Measurements

for Engineering

and other surveys

PRENTICE-HALL CIVIL ENGINEERING AND ENGINEERING MECHANICS SERIES

N. M. NEWMARK, *Editor*

MICHAEL V. SMIRNOFF

Associate Professor of Civil Engineering
North Carolina State College of the
University of North Carolina

Measurements
for Engineering

and other surveys

Englewood Cliffs, New Jersey

PRENTICE-HALL, INC.

Preface

This book presents, in the odd-numbered chapters, a comprehensive theoretical approach to engineering measurements. Field instructions in the use of surveying instruments and equipment are given in the even-numbered chapters. The later chapters deal also with practical applications of surveying measurements, especially those that are used on engineering projects.

The introduction of new methods and instruments in surveying measurements requires a thorough understanding of the general theory of measurements, which, incidentally, can also be used in other engineering applications. Accordingly, such topics as precision and accuracy, significant figures, theory of errors, repeated measurements, etc., are adequately covered in this text. Numerous applications of these topics to surveying measurements are presented throughout the book.

The uses of electronic measuring instruments and of the photogrammetric methods are briefly discussed in connection with surveying measurements, where those instruments and methods apply.

A comprehensive set of problems is given at the end of each odd-numbered chapter, and recommended field exercises appear at the end of each even-numbered chapter. In all problems three sets of data are given in each problem under (A), (B), and (C). The answers are given in all A problems.

This volume includes not only the topics that are normally given in an introductory surveying course but also those that are often given in the second semester of surveying instructions. Thus the book includes discussions on engineering astronomy, plane table, mine surveys and hydrographic surveys. Slide rule instructions, public land surveys and property surveys are discussed, respectively, in Appendixes B, C, and D.

A new, accurate method for the adjustment of traverses is given in this book. This method, and some new equations developed in other surveying problems, appear here in print for the first time.

The author wishes to express sincere thanks to his former colleague on the faculty of the University of California in Los Angeles, Paul E. Wylie, who read the manuscript and made constructive suggestions.

v

Acknowledgment is also made here of wonderful cooperation received, in preparation of illustrations, from the following organizations: U.S. National Bureau of Standards; U.S. Coast and Geodetic Survey; Keuffel and Esser Company; Eugene Dietzgen Company; W. and L. E. Gurley; C. L. Berger and Sons, Inc.; Wild Heerbrugg Instruments, Inc.; Kern Instruments, Inc.: Tellurometer, Inc.; Zeiss Aerotopograph; Kelsh Instrument Company, Inc.; Abrams Instrument Corporation; Lenker Manufacturing Company; American Paulin System; Los Angeles Scientific Instrument Company; C. J. Van Leeuwen; Fairchild Camera and Instrument Corporation; Fairchild Aerial Surveys, Inc.; and Charles Bruning Company, Inc.

Sincere thanks are also due Professors N. M. Newmark and H. M. Karara of the University of Illinois for their fine suggestions.

Contents

Contents

CHAPTER 1

Introduction

Classification of Surveys

1-1. Definition. According to Webster's dictionary, surveying is "that branch of applied mathematics which teaches the art of determining the area of any portion of the earth's surface, the lengths and directions of the bounding lines, the contour of the surface ... and of accurately delineating the whole on paper."

As far as engineering surveys are concerned, the definition should be broadened to include "the establishment of any line, grade, or elevation as may be required on various engineering projects."

1-2. Prerequisite requirements. In order to be able to measure distances and angles and to determine direction of lines and elevation of points on the earth's surface for any engineering project, and to make computations to solve problems connected with those measurements, a person needs a fundamental knowledge of algebra, geometry, and trigonometry.

1-3. Surveying instructions. Surveying, as it is taught in colleges and universities, consists of lectures and field practice. Surveying lectures deal mostly with theory of measurements, solution of problems encountered on various types of surveys, and explanation of the principles involved (a) in measurements, (b) in computations based on such measurements, and (c) in construction and uses of various surveying instruments. This part of surveying instruction belongs to the *science of engineering*.

Surveying field practice, on the other hand, deals with proper use of surveying instruments and equipment and thus is related for the most part to the *art of engineering*. Surveying field exercises also enable students to understand what kinds of instruments and equipment are appropriate to the various types of surveys, and how to do the actual field work in order to meet widely varying accuracy requirements. Part of the time assigned to the surveying laboratory is normally devoted to office work such as making computations and drawings. The drawings are usually plans showing surveying work done in the field.

1-4. The shape of the earth. The mean radius of the earth approximates 4000 miles, and the highest mountain, Mount Everest, has a summit elevation of about 29,000 feet (about 5.5 miles) above the mean sea level. This shows that the irregularities of the earth's surface are not great as compared to the size of the earth. Thus the earth, for many practical purposes, may be regarded as the ellipsoid of revolution having its polar axis equal to 41,711,940 ft and its equatorial axis equal to 41,852,860 ft. This ellipsoid of revolution is known as *Clarke's spheroid of 1866*.

1-5. Geographic coordinates. Geographic or *geodetic* coordinates for locating a point on the surface of the earth are latitude and longitude.

The geodetic latitude of a point on the earth's surface is the angle between the normal to the Clarke's spheroid, at the point in question, and the plane of the equator. Thus latitudes vary from 0° to 90°. The points in the Northern Hemisphere have north latitudes and the points in the Southern Hemisphere have south latitudes.

The longitude of a point on the earth's surface is the angle between two meridional planes, one passing through Greenwich Observatory in England and another through the point in question. The meridional plane passing through Greenwich has zero longitude and all points along that meridian have zero longitude. The longitudes of other points are measured east and west from Greenwich meridian. Thus longitudes vary from 0° to 180°. Points east of Greenwich have east longitudes and points west of Greenwich have west longitudes.

A *point*, as used in the above discussion, has a figurative meaning since, strictly speaking, a point has no dimensions. In surveying, a point is a dot, or a tack, very often a stake, or even a spot of considerable dimensions. For instance, a point on the surface of the earth described to the nearest second of latitude and longitude is determined only within a radius of about 100 ft, since the arc on the surface of the earth, subtended by an angle of one second of latitude, has an approximate length of 100 ft.

1-6. Directions. A person moving continuously from a point on the equator east or west may expect eventually to come to the point of beginning. A person imagined to be at the North Pole cannot move either east or west; any direction that he may choose will be south. A person beginning to move east or west from a point located between the North Pole and the equator, and continuing to move along what would appear to him to be a straight line, will eventually cross the equator, thus moving into the Southern Hemisphere.

On engineering projects extended over considerable distances, such as the construction of a long highway, a railroad, a pipe line, a canal, or a transmission line, due cognizance must be taken of the fact that the route of the project is along a spherical surface. A straight line on such a surface, as prolonged by surveying instruments, is a line of constantly changing direction.

1-7. Elevations. Elevations on the surface of the earth are measured from a frame of reference known as the *mean sea level,* which is said to be at zero elevation. Elevations above zero elevation are positive and those below zero elevation are negative. The highest elevation on the North American Continent is Mount McKinley in Alaska, having an elevation of 20,300 ft. The lowest point in the Western Hemisphere is in Death Valley, California, having an elevation of −276 ft.

A level surface to which the elevations of points are referred is called *datum.* Beside the mean sea level datum some arbitrarily chosen datum is often used in surveying work.

1-8. Level surface. A level surface is a curved surface perpendicular to the direction of gravity at all points. Starting with a point of zero elevation and continuing in any selected direction along a straight, horizontal line at that point, one will discover that all other points on the line are above zero elevation. For instance, the elevation of a point 1 mile along the line will be 0.57 ft, and the elevation of a point 10 miles away will be 57.4 ft above mean sea level. Thus, for a long horizontal line of sight, corrections for the curvature of the earth and the atmospheric refraction must be taken into consideration in determining the elevation of points. In surveying, such corrections are negligible for the length of sights up to about 200 ft.

1-9. Geodetic surveys. Certain agencies of the Federal Government, such as the United States Coast and Geodetic Survey (USC&GS) or the United States Geological Survey (USGS), are charged with conducting country-wide surveys for various purposes.

USC&GS, for instance, is charged with establishing, throughout the country, points tied to a single surveying net in their relative horizontal positions. Such points, usually stone monuments with a properly inscribed brass disc on top, constitute so-called *horizontal control* in this country. Any survey tied to those points is also tied to the national net of horizontal control. Such surveys could be re-established in their original location even if all local survey markers were obliterated.

Likewise, USC&GS establishes points of ***vertical control,*** all referred to the same level surface, or a datum. The datum normally is *1929 mean sea level datum.* The mean sea level is subject to slight variations from year to year.

One of the main functions of the USGS is to prepare topographic maps, commonly known as the USGS quadrangle sheets. These maps vary in scale from 1:24,000 to 1:250,000; they may be obtained from the agency itself or locally in certain stores.

The surveys conducted by these agencies are of such extent that the sphericity of the earth must be taken into consideration in all measurements. Such surveys are called ***geodetic surveys.***

1-10. Plane surveying. On surveys of limited extent the corrections to measured distances, angles, and directions due to sphericity of the earth may be so small that the required accuracy of a survey is not seriously impaired if those corrections are neglected. In such cases the surveying measurements are made as if the surface of the earth were a plane surface. Thus all angles, distances, and elevations are measured in reference to a plane surface. When such surveys are continued in extent they automatically follow a curved surface of certain elevation from place to place. This type of surveying is called ***plane surveying.***

Practically all engineering surveys are conducted by the plane surveying method. On such surveys as route surveys it is necessary to apply corrections to changing directions due to convergence of meridians, but otherwise the work is conducted by the plane surveying method.

1-11. Surveying categories. Various techniques, instruments, and equipment are used in different categories of surveying work. There are four main categories or subdivisions of plane surveying: *planimetric* surveys, *topographic* surveys, *hydrographic* surveys, and *photogrammetric* surveys. Table 1-1 shows these four categories as the headings of four columns.

Surveying may also be subdivided or classified according to the purpose for which it is intended—for instance, public land surveys, property surveys, route surveys, bridge surveys. These classifications are shown in the first vertical column of Table 1-1.

Table 1-1 also shows cross marks to indicate that for a given purpose several types of surveying work may be needed. For instance, planimetric, topographic, hydrographic, and photogrammetric surveying may be required for planning, design, and construction of a highway.

Public land surveys (item 1 in Table 1-1) are currently conducted in this country under the supervision of the Bureau of Land Management, formerly the General Land Office. With the exception of the thirteen original states and Kentucky, Tennessee, and Texas, public lands are subdivided into townships, sections, and quarter sections. Normal size of a quarter section is 160 acres.

Where the land passes into the hands of private owners, further subdivisions are made by practicing land surveyors whose main business is to make property surveys. Property surveys, sometimes called *cadastral surveys,* are shown under item 2 in Table 1-1. Most states require their practicing land surveyors to be registered by the appropriate

TABLE 1-1. CLASSIFICATION OF SURVEYS

Item	Classification of Surveys According to Purpose	Classification of Surveys According to Type of Work			
		Plani-metric Surveys	Topographic Surveys	Hydrographic Surveys	Photogram-metric Surveys
1	Public land surveys	x			
2	Property surveys	x			
3	Route surveys	x	x	x	x
4	Bridge surveys	x	x	x	x
5	Building surveys	x	x		
6	Dam surveys	x	x	x	x
7	Reservoir surveys	x	x	x	x
8	Mine surveys*	x	x		x
9	Harbor surveys Etc.	x		x	x

* Mine surveys should be considered as a special type of underground surveying.

State Board of Registration; when so registered they are called *licensed land surveyors.*

College students preparing themselves for an engineering career are required to take surveying courses so that they can conduct or supervise surveying work on engineering projects. Various kinds of engineering surveys are shown in Table 1-1. Although a practicing engineer may be engaged in property surveys, such activity normally is incidental to other work that he may be doing in the field of engineering. Most engineering projects require location of structures in reference to existing property lines.

Although property surveys may and should be regarded as engineering surveys, it is important to recognize that special training is necessary for this type of surveying practice. Competence in cadastral surveying requires not only the technical knowledge of how to operate surveying instruments and equipment, but also the knowledge of legal principles involved and familiarity with existing local regulations. Although engineers are responsible for the surveys conducted under their supervision, actual operation of surveying instruments and equipment may be carried out by trained technicians. Beside the instrumentman, such trained help includes tapemen and rodmen.

1-12. Planimetric surveying. Planimetric surveys, as the name implies, are conducted for the purpose of making plan views of an area without showing contours (i.e., topographic features) of the land. A plan view of an area is needed on engineering projects to show the location and the horizontal dimensions of proposed structures in a given area. The finished drawing is called a *plan*. Its scale varies from about 1 in. equal to 40 ft to about 1 in. equal to 500 ft. Locations of property lines are also shown on such plans when necessary. A plan view of a large area shown to a scale of about 1:1000 or smaller is called a *map*. Ordinary road maps are typical examples of planimetric maps made for a specific purpose. The word "map" is often loosely used to signify a plan.

1-13. Topographic surveying. Topographic surveys are normally conducted for the purpose of showing both planimetric and topographic features of an area. It would be impossible to make designs of roads, dams, reservoirs, bridges, and other structures without knowing the topography of the ground. The USGS quadrangle maps are typical examples of topographic maps.

1-14. Hydrographic surveying. Hydrographic surveys are made for such purposes as navigation, water supply, subaqueous mapping, construction of harbors, channel dredging, and construction of bridges. Special techniques used in *taking soundings*, to determine the depth of water, and to measure the velocity of flow and the amount of water discharge, characterize this type of survey.

1-15. Photogrammetric surveying. Photogrammetry is defined as a branch of science which teaches how to make measurements using photographs. In the last two or three decades photogrammetry has progressed to such an extent that it is now used on all important engineering projects.

Aerial photogrammetry employs photographs taken from the air and *terrestrial photogrammetry* uses photographs taken from the ground. Aerial photographs are often used on engineering projects. The aerial survey companies which specialize in this kind of work use special cameras for taking photographs and special apparatus for making planimetric and topographic maps. Other uses of photographs include the finding of suitable sites for structures, the study of land use, location of suitable construction material, determination of type of soil and drainage conditions, and preliminary studies for route locations.

USGS maps are made at present almost exclusively by photogrammetric methods.

1-16. Engineering surveys.   Table 1-1 shows that some surveying work must be done on every engineering project.   When a project is in the *planning stage*, usually some rough field measurements are necessary for proper planning of the location and the size of structures.   When a project reaches the design stage or *drafting board stage*, the designers use surveying field data shown on various drawings, such as profiles, cross sections, and stake-out plans, for location of structures, drainage, and various details.   When the design is completed, the engineers turn out a complete set of construction plans.   Finally, when the contract is signed with a construction contractor, the project reaches the *construction stage*. At this stage the alignment and the elevation of all structures to be erected must be staked out on the ground by surveying field parties.

If an engineer is working for a company which designs the engineering works, he may be assigned as inspector of construction for his company. His duties are to see that the work is done according to plans.   The inspector of construction must know how to operate surveying instruments, since his duties may require checking of distances, angles, and elevations for various structures erected by the contractor.

If an engineer is working as a chief of party on field surveys conducted for an engineering project, he must know not only how to make field measurements and how to record them in the field notebook, but also how to supervise and to direct the work of other men in his party.

If an engineer is working for a contractor, he is directly responsible for all measurements made on the job and for proper construction of all works called for in the contract.

All of these duties and responsibilities of an engineer bear a direct or indirect relation to engineering surveys.   Such surveys may include measurement of distances and elevations, finding direction of lines, measurement of horizontal and vertical angles, computation of areas, and work on plans showing various planimetric and topographic features of construction sites.   This type of surveying work and the necessary theories for its proper execution are discussed in chapters that follow.

Linear Measuring Units

1-17. What is measurement?   A measurement may be direct or indirect.   Measuring a distance with a tape is *direct measurement*, but finding distances of two sides of a triangle by measuring the third side and two angles is *indirect measurement*.

Direct measurement is a comparison of the measured quantity with a measuring unit or units employed for measuring a quantity of that kind. Several measuring units may be employed in measuring a given type of quantity. For instance the inch, the foot, the meter, and the mile are all linear measuring units. However, in all such cases only one unit is considered to be a measuring standard unit, and all other units are derived from such a standard.

1-18. Standard units of length. Although the foot, the pound, and the second, known as the British system of measuring units, are commonly regarded in the United States as standard units for measuring length, mass, and time, the standard length of a foot is really derived from the meter. The United States is a member of a group of nineteen nations which accepted a distance marked on a standard metal bar kept in the International Building in Sèvres, France, as representing the length of the standard meter. It has also been decreed by an Act of Congress of the United States that there will be exactly 39.37 inches in one standard meter. Twelve such inches establish the foot. In Great Britain the meter contains 39.37011 inches.

In 1958 the nations using the foot agreed to use in international relations the length of 1 inch equal exactly to 2.54 centimeters. There are 39.370078 ... such inches in the standard meter.

TABLE 1-2. UNITS OF LENGTH

Unit	Inches (In.)	Feet (Ft)	Yards (Yd)	Rods (Rd)	Meters (M)
1 inch	1	0.08333	0.02778	0.00505	0.02540
1 foot	12	1	0.3333	0.0606	0.3048
1 yard	36	3	1	0.1818	0.9144
1 rod	198	16.5	5.5	1	5.0292
1 mile	63,360	5,280	1,760	320	1,609.35
1 meter	39.37	3.281	1.094	0.199	1

TABLE 1-3. METRIC UNITS OF LENGTH

Unit	Microns (μ)	Millimeters (Mm)	Centimeters (Cm)	Decimeters (Dm)	Meters (M)
1 micron	1	0.001	0.0001		
1 millimeter	1,000	1	0.1	0.01	0.001
1 centimeter	10,000	10	1	0.1	0.01
1 decimeter	100,000	100	10	1	0.1
1 meter	1,000,000	1,000	100	10	1

1 meter = 0.1 decameter = 0.01 hectometer = 0.001 kilometer.

TABLE 1-4. MARINER'S MEASURING UNITS

1 fathom = 6 ft
1 cable = 120 fathoms = 720 ft
1 international nautical mile* = 6076.10 ft

* Used by all U.S. Government agencies.

TABLE 1-5. UNITS USED IN LAND MEASUREMENTS

1 Gunter's chain (100 links) = 66 ft = 4 rods or poles or perches
80 Gunter's chains = 1 mile
1 vara = 32.993 in. in Mexico, 33 in. in California, and 33⅓ in. in Texas

TABLE 1-6. SQUARE MEASURES (MIXED)

Square Centimeters	Square Inches	Square Feet	Square Yards	Square Meters
1	0.15500	0.00108		
6.4520	1	0.00694	0.000772	0.000645
929.03	144	1	0.11111	0.09290
8361.3	1296	9	1	0.83613
10,000	1550	10.764	1.1960	1

1 sq mile = 6,400 sq chains = 640 acres
1 acre = 10 sq Gunter's chains = 160 sq rods = 43,560 sq ft
      = 4046.87 sq m
1 centare = 1 sq m
1 are = 100 sq m
1 hectare = 100 ares = 10,000 sq m

Tables 1-2 through 1-6 show various linear and square measuring units and their relation to each other.

The *meter* is the standard unit of length in the metric measuring system which employs *centimeter, gram,* and *second* as measuring units of length, mass, and time. Table 1-3 shows metric measuring units and their relation to each other.

1-19. National Bureau of Standards. The National Bureau of Standards (NBS), established by an Act of Congress in 1901, serves the government, industry, and the public in many capacities. Some functions of the NBS are mentioned here.

Custody of Standards. The NBS is responsible for the maintenance and development of the national standards of physical measurements.

Figure 1-1 shows a display of meter bars and kilograms. Other standards may include those for screw threads, for isotopes, for color, temperature, viscosity, frequency, time, electrical units, and many others
too numerous to be mentioned here. Besides keeping established standards, NBS is constantly developing new standards as the need arises.

  Research. Continuous demand by industry for more precise measurements makes research on various properties of materials and on better

Fig. 1-1. Standard units of length and mass. (Courtesy U.S.
National Bureau of Standards.)

methods of measurement one of the main activities of the NBS. This
agency not only develops new standards but also devises new instruments and methods for various types of measurements. Demand for the
accuracy of measuring devices often runs high. For instance, the master
gage blocks used in industry are calibrated with an accuracy of one-
millionth of an inch per inch of length.

  Services to Government, Industry, and the Public. NBS performs valuable services to the Government and it also makes many services available
to industry and to the public. For example, it will calibrate measuring
instruments sent to the Bureau for that purpose. Figure 1-2 shows a
certificate, issued by the Bureau, recording the results of calibration of a
100 ft steel tape of the type used in engineering and land surveying work.

NBS 579
Rev. 3-1-41

UNITED STATES DEPARTMENT OF COMMERCE
WASHINGTON

National Bureau of Standards

Certificate
100-Foot
Steel Tape

Maker: The Lufkin Rule Co.   Submitted by   NBS No. 11171
No.

University of North Carolina
North Carolina State College of Agriculture and Engineering
Department of Civil Engineering
Raleigh, North Carolina

This tape has been compared with the standards of the United States, and the intervals indicated have the following lengths at 68° Fahrenheit (20° centigrade) under the conditions given below:

Supported on a horizontal flat surface; tension, 10 pounds
Interval   Length
0 to 100 feet   100.000 feet

The weight per foot of this tape is 0.01233 pound.

See Note 3(a) on the reverse side of this certificate.

For the Director
National Bureau of Standards

Test No. 2.4/G-21965
Date: July 3, 1957

Lewis V. Judson

Lewis V. Judson
Chief, Length Section
Optics and Metrology Division

10—49599—3

Fig. 1-2. Certificate of steel tape calibration.

PROBLEMS

1-1. Given a triangular field ABC. $a = 1042.71$ ft, $b = 528.96$ ft, and $c = 723.49$ ft.   Using six-place logarithmic tables find respective angles, shown under parts (A), (B), and (C) below, to the nearest second.   Do not use

12   **Introduction**

cosine law formula. See trigonometric formulas on p. 400. Arrange all computations in four columns as shown below.

Solution:

$$\sin \frac{A}{2} = \sqrt{\frac{(s-b)(s-c)}{b \cdot c}}$$

$$2 \log \sin \frac{A}{2} = \log (s-b) + \log (s-c) + \text{colog } b + \text{colog } c$$

Symbol	Value	Log or Colog	Value
a	1042.71		
b	528.96	colog	$7.276577 - 10$
c	723.40	colog	$7.140567 - 10$
$\dfrac{a+b+c}{2}$	1147.58		
$s-b$	618.62	log	2.791424
$s-c$	424.09	log	2.627458
$\dfrac{A}{2}$		2 log sin	$19.836026 - 20$
$\dfrac{A}{2}$	55°53′26″	log sin	$9.918013 - 10$
A	111°46′52″		

(A) Find angle A.   *Ans.* 111°46′52″
(B) Find angle B.
(C) Find angle C.

1-2. In an oblique triangle ABC are given two sides and the included angle. Using tangent formula and the tabular form for computations as shown in Problem 1-1 above, find two other angles. Use six-place logarithmic tables.
(A) Given: $a = 554.29$ ft, $b = 482.23$ ft, $C = 49°23′56″$.
                                             Ans. 73°53′45″, 56°42′19″
(B) $a = 100.43$ ft, $c = 302.76$ ft, $B = 150°28′20″$.
(C) $b = 253.75$ ft, $c = 371.40$ ft, $A = 72°15′24″$.

1-3. Three sides of a triangular field have been measured to the nearest 0.01 ft; it is required to find the area of the field in square feet using six-place logarithms and the tabular method of computations as shown in Problem 1-1.
(A) $a = 302.49$, $b = 507.09$, $c = 699.07$.   *Ans.* 68,234 sq ft
(B) $a = 1042.71$, $b = 528.96$, $c = 723.49$.
(C) $a = 554.29$, $b = 482.23$, $c = 378.75$.

The following exercises are given for practice with the slide rule.

1-4. Determine on the slide rule the values of trigonometric functions entering expressions given below. Substitute these values in the expressions and evaluate the result on the slide rule. Next, check the result obtained by running the slide rule continuously without determining beforehand the numerical values of the functions.

(A) $x = \dfrac{\sin 25°30' \times 13.7 \times \cos 43°15'}{\tan 4°18' \times 192.5 \times 2.375}$.   *Ans.* 0.125

(B) $y = \dfrac{\cot 75°20' \times 257.3 \times \sin 3°24'}{372.3 \times \tan 37°48' \times 10.25}$.

(C) $z = \dfrac{\cos 62°12' \times 35.19 \times 0.731}{1.725 \times \tan 15°36' \times \sin 2°15'}$.

1-5. In a triangle ABC find angles B and C and the side c using slide rule and the sine law formulas.

(A) $a = 10.4$ ft, $b = 5.29$ ft, $A = 111°46'$.   *Ans.* $B = 28°12'$

(B) $a = 28.7$ in., $b = 18.9$ in., $A = 117°24'$.

(C) $a = 17.2$ in., $b = 32.5$ in., $A = 125°18'$.

1-6. Evaluate on the slide rule deflection δ of a beam in inches, by substituting given values in the formula

$$\delta = \frac{PL^3}{48EI}$$

where P is concentrated load in pounds

L is the span in inches

E is the modulus of elasticity in lb/sq in.

I is the moment of inertia of the beam in in.⁴

(A) $P = 1210$ lb, $L = 17'-4''$, $E = 30,000,000$ lb/sq in., $I = 24$ in.⁴

                                                   Ans. 0.315 in.

(B) $P = 14,300$ lb, $L = 12'-0''$, $E = 30,000,000$ lb/sq in., $I = 183.4$ in.⁴

(C) $P = 9500$ lb, $L = 15'-3''$, $E = 30,000,000$ lb/sq in., $I = 95.3$ in.⁴

CHAPTER 2

Field Instructions—Surveying Instruments and Equipment

Measuring Tapes

2-1. Steel tapes. The tapes are used for measuring distances. Steel tapes 100 ft long are commonly used in surveying work. These tapes vary in width from about $\frac{1}{4}$ in. to $\frac{3}{8}$ in. and in thickness from about 0.01 in. to 0.02 in. A light 100 ft tape weighs about 1.25 lb. The tapes used in surveying must be graduated into feet throughout and into tenths and hundredths of a foot at both ends or throughout. Normally only the first and the last foot are so graduated.

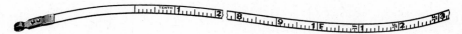

Fig. 2-1. Steel tape graduated into hundredths of a foot. (Courtesy Keuffel & Esser Co.)

Figure 2-1 shows the end of a graduated tape. There are also tapes on the market which have an extra foot, with graduations, at each end. Such tapes are cumbersome to use when a spring balance (Fig. 2-6) is attached to a tape.

The present-day practice is to keep 100 ft tapes wound on reels. Figure 2-2 shows a tape wound on one of commonly used reels. The

14

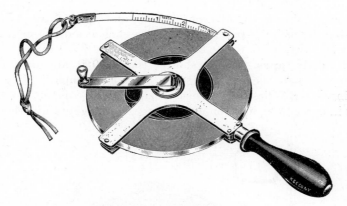

Fig. 2-2. Steel tape on reel.   (Courtesy Keuffel & Esser Co.)

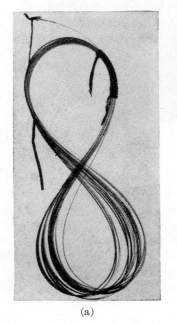

(b)

Fig. 2-3. (a) Steel tape wound into 5 ft loops. (b) Same tape "thrown" into circle.

(a)

figure shows also a leather thong attached to the end of the tape to stretch it and hold it during measurements.   Occasionally, one may still see tapes used without a reel.   When not in use such tapes are wound into 5-foot loops (Fig. 2-3a) and then "thrown" into a circle about 8 inches in diameter (Fig. 2-3b).   Such tapes may be recommended for school exercises since they give practice to students in winding, unwinding, and handling a tape when a reel is not available.

There are also on the market 200, 300, and 500 ft tapes.   These are used primarily on long-span measurements, such as a direct measurement across a small river.

2-2. Cloth tapes.   Tapes shorter than 100 ft are often used for short approximate measurements.   A 50 ft cloth tape is often used in surveying to make ties, i.e., to measure approximate distances to various objects in order to fix location of a stake, a building, or any other object.

Fig. 2-4. Cloth tape with case.   (Courtesy Eugene Dietzgen Co.)

Short tapes are normally enclosed in a case, as shown in Fig. 2-4.   A small handle on one side of the case is used to wind the tape inside the case.

Cloth tapes are not used for accurate measurements.   Some cloth tapes have metal strands woven into their fabric and are called *metallic tapes*.   Others are normally labeled as *nonmetallic tapes*.

A few other tapes used on special kinds of work are briefly described below.

2-3. Builder's tapes are somewhat lighter than surveyor's tapes. They come in various lengths and are graduated in feet and inches. They are used in building construction, since the dimensions shown on construction plans are given in feet and inches.

2-4. Invar tapes are made of an alloy of nickel and steel.   They have a low coefficient of expansion and require very careful handling since they are much softer than surveyor's steel tapes.   Invar tapes are used on various precise measurements, such as measurement of a base line in triangulation work.   Lovar tapes are similar to invar tapes. They have a slightly different composition and coefficient of expansion.

2-5. Chains are nowadays used only on special types of land surveying work (Fig. 2-5). The surveyor's chain, also called *Gunter's chain*, is 66 ft long and contains 100 links, so that distances may be recorded in chains and in decimal parts of the chain. Public land surveys in the United States are conducted with the use of a chain or, more recently, with the use of a 66 ft tape divided into 100 parts. Each part, still called a link, is 0.66 ft long.

Land surveyors generally use regular 100 ft tapes in property survey work.

Metric tapes, 50 ft long and divided into meters, are used by the USC&GS in measuring base lines in triangulation work.

Taping Accessories

2-6. Spring balance. A spring balance (Fig. 2-6), also called a *tension handle,* is used at the end of a tape for reading the tension or the *pull,* in pounds, applied to the tape during measurements. The scale on such balances is usually graduated from zero to 30 pounds. Spring balances are used in accurate taping. They are usually dispensed with in measuring

Fig. 2-5. Gunter's chain. (Courtesy Keuffel & Esser Co.)

distances with ordinary accuracy, which is about 1:3000. In such measurements the tapemen apply a 10 lb pull to the tape by estimation.

2-7. Tape clamp. The clamps (Fig. 2-7) are used during measurements to hold the tape under tension at any place between the zero and 100 footmarks. Holding the tape without a clamp may result in a slight bending of the tape which in turn will cause a kink. The kinks, once produced, cannot be entirely straightened out.

2-8. Plumb bob. In taping, plumb bobs are used to plumb the tape over a point when the tape must be suspended above a measured line. Although there are iron plumb bobs on the market they are not popular with tapemen. The commonly used plumb bob is a brass bob (shown in Fig. 2-8). They come in various sizes, varying in weight from about 6 oz to 18 oz.

Plumb bobs are used also to set a transit (Fig. 2-18) over a point.

2-9. Stakes and tacks. Wooden stakes or hubs about $1\frac{1}{2}$ in. by $1\frac{1}{2}$ in. by 12 in. (Fig. 2-9) are used in surveying to establish certain points on the ground. These ground points, often called *stations* on engineering surveys, are needed to stake out a building, to run a center line for a road, and to stake out any line or a grade.

Fig. 2-7. Tape clamp.

Fig. 2-8. Brass plumb bob.

Fig. 2-6. Spring balance.

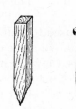

Fig. 2-9. Hub (left).
Surveying tack (right).

Fig. 2-10. Tally pin.

(Courtesy Keuffel & Esser Co.)

18

After the hub is driven into the ground, the point on the top of the hub is established by driving a special tack (Fig. 2-9). A special feature of the surveying tack is that it has a depression in its head.

2-10. Tally pins.   Tally pins or *arrows* (Fig. 2-10) are used to mark the ends of measured tape lengths on the ground. Tally pins are kept in a set of 11 pins on a circular ring. A common size of a tally pin is $\frac{1}{4}$ in. in diameter and 14 in. in length.

Tally pins are seldom used on engineering projects. They are useful, however, in school exercises where they may be used in place of stakes supposedly driven into the ground.

2-11. Thermometers.   Pocket thermometers (Fig. 2-11) are used to obtain the temperature of the air and thus to determine the approximate temperature of the tape during measurements. There are also tape

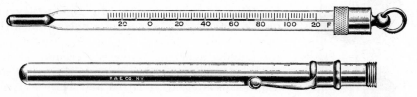

Fig. 2-11. Pocket thermometer.   (Courtesy Keuffel & Esser Co.)

thermometers on the market which can be easily attached to a tape when needed. Tape thermometers are used only on precise measurements.

2-12. Crayons.   Crayons or *keels* used in surveying are "lumber crayons." They are hexagonal in cross section, about $\frac{1}{2}$ in. across and about 4 in. long (Fig. 2-12). They come in various colors, the most

Fig. 2-12. Lumber crayon.

popular being red, blue, and yellow. Crayons are used for marking stations or cross marks on pavements and sidewalks to serve as points for the positioning of an instrument, for holding a rod, and for other purposes. Dark crayons are used, for instance, to mark the station number or some other identification on a guard stake driven over the hub representing the station.

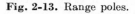

Fig. 2-13. Range poles.

2-13. Range poles.   Range poles (Fig. 2-13) are rods, normally 6 or 8 ft in length and from 1 to about $1\frac{1}{2}$ in. in diameter.   There are steel and wood range poles on the market. Wooden poles have a pointed metal end, called a *shoe*, to assure rod penetration into the ground when the poles are set in a vertical position. Range poles are employed mostly in marking the location of ground points.   In taping they are used to mark the direction of a line in which the taping must proceed.   For better visibility and for judging a height above the ground when a pole is stuck into the ground, the poles are painted in alternate 1 ft red and white sections.

Fig. 2-14. Philadelphia leveling rod with target. (Courtesy Keuffel & Esser Co.)

2-14. Leveling rod.   A leveling rod most commonly used in surveying work is the so-called *Philadelphia rod* (Fig. 2-14).   This rod usually consists of two sliding sections so that it can be extended to a length nearly double its size. When closed, the rod is about $1\frac{5}{8}$ in. by $1\frac{5}{8}$ in. in cross section, and usually either 6 ft 6 in. or 7 ft long.   A 6 ft 6 in. rod extends to 12 ft, and a 7 ft rod extends to 13 ft.   When a rod is fully extended, the graduations run continuously up from zero at the foot of the rod.   Graduations are made in feet, and in tenths and hundredths of a foot.

Leveling rods are used in conjunction with an instrument called the *level* to determine differences of elevation of various points.   A detailed description of leveling rods and their uses is given in Chapter 9.

2-15. Hand level.   The most commonly used hand level is in the shape of a brass tube about $\frac{5}{8}$ in. in diameter and about 6 in. long (Fig. 2-15).   At one end the tube has a peep-sight opening for viewing the objects and at another

Fig. 2-15. Hand level.   (Courtesy Keuffel & Esser Co.)

end the tube is enclosed by plain glass.   A small spirit-level tube is attached to the hand level, near the objective end, above a small slot in the tube.   The level's bubble is projected to the eye opening by means of a prism or a mirror placed inside the tube.   The mirror occupies only one-half of the inside cross section of the tube so as to allow clear view of objects through the other half of the tube.   This arrangement permits a person holding the hand level horizontally in front of an eye to view an object and the bubble simultaneously.

When the user raises or lowers the objective end of the level slightly, the bubble appears to move up and down.   When the bubble is at a short horizontal hair, etched on a glass inside the tube, the hand level produces a horizontal sight.

Hand levels have no magnification; the length of sight at which graduations on a leveling rod may be read with normal eyesight is limited to about 50 ft.

The hand level is used in taping, for finding approximate difference in elevation of points, and in other field operations where it is required to produce a level sight.

2-16. Clinometer.   A clinometer consists essentially of a hand level tube with a graduated arc attached to its side.   An Abney type hand level and clinometer is shown in Fig. 2-16.   The level tube on the clinometer is attached to the top of the arc and thus is rotated through the same angle as the arc.   The arc can be rotated through a 45° angle both ways from its zero position.

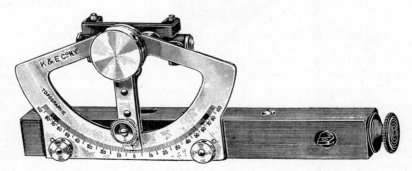

Fig. 2-16. Abney type hand level and clinometer.   (Courtesy Keuffel & Esser Co.)

The arc is graduated in degrees from zero in the middle to 45° both ways.   When the arc is set on zero, the clinometer can be used as a hand level since in such position of the arc the level tube is parallel to the barrel of the clinometer, as in a hand level.   But when the arc is set to read an angle, the level tube is rotated through that angle, and in order to bring it to a level position the objective end of the tube must be either raised or lowered, as the case may be, through the same angle.   Thus when the bubble is brought to the horizontal hair of the clinometer, the line of sight is inclined through the angle that was set on the arc.

A small vernier is often attached to the turning knob of the clinometer so that the scale of the clinometer can be read to about 10'.   The Abney type clinometer also has another scale which reads the slope of a line in per cent.   This scale is used mostly on route survey work.

Surveying Instruments

2-17. Engineer's level.   The engineer's level is used in determining the elevation of points.   It consists (see Fig. 2-17) of a telescope and

Fig. 2-17. Engineer's dumpy level.   (Courtesy Eugene Dietzgen Co.)

a spirit level tube fixed under the telescope.   The telescope can be rotated only about the level's vertical axis.   Four foot-screws are used for leveling the instrument.   When in use the instrument is secured on a tripod.   Other parts include a clamp screw for arresting rotation of the instrument, a tangent screw for slow rotational motion, a knob on the telescope for forcusing the telescope on an object, and an eyepiece for focusing the cross hair.   The level is used mostly in conjunction with a leveling rod to find the elevations of points needed for ground contours, for erecting structures, and for running ground profiles.   It is an important surveying instrument since the elevation of points must be determined on almost all engineering surveys.

A more detailed description of levels and their use is presented in Chapter 9.

2-18. Engineer's transit.   The transit is another instrument which is used on almost all surveys.   Its versatility comes from the many uses to which it can be put.   The main function of the transit is to measure

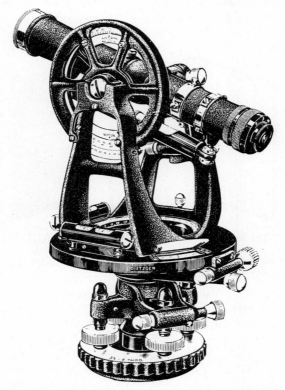

Fig. 2-18. Engineer's transit.   (Courtesy Eugene Dietzgen Co.)

horizontal and vertical angles, but it may be used also for leveling, for special topographic work called *stadia* (Chapter 17), and for many other purposes.   For instance, transits are used in the aircraft industry for the alignment of jigs.

Since a detailed description of the transit is given in Chapter 11, and work with transits is described in subsequent chapters, only the main parts of the transit are mentioned here.

Referring to Fig. 2-18, the following transit parts may be clearly seen: the telescope supported by the horizontal axis of the instrument; the vertical circle mounted on the horizontal axis and used for measuring vertical angles; the horizontal circle with scales for measuring horizontal angles and usually with a compass on top; and four leveling screws supporting the instrument on a foot plate. Like a level, the transit is attached to a tripod by standard threads, $3\frac{1}{2}$ in. in diameter, 8 threads per inch. When not in use, the transit is kept in a wooden box which comes with each instrument.

2-19. Field notebook. There are several types of field notebooks. The one commonly used by engineers for recording surveying field data is shown in Fig. 2-19. Its size is close to $4\frac{1}{2}$ in. by $7\frac{1}{2}$ in. so that it can

Fig. 2-19. Engineer's notebook. (Courtesy Keuffel & Esser Co.)

be carried in a pocket. This is rather important, since on many surveys the notes may be kept either by an instrumentman or by a head tapeman, both of whom need both hands when operating their respective instruments and equipment.

The left page of the field book has horizontal lines and six columns; the right page has cross lines and a single red line through the middle of the page lengthwise. The horizontal lines of the right page coincide with the horizontal lines of the left page, so that explanation notes or computations written on the right page may correspond to the field data recorded on the left page.

Spiral-bound field books are quite popular with field men because these books can be very easily double-folded on any page. Loose-leaf notebooks are also widely used.

FIELD EXERCISES

2-1. Use of instruments and equipment. The first meeting of a field class should be devoted to general explanations pertaining to the use and proper handling of surveying instruments and equipment.

It may be well worth while to demonstrate before the class every instrument and all equipment used in surveying. Specifically the demonstration may include the following:

(a) How to wind and unwind 100 ft tapes without using a reel.

(b) How to wind the string on a plumb bob and how to tie a slip-loop knot.

(c) How to attach a spring balance to the tape.

(d) How to use a plumb bob with suspended tape.

(e) Proper position of a tapeman with respect to tape during measurements.

(f) How to carry the level and the transit when not in an open field (under the arm with the instrument in full view of the carrier).

(g) Uses of various instruments and equipment.

(h) How to set up instruments on tripods.

(i) Last, but not least, how to start keeping notes properly—to use the first half-page for the index; to page each double page with a single page number in the upper right-hand corner; to have the title of the exercise at the top of the left page and other data pertaining to the exercise at the top of the right page; and to record all field data on the left page. It should also be demonstrated *how to letter*—both the letters and the numbers.

CHAPTER 3

General Theory of Measurements

3-1. Introduction. Perhaps the first thing a person must learn about measurements is that no exact measurement is possible. For a measurement to be exact it must, theoretically, contain an infinite number of figures or an infinite number of zeros after the last recorded decimal. For instance, when Congress decreed that the standard meter should contain exactly 39.37 inches in this country, it meant that all decimals after 7 must be zeros. However, since it is impossible to determine an infinite number of digits, i.e., an infinite number of *significant figures* in a measured quantity, all measurements, no matter how accurate, will contain some errors.

The error is defined as the difference between the true value and the measured value of a quantity. But since no true value of a quantity can ever be ascertained by measurements, no exact value of an error can be found in such measurements. Such a situation may appear a bit discouraging, but in practical applications it is not as bad as it looks. Ordinarily, a scientific measurement is the kind of measurement that carries with it a fairly good indication of its accuracy. Thus all one needs to know in a practical application is whether the degree of accuracy of a given measurement is sufficient for a given application. If not, a better precision in the measurement must be specified.

Modern technology has advanced to the point where superficial knowledge of measurements is no longer adequate. Many costly and perhaps tragic failures may be avoided with a better understanding of the theory of measurements.

26

3-2. Accuracy and precision.   The accuracy of a measurement is
its conformity to a true value.   Thus if one measurement was carried out
with an estimated error of ± 0.01 in., and another with an estimated error
of ± 0.01 ft, it is said that the first measurement was carried out with a
greater accuracy than the second.

Thus if one wishes to describe the extent of accuracy numerically,
the total amount of error—or at least the estimated amount of error—
in a given measurement must be found.

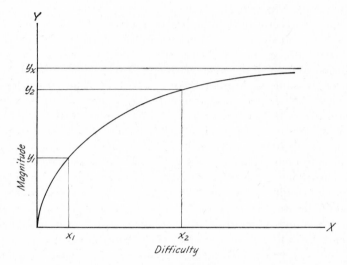

Fig. 3-1. Magnitude   of   measured   quantity   versus   difficulty
involved.

The total amount of error, however, does not give a good idea of the
extent of care that must be exercised in a measurement in order to achieve
a required accuracy.   It may be readily imagined, for instance, that
although measuring 1 inch to the nearest 0.01 of an inch is easily accomplished, measuring 100 feet with the same accuracy may present considerable difficulties.   In fact, the difficulty of maintaining the same
accuracy mounts rapidly with the increase in magnitude of a measured
quantity.

In plotting a curve showing the difficulty in measuring a certain
quantity with the same accuracy as the abscissa, and the magnitude of
the quantity as the ordinate, the curve would have a shape similar to that
shown in Fig. 3-1.   It may be seen from this figure that when the magnitude of a quantity reaches a certain value y_x, the difficulty approaches
infinity; i.e., it becomes insurmountable.   One may readily imagine, for

instance, that it is well-nigh impossible to measure one mile within one hundredth of an inch.

The above discussion points out that a statement of the total amount of error in a given measurement does not convey satisfactory information about the measurement unless the error is related to the magnitude of the measured quantity. For this reason the *relative error* or the ratio of the error to the measured quantity is used to indicate the accuracy of a measurement, which in its proper definition is **the degree of refinement obtained in a measurement.**

Relative error or relative accuracy is expressed by a fraction having the magnitude of error in the numerator and the magnitude of a measured quantity in the denominator, both expressed in the same units. Thus the accuracy of measuring 1 inch to the nearest 0.02 in. may be expressed as a fraction, $0.02/1$ or $\frac{1}{50}$, also written as $1:50$. The numerator in such fraction expressions is normally reduced to 1 in order to render an easy comparison with other measurements. For instance, comparing the above example with measuring one mile to the nearest foot, where relative accuracy would be expressed as $\frac{1}{5280}$, one may say that measuring one mile to the nearest foot is, relatively, about one hundred times as accurate a measurement as measuring 1 inch to the nearest 0.02 in.

The accuracies prescribed by various specifications for engineering measurements indicate not only the type of instruments and equipment that should be used in a given measurement, but also how close those instruments should be read in order to achieve the prescribed accuracies. In other words, a prescribed accuracy determines the *precision* with which to carry out a given measurement. Thus the precision may be defined as **the degree of refinement used in a measurement.** For instance, measuring one tape length with a 100 ft tape within 0.1 ft would indicate the precision of $\frac{1}{1000}$, while the same length measured within 0.01 ft would indicate precision of $\frac{1}{10,000}$. Such fractions, when applied to the precision of measurements, are called **precision ratios.**

It should be noted that, barring accumulation of personal and systematic errors, a measurement carried out with a higher degree of precision should result in a higher accuracy. For instance, in the tape measurements discussed above it is natural to expect a higher accuracy in a measurement made with $1:10,000$ precision than in one made with $1:1000$ precision. However, such may not always be the case. Assuming, for instance, that a mistake of 1 ft was made in the measurement of 100 ft carried out with $1:10,000$ precision, the resultant accuracy of measurement would be only $1:100$. In such a case, $1:10,000$ precision used in measurement resulted in $1:100$ accuracy obtained in measurement.

How one should go about selecting proper instruments and determining proper precision in reading them depends considerably on the judgment and the experience of the person planning and carrying out measurements. Some helpful ideas in this respect are discussed in Chapter 5.

3-3. Repeated measurements. It is possible to increase the accuracy of a measurement by making repeated measurements of the same quantity and taking the average of the results. The method of repeated measurements is used in all cases when precision of the instrument is lower than the prescribed accuracy. For instance, it may be required to measure an angle within 10″ with a transit which reads the angles only to the nearest minute.

Let it be assumed for instance that an angle known to be 5°10′13″ is measured with a one-minute transit. Since the transit used in this example reads only to the nearest minute, the scale reading after first measurement should be 5°10′, and after accumulated second measurement, 10°20′. However, after measuring the angle the third time the reading should be 15°31′, since 13″ repeated three times will accumulate to 39″ thus giving one extra minute on third reading. Similarly, after ten repetitions the recorded angle should be 51°42′. Dividing this value by 10 gives 5°10′12″. This result is only one second less than the known value. In this case an accuracy of one second has been achieved by a one-minute transit. The results will not always be as dramatic as in this example; nevertheless the example gives a good illustration of how accuracy may be improved by repeated measurements.

In those instances when the readings cannot be accumulated in repeated measurements, the prerequisite condition for improving the accuracy is that measurements must be of such an order of precision that there will be some variations in recorded values.

For instance, in measuring a length of about 100 ft with a 100 ft tape ten times under the same conditions, the readings may show variations within, say, ±0.02 ft. Thus measuring a length, known to be 99.500 ft, ten times, the recorded values may be as follows: 99.51, 99.50, 99.49, 99.48, 99.51, 99.52, 99.49, 99.52, 99.50, and 99.49. The average of these readings gives 99.501, which value is within 0.001 ft of the correct length. Here, again, reading the tape to the nearest 0.01 ft, or with a precision ratio of about 1:20,000, yielded 1:100,000 accuracy in the result, because of repeated measurements. In this connection it must be pointed out that the increased accuracy of the mean value of repeated single measurements is possible only if the discrepancies in measurements are entirely due to so-called accidental errors (see Art. 5-2 below).

It should be observed in the above example that if the precision ratio in measuring 99.50 ft were 1:100, all ten measurements would be recorded as 99.5 and the average still would be 99.5. In other words, *at a low order of precision no increase in accuracy will result from repeated measurements.*

Significant Figures in Measurements*

3-4. Definitions. This article presents the question of the significance of figures employed in recording observed values of measurements and in computations.

Since the true values of measured quantities must remain forever unknown, it is possible to obtain by measurements only approximations to true values. Such approximations are called *most probable values*, abbreviated sometimes as *MPV*. Thus a length measured to the nearest foot and recorded as 352 ft has this measurement as the most probable value of the length measured. If, however, the same length is measured to the nearest 0.1 ft and recorded as 352.0 ft, then this last measurement becomes the most probable value of the length measured, since it is a better measurement than the former. In each of the above two examples every recorded digit has a meaning and thus is a *significant figure*. There are three significant figures in 352 and four in 352.0. It should be obvious that it would be incorrect to record 352.0 in the first measurement or 352 in the second.

Not all recorded figures in a measurement may be accurate. For instance, a distance recorded as 438 ft might have been measured by pacing, in which case one could be quite sure that there are 4 hundreds in the measured distance and also reasonably sure that there are 3 tens. However, the number of units recorded as 8 may be in doubt, perhaps by as much as 7, 8, or more feet. The question arises then whether the 8 in 438 is still a significant figure.

It is said that *a figure is a significant figure if its uncertainty is less than 10 units in its place.* Thus the 8 in 438 will cease to be a significant figure when it is in doubt by 10 or more units. Similarly, 3 in 438 will not be a significant figure if its uncertainty is 10 or more units in its place, and so on. However, showing 438 as 440, if units are not significant, would be misleading, since recorded zero might be taken as being a significant figure. There seems to be no standard way to designate the last significant figure in a recorded measurement. The method followed in this book will show the last significant figure by underscoring. Thus 43̲0 will signify that units are not significant and 4̲00 will signify that tens as well as units are not significant. But a measurement recorded as 400 must be taken as having three significant figures.

It must also be noted that any zero preceding the first non-zero digit is not counted as a significant figure. For instance, a measurement recorded as 0.050 has only two significant figures.

* First published by the author in the *Journal of Industrial Engineering*, American Institute of Industrial Engineers, Inc., March–April 1959, p. 91.

3-5. Exact numbers. Since no measurement may have an exact value, the exact numbers, i.e., mathematically correct numbers, may be found only in non-measured values. Counting, for instance, may be recorded by an exact number, such as counting three sides of a triangle. This 3 may be recorded as 3.000 ... *ad infinitum.* It has an infinite number of significant figures; nevertheless it must be correctly written as 3, since it is not a measured quantity. Many constants in formulas have an infinite number of significant figures, such as 2 in the area $ab/2$ of a right-angled triangle having sides a and b.

3-6. Significant figures in computations. It is important to know how to ascertain the number of significant figures in the result of computations involving measured quantities. Often one can determine the number of significant figures in a result by a rule of thumb, but sometimes it is advisable to make a few simple calculations.

3-7. Addition. Let it be required to add three measured quantities, 3.75, 7.912, and 4.526. Whether the empty space where thousandths should have been recorded in 3.75 has any significance depends on how close the hundredths were ascertained. For instance, if 3.75 is known only to the nearest 0.02 units, the true value must be between 3.740 and 3.760. This range makes thousandths not significant because they are uncertain by ± 10 units in their place. However, should 3.75 be known to the nearest 0.01 unit, the range of uncertainty will be from 3.745 to 3.755, which makes thousandths uncertain only by ± 0.005 or by ± 5 units in their place. This makes thousandths significant even though they were not recorded.

The implication is that in adding 3.75, 7.912, and 4.526, the thousandths must be retained and the sum given as 16.188.

Of course the argument for retention of thousandths in the above example would be much weaker if two out of three given numbers did not have thousandths recorded, as in the set of numbers 3.75, 7.91, and 4.526. However, a careful computer would add these three numbers as 16.186 and then, if it were the last operation to be performed, he would give 16.19 as the final result, thus rounding it off to hundredths.

3-8. Rounding off numbers. In rounding off a number, i.e., in discarding the final digit (or digits), 1 must be added to the last retained figure if the first discarded figure is 5, 6, 7, 8, or 9 (five altogether), and the last retained figure must be left unchanged if the first discarded figure is 0, 1, 2, 3, or 4 (also five altogether). The so-called "computer's rule" in rounding off the numbers should not be applied to measured quantities. The rule is apparently devised for non-measured values where a zero at the end of a number like 5.460, being superfluous, normally would not be recorded. It is not superfluous in a measured quantity.   Zero is a number, and in measurements it must be treated like any other digit.

3-9. Subtraction.   Subtraction is the reverse of addition; thus the same rules used for addition must hold true for subtraction.

3-10. Multiplication.   The rule for the retention of significant figures in multiplication may be worked out for two measured quantities, a and b, and then extended to any number of factors.   Let Δa and Δb be the errors in a and b respectively.   Also let ΔP be the resulting error in the product, $P = ab$.   All the above errors could be either plus or minus, but in the process of derivation of expressions below only the positive sign for deltas is used.   The errors thus computed are the maximum errors, since no cancellation of terms is possible.

If we apply respective deltas to a, b, and P, the following equation will result:

$$P + \Delta P = (a + \Delta a)(b + \Delta b) \tag{3-1}$$

By multiplying out and discarding a relatively small term $\Delta a \cdot \Delta b$, Eq. (3-1) is reduced to

$$P + \Delta P = ab + \Delta a \cdot b + \Delta b \cdot a \tag{3-2}$$

By subtracting $P = ab$ from Eq. (3-2), and then dividing the result by $P = ab$, one obtains a very useful equation.

$$\frac{\Delta P}{P} = \frac{\Delta a}{a} + \frac{\Delta b}{b} \tag{3-3}$$

The same type of equation may be derived for any number of factors. For instance, Eq. (3-4) below may be derived for the product $P = abc$.

$$\frac{\Delta P}{P} = \frac{\Delta a}{a} + \frac{\Delta b}{b} + \frac{\Delta c}{c} \tag{3-4}$$

Every term in Eq. (3-4) shows the ratio of the error of a quantity to the quantity itself.   Thus, in words, Eq. (3-4) states that *the relative accuracy (error) of a product is equal to the sum of the relative accuracies (errors) of its factors.*   Since the word *accuracy* means proximity to a true value, the smaller the error, the greater the accuracy.

Of course every term in Eq. (3-4) may be multiplied by 100, in which case the equation can be stated in still another manner, namely: *the per cent of error in a product is equal to the sum of the per cent of errors in its factors.*

By solving Eq. (3-3) and Eq. (3-4) for ΔP, one can easily determine the number of significant figures in a product.

Example 3-1. Two sides of a right-angled triangle were measured as $a = 3.72$ ft and $b = 7.54$ ft. The respective accuracies in these measurements were $1:200$ and $1:500$. It is required to express the area of the triangle to a proper number of significant figures.

Solution: Carrying out complete multiplication,

$$P = \frac{ab}{2} = 14.0244$$

and from Eq. (3-3)

$$\frac{\Delta P}{14.0} = \frac{1}{200} + \frac{1}{500}$$

Solving for ΔP, $\Delta P = 0.098$.

Rounding to the nearest 0.01, and introducing a plus-or-minus sign in front of the result, $\Delta P = \pm 0.10$.

This shows that the uncertainty of hundredths is 10 units in their place; thus hundredths in the area are not significant and the area should be given as $P = 14.0$ sq ft.

It may be noted in the above example that both lengths a and b were measured to three significant figures, and that the product, P, also came out with three significant figures. This, however, will not always be the case, because if a had been given as, say, 2.92 instead of 3.72, the hundredths in the product would be significant and the area would have four significant figures.

As a rule, *the number of significant figures in a product is either the same as the number of significant figures in the least significant factor, or greater by one significant figure.* The least significant factor is one which has the smallest number of significant figures.

Since it would be a greater blunder to lose significant figures in computation than to retain those that are not significant, the safe rule in multiplication should be to *retain in the product one significant figure over those in the least significant factor.* If more accurate results are required, the proper number of significant figures can be ascertained by using Eq. (3-3).

Multiplication of any two measured quantities, expressed in the same units, can be represented graphically by the area of a rectangle as shown in Fig. 3-2. The shaded portion of the area represents the uncertainty in the product owing to errors Δa and Δb in the factors a and b. The crosshatched corner of the area represents the product $\Delta a \cdot \Delta b$ which was discarded in the derivation of Eq. (3-3) as being negligible.

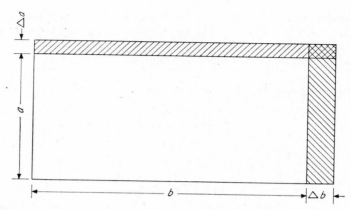

Fig. 3-2. Graphical representation of the product of two measured quantities.

3-11. Division. The same rules which apply to multiplication will apply to division, since division of two numbers like $\frac{a}{b}$ may always be represented as a product of a and $\frac{1}{b}$, where $\frac{1}{b}$ will have the same number of significant figures as b.

It may be easily proved that the maximum ΔQ in a quotient $Q = x/y$ may be obtained from the equation

$$\frac{\Delta Q}{Q} = \frac{\Delta x}{x} + \frac{\Delta y}{y} \tag{3-5}$$

3-12. Powers. Elevation into a power is the same as successive multiplication of a number by itself, the number of times being given by the exponent. Thus multiplication rules also apply in this case.

3-13. Roots. Consider a general expression, $\sqrt[n]{A} = x$. Elevating both sides of this expression to the n-th power, $A = x^n$. Thus

$$\frac{\Delta x}{x} = \frac{1}{n} \frac{\Delta A}{A} \tag{3-6}$$

This shows that *the per cent of uncertainty in a root is equal to the per cent of uncertainty in the radicand divided by the power of the root.* Let it be required, for instance, to find the number of significant figures in $\sqrt[3]{125}$. If it be assumed that 125 is known within, say, 1 unit, then $\Delta A/A = \frac{1}{125}$, $n = 3$, and $x = 5$. Substituting these values in Eq. (3-6), and solving for Δx, $\Delta x = \frac{1}{75} = 0.01$ approximately. This means that hundredths in $\sqrt[3]{125}$ are significant, so that the answer must be given as 5.00. Applying this dimension to the side of a cube, it means that in order to have the volume of the cube correct to the nearest cubic foot, 5-foot sides must be measured to the nearest 0.01 ft.

As a rule, *the number of significant figures in a root is either equal to the number of significant figures in the radicand, or is greater by one significant figure.* For instance, $\sqrt{3}$ must be given as 1.7 if 3 is known to the nearest unit. When in doubt, the question may be easily resolved by application of Eq. (3-6).

PROBLEMS

3-1. A rectangular field was measured by a Gunter's chain. Determine its area in square chains, in square feet, and in acres, giving in each case the answer to a proper number of significant figures, if field dimensions were recorded as:
(A) 15 ch. 5 lks. by 23 ch. 20 lks.
Ans. 349.2 sq ch., 1,520,900 sq ft, 34.92 acre
(B) 9 ch. 28 lks. by 30 ch. 72 lks.
(C) 24 ch. 17 lks. by 19 ch. 42 lks.

3-2. A right-angled triangular field was measured with a 100 ft tape. Determine its area in square feet and square miles, to a proper number of significant figures, if two sides of the field were measured as
(A) 72.31 ft and 152.7 ft.   *Ans.* 5521 sq ft, 0.00019804 sq mile
(B) 378.24 ft and 125.0 ft.
(C) 245.7 ft and 78.5 ft.

3-3. It is required to measure X ft with an accuracy of 1:5000, using a 100 ft tape. Determine maximum admissible error in measuring required distance and maximum admissible error in measuring 100 ft if X values are:
(A) 421.56 ft.   *Ans.* ± 0.084, ± 0.02
(B) 372.39 ft.
(C) 1538.5 ft.

3-4. Two sides, *EF* and *FG*, of a right-angled triangular field were measured with the same care, i.e., approximately with the same precision ratio, in order to obtain the area of the field with the accuracy of 1:300. Determine (a) precision ratio needed for measuring the sides; (b) maximum allowable error in measuring each side; and (c) maximum allowable error in determining the area of the field, if the measurements of the sides were recorded as shown below. Discuss whether recorded measurements were adequate to meet the accuracy required in the problem. Also give the area to a proper number of significant figures.
(A) *EF* = 32.2 ft, *FG* = 5.74 ft.
Ans. (a) 1:600, (b) ± 0.054 ft, ± 0.0096 ft, (c) ± 0.31 sq ft, 92.4 sq ft
(B) Required accuracy for the area is 1:400;
          EF = 41.6 ft, *FG* = 6.52 ft.

(C) Required accuracy for the area is 1:100;
$EF = 179.3$ ft, $FG = 231.5$ ft.

3-5. Each measurement DE and EF of the two sides of a right-angled triangle is known to be correct within 0.1 ft.   (a) compute maximum possible error in the area and (b) give the area to a proper number of significant figures underscoring the last significant digit.
  (A) $DE = 18.0$ ft, $EF = 22.6$ ft.   *Ans.* (a) ± 2.0 sq ft, (b) 20$\underline{3}$ sq ft
  (B) $DE = 125.7$ ft, $EF = 172.3$ ft.
  (C) $DE = 347.2$ ft, $EF = 282.4$ ft.

3-6. You, as the engineer on a job, must determine how precisely the two sides GH and HJ of a rectangular field must be measured in order to obtain the area to the nearest 10 sq ft.   (a) Find the precision ratio for measuring the sides with equal precision ratios; (b) determine the maximum admissible error in measuring each side; (c) determine whether the measurements must be made to the nearest foot, tenth, or hundredth of a foot.   The approximate lengths of sides are:
  (A) $GH = 240$ ft, $HJ = 150$ ft.
                   Ans. (a) 1:7200, (b) ± 0.033 ft, ± 0.021 ft, (c) 0.01 ft
  (B) $GH = 750$ ft, $HJ = 525$ ft.
  (C) $GH = 420$ ft, $HJ = 630$ ft.

3-7. Express the volume of a rectangular structure, having dimensions p, q, and z, with a proper number of significant figures, underscoring the last significant digit, if each dimension is reliable to 1 part in 200.
  (A) $p = 10.0$ ft, $q = 15.2$ ft, $z = 25.7$ ft.   *Ans.* 391$\underline{0}$ cu ft
  (B) $p = 17.3$ ft, $q = 28.5$ ft, $z = 20.4$ ft.
  (C) $p = 14.9$ ft, $q = 18.3$ ft, $z = 16.5$ ft.

3-8. The frontage length KL of a rectangular property is known to be correct to 1 part in 5000 and the width LM is known to be correct to 1 part in 1000. (a) Compute the amount of the uncertainty in the area and (b) express the area with a proper number of significant figures, underscoring the last significant digit.
  (A) $KL = 375.00$ ft, $LM = 200.00$ ft. *Ans.* (a) ± 90 sq ft, (b) 75,0$\underline{00}$ sq ft
  (B) $KL = 252.50$ ft, $LM = 175.00$ ft.
  (C) $KL = 156.00$ ft, $LM = 315.50$ ft.

3-9. The inside radius r of a circular concrete cistern and the height h are each known to be correct within 0.01 ft.   (a) Compute maximum possible error in the volume, (b) compute the volume and show it to a proper number of significant figures underscoring the last significant digit.
  (A) $r = 22.59$ ft, $h = 12.76$ ft.   *Ans.* (a) ± 34.1 cu ft, (b) 20,4$\underline{60}$ cu ft
  (B) $r = 10.34$ ft, $h = 8.72$ ft.
  (C) $r = 9.25$ ft, $h = 7.33$ ft.

3-10. The square base of a pyramid has the side d, which is known within 0.01 ft, but the height h is known only within 0.1 ft.   (a) Compute maximum possible error in the volume; (b) compute the volume and show it to a proper number of significant figures underscoring the last significant digit.

(A) $d = 14.32$ ft, $h = 27.8$ ft.   *Ans.* (a) ± 9.5 cu ft, (b) 190\underline{0} cu ft

(B) $d = 9.75$ ft, $h = 32.4$ ft.

(C) $d = 12.84$ ft, $h = 20.3$ ft.

3-11. If a cubic structure must be built so that its volume comes out correct within 1%, determine (a) the precision ratio for measuring the sides and (b) the maximum admissible error in measuring the sides, the length of which is given as follows:

(A) 6.50 ft.   *Ans.* (a) $1:300$, (b) ± 0.022 ft

(B) 10.32 ft.

(C) 8.45 ft.

CHAPTER **4**

Field Instructions—Measurements with Tape

4-1. General. This chapter describes in detail the way a steel tape and taping accessory equipment should be used in measuring distances if one is to achieve prescribed accuracies in such measurements.

The first thing a student must learn in surveying field practice is how to handle various instruments and equipment in order to achieve best results in measurements, and how to avoid any damage to measuring devices so that their usefulness will not be impaired or destroyed.

4-2. Winding and unwinding the tapes. Although there are rustproof tapes on the market, they are expensive. Commonly used dark gray steel tapes are made of hard steel but they are not rustproof. To prevent rusting after using such a tape on wet ground, one must wipe the tape first with a dry cloth and then with an oily cloth. The last operation is usually done while winding the tape into 5 ft loops or on a reel. The winding of a tape into loops can be best demonstrated by the field instructor. Unwinding the tape is the reverse of winding and also must be properly demonstrated in the field in order to forestall improper handling and possible damage to the tape. Winding and unwinding the tapes on reels (Fig. 2-2) require no special skills.

When the tape is being unwound and stretched on the ground, it must be free of loops and it must not be trampled upon. The tape will break when a loop is tightened. Stepping on the tape, especially with the heels, will produce a kink, and the tape will eventually break at that spot. With proper handling, a tape may last many years and still remain as straight as an arrow when stretched.

The operation of winding a tape into 5 ft loops starts at the zero end of the tape and proceeds in successive "figure-8 loops" (see Fig. 2-3a) to the 100 ft end. When the loops of a wound tape are stretched diametrically between two hands, a twist of each wrist "throws" the tape into a $2\frac{1}{2}$ ft circle (Fig. 2-3b). The operation is reversed in unwinding, so that the 100 ft mark is dropped near the point of beginning of measurement, and successive loops are dropped one by one as the person unwinding the tape proceeds in the direction of a line to be measured.

When the tape is wound on a reel (Fig. 2-2), the winding starts with the 100 ft end, thus leaving the zero end on the outside. In unwinding this tape along a measured line, the rear tapeman holds the reel at the point of beginning while the head tapeman walks ahead holding the zero end. Thus in unwinding a tape wound into loops or the one wound on a reel, the zero end of the tape is always carried forward.

Fig. 4-1. Holding the tape with spring balance over a point.

4-3. Aligning the tape. The tape must be aligned along the direction of a measured distance. On certain types of projects, such as route location, the alignment may be done by the transitman sighting with his transit telescope along the measured line. In the absence of a transit the rear tapeman aligns the head tapeman. The proper position of either tapeman with respect to the tape is standing or kneeling alongside the tape and holding it by the leather thong attached to the end of tape. In such position either tapeman may see the range poles set along the line of measurement (see Fig. 4-1).

4-4. Stretching the tape. The man carrying the zero end of the tape ahead is called the *head tapeman* and the one holding the 100 ft end or any intermediate footmark is called the *rear tapeman*. The head tapeman sets the pace of measurements and is generally the boss of the taping party.

In any taping for engineering purposes or for land surveying, the desired distance is the horizontal distance. Thus after the tape is unwound, it is stretched so that both ends are held at the same elevation. When the ground is not level or is covered by vegetation it is necessary to use plumb bobs either at one end of the tape (the downhill end) or at both ends.

When the accuracy required in taping is 1:3000 or better, the hand level (Fig. 2-15) is used to bring both ends of the tape to the same elevation. When the accuracy of taping is lower than 1:3000, the level line is estimated by eye. If three persons are doing the taping the hand level may be operated by the notekeeper. With only two men available for taping, the hand level is operated by the head tapeman on level ground, or by the downhill man on sloping ground.

In measuring over smooth, level ground, the tape is stretched on the ground and the 100 ft mark is held by the rear tapeman at the point of beginning while the head tapeman applies the desired tension (normally 10 lb) to his end of the tape. When required accuracy in taping is 1:3000 or lower, the 10 lb tension is estimated; for better accuracies the tension handle (Fig. 2-6) should be used. The tension handle is attached to the ring at the zero end of the tape. The first measuring operation is called *stretching for the stake*. The head tapeman finds the spot on the ground where the zero mark falls and drives the stake. When measurement of long distances is involved, a stakeman carrying a bag of stakes and a sledge hammer should be added to the taping party. The stakeman drives the stakes at the direction of the head tapeman. On engineering surveys the stake is driven flush, or nearly so, with the ground and a flat ($\frac{1}{2}$ in. by 2 in.) *guard stake* is driven at the spot before the party proceeds. A guard stake should project about 7 in. above the ground and should be driven at an angle in order to protect crayon marks on the underside of the stake from being washed off by rains.

4-5. Measuring a full tape length. After "stretching-for-the-stake," the tape is stretched a second time between the same points. This time the rear tapeman calls, "All right!" as soon as the footmark which he is holding is on the point. The head tapeman then marks his own point, where the zero mark falls on the stake, and drives there a tack (Fig. 2-9). The head tapeman may call for a check measurement or he may call, "Come ahead!" when he starts dragging the tape forward. The rear tapeman follows the 100 ft end of the tape and calls, "Tape!" when the tape approaches the stake set by the head tapeman. From there on the new length is measured in the same way.

4-6. Measuring a length shorter than 100 feet. In measuring a length shorter than 100 feet, the procedure is much the same as described above except that the rear tapeman holds some intermediate footmark instead of the 100 ft mark.

Let it be required, for instance, to measure 72.34 ft. Since only the last foot at each end is graduated into tenth and hundredth parts of a foot, the head tapeman subtracts 72.34 from 73.00 and obtains 0.66. Then he calls to the rear tapeman, "Hold 73!" and proceeds to set the stake and the tack 0.66 ft from the zero mark of the tape.

If two points, say 72.34 ft apart, are already on the ground, and it is required to measure that distance, the head tapeman holds the zero mark near his point and asks the rear tapeman what mark he is holding. If the rear tapeman attempts to hold the 72 ft mark on his point, the zero mark will fall short of the point over which the head tapeman is standing. The head tapeman then calls to the rear tapeman, "Hold 73!" and reads 0.66 ft at his end of the tape. He then calls, "Cut zero point six six!" The rear tapeman subtracts 0.66 from 73.00 and calls, "Seventy-two point three four!" If the head tapeman checks this number then the notekeeper enters that length in the field notebook.

When the tape is held at an intermediate footmark, the use of a tape clamp (Fig. 2-7) is recommended. The tape clamp allows the tape to be held without bending when tension is applied.

4-7. Use of plumb bobs. When the ground is covered by low brush, or when the surface is on a slope, it is necessary to use plumb bobs (Fig. 2-8) at one or both ends of a measured length. When it is possible, the uphill end of the tape should be held on the ground. It requires a bit of skill to make accurate measurements with a suspended tape, since the swinging of plumb bobs may throw off the measurement a few tenths of a foot. With a little practice it is possible to develop such teamwork that the readings are made when both plumb bobs are practically at a standstill.

When measuring a length between two established points, the head tapeman holds the string of the plumb bob over the tape with his thumb, so that he can slide it left or right until the bob is over the point (see Fig. 4-1). He can then read the tape after releasing the tension. In setting a point he holds the string over the tape at a desired graduation and watches only the plumb bob. When he hears repeated calls of the rear tapeman, "All right ... all right," he lowers his hands until the plumb bob touches the ground and notes the spot where the stake is to be driven. He also checks the graduation over which the string was held. The same procedure as that used for setting the stake is followed in setting the tack in the top of the stake.

4-8. Use of tension handle. The use of the plumb bob in measurements gets a bit more complicated when a tension handle (Fig. 2-6) is attached to the end of the tape (see Fig. 4-1). If one end of the tape is held on the ground and the other end is suspended, it is preferable to attach the tension handle at the ground end of the tape, since the tapeman at that end will not be watching a plumb bob and will have the firm support of the ground for his hands.   When both ends of the tape are elevated, the tension handle may be applied at the zero end of tape going forward, and at the 100 ft end going back.   This will allow the tapemen to check each other on the applied tension.

When a tapeman is holding both the plumb bob and the tension handle, it may be said that he, in a way, keeps one eye on the scale of the handle and another on the plumb bob.   His final sight must always be on the plumb bob before marking the point.

4-9. Closure in measurements.   No field measurement is made without a check or—as it is often said in surveying—without a closure. To effect a check in a linear measurement, the measurement is made both ways forward and back.   The average of the two measurements is then taken as the final value of a measured distance if no corrections need to be applied to the recorded lengths.   If there are corrections, the average of the corrected lengths is the distance measured.

Repeated measurements of a line may be made in order to increase the accuracy of measurements.   How the measurements should be made is normally left to the discretion of the engineer.

4-10. Recording of data.   The recording of field data is just as important as the measurement itself, since any care exercised in taking a measurement is useless unless a clear and legible recording is made.

The engineer's field notebook (Fig. 2-19), used for recording field data, is $4\frac{1}{2}$ by $7\frac{1}{2}$ in.   It has horizontal lines, and six vertical columns on the left page, and cross lines on the right page.   The right page also has a red line lengthwise through its center.   A single page number is placed in the upper right-hand corner of each double page.   The single page at the beginning of the book is used for an index showing the titles of the exercises and the page numbers.

All data taken in the field are recorded in the columns on the left page under the proper heading for each column.   At the top of the left page is recorded the title of the exercise or the type of work done (see Fig. 4-2).   At the top of the right-hand page the following data are recorded: date, weather, number of each instrument used in making measurements, number of the party, and names of the men doing the exercise.   Since in school exercises the duties of the students may be rotated during an exercise, the recording of only the names of the men should suffice.   In actual practice their duties are also recorded (Fig. 4-2).

It is very important that the recording be as neat as possible so that no errors will result in the copying of field data by office workers who are using those data for plotting and design purposes.   The headings and preferably all recordings should be lettered.   If a student has never practiced lettering he should start doing this with the first field exercise.

Special care must be taken to produce perfectly legible numbers. "5's" that look like "S's," "1's" that resemble "7's," or zeros that may be taken for "6's" are not tolerated. There is no place for such careless recordings since the errors may easily result in loss of time and money and on engineering projects may even result in failure of structures that endanger the lives of people.

All surveying textbooks recommend that recordings be made with a hard pencil, about 4-H, and that no erasures be made in the recorded field data. There is a good reason for such recommendations, since a

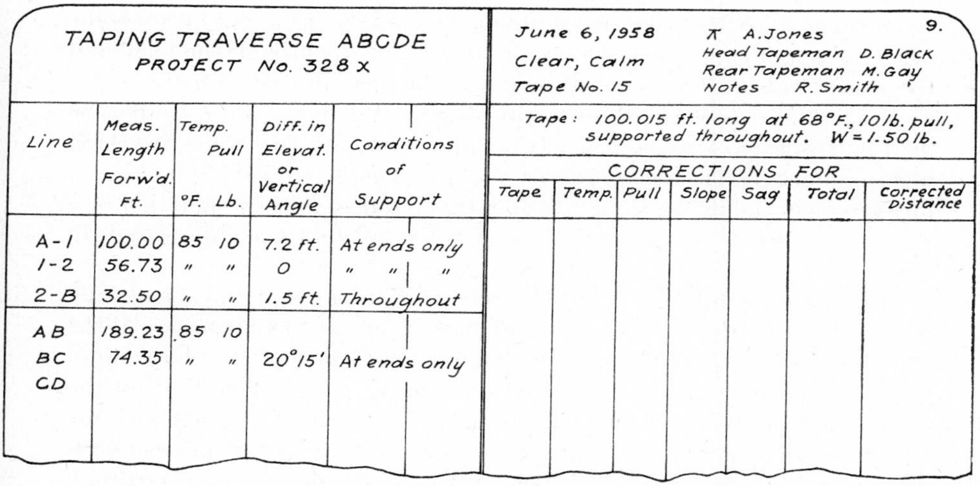

Line	Meas. Length Forw'd. Ft.	Temp. Pull °F. Lb.	Diff. in Elevat. or Vertical Angle	Conditions of Support	Tape	Temp.	Pull	Slope	Sag	Total	Corrected Distance
A-1	100.00	85 10	7.2 ft.	At ends only							
1-2	56.73	" "	0	" " "							
2-B	32.50	" "	1.5 ft.	Throughout							
AB	189.23	85 10									
BC	74.35	" "	20°15'	At ends only							
CD											

TAPING TRAVERSE ABCDE
PROJECT No. 328 X

June 6, 1958   ⚡ A. Jones   9.
Clear, Calm   Head Tapeman D. Black
Tape No. 15   Rear Tapeman M. Gay
               Notes   R. Smith

Tape: 100.015 ft. long at 68°F., 10 lb. pull, supported throughout. W = 1.50 lb.

CORRECTIONS FOR

Fig. 4-2. Recording of tape measurements.

soft pencil will smear, and erased data would not stand in court as a *bona fide* evidence of original measurements. Although such rules are important for practicing land surveyors, they are sound enough to be recommended also on engineering surveys.

A number recorded in the notebook and needing correction should be voided by a single line drawn through the number with the correct number written directly above the original one. For this reason, and for the sake of neatness and clearness of recorded data, field notes must not be crowded. The recording of a single exercise may be continued on the next page by writing at the top, "Exercise No. X, continued." However, if the same exercise is continued on a different date, a new page must be used with the new explanatory data at the top of the right-hand page.

The importance of *complete* recording of data hardly needs to be emphasized. For instance, it must be clear from the study of significant figures that a 100 ft distance, measured to the nearest hundredth of a foot, is not properly recorded if indicated merely as 100 ft, even though there might actually have been measured zero tenths and zero hundredths. A zero that comes after the decimal point is just as significant in measurements as any zero recorded to the left of the decimal point.

If any computations are made on the left page of the field notebook, they must be labeled to distinguish them from recorded measurements. It is a good practice, though, to use the right-hand page for computations, for making sketches, and for writing necessary explanations and descriptions to supplement the data recorded on the left page.

If it becomes desirable to rewrite an entire page, or to void it for some other reason, a single diagonal line must be drawn through the page and the word "void" must be written across the page in large letters.

4-11. Tape measurements on slope. When the tape cannot be held horizontally because of a steep slope, there are two ways of taking measurements—(1) *breaking tape* and (2) *slope measurement*, i.e., a measurement along the slope. The latter requires a later reduction of a measured length to corresponding horizontal distance (discussed in Chapter 7).

4-12. Breaking tape. The term *breaking tape* simply means making horizontal measurements in practical short lengths. For instance, if the whole tape length is to be measured on a downward slope, the zero end of tape is carried the whole tape length ahead of the last point set on the ground. Then the head tapeman returns and picks up the tape at some footmark which will allow him to hold horizontally the length between himself and the rear tapeman. Let it be assumed that the head tapeman holds the tape at the 80 ft mark. He then proceeds to measure the 20 ft span by the usual method, suspending the length between the 100 ft and 80 ft marks. After he sets the stake with the tack (or a pin) in the ground and is ready to measure the next short length, he calls to the rear tapeman, "Holding eighty." Then he drops the tape to the ground and proceeds to hold the tape at some other convenient footmark while the rear tapeman moves forward to hold the 80 ft mark on the point set by the head tapeman. From here on the procedure is repeated until the whole tape length is measured.

Let it be assumed that the head tapeman held the tape at 80, 30, and zero footmarks. The notekeeper would then record, under *Measured Length*, "100.00 ft," and under *Conditions of Support*, "supported at 100, 80, 30, and 0." This would mean that the suspended spans were 20, 50, and 30 ft. The procedure is the same when a measurement is made uphill, except that the tape footmarks picked up by the head tapeman are held, when possible, on the ground and the plumb bob is applied at the footmarks held by the rear tapeman.

4-13. Measuring along the slope.   In another method of measurement on sloping ground, the zero end of the tape is carried a full tape length ahead as before and a stake with tack is set at the zero end. The measurement is then made along the slope.   This method is practical only when the slope is uniform and when the unsupported spans along the tape do not exceed about 30 ft, which makes correction for sag negligible.   The recording is made as follows: under *Measured Length*, "100.00 ft on slope"; and under *Conditions of Support*, "Supported throughout" (see Fig. 4-2).

As far as horizontal measurement is concerned, the last measurement is not complete.   The stakes must be identified in the recording, preferably by letters, so that after the taping is completed the difference in elevation of those points can be determined by using either an engineer's level (Fig. 2-17), or a hand level, and a level rod (Fig. 2-14).   Such operations are described in detail in Chapter 9.

If the difference in elevation of points is needed only for the purpose of making corrections to slope measurements in order to reduce them to horizontal distances, the use of a hand level, a range pole, and a level rod may be found quite satisfactory on slopes not exceeding about 2% and for distances not exceeding 50 ft.   On a 2% slope the horizontal correction for a slope distance may be computed within 0.01 ft if the difference in elevation of points 50 ft apart is known within 0.1 ft.

4-14. Difference in elevation of points.   The procedure for determining the difference in elevation of two points by the use of a hand level is as follows: The hand level is held a certain number of feet above the higher of the two points.   This is done by holding a range pole vertically on the point and holding the hand level at a convenient footmark on the range pole.   For instance, assume this height to be 5 ft above the point. A level rod, graduated to hundredths of a foot, is then held on the lower point.   When the bubble of the hand level shows that the level is horizontal, the reading of the level rod is taken to the nearest 0.1 ft.   No finer readings should be attempted with a hand level.   Let such reading be 7.4 ft.   The difference in elevation of the two points is then $-7.4 + 5.0 = -2.4$ ft.

Since a range pole does not provide a satisfactory support for the hand level, special staffs, usually 5 ft long, are often made to support the hand level.   While a reading is taken the level is held in a notch made at the top of the staff.

When the hand level is used for determining the difference in elevation of points, such difference is recorded in the field notebook in a separate column, as shown in the sample of field notes (Fig. 4-2).   However, when the leveling operation is done with the engineer's level, the recordings are made on a separate page, explained in Chapter 9 and shown on Fig. 9-6.   In the latter case the differences in elevation of points for slope correction are computed from the data shown on the leveling page and are entered then in the proper column of the page containing taping data.

4-15. Slope measurement with clinometer.   A clinometer (Fig. 2-16) is a handy instrument for an approximate measurement of slopes. If the clinometer has a vernier for reading angles to 10′, the error of sighting on a point may be greater than 10′ owing to the difficulty of

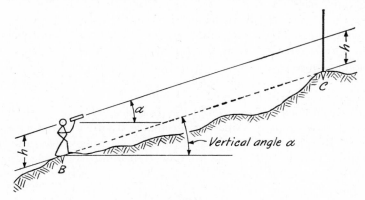

Fig. 4-3. Measuring vertical angle with clinometer.

holding the level bubble still.   It may be assumed that an error of 0.2 ft may result when one is determining the difference in elevation of points 50 ft apart.

It must be borne in mind that *correction for slope is proportional to the square of the difference in elevation of points.*   For instance, if the difference in elevation of two points is 1 ft, correction for slope is 0.005 ft in a distance of 100 ft.   Neglecting such a correction still would give 1:20,000 accuracy if no other errors were present.   However, if the same error of 1 ft is made in determining the difference in elevation of points when one is 10 ft higher than another, the error in slope correction will be $11^2 - 10^2 = 21$ times as great as 0.005, making it equal to 0.105 ft per 100 ft.   This gives only 1:1000 accuracy.   Thus *the greater the difference in elevation of points, the more accurately the difference should be determined.*

In measuring a vertical angle between two points set on the ground, the man using the clinometer stands over one of the points and determines the height of his eye by holding a graduated rod in front.   He sights then with the clinometer on the same point on the rod when it is held on the other point (see Fig. 4-3).   The angle that he reads on the clinometer is the vertical angle between the two ground points.

4-16. Slope measurement with transit. When the required accuracy of tape measurements is 1 : 3000 or better, and the vertical angle of a slope is greater than about 3°, neither hand level nor clinometer should be used to find the difference in elevation of points for tape measurements. If direct horizontal measurements are not practical because of a steep slope, a transit (Fig. 2-18) should be used for measuring vertical angles; or the difference in elevation of points should be accurately determined by the use of the engineer's level.

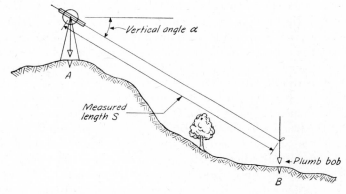

Fig. 4-4. Measuring vertical angle with transit.

Figure 4-4 shows two ground stakes marked by letters A and B. Let it be required to measure the horizontal distance AB using transit and tape. The transit may be set up at either point. Let it be at point A. By sighting point B through the transit's telescope, it is possible to measure the vertical angle that the line of sight makes with the horizontal. If point B is not visible because of an obstruction, the range pole may be held at B and the sight may be taken on any footmark along the range pole.

At the same time as the vertical angle is being measured, the tape is stretched from the horizontal axis of the instrument to the same footmark on the vertically held range pole to which the sight was taken with the transit. After measuring the slope distance S and the vertical angle α, it is possible to find horizontal correction S *vers* α to the measured slope distance S.

A taping party normally does not carry a range pole; thus instead of holding a range pole on point B, as described above, the plumb bob may be held at B. The sight is taken on a loop knot made on the plumb bob string. A slope measurement with the tape is then taken to the same point on the string.

4-17. Recording of data. In the measurement of distances over a rolling terrain, some tape spans may be measured horizontally while others may be measured along a slope. For finding horizontal correction to slope distances, in some cases the difference in elevation of points may be used while in others the measurement of vertical angle between points may be necessary or preferable. Thus it is important to adopt a method of recording the taping data which will clearly indicate how various span measurements were made.

Figure 4-2 shows the type of notes that are adaptable for almost any kind of tape measurements. The vertical angles that may be measured on some spans may be recorded in the "Difference in Elevation" column and, if desired, the column heading may be changed to read "Difference in Elevation or Vertical Angle." Sample recordings shown in Fig. 4-2 clearly indicate how measurements were made and should leave no doubt as to how horizontal corrections should be computed in each case.

4-18. Measurements with tally pins. On certain long-distance measurements, only the end points need be marked by stakes. For instance, in surveying property lines the stakes or monuments are often left only at the property corners. If all tape spans on such measurements are made in the same manner, i.e., with the tape either suspended or supported throughout, there is no need to record in the notebook each measured span; thus only total distances are recorded. However, in recording a distance like 2573 ft, it is easy to miscount the number of tape lengths measured. On such measurements tally pins (Fig. 2-10) must be used.

There are 11 tally pins on a ring. Leaving one pin with the rear tapeman at the point of beginning, the head tapeman carries ahead ten pins which he will use up after measuring ten full tape lengths. By this time the rear tapeman will have picked up nine pins from the ground. With the one that he had at the beginning he will hold ten pins, which he gives back to the head tapeman. This makes *the number of pins that the rear tapeman is holding, at any time, equal to the number of measured tape lengths, if measured distance is 1000 ft or less.*

After giving ten pins to the head tapeman the rear tapeman will again be left with one pin, which is the last pin that has been stuck in the ground and which has not been picked up at the end of measuring ten tape lengths, or 1000 ft, called a *tally.* Thus after measuring each tally, the procedure repeats itself until the end of the distance is reached. *The measured number of tape lengths is equal then to 10 times the number of tallies plus the number of pins in the hands of the rear tapeman* at the end of the measured distance. To this number multiplied by the length of the tape must be added an odd number of feet measured at the end of a line.

In order to keep the system practical on slope measurements with breaking-tape procedure, the rear tapeman retains only the pins picked up at the end of each 100 ft span. Any pin picked up by him at any intermediate footmark is passed immediately to the head tapeman.

The tally-pin procedure is important in property surveys. Tally pins are seldom used on engineering surveys.

FIELD EXERCISES

4-1. Calibration of Tapes

Party: Three or four men.

Equipment: 100 ft tape, spring balance, two pieces of masking tape, a short scale graduated to thousandths of a foot.

Object: To show how a tape may be calibrated during a laboratory period. Although laboratory calibration may not be as accurate as that of the National Bureau of Standards (NBS), it should meet requirements for accurate taping.

Procedure: If there are no tapes available that have been calibrated by the NBS or some other agency, the instructor may set aside a good tape and use it as a standard tape to calibrate other tapes. This will assure uniformity in all linear measurements made during subsequent field exercises.

It may be assumed that the standard tape is 100.000 ft long at 68°F and 10 lb pull, supported throughout, unless a calibrated tape is available.

For this exercise it is necessary to have enough floor space to stretch 100 ft tapes. Usually it is possible to find on the campus some unused hall or a corridor. If indoor space is not available it may be possible to find some shaded unused paved road or a walk.

The standard tape is stretched out and two pieces of masking tape are applied on the floor, one at the zero mark of the tape and another at the 100 ft mark. With a sharp, hard pencil and with the aid of a pocket straight edge, a short tick-line is next marked on the masking tape at one end of the tape, say at the 100 ft end.

A 10 lb tension is then applied to the tape by means of a spring balance. Since there will be some friction between the tape and the floor, it is advisable to use two spring balances, one at each end of the tape. When the 100 ft mark coincides with the marked line on the masking tape, the man at that end calls repeatedly, "All right ..." The man at the other end of tape should be ready to mark a dot (with a sharp pencil) opposite the zero mark of the tape when the tension at his end also indicates 10 lb. The same procedure is repeated several times and a tick-line is finally marked on the masking tape at the average position of the marked dots.

This procedure establishes a 100 ft distance for calibrating the tapes.

If due care is taken the marked distance may be reliable within one or two thousandths of a foot. When the 100 ft distance is marked on the floor, it is important that the tapes to be calibrated be stretched out on the floor at the same time as the standard tape so that all tapes will acquire the same temperature. This will eliminate the necessity of any temperature correction.

The tapes to be calibrated are then stretched one by one as described and the difference between the length of each tape and the distance set on the floor is measured by a scale divided into thousandths of a foot.

						3.
EXERCISE 4-1 CALIBRATION OF TAPE No.17				Sept. 20, 1958 Indoors Tape No.17	M.P. SMITH G.R. WOODS N.K. BLACK C.P. MOORE	

TRIAL NO.	LENGTH FT.	TENSION LB.		CONDITIONS OF SUPPORT		
1	100.002	10		Throughout		
2	100.003	"		"		
3	100.001	"		"		
4	100.005	"		"		
5						
etc.						

Fig. 4-5. Tape calibration recording.

Several trials for each tape are desirable. The average length of each tape from all trials is recorded then in the notebook as the calibrated length of tape No. X, at 68°F, 10 lb pull, supported throughout.

Notebook Recordings. Sample recordings given in Fig. 4-5 show recordings on the left-hand page of the field notebook.

4-2. Horizontal Taping
Party: Four men.

Equipment: 100 ft tape, two plumb bobs, one hand level, two range poles, two stakes, one set of tally pins, one tape clamp, one hatchet.

Object: To acquire practice in taping long distances, holding the tape horizontally; also to acquire practice in proper recording of measured distances.

Procedure: The instructor will assign, by setting range poles at terminal points, separate distances to be measured by each party. Each party will drive two stakes, one at each terminal point, and will proceed to tape the assigned distances between them by employing the method of holding both ends of the tape at the same elevation.

Each man should practice holding the tape in one hand and the plumb bob in the other, while holding the tape over a point. The duties of the men in a party should be divided as follows: one rear tapeman, one head tapeman, one stakeman, and one notekeeper. The notekeeper may also act as the chief of party for the group. The stakeman may use tally pins for stakes at all intermediate points. Although the hand level is normally operated by one of the tapemen, it would be well to give the hand level to the stakeman since it is hard for an inexperienced tapeman to use the tape, the bob, and the hand level. Besides, the stakeman's duties are light, since he is carrying only tally pins instead of the bag of stakes and the sledge hammer he would carry on actual engineering surveys.

In measuring the first span the rear tapeman is at the point of beginning and the head tapeman is holding the zero end of the tape and the plumb bob at the zero mark. The rear tapeman aligns the head tapeman with the range pole set up at the far end of the line. The stakeman, using a hand level, tells the tapemen to raise or lower their hands until the ends of tape are held at approximately the same elevation. When the rear tapeman calls, "All right here," the head tapeman lowers his hands slightly until the end of the plumb bob touches the ground. He does so when he estimates that the pull on the tape is about 10 lb, and when the plumb bob is fairly calm (not swinging). The stakeman then inserts the pin at about a 45° angle where the plumb bob touches the ground. The party then proceeds to measure the next span.

The notekeeper records each measured tape length, estimated or measured tension, and conditions of support for each span. In accurate taping he also records the temperature. In accurate taping the spring balance must be used.

In measuring the second span the rear tapeman proceeds to the pin set by the head tapeman and the same procedure is repeated until the end point is reached. The tape is then reversed and the same distance is measured in the opposite direction.

Figure 4-2 shows a sample of recordings of the measurement of several spans, going forward. Notes of the same type are used to record measurements made in the opposite direction; that is, "Measurements Back." It should be noted that recordings are made in such a way that corrections owing to variations in temperature, sag, or pull can be made after the field work is completed. Such corrections, which are caused by systematic errors in taping, are discussed in Chapter 7.

A separate page is used to show average values of corrected distances, as shown in Fig. 8-5. Notes of the type shown on this figure are also used when no tape corrections are necessary. The recordings shown on Fig. 4-2 are then omitted altogether.

CHAPTER 5

Accidental or Random Errors
in Measurements

Measurements of Equal Weight

5-1. Three types of errors. Discussion of measurements presented in Chapter 3 indicates that much in the theory of measurements depends on errors. There are three types of errors that may occur in a recorded measurement—*accidental, systematic,* and *personal.*

5-2. Accidental error. Assume that a distance closely equal to 100 ft is measured with a 100 ft tape graduated into tenths and hundredths of a foot. The result of a measurement may show that the measured distance is between 99.92 and 99.93 ft. When measuring with a tape graduated to hundredths of a foot, it is possible to estimate the thousandths, say, within about ± 0.002 ft. Thus the final result may show the length for instance as 99.924 ± 0.002 ft.

The plus and minus signs for the estimated error of 0.002 show that it is only the magnitude of the error that can be estimated—not its sign. Such errors are called **accidental** or **random errors.** Although random errors are present in all measurements, their magnitude becomes evident only when the precision of a measurement is such as to throw a certain amount of doubt on the validity of the last recorded digit. For instance, variations in the hundredths place in ten measurements of a distance, shown in Art. 3-3, are due to the presence of accidental errors.

Accidental errors may be greatly reduced but they cannot be completely eliminated.

5-3. Systematic error.   Other errors may also occur in the above-given measurement of 99.924 ± 0.002. For instance, the calibrated length of the tape might be equal to 100.010 ft, which means that each time 100.00 ft is read on the tape, the actual measured length is 100.01 ft; i.e., the recorded measurement is 0.01 ft short.   Thus the correction to be applied to a 100 ft measured length must be +0.01 ft.   This type of error will repeat itself in other measurements with the same sign and thus will accumulate.   For this reason this type of error is called *cumulative* or *systematic error*.   Measuring instruments may be calibrated for various measuring conditions and their systematic errors may be ascertained with a desired accuracy.   Corrections for systematic errors in taping are considered in Chapter 7.

5-4. Personal error.   The third type of error that may be present in a recorded measurement is the *personal error.*   Personal errors are mistakes made either in reading an instrument or in recording the results of measurements.   These errors may be easily eliminated by using appropriate checking procedures in taking and recording the measurements.

Of the three types of errors mentioned above the most elusive errors, and consequently those that are likely to cause most trouble in accurate measurements, are accidental errors.   The rest of this chapter is devoted to the explanation of the theory underlying these errors.

5-5. Law of chance.   The magnitude of accidental errors is seldom estimated by guessing.   There is a mathematical theory called the *theory of probability* which expounds the laws governing the behavior of accidental errors.

The theory of probability is based on the law of chance which in its simplest form may be demonstrated by tossing a coin.   The coin, it will be assumed, has an equal chance to show either head or tail.   Thus there are 50 chances for heads and 50 chances for tails in 100 throws.   This means that if the probability of all possible cases (heads plus tails in this case) is made equal to 1, the probability of getting heads will be $\frac{1}{2}$ and the probability of getting tails will be $\frac{1}{2}$, i.e., in each case, one-half of total occurrences of all events.

It should be immediately apparent that the occurrence of any doubtful event will conform more and more to this law of chance as the number of events increases.   For instance, when tossing a coin twice one may easily expect two heads or two tails in a row, but it is most improbable that either 100 heads or 100 tails will occur if one tosses a coin 100 times.

The theory of probability assumes an infinite number of occurrences of all possible events; however, the theory may be applied with good results to a limited but fairly large number of observations.

The probability of occurrence of a single event or of a combination of a few events may be computed mathematically for a small number of possibilities without much difficulty, as it was done above in the case of tossing a coin. However, as the number of possible events increases, the mathematics becomes more complicated. Therefore, it becomes necessary to learn about a general pattern that the occurrence of various events is most likely to follow.

The accidental errors in measurements are analogous to any doubtful events that must follow the law of chance in a large number of observa-

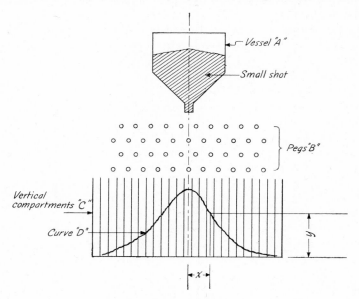

Fig. 5-1. Shot apparatus.

tions. The general pattern of distribution of accidental errors of various magnitudes may be studied in a *shot apparatus* shown diagrammatically in Fig. 5-1.

5-6. Shot apparatus. Small shot, held in a vessel A, are allowed to drop one by one through the opening at the bottom of the vessel. The shot are collected in the vertical compartments C. A number of pegs B are inserted between the vessel and the vertical compartments.

If there were no interference by the pegs, all the shot would fall into the same vertical compartment directly under the opening of the vessel. This direction of fall may be regarded as the true direction, synonymous with a true value of a measurement; i.e., one which has zero error. However, owing to the obstacles afforded by pegs, the shot will distribute itself in a certain pattern, so as to form a curve D. The shape of this curve, shown in Fig. 5-1, is typical of the random distribution of deviations of the shot from the true direction.

If one draws an analogy of a number of repeated measurements of the same quantity with the number of the shot dropped, the pegs represent all those conditions which make an exact measurement impossible. The manner in which the pegs are spaced is synonymous with a variance in those conditions and will affect the shape of the curve. The deviation of fallen shot from the vertical line of symmetry corresponds to the magnitude of accidental errors obtained in repeated measurements. It is apparent that in order to obtain a smooth, symmetrical curve by plotting the number of measurements along the y-axis and the errors

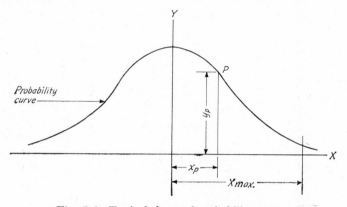

Fig. 5-2. Typical shape of probability curve.

along the x-axis, as shown in Fig. 5-2, a great number of measurements must be taken.

5-7. Probability curve. Theoretically, a perfectly smooth and symmetrical curve of errors, or *probability curve*, will be obtained from an infinite number of measurements. The ends of this curve approach the x-axis *asymptotically*, which means that, theoretically, there is an infinitely small chance for the magnitude of some errors to be equal to infinity. However, in practical applications the maximum magnitude of an accidental error in a series of measurements is assumed to be at some value x_{max} (Fig. 5-2) which is easily estimated from the magnitude of a *probable error* as described below.

The area under the curve D in Fig. 5-1 includes the number of all shot dropped, and the height of shot in any compartment represents the number of shot having a certain deviation from the central vertical line. In case of measurements, the area under the curve is considered to be equal to *unity*, meaning that the probability of occurrence of all possible errors has been included under the curve. Thus the y-ordinate (Fig. 5-2) to any point P on the curve, having the abscissa equal to x, is a number representing the probability of occurrence of the error of magnitude x. For instance, in the case of tossing a coin the probability of occurrence of the head is $\frac{1}{2}$ and the probability of occurrence of the tail is also $\frac{1}{2}$, based on probability of occurrence of all events equal to 1. Thus the probability curve in the case of tossing a coin is a straight line, having the ordinate equal to $\frac{1}{2}$, and the equation of the probability curve is $y = \frac{1}{2}$. For each throw of a coin an ordinate may be plotted, to the right of the y-axis, say for heads, and to the left of y-axis for tails.

In case of a great number of possible events, such as accidental errors in a great many repeated measurements, there are, theoretically speaking, an infinite number of possible ordinates, and the general equation of the resulting probability curve may be mathematically derived to be

$$y = \frac{h}{\sqrt{\pi}} e^{-h^2 x^2} \tag{5-1}$$

In Eq. (5-1), y is the probability of occurrence of accidental error of magnitude x, e is the base of natural logarithms, and h is a constant for a given series of observations. This constant determines the height of rise of the probability curve in the middle and the rate of rise and fall on each side of the y-axis.

Let it be assumed for example that the true value of a quantity is 6.00 of some unit, that 24 measurements were made of this quantity, and that they were tabulated in column 2 of Table 5-1 under m. For the convenience of analysis these measurements are arranged in the order of magnitude.

The mean value of these measurements, shown at the bottom of column 2, is 6.0075 or 6.01 to the nearest hundredth of a foot. In the absence of better measurements this mean value is *the most probable value.* In order to be able to estimate the respective errors of individual measurements it must be assumed that the most probable value is the true value of the quantity being measured. Then the estimated error in any single measurement may be found as the difference between the measurement and the most probable value of the measured quantity. Such difference is called a *residual* or a *deviation.* In Table 5-1 the residuals are designated by letter v and are shown in column 3. The heavy lines in this column show that there is one error which falls between the limits -0.3 and -0.4, two errors between -0.2 and -0.3, four between -0.1 and -0.2, and so on.

5-8. Frequency-distribution diagram. By plotting the errors shown in column 3 along the x-axis as abscissas and the numbers of errors that fall between the indicated limits along the y-axis as ordinates, one

TABLE 5-1

1	2	3	4
	m	v	v^2
1	5.63	−0.38	0.1444
2	5.71	−0.30	0.0900
3	5.78	−0.23	0.0529
4	5.82	−0.19	0.0361
5	5.84	−0.17	0.0289
6	5.86	−0.15	0.0225
7	5.87	−0.14	0.0196
8	5.92	−0.09	0.0081
9	5.93	−0.08	0.0064
10	5.95	−0.06	0.0036
11	5.97	−0.04	0.0016
12	6.01	0.00	0.0000
13	6.02	0.01	0.0001
14	6.05	0.04	0.0016
15	6.06	0.05	0.0025
16	6.07	0.06	0.0036
17	6.13	0.12	0.0144
18	6.15	0.14	0.0196
19	6.16	0.15	0.0225
20	6.19	0.18	0.0324
21	6.21	0.20	0.0400
22	6.23	0.22	0.0484
23	6.27	0.26	0.0676
24	6.35	0.34	0.1156
Avg = 6.0075	$\dfrac{[v]}{n} = 0.15$	$\Sigma v^2 = 0.7824$	

$$\Sigma\,(-v) = -1.83, \quad \Sigma\,(+v) = 1.77$$

obtains a broken line shown in Fig. 5-3. This broken line represents a so-called *frequency-distribution diagram*. If a smooth curve is drawn through the broken line, it becomes evident that one may closely approximate the shape of the probability curve by plotting the deviations of a limited number of observations and by using the mean value of repeated measurements as representing the true value of a measured quantity.

5-9. The probable error. There are other important conclusions that may be derived from the results plotted in Fig. 5-3. For instance,

the average value of all negative errors (residuals) shown in Table 5-1 is
$-1.83/11 = -0.167$, and the average value of all positive errors (residuals) is $1.77/13 = 0.136$, although the average absolute value of all errors is equal to 0.15. If the curve were symmetrical about the y-axis the average negative error would be -0.15 and the average positive error would be $+0.15$. The significant thing about this number (±0.15) is that close to 50 per cent of the negative errors are greater than -0.15 and close to 50 per cent of the negative errors are less than -0.15.

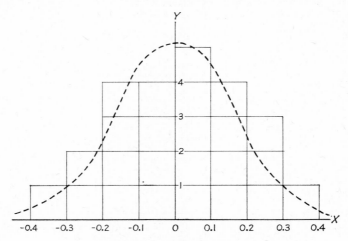

Fig. 5-3. Frequency-distribution diagram.

Also there are close to 50 per cent positive errors which are greater than $+0.15$ and close to 50 per cent positive errors which are less than $+0.15$.

By definition an error with a probability of 0.5, or a *50 per cent error*, is called the ***probable error*** of a single observation. In order to obtain the value of this probable error from a symmetrical probability curve (Fig. 5-4), the area under the curve may be so divided as to make the central (shaded) portion equal to one-half the total area. This makes the probable error equal to $\pm x_p$, as shown in Fig. 5-4.

In practice, however, the value of the probable error can be closely approximated by multiplying the average residual, irrespective of sign, by the constant 0.845. Thus, by designating the probable error of a single observation by E, one may state that

$$E = \pm 0.845 v_{\text{avg}} \quad \text{(very closely)} \tag{5-2}$$

Applying Eq. (5-2) to the example of Table 5-1,

$$E = \pm 0.845 \times 0.15 = \pm 0.127$$

The probable error multiplied by 3 gives a 95 per cent error, which is so called because, theoretically, 95 per cent of the measurements will have errors smaller than the 95 per cent error. Since the theoretical value of the maximum error is equal to $\pm \infty$, which never can occur in practice, the 95 per cent error may be regarded as the maximum error in all practical applications.

For the example given in Table 5-1 the maximum error may be estimated as $\pm 0.127 \times 3 = \pm 0.38$. Table 5-1 shows that this is a very reasonable estimate, since maximum negative error is given as -0.38 and maximum positive error as 0.34.

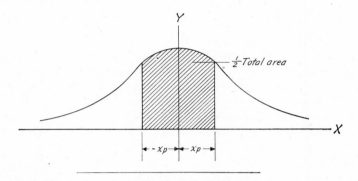

Fig. 5-4. Magnitude of probable error.

When the coefficient of Eq. (5-2) is multiplied by 3, one obtains the following approximate expression for the maximum random error:

$$E_{\max} = \pm 2.54 v_{\text{avg}} \quad \text{(approximately)} \tag{5-3}$$

5-10. Computation of probable error according to the theory of probability. Computation of probable error of a single observation according to the theory of probability is slightly more complicated. First, all residuals are squared, as shown in column 4 of Table 5-1, giving the values of v^2. The summation of these values, written as Σv^2, divided by $n - 1$ gives $\Sigma v^2/(n - 1)$, where n is the total number of observations. The quantity $\Sigma v^2/(n - 1)$ is called the **variance,** and the square root of the variance is called the **standard error,** the **standard deviation,** or the **mean square error.** Thus

$$\text{standard error} = \sqrt{\frac{\Sigma v^2}{n - 1}} \tag{5-4}$$

The standard error multiplied by the constant 0.6754 gives the probable error E of a single observation.   Thus

$$E = 0.6745 \sqrt{\frac{\Sigma v^2}{n - 1}} \tag{5-5}$$

Applying Eq. (5-5) to the example given in Table 5-1,

$$E = 0.6745 \sqrt{\frac{0.7824}{23}} = \pm 0.124$$

This value is very close to the probable error ± 0.127 computed by Eq. (5-2), using the average of the absolute values of deviations.

5-11. Practical deductions.   Rounding off the probable error, computed above to ± 0.13, it may be said that any single measurement of the example given in Table 5-1 has probable error ± 0.13.   For instance, applying this probable error to 5.78, which is the third measurement shown in the table, one may write 5.78 $\pm$ 0.13.   This gives two limits for the measurement, 5.65 and 5.91, which, according to the definition of probable error, means that there is only a 50-50 chance that the true value of the measured quantity falls between these two limits.   Or, expressing it mathematically, the probability of occurrence of true value between those limits is $\frac{1}{2}$ and beyond those limits it is also $\frac{1}{2}$.   In this case the true value, which was assumed to be 6.00, falls outside those limits.

If, however, the estimated maximum error ± 0.38 is applied to any single measurement, one may be reasonably sure that the true value of the measured quantity will fall between the obtained limits.   For instance, 5.78 $\pm$ 0.38 gives 5.40 and 6.16 as the two limits, and the assumed true value does fall between these limits.

5-12. Probable error varies as the square root of the number of observations.   It is a well-established fact that a probable error tends to increase or decrease, as the case may be, in proportion to the square root of the number of observations.   As the accuracy of a measurement increases, the probable error gets smaller, and as the accuracy decreases the probable error gets larger.   For instance, in the example shown in Table 5-1, the mean value of 24 measurements was computed to be 6.01, which is a better value of the measured quantity than a random value of a single measurement.   Thus the probable error of the mean value must be smaller than the probable error of a single observation.   Furthermore, it is not 24 times smaller, but $\sqrt{24}$ times.   In other words, the probable error of the average value 6.01 is $0.13/\sqrt{24} = \pm 0.0265$ or ± 0.03.

By designating the probable error of a mean value by E_m and the probable error of a single measurement by E as before, one may write that

$$E_m = \frac{E}{\sqrt{n}} \qquad (5\text{-}6)$$

where n is the number of repeated measurements.

Substituting in Eq. (5-6) the value of E given by Eq. (5-5),

$$E_m = 0.6745 \sqrt{\frac{\Sigma \, v^2}{n(n-1)}} \qquad (5\text{-}7)$$

It is just as important to be able to estimate the probable error E_s of the sum of several measurements if the probable error E of a single measurement is known. For instance, ± 0.13 might have been the probable error of measuring a 100 ft distance with a 100 ft tape. What then will be the probable error of measuring 400 ft with the same tape? In this case four new measurements must be made with the tape, and this will cause the probable error E to increase $\sqrt{4}$ times. Thus probable error in measuring 400 ft is $\pm 0.13 \times 2 = \pm 0.26$ ft.

Showing this by a general expression, one may write that

$$E_s = E \sqrt{n} \qquad (5\text{-}8)$$

where n is the number of measurements added together, and each measurement has probable error equal to E.

Measurements of Unequal Weights

5-13. Weighted mean of repeated measurements. Since nothing was said in the example shown in Table 5-1 about varying conditions of measurements, it must be assumed that all 24 measurements were made under similar conditions. Measurements made under similar conditions are said to be of equal reliability or to have equal **weights.** This may not always be the case. Assume, for instance, that a distance between two established points on the ground was measured on two different occasions. On the first occasion the weather was calm and mild and the result of measurements was recorded as 200.73 ft. On the second occasion it was windy and cold and the result was recorded as 200.80 ft. In order to be able to average these two results properly, one should estimate relative reliability of recorded values, i.e., apply certain weights to them.

The assignment of weights to the observed values is often a matter of judgment. A person experienced in observations for which the weights are applied would naturally be expected to exercise better judgment than an inexperienced person.

When two values are averaged, as in the example given above, it is necessary first to apply corrections for any possible systematic errors present in these values. Assuming that such corrections have been made, one might assign a weight of 2 to the first measurement and a weight of 1 to the second. This means that the recorded measurement of 200.73 ft is regarded as being twice as reliable as the measurement of 200.83 ft. Since it is only the relative weights that are significant, any weights in the ratio of 2 to 1 may be assigned instead of 2 and 1. For instance, the weights may be 4 and 2 or 1 and $\frac{1}{2}$.

In the averaging of the weighted values, each value is multiplied by its weight and the sum of the products is divided by the sum of the weights. These operations are shown below.

$$200.73 \times 2 = 401.46$$
$$200.80 \times 1 = 200.80$$

summations   3   602.26

$$\text{the weighted mean} = \frac{602.26}{3} = 200.75$$

It may be observed that instead of multiplying recorded values by their weights, it is sufficient to apply weights to the differences between recorded values and any arbitrary number. In the above example, for instance, the weighted mean could have been taken of 0.73 and 0.80 which gives $(1.46 + 0.80)/3 = 0.75$. This is then added to 200.00, which is the number that has been subtracted from the recorded values. Thus the computed mean value is 200.75—the same as that obtained above.

5-14. The weights are directly proportional to the number of repeated observations. It is a common occurrence in measurements that all single measurements may be of equal reliability but that some quantities may be measured more times than the others. In such cases the weights applied to a mean value of several measurements must be proportional to the number of repetitions used in those measurements. For instance, if a quantity was measured n_a times on one occasion and n_b times on another, the ratio of the weight W_a applied to the mean value of n_a measurements to the weight W_b applied to the mean value of n_b measurements must be in direct proportion to the number of measurements, or

$$\frac{W_a}{W_b} = \frac{n_a}{n_b} \tag{5-9}$$

5-15. Corrections applied to measurements are inversely proportional to the number of repeated measurements.   It is logical to assume that if one measurement is twice as reliable as another, the correction that must be applied to the first measurement should be one-half of that applied to the second measurement.   In other words, corrections applied to various observations must be inversely proportional to their weights, or

$$\frac{C_a}{C_b} = \frac{W_b}{W_a} \tag{5-10}$$

where C_a and C_b are corrections applied to the quantities having respective weights W_a and W_b.

By combining Eqs. (5-9) and (5-10), one obtains

$$\frac{C_a}{C_b} = \frac{n_b}{n_a} \tag{5-11}$$

Equation (5-11) means that corrections applied to mean values of various quantities must be inversely proportional to the number of repeated measurements of the respective quantities.

Assume for instance that three angles of a triangle ABC were measured as follows: angle A was measured six times, angle B four times, and angle C twice.   It is required to apply corrections to each angle if the sum of the average values of these angles is equal to $180°01'00''$.

According to Eq. (5-9) the weights W_a, W_b, and W_c applied to angles A, B, and C respectively must be in direct proportion to the number of measurements; i.e., $W_a:W_b:W_c = 6:4:2$.   This proportion does not change if the numbers on the right side of the equation are multiplied by $\frac{1}{2}$, thus giving a simpler ratio of $3:2:1$.   Thus the weights may be given as $W_a = 3$, $W_b = 2$, and $W_c = 1$.

Also, according to Eq. (5-10), corrections C_a, C_b, and C_c applied to three angles must be inversely proportional to the weights.   Or, $C_a:C_b:C_c = \frac{1}{3}:\frac{1}{2}:1$.   Here again the ratios on the right side of the equation may be simplified by multiplying each number by the common denominator, i.e., by 6, giving $C_a:C_b:C_c = 2:3:6$.

The total number of parts in the last proportion is $2 + 3 + 6 = 11$.   Thus corrections applied to angles A, B, and C must be, respectively, $\frac{60}{11} \times 2 = 11''$, $\frac{60}{11} \times 3 = 16''$, and $\frac{60}{11} \times 6 = 33''$, where $60''$ was the excess of the sum of three angles over $180°$.   As a check, the total correction applied is $11 + 16 + 33 = 60''$.   It should be noted that the proportional parts of corrections can be worked out directly from Eq. (5-11).

Computations in problems of this type may be conveniently arranged in tabular form as in Table 5-2.

Example 5-1. Four angles a, b, c, and d were measured around the horizon (around a point) with the results shown in Table 5-2 below. It is required to adjust the measured angles.

The solution is arranged in tabular form in Table 5-2 by using Eq. (5-11), i.e., by computing corrections to measured angles in inverse proportion to the number of measurements.

TABLE 5-2

Angle	No. of Measurements	Average Values	$\frac{1}{n}$	Relative Parts of Correction	Actual Corrections	Adjusted Angles
a	1	30°15'12"	$1 = \frac{12}{12}$	12	$12'' \cdot \frac{12}{25} = 5.8''$	30°15'06.2"
b	2	25°10'05"	$\frac{1}{2} = \frac{6}{12}$	6	$12'' \cdot \frac{6}{25} = 2.9''$	25°10'02.1"
c	4	170°27'25"	$\frac{1}{4} = \frac{3}{12}$	3	$12'' \cdot \frac{3}{25} = 1.4''$	170°27'23.6"
d	3	134°07 30"	$\frac{1}{3} = \frac{4}{12}$	4	$12'' \cdot \frac{4}{25} = 1.9''$	134°07'28.1"
Σ	10	360°00'12"		25	12.0	360°00'00"

5-16. Probable errors in measurements of unequal weights. It has been discussed above how to apply weights to various measurements and how to adjust the measurements according to the number of observations. In some instances, however, the probable errors of various observations may be known, making it necessary to apply weights according to the probable errors.

Equation (5-6) shows that probable errors vary inversely as the square root of the number of observations, since the equation may be written as $E_m : E = \sqrt{1} : \sqrt{n}$. Or in general, if E_a is the probable error of the mean value of n_a observations, and E_b is the probable error of the mean value of n_b observations of the same quantity, $E_a : E_b = \sqrt{n_b} : \sqrt{n_a}$. By squaring both sides of this proportion, one obtains

$$\frac{E_a^2}{E_b^2} = \frac{n_b}{n_a} \tag{5-12}$$

Substituting in this equation the value of n_b/n_a from Eq. (5-9),

$$\frac{E_a^2}{E_b^2} = \frac{W_b}{W_a} \tag{5-13}$$

Equation (5-13) shows that *the weights vary inversely as the squares of probable errors.* Substituting further in Eq. (5-13) the value of W_b/W_a from Eq. (5-10), one obtains

$$\frac{E_a^2}{E_b^2} = \frac{C_a}{C_b} \qquad (5\text{-}14)$$

Equation (5-14) shows that **adjustment of observations may be made in direct proportion to the square of probable errors.** Equation (5-14) has a wide application in adjustment of measurements which *do not close* because of the presence of random errors. For instance, the data given in Example 5-1 show that the angles measured around the horizon do not close to 360° owing to the presence of random errors in measurements. If in this example the probable error of each angle were known instead of the number of measurements, the angles could have been adjusted by application of Eq. (5-14).

Example 5-2. A quantity was measured repeatedly on three different occasions and the probable error of each mean value was computed with the following results:

First set of measurements	112.12 ± 0.07
Second set of measurements	112.30 ± 0.02
Third set of measurements	112.36 ± 0.05

It is required to obtain the weighted mean of the three sets of measurements.

Solution: According to Eq. (5-13) the weights applied to each set of measurements must be in inverse proportion to the square of probable errors.

TABLE 5-3. SOLUTION OF EXAMPLE 5-2

(1)	(2)	(3)	(4)	(5)	(6)
$m - 112.00$	E	E^2	$\dfrac{1}{E^2} = W$	Relative W	(1) $\times$ (5)
0.12	0.07	0.0049	204	1.0	0.12
0.30	0.02	0.0004	2500	12.2	3.66
0.36	0.05	0.0025	400	2.0	0.72
Summations				15.2	4.50

These weights are computed in column 4 of Table 5-3. Column 5 shows relative weights, in the same proportion as those given in column 4, by assigning the value of 1.00 to the smallest weight. Next, the weighted mean is obtained of the differences between the measured mean values and an arbitrary number 112.00, chosen here for convenience of computation. In the final operation the weighted mean of the differences is added to 112.00 giving 112.296 as the weighted mean of given measurements.

$$\text{weighted mean} = 112.00 + \frac{4.50}{15.2} = 112.296$$

It is also possible to compute the probable error of this weighted mean value, but it is first necessary to show how probable errors may vary as the result of addition, subtraction, multiplication, and so forth.

Probable Errors in Computed Quantities

In the following discussion it is assumed that E is the probable error of a single measurement L of a quantity.

5-17. Addition. Since the probable error of measuring $2L$ is, according to Eq. (5-8), $E\sqrt{2} = \sqrt{E^2 + E^2}$, the probable error E_s of the sum of two or more measured values $L_1, L_2, \ldots L_n$, having probable errors $E_1, E_2, \ldots E_n$ respectively, is

$$E_s = \sqrt{E_1^2 + E_2^2 + \ldots + E_n^2} \tag{5-15}$$

5-18. Subtraction. A difference of two measured values L_1 and L_2 may be represented as a sum $L_1 + (-L_2)$. Thus the probable error of a difference of two quantities is the same as the probable error of the sum, since E_1 and E_2 go under the radical in Eq. (5-15) as squares. Designating probable error of $L_1 - L_2$ by E_d,

$$E_d = \sqrt{E_1^2 + E_2^2} \tag{5-16}$$

where E_1 and E_2 are the probable errors of L_1 and L_2 respectively.

5-19. Multiplication by a constant. The result of multiplication of $L \pm E$ by a constant C is $CL \pm CE$. Thus probable error E_c of a product CL is

$$E_c = \pm CE \tag{5-17}$$

5-20. Multiplication of measured quantities. Multiplication of $L_1 \pm E_1$ by $L_2 \pm E_2$ would give $L_1L_2 \pm L_1E_2 \pm L_2E_1$, neglecting a small term E_1E_2. Applying Eq. (5-15) to the sum of probable errors $\pm L_1E_2 \pm L_2E_1$, it may be written that the probable error E_p of a product L_1L_2 is

$$E_p = \sqrt{L_1^2E_2^2 + L_2^2E_1^2} \tag{5-18}$$

Similarly, it can be shown that the probable error of a product of several quantities is

$$E_p = L_1L_2L_3 \ldots \sqrt{\left(\frac{E_1}{L_1}\right)^2 + \left(\frac{E_2}{L_2}\right)^2 + \left(\frac{E_3}{L_3}\right)^2 + \ldots} \tag{5-19}$$

5-21. Division. Division of L_1 by L_2 may be regarded as multiplication of L_1 by $1/L_2$. This makes the probable error E_q of the quotient L_1/L_2 the same as for the product except that it will be reduced by a factor $1/L_2^2$. Thus

$$E_q = \frac{1}{L_2^2} \sqrt{L_1^2 E_2^2 + L_2^2 E_1^2} \qquad (5\text{-}20)$$

5-22. Elevation into a power. The elevation of a quantity L into a power n may be regarded as successive multiplications of L by itself n times. If in this multiplication one applies Eq. (5-19), the probable error E_e of L^n is

$$E_e = E L^{n-1} \sqrt{n} \qquad (5\text{-}21)$$

5-23. Extraction of a root. If E is the probable error of L, it is required to find the probable error E_r of $\sqrt[n]{L}$. Let $R = \sqrt[n]{L}$ or $R^n = L$. Thus E is the probable error of R^n and E_r is the probable error of R. Applying Eq. (5-21), $E = E_r R^{n-1} \sqrt{n}$, where $R^{n-1} = R^n/R = L/\sqrt[n]{L}$. Thus

$$E_r = \frac{E \sqrt[n]{L}}{L \sqrt{n}} \qquad (5\text{-}22)$$

Example 5-3. Determine the probable error of the weighted mean value 112.296 of Example 5-2.

Solution: It is necessary to follow all operations that were performed with measured values in Example 5-2. First they were multiplied by their respective weights, i.e., constants; next the results were added together and finally divided by the summation of weights. The same operations must be performed on the probable errors of the three measured values, employing for this purpose successively Eq. (5-17), Eq. (5-15), and again Eq. (5-17). These computations may be conveniently arranged in tabular form as shown in Table 5-4.

TABLE 5-4. SOLUTION OF EXAMPLE 5-3

E	W	WE	W^2E^2
0.07	1.0	0.07	0.0049
0.02	12.2	0.24	0.0576
0.05	2.0	0.10	0.0100
Σ	15.2		0.0725

$$\text{probable error of the mean} = \frac{\sqrt{0.0725}}{15.2} = \pm 0.018$$

This answer makes the maximum random error equal to ± 0.054, making the thousandths in 112.296 not significant. Thus the correct answer in Example 5-2 is 112.30.

Example 5-4. Determine the maximum random error of the area of a rectangular field if two sides are given as 120.37 ± 0.08 and 352.50 ± 0.21, where 0.08 and 0.21 are maximum random errors. Also express the area with a proper number of significant figures.

Solution: Applying Eq. (5-18) for the product,

$$E_p = \sqrt{120^2 \times 0.21^2 + 353^2 \times 0.08^2} = \pm 38$$

This shows that the units in the area are not significant and the area should be given as 42,430 sq ft.

Example 5-5. Three sides of a triangle were measured with a 10 ft tape with the following results: $a = 20.32$ ft, $b = 40.00$ ft, $c = 49.87$ ft. If the probable error of measuring 10 ft is E, find the probable error of the area of the triangle in terms of E.

Solution: For the purpose of computation of probable error, assume the sides to be 20, 40, and 50 ft respectively. The area

$$A = \sqrt{s(s - a)(s - b)(s - c)}$$

where $s = (a + b + c)/2$. The computations are arranged in Table 5-5.

TABLE 5-5. SOLUTION OF EXAMPLE 5-5

Symbol	Value	Probable Error
a	20	$E\sqrt{2}$
b	40	$E\sqrt{4}$
c	50	$E\sqrt{5}$
$a + b + c$	110	$\sqrt{2E^2 + 4E^2 + 5E^2} = E\sqrt{11}$
s	55	$E\dfrac{\sqrt{11}}{2} = E\sqrt{2.75}$
$s - a$	35	$\sqrt{2.75E^2 + 2E^2} = E\sqrt{4.75}$
$s - b$	15	$\sqrt{2.75E^2 + 4E^2} = E\sqrt{6.75}$
$s - c$	5	$\sqrt{2.75E^2 + 5E^2} = E\sqrt{7.75}$
$s(s - c)$	275	$\sqrt{2.75E^2 \times 5^2 + 7.75E^2 \times 55^2} = E\sqrt{23,512}$
$(s - a)(s - b)$	525	$\sqrt{4.75E^2 \times 15^2 + 6.75E^2 \times 35^2} = E\sqrt{9337}$
A^2	275×525	$\sqrt{23,512E^2 \times 525^2 + 9337E^2 \times 275^2}$ $= 275E\sqrt{95,156}$
A	380	$\dfrac{275E\sqrt{95,156}}{380\sqrt{2}} = 158E$

Assuming that the probable error of measuring 10 ft is ±0.01, the probable error of the area is then ±158 × 0.01 = ±1.6 sq ft.

PROBLEMS

5-1. A line was measured with a 100 ft tape and recorded as being X ft long. If the actual length of tape under measuring conditions was 100.075 ft and the accuracy achieved in this measurement is believed to be 1:5000, (a) correct the recorded length for incorrect length of tape, (b) compute the amount of uncertainty in the measured distance, (c) give the answer to a proper number of significant figures if X is:

(A) 2679.03 ft.   *Ans.* (a) 2681.04 ft, (b) ±0.5, (c) 2681.0 ft
(B) 1825.84 ft.
(C) 3740.25 ft.

5-2. It is required to lay out given dimensions x and y of a rectangular field within ±0.05 ft. A 100 ft tape that must be used has a splice between the 10 and 11 ft marks, which makes the actual length of the tape 99.870 ft. Assuming that the rest of this tape is correct and that in the measurement of x and y ft the zero end of the tape is carried forward, determine (a) the amount of discrepancies in x and y dimensions if they were measured by the given tape, (b) the lengths that must be measured with the given tape, (c) the best accuracy required in measurements, if x and y are as follows:

(A) $x = 50.35$ ft, $y = 172.83$ ft.
             Ans. (a) 0.13, 0.26, (b) 50.48 ft, 173.09 ft, (c) 1:3460
(B) $x = 125.32$ ft, $y = 270.85$ ft.
(C) $x = 175.48$ ft, $y = 325.42$ ft.

5-3. It was determined that the probable error of measuring 100 ft with a 100 ft tape under certain conditions is ±0.008. Determine the probable error of measuring

(A) 800.00 ft 5 times.   *Ans.* ±0.010
(B) 500.00 ft 7 times.
(C) 600.00 ft 6 times.

5-4. A set of ten readings was made in measuring a quantity. Find the following: (a) the most probable value of the measured quantity, (b) average deviation (error) multiplied by 0.845, (c) probable error of single measurement using Eq. (5-5), (d) probable error of the mean value of measurements, if the set of ten readings is as follows:

(A) 2.421, 2.419, 2.425, 2.422, 2.417, 2.420, 2.419, 2.424, 2.418, and 2.423 amp.   *Ans.* (a) 2.421 amp, (b) 0.0015, (c) ±0.0018, (d) ±0.0006
(B) 13.12, 13.10, 13.12, 13.09, 13.11, 13.13, 13.13, 13.10, 13.13, and 13.11 ft.
(C) 42.3, 42.2, 42.0, 41.8, 41.5, 41.9, 42.2, 42.1, 42.0, and 41.8 min.

5-5. The interior angles in a quadrilateral $ABCD$ were measured as follows: angle at A once, angles at B and C twice, and angle at D four times. Determine the most probable values of the angles, arranging all computations in

tabular form, if measured angles were as follows:
(A) $A = 75°21'52'', B = 103°37'22'', C = 132°15'17''$, and $D = 48°45'07''$.
                     Ans. $75°22'01.8'', 103°37'26.9'', 132°15'21.9'', 48°45'09.4''$
(B) $A = 114°25'30'', B = 82°17'15'', C = 53°43'00''$, and $D = 109°34'52''$.
(C) $A = 97°35'00'', B = 128°22'30'', C = 65°42'00''$, and $D = 68°19'45''$.

5-6. Two sides of a rectangle were measured as x and y with probable errors of ± 0.015 and ± 0.019 respectively. Find (a) the probable error of the area, (b) estimated accuracy in measuring each side, (c) the area given to a proper number of significant figures, if x and y are as follows:
(A) $x = 21.32$ in., $y = 15.74$ in.
                   Ans. (a) ± 0.47 sq in., (b) 1:473, 1:276, (c) 336 sq in.
(B) $x = 75.32$ ft, $y = 87.25$ ft.
(C) $x = 17.84$ chains, $y = 24.43$ chains.

5-7. If the probable error of measuring the side of a cube is ± 0.003 ft, find (a) the probable error of its volume, (b) the volume given to a proper number of significant figures, if the side was measured as
(A) 3.510 ft.   *Ans.* (a) ± 0.064, (b) 43.2 cu ft.
(B) 7.135 ft.
(C) 9.812 ft.

5-8. If the probable error in measuring 100 ft is ± 0.04 ft, what is the probable error of measuring the perimeter of a closed figure having its sides measured as shown below? [*Hint:* Probable errors should be taken in each case proportional to the square root of the number of measured 100 ft spans, including fractions thereof.]
(A) 231.5, 352.6, 73.7, and 134.6 ft.   *Ans.* ± 0.11
(B) 517.2, 275.0, 139.7, and 82.3 ft.
(C) 451.3, 310.7, 152.3, 72.9, and 159.4 ft.

5-9. A quantity was measured repeatedly on two occasions with the results as shown below, where the plus-minus quantities are the maximum random errors. (a) Determine the weighted mean of the results of two measurements, (b) determine the maximum random error of the mean, (c) express the weighted mean with a proper number of significant figures.
(A) 372.51 ± 0.05 and 372.45 ± 0.10.
                   Ans. (a) 372.50, (b) ± 0.05, (c) 372.50
(B) 232.30 ± 0.04 and 232.35 ± 0.07.
(C) 73.91 ± 0.007 and 73.82 ± 0.012.

5-10. It was found by repeated measurements that the maximum random errors in measuring the sides of a rectangular structure were ± 0.03 ft, ± 0.07 ft, and ± 0.02 ft. The respective dimensions of the sides are given below. Find (a) the maximum random error in the volume and (b) the volume to a proper number of significant figures.
(A) 23.52, 37.31, and 17.90 ft.   *Ans.* (a) ± 40, (b) 15,7$\underline{1}$0 cu ft
(B) 13.71, 28.19, and 10.34 ft.
(C) 33.12, 51.37, and 27.58 ft.

CHAPTER **6**

Field Instructions—Referencing
Objects and Measuring Angles
with Tape

Ties, Offsets, and Random Lines

6-1. Ties. A considerable time may elapse between the preliminary survey of an engineering project and its final, or location, survey. The preliminary survey is made to obtain data for design when the project is started. The location survey is made after the project is designed and the contract for building it is signed. Points set on the ground during preliminary surveys are often used again in the location survey; thus it is important not only to preserve the control points set on the ground but also to be able to find them after the lapse of months or even years. For this purpose surveying control points are referenced by *ties*.

A tie is a measurement which gives the distance from a stake or an object to near-by permanent or semi-permanent landmarks, or to a transit line. The process of measuring ties is called ***referencing.*** Figure 6-1 shows ties referencing a hub to trees and to a brick building. Field notes must show the sketch of ties.

A stake may also be referenced by distances and angles. This method may be especially useful in tying a point in an open field to distant objects. In such cases it may be necessary to tie a stake to other stakes

71

set in the ground, preferably to a stake in line with some distant object, such as a church steeple or a radio tower.

Figure 6-2 indicates a point tied to four stakes set in line with distant objects. It is a good practice to measure more ties than seem necessary, especially in referencing an important control point, so that the point can be relocated even though some of the reference stakes are destroyed.

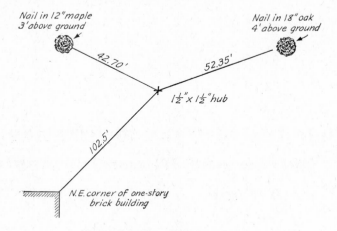

Fig. 6-1. Ties to near-by objects.

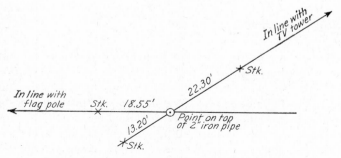

Fig. 6-2. Ties to stakes and distant objects.

6-2. Range lines. It is a common procedure to tie various objects to the transit line. The objects must be tied to the line so as to facilitate quick and accurate plotting of all the tied features on the construction plan. For this purpose field men often use ***range lines*** to tie a building. A range line is a line determined by the face of a building, or other structure, produced to an intersection with the transit line.

In locating various details in the field some consideration must be given to convenience and accuracy in plotting details on paper. For instance, a field man may prefer to locate all objects by angles and distances, so that the plotting would necessarily be done with protractor and scale.   However, the use of the protractor in plotting is cumbersome and not very accurate; thus other methods of referencing objects should also be used whenever they promise advantages in accuracy or convenience in plotting.

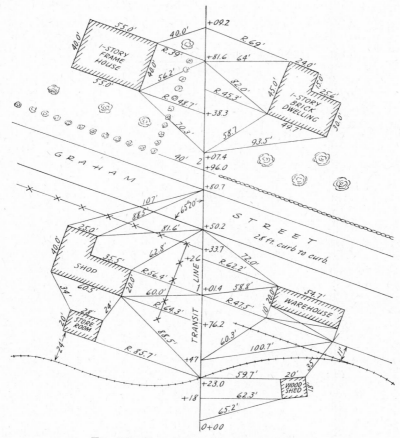

Fig. 6-3. Transit line ties and range lines.

Figure 6-3 shows ties and range lines referred to the transit line marked by stations.   It should be noted that all ties are made so that the angles between them are not less than about 30°.   Range lines are marked by letter *R*.   Some of the structures are tied to other buildings when direct ties to the transit line are not convenient.   Also, all main buildings shown on the figure are provided with at least one check tie (an extra tie), to make possible better accuracy in plotting.   In addition, all horizontal dimensions of buildings are shown.

6-3. Offsets. On engineering surveys it may be necessary to run a line through a building or some other obstacle, or to measure a line along a hedge or a fence. Since in such cases direct measurements along the line may be impossible, convenient right-angle *offsets* may be measured from the line in order to establish a line parallel to the one which runs through the obstruction. Figure 6-4 shows right-angle offsets. The

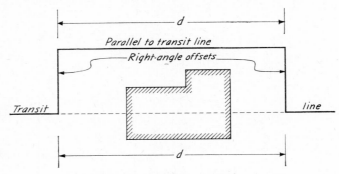

Fig. 6-4. Right-angle offsets.

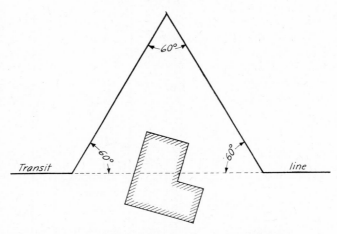

Fig. 6-5. Indirect measurement by 60° offsets.

accuracy required in measuring right angles for the offsets depends on the specified accuracy of the survey, but in any event the angles should be measured with a transit.

In other cases it may be more convenient to circumvent an obstacle by running two lines at 60° angles to the transit line, thus forming an equilateral triangle (Fig. 6-5). The base of the triangle running through the obstruction is equal to either of the other sides of the triangle. Both sides should be measured as a check on the measured 60° angles.

The best way to get around a small obstruction, where the prolongation of the line may be established beyond the obstruction, is to measure only one right angle at a point near the obstruction and just beyond it, as is shown in Fig. 6-6. Then by measuring the short side $bc = h$ and the hypotenuse $ac = s$, one may easily obtain the required distance ab by applying correction C_s, given by Eq. (7-6), to the measured hypotenuse s. Where the small angle of the triangle does not exceed 9° and the measured hypotenuse is 100 ft or less, only the first term in Eq. (7-6), $h^2/2s$, need be applied to find the distance ab correct to a hundredth of

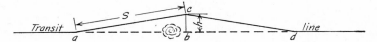

Fig. 6-6. Surveying around a small obstacle.

a foot. In the case shown in Fig. 6-6 the taping may be continued from point b along established direction bd, or sometimes it may be preferred to measure another hypotenuse cd and apply to it correction giving the distance bd.

6-4. Random lines. Still another method of measuring a line between two points which are not intervisible consists of running a *random line*. A random line is a line run in an arbitrary direction close to the line to be measured. Figure 6-7 shows two points A and B with some obstruction lying between the points, so that distance AB cannot be measured directly.

If some arbitrary direction, AF, has been chosen for the random line, the problem is to measure a right-angle offset, BC, to the random line

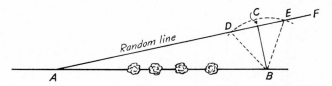

Fig. 6-7. Random line and swing offsets.

and also to measure the side AC in the right triangle ACB. Knowing $BC = h$ and $AC = d$, one may obtain the distance AB by applying a proper positive correction to the measured length AC, as is shown by Eq. (7-8). With the angle at A not exceeding 9° and the measured side AC being 100 ft or less, only the first term, $h^2/2d$, is needed to obtain length AB correct to one hundredth of a foot.

In order to locate point C along the line AF, the transit is set up at A and a sight is taken along the direction AF. At the same time the zero end of the tape is held at point B and the tape is stretched along an arbitrary direction BD, making the angle DBC any value between about 30° and 50°. Some footmark is held along the tape with the plumb bob string at that footmark. The tape is then swung around until the line of sight of the transit falls on the plumb bob string. This procedure establishes point D, which is marked on the ground by a pin or a stake.

The same procedure is repeated, using the same footmark, to establish point E. The chord DE is measured and bisected to establish point C. Location of point C directly by swing offset BC should not be attempted. It will result in low accuracy in measuring the line AC, since the intersection point C cannot be accurately located by sighting along the line AC.

If a transit is not available, it is possible for a man standing at A to align a plumb bob string held at D with a range pole placed somewhere along the random line, for instance at F. This method is not as accurate as the one described above and is limited to relatively short distances.

Laying Out and Measuring Angles with Tape

6-5. Laying out a 90° angle with tape. A tape is seldom used on engineering projects for measuring or laying out angles. However,

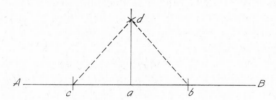

Fig. 6-8. Right-angle direction by swing offsets.

there may be cases when a transit is not available and when an angle needs to be measured only within about 5′ or 10′. In such cases measurements with tape give satisfactory results.

When the direction of a perpendicular to a line is required at a given point, as in laying out a corner for a building, there are two methods which may be followed. The simplest method is shown on Fig. 6-8, where erection of a perpendicular is required at point a of the line AB. Two equal distances, ab and ac, are measured on each side of point a. Then swing offsets of an equal length are made from points b and c. The intersection of the two arcs at point d gives the desired perpendicular ad.

It is possible to lay out a 90° angle quite accurately by the above method if a hub is driven at the intersection of arcs at d, and if equal distances, bd and cd, are measured with small arcs marked on the hub.

By this method point d may be established within about two or three hundredths of a foot. Thus if distance ad is about 30 ft, the 90° angle is measured with a maximum error of about 3′.

Another method of erecting a perpendicular at a point is shown in Fig. 6-9. In this method three sides of a triangle are made equal to 3-4-5 multiples of some number, for instance 12 ft. This produces a triangle with sides equal to 36, 48, and 60 ft respectively, and with a

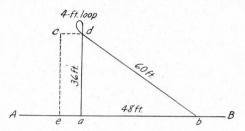

Fig. 6-9. Right-angle direction by constructing right-angled triangle.

right angle lying between the 36 ft and the 48 ft sides. Thus if line ab is measured to be 48.00 ft, the zero end of the tape may be held at a and the 100 ft end at b while the rest of the tape is stretched out toward point d to make sides $ad = 36$ ft and $bd = 60$ ft. This is accomplished by holding a 4 ft loop at d by bringing together the 36 and 40 ft marks.

The problem is slightly different if a perpendicular to line AB is required to pass through some point c (Fig. 6-9). In this case the position of the foot of the perpendicular is estimated by eye to fall at a, and a 36-48-60 triangle is constructed at point a. By stretching the tape along the perpendicular ad, and by measuring offset cd, one finds the distance $ea = cd$ for moving the foot of the perpendicular to point e.

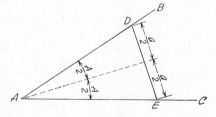

6-6. Measuring an angle with tape. Let it be required to measure

Fig. 6-10. Measuring angle with tape.

the angle BAC shown in Fig. 6-10. Two equal radial lines, AD and AE, are measured along known directions AB and AC. After points D and E are establshed, the chord DE is measured and bisected. Then,

$$\sin \frac{A}{2} = \frac{DE}{2AD}$$

The accuracy of measuring the angle with a tape depends on the care exercised in taping and in setting points D and E on the ground. With care the angle may be measured within one or two minutes.

All the procedures described for measuring or laying out angles with a tape depend on favorable conditions of terrain. A measurement would be cumbersome to make in high brush or on very irregular ground. For this reason, and because no time is saved by making such a measurement, the transit should be used to measure or lay out angles on engineering projects.

FIELD EXERCISES

6-1. Measurements of distances by pacing and determination of heights of objects

Party: Two men.

Equipment: Two range poles, tape, two yardsticks, pencils (about 5 in. long).

Objects:
  (a) To determine how closely distances can be measured by pacing.
  (b) To determine the average length of pace for each person.
  (c) To find how closely heights can be measured with pencil and yardstick.

Procedure—Part 1: Each party will set up two range poles about 150 paces apart, and each person will proceed to pace this distance ten times, five times in each direction. Each measurement must be recorded in a column on the left-hand page of the field notebook. When this is completed the following computations are required:

  (a) The most probable value of a paced distance (in individual's paces).
  (b) The average deviation.
  (c) The estimated relative accuracy of a single measurement.
  (d) The distance in feet equivalent to the individual's 100 paces, and the number of paces equivalent to 100 ft. [*Note:* The required distance and paces may be computed after measuring the paced distance with a tape. This must be done after pacing is completed. The right-hand page may be used for computations, which should be set in line form. For example, $2.37 \times 15.31 = 36.28$.]

Procedure—Part 2: Each person is required to measure the height of an assigned tall building or another structure, as is shown on the sketch (Fig. 6-11).

For this type of measurement, the paced distance may be assumed to be equal to AC shown on the sketch. Using similar triangles, ABC and ADE, set up an equation for the unknown height BC in letters, then

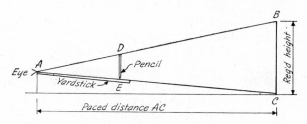

Fig. 6-11. Approximate measurement of heights of objects.

substitute known numerical values of lines and compute the required height in feet.

6-2. Area of a triangular field by three methods

Party: Three men.

Equipment: Tape, tally pins, two plumb bobs, two range poles.

Objects:

(a) To gain some experience in making measurements with a tape.

(b) To learn how to measure angles with tape.

(c) To determine the area of a field by three different methods.

(d) To compare the results and to determine the proper number of significant figures in the answer.

Procedure: Each party will be assigned or will select a place for a triangular field about 80 ft by 110 ft by 150 ft. These dimensions can be determined approximately by pacing. All distances will be measured horizontally by taping, with an estimated tension of 10 lb. It will not be necessary to apply corrections to the measured lengths in this exercise. Try to make measurements as uniform as possible.

Part 1. Find the area of the triangle by its three sides.

Make a sketch of the field on the right-hand page of the notebook and assign letters to the lines to be measured. Record measurements on the left page in two columns headed "Forward" and "Back." Obtain the average of measured lengths and compute the area by the formula

$$A = \sqrt{s(s - a)(s - b)(s - c)}$$

Part 2. Find the area of the triangle by two sides and the included angle.

Select one of the vertices of the triangle and measure from it 100 ft along each side. Mark the ends of lines by tally pins. Measure the distance between the two tally pins. This will give sufficient data to compute the angle at the selected vertex. Using this angle and the lengths of two sides (from Part 1) compute the area by the formula

$$A = \frac{ab \sin C}{2}$$

Part 3. Find the area by base-altitude method.

Select one side of the triangle and erect a perpendicular that will pass through the opposite vertex. First, estimate the point along the selected side as a base of such perpendicular. Then measure 48 ft from this point along the selected side and mark the ends of the 48 ft line by two tally pins. Hold the zero end of the 100 ft tape at one pin and the 100 ft end at another, say at the base of the perpendicular. Stretch the tape from the two ends outward, holding the 60 and 64 ft marks together, thus forming a 4 ft loop. This will make a 36-48-60 or 3-4-5 right triangle with the right angle at the estimated point on the selected side. Mark the third point of this triangle by a pin and stretch the tape along the established perpendicular. Measure the distance by which the opposite vertex was missed and move the base of the perpendicular this distance in a proper direction. Measure the finally established altitude of the triangle and compute the area by the formula

$$A = \frac{bh}{2}$$

Record all measurements for the three parts on the left-hand page and use the right-hand page for the necessary sketches and computations. Arrange computations in line form and in proper sequence.

The three answers obtained in this exercise cannot be expected to agree very closely. Determine the most probable value of the area by assuming that the method of Part 1 is three times as reliable and the method of Part 2 is twice as reliable as the method of Part 3. Compute the average deviation for the area and determine the estimated relative accuracy for the answer. Knowing the estimated error, give the area to a proper number of significant figures by underscoring the last significant digit.

CHAPTER 7

Measurement of Distances

Various Methods of Measuring Distances

7-1. General. The method to be employed in measuring a distance depends upon the required accuracy of the measurement, and this in turn depends upon the purpose for which the measurement is intended. It is a common practice, for instance, to pace distances for small-scale mapping, for estimate purposes, for making rough plans, and so on. Other rough measurements can be made by using an odometer or a range finder. Measurements of principal distances for preliminary and location surveys on engineering projects, however, are made with a tape, although topographic features of the ground are usually delineated by transit-stadia measurements or by photogrammetry. In measuring long distances, which may extend over many miles, as for example on extensive surveys in triangulation work, electronic devices such as the geodimeter and the tellurometer are used in modern surveys. Brief accounts of these distance-measuring techniques are given below.

7-2. Pacing. Everyone who has anything to do with field measurements should determine factors for converting the number of his paces to a corresponding distance in feet, and vice versa. The first conversion factor is needed for measuring distances by pacing, and the second for laying out distances by pacing.

Pacing down a slope will produce fewer paces than pacing the same distance up the slope. Thus, a horizontal distance is approximated by pacing it an equal number of times in each direction. The average value

81

of two such measurements should give the required distance within about 1 per cent; that is, with 1:100 accuracy. Usually it is best to count strides rather than paces. A ***stride*** consists of two paces. A tally register operated by hand is a convenient device for counting paces or strides.

7-3. Odometer. The odometer is a device similar to the distance recorder in an automobile's speedometer. The odometer is attached to a wheel which is rolled over a distance to be measured. On level ground the odometer may be expected to give 1:200 accuracy. However, the accuracy of odometer measurements depends on topography since the wheel follows the irregularities of the surface. Thus, the recorded distances are usually greater than the required horizontal values. The odometer may be used for measuring distances in small-scale mapping.

7-4. Stadia. The principle of the stadia method, described in detail in Chapter 17, is based on two short horizontal hairlines, called

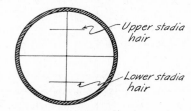

Fig. 7-1. Cross-hair ring with stadia hairs.

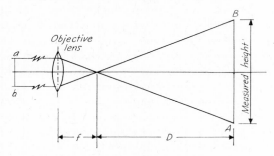

Fig. 7-2. Horizontal distance by stadia measurement.

stadia hairs, which are etched on a glass plate inside the transit telescope (see Fig. 7-1). When a graduated rod is viewed through the transit telescope and a certain graduated distance AB, called ***stadia intercept*** (Fig. 7-2), is seen included between the upper and the lower stadia hairs, the ratio of that distance to the distance ab between the stadia hairs is the same as the ratio of the distance D (from the rod to the front focal point of the objective lens) to the focal distance f of the lens. Thus

$D = AB(f/ab)$. The ratio f/ab is constant for a given instrument and is normally made equal to 100 in instruments of American manufacture. Thus by reading a stadia intercept on a rod, one can determine the distance from the rod to the instrument.

It is also possible to determine difference in elevation of points by the stadia method. Horizontal distances can be measured by the stadia method approximately with 1:500 accuracy. Since this accuracy is too low for running the lines on engineering surveys, the stadia measurements are used mostly in topographic map making, where the scale of the map is consistent with the accuracy of stadia measurements.

7-5. Taping. Measurement by tapes is the most important method of measuring distances for the construction of roads, buildings, bridges, dams, reservoirs, and other engineering works. The tape is also used almost exclusively on property land surveys. The versatility of tape measurements is explained by the wide range of accuracies which tape measurements may produce. The taping may vary from a low order of about 1:1000 accuracy to a precise taping of 1:25,000 or better.

Accurate taping of 1:5000 or better is used on many engineering projects. This is known as the *third order accuracy* (see Table 7-1).

7-6. Photogrammetry. The type of photographs used for measurements are mostly *vertical aerial photographs,* i.e., photographs taken from an airplane with the camera axis in vertical position. The scale of aerial photographs depends on the flying altitude of the airplane. The higher the altitude, the smaller the scale and consequently the larger the coverage of the terrain on the photographs. Thus smaller-scale photographs cost less for the same coverage, but measurements made on such photographs may be expected to be of lower order of accuracy, assuming other conditions are equal.

Measurements of distances on photographs may be performed with an accuracy of about 1:3000 if precise cameras and equipment are used. In other words, photogrammetry has developed to such a degree of precision that it is possible to make some property surveys by means of photographs. However, such surveys are quite expensive and thus are not practical when the area to be measured is small.

On engineering projects photogrammetry is used mostly for making topographic maps of various scales, as they may be required for reconnaissance of the ground, preliminary studies of location, and design of various structures. The surveys necessary for many engineering projects such as route construction often cover enough ground to make the photogrammetric method cheaper than ground surveys. Extensive topographic surveys are made nowadays almost exclusively by the photogrammetric method. An additional description of the photogrammetric method is given in Chapter 17.

One important advantage of photogrammetric surveys of large areas is that they can be accomplished rapidly and without trespassing on private property. The time element depends to a great extent upon the size of the area being surveyed. For instance, while it would be much quicker to survey a small lot by a ground-surveying crew, it would take only a fraction of the corresponding ground-surveying time to make a topographic map of an area equal to, say, 100 square miles.

7-7. Subtense bar. The subtense bar is a device used for indirect measurement of distances (see Fig. 7-3). This device consists of an invar bar with a target placed at each end, and a tripod. The bar is mounted on the tripod so that it may be set in the horizontal position over a point. By measuring the angle subtended by the precisely known bar length between the bar targets, with an instrument set at a distance perpendicular to the bar direction, the distance between the bar and the instrument can be easily computed.

Assuming that the distance between the targets is d and the measured horizontal angle is α, the horizontal distance between the theodolite and the subtense bar is $d/2 \cot (\alpha/2)$.

Since distance d is normally determined by the bar manufacturers within a fraction of 1 mm, the accuracy of the subtense bar method depends mainly on the accuracy with which angle α is measured. Normally a precise theodolite is used for measuring angles subtended by the subtense bar. Figure 11-8, p. 173, shows the Wild T-2 theodolite which reads angles directly to $1''$.

Although subtense bars may be of various lengths, the length commonly used is 2 m between the targets. Since the bar is made of invar, an alloy having a low coefficient of expansion, the distance between the targets remains very nearly constant at all temperatures encountered in field measurements. A 40°F change of temperature changes the length of the bar by less than 0.03 of 1 per cent.

By means of an optical plummet and a circular level, the bar is placed with its mid-point over a ground point and also at a right angle to the distance between the bar and the theodolite. If the distance between the targets on the bar is 2.000 m and the measured horizontal angle between the targets is α, the horizontal distance between the bar and the transit is equal to $\cot (\alpha/2)$ meters. Thus the measured distance is directly proportional to $\cot (\alpha/2)$, so that the greater the distance the smaller is angle α and the greater will be the relative error in measuring α. Thus the accuracy of the method depends on the distance measured. With a $1''$ theodolite and with measured spans not exceeding 200 ft it is possible to measure distances with 1:3000 or better accuracy.

Distance measurement with the subtense bar is not commonly used on engineering surveys because of the high cost of the precise theodolite

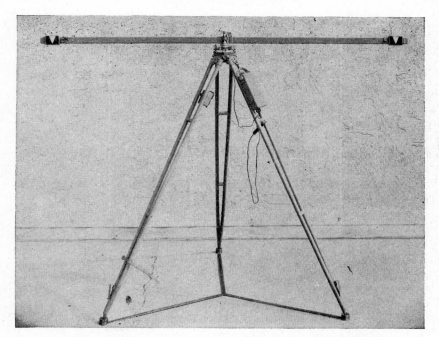

Fig. 7-3. Subtense bar.   (Courtesy Wild Heerbrugg Instruments, Inc.)

and the subtense bar.   This method of measurement may be used to advantage on surveys where the required accuracy is of the ordinary or lower order of accuracy, and where direct tape measurements present substantial difficulties.

7-8. Geodimeter.   The geodimeter is an electro-optical device which compares the phase of a highly modulated beam of light, projected by one unit of the instrument, with the phase of the same beam reflected from a distant unit.   On account of the tremendous velocity of light, the comparison of phase displacement, which is a function of the distance traveled by light, is made billions of times per second and the final answer is really statistical average of a great number of individual measurements.

The geodimeter is best adapted to measuring long distances since the magnitude of its probable error is practically the same irrespective of the distance.   Although in heavy models the probable error is close to ± 0.5 in., the light model has a probable error of about ± 4 inches.   This produces 1:16,000 accuracy in measuring 1 mile and 1:190,000 in measuring 20 miles, which is about the maximum range for this instrument.

The geodimeter is used chiefly on geodetic surveys for establishing first and second order stations of horizontal control.

7-9. Tellurometer system. The tellurometer system is an electronic device for measuring distances. Its main application up to the present time has been in triangulation work on geodetic surveys. The tellurometer system uses radio waves instead of light waves. Its heaviest unit weighs only 28 lb. The time required to measure a distance is about 30 minutes. It has many important advantages over the geodimeter: It is easier to operate and to transport; it can be operated under any atmospheric conditions; and it may be used in daylight.

Fig. 7-4. Tellurometer system. (Courtesy Tellurometer, Inc.)

The new units coming into use will weigh only 16 lb, and will have 20 in. by 19 in. by 9 in. over-all dimensions. Power consumption is 6 v, 8 amp, DC.

The accuracy of the tellurometer system and of the geodimeter depends on a knowledge of the correct value of the velocity of light *in vacuo*. This value does not seem to be established with a better certainty than about ±2 km/sec (kilometers per second). The value accepted in 1954 by the International Scientific Radio Union is 299,792.0 km/sec. with uncertainty of perhaps ±2 km/sec. With this limitation, the probable error claimed for the instrument in measuring distances is 3 p.p.m. (parts per million) ± 2 in. This will produce an accuracy of 1:30,000 in measuring one mile but only 1:3000 in measuring 500 ft.

The 3 p.p.m. probable error results not only from the probable error in the accepted velocity of light but also from uncertainties in the corrections for atmospheric conditions, although these corrections may be determined fairly accurately by simple meteorological measurements.

The standard equipment of a tellurometer system outfit includes, besides the master and the remote station units, an aneroid barometer, a whirling hygrometer, and a built-in duplex radio telephone circuit. Figure 7-4 shows the transmitting and receiving stations of the tellurometer system.

7-10. Accuracy in measurements. Table 7-1 shows that, because of the great variation in the accuracies which may be obtained from various measuring devices, it is important to select proper "tools" to be used on various engineering surveys. It is the responsibility of the engineer in charge of surveys to select the instruments and equipment that will do the work most efficiently.

TABLE 7-1. ACCURACIES IN MEASURING DISTANCES

Method		Expected or Required Accuracies	Use
Pacing		1:100	Estimations; rough plans; details in small-scale mapping.
Odometer		1:200	Details in small-scale mapping; approximate distances for planning a project.
Stadia		1:200 to 1:1000	Topographic mapping; rough traverses.
Taping	Low Order	1:1000 to 1:3000	On some preliminary and construction surveys; location of details on plans; land surveying of low accuracy.
	Ordinary	1:3000 to 1:5000	On many engineering surveys where greater accuracy is not required; land surveys; building construction.
	Third Order*	1:5000 to 1:10,000	Traverses tied to the national net; important engineering works; city surveys; accurate land surveys.
	Second Order*	1:10,000 to 1:25,000	Triangulation or traverses connecting first order stations; accurate surveys.
	First Order*	1:25,000 or better	Any precise survey; base line measurements on first order horizontal control network.
Subtense bar with 1 sec theodolite		1:1000 to 1:5000	Where taping is difficult or impossible.
Geodimeter		1:16,000 on 1 mile 1:190,000 on 20 miles	Triangulation; base line measurements; trilateration.
Tellurometer		1:30,000 on 1 mile 1:225,000 on 30 miles	Triangulation; base line measurements; trilateration; traverses for establishing stations of first and second order control.

* Taken from definition of order of accuracy in triangulation and traverses by the United States Board of Surveys and Maps, May 1933.

The first question any engineer or land surveyor must ask on surveying jobs is, "How accurately must it be done?" Then he may plan the method of work accordingly. Table 7-1 also shows that despite the large number of measuring devices available, the tape remains the main tool in measuring distances on engineering projects and on land surveys. Thus it is important to know not only how to make tape measurements but also how to apply corrections for their systematic errors.

Systematic Errors in Taping

7-11. Various types of systematic errors. How accidental errors are likely to affect a measurement, and how one can estimate or compute a probable error or a maximum random error, has been discussed in Chapter 5. The total amount of error present in a measurement recorded in the field is equal to the algebraic sum of all random errors and all systematic errors contained in the measurement. The systematic errors in taping may be caused by the following conditions present during measurements:

(a) The length of the tape is not its nominal length.
(b) The temperature of the tape during measurements is not that at which the tape was standardized.
(c) The tension (pull) applied to the tape is not that at which the tape was standardized.
(d) Measurements are made along slopes instead of in a horizontal direction.
(e) Measurements are made with the tape suspended.

7-12. Incorrect length of tape. This has already been briefly discussed in previous chapters. It will be shown here that a "long tape measures short" and that a "short tape measures long."

Assume that the actual length of a 100 ft tape is 99.992 ft and that a distance was measured with this tape and recorded as 1375.4 ft. It is required to correct the recorded distance for the incorrect length of tape.

Each time one full tape length was measured, 100.00 ft were recorded. Thus there were 13.754 tape lengths measured, each length being only 99.992 ft. Therefore the correct length must be 99.992 × 13.754 ft. This operation should be performed as follows:

$$(100.000 - 0.008) \times 13.754 = 1375.4 - 0.11 = 1375.3 \text{ ft}$$

Since 1375.4 ft is the recorded length, correction for the recorded length may be computed by multiplying the difference between the nominal length of the tape and the actual length by the number of times the tape length was measured.

7-13. Correction for temperature. The coefficient of expansion of the steel used in common tapes is 0.00000645 per 1°F. If the length of a tape is known at some temperature t_0 at which the tape was standardized, the correction C_t for a recorded distance L measured at a different temperature t is equal to the change in length of tape per foot multiplied by the number of feet measured. Also since change in length per foot of tape is equal to the coefficient of expansion multiplied by the difference in temperatures $t - t_0$,

$$C_t = 0.00000645(t - t_0)L \qquad (7\text{-}1)$$

7-14. Correction for pull. Tapes are standardized at some specified tension P_0. If the tension applied to the tape during measurements is equal to P, then a measured distance L should be corrected for the difference in tension $P - P_0$. In this connection a few definitions must be introduced.

The modulus of elasticity of a material is defined as the ratio of unit stress to unit strain.

The unit stress of a prismoidal body is equal to the total axial stress applied to the body divided by its cross-sectional area.

The unit strain (deformation) of a prismoidal body is equal to the total longitudinal strain of the body divided by its length.

Designating by C_p the total correction that need be applied to a measured distance L owing to application of additional tension $P - P_0$ to the tape, the unit strain of the tape is C_p/L owing to unit stress $(P - P_0)/A$, where A is the cross-sectional area of the tape. Thus by definition of the modulus of elasticity, E, it may be stated that

$$E = \frac{(P - P_0)/A}{C_p/L} \qquad (7\text{-}2)$$

When Eq. (7-2) is solved for C_p, the following expression for the correction of a measured length, L, for difference in pull, $P - P_0$ is obtained:

$$C_p = \frac{(P - P_0)L}{A \cdot E} \qquad (7\text{-}3)$$

The cross-sectional area A of a tape may be computed from the following data:

W_0 lb = weight of a 100 ft tape

490 lb per cu ft = unit weight of steel

$\dfrac{A}{144}$ sq ft = cross-sectional area of the tape, where A is in square inches

Using these data, the weight of the tape must be equal to its volume multiplied by the unit weight of steel, or

$$W_0 = 100 \times \frac{A}{144} \times 490$$

Solving this equation for A and simplifying,

$$A = 0.00294W_0 \tag{7-4}$$

By substituting Eq. (7-4) in Eq. (7-3) and using as the modulus of elasticity of steel, $E = 30,000,000$ lb per sq in., one finds that the correction for pull to measured length L reduces to

$$C_p = \frac{(P - P_0)L}{8.82 \times 10^4 W_0} \tag{7-5}$$

7-15. Correction for slope.   In reducing slope measurements to the horizontal length d it is necessary to apply a correction to the measured

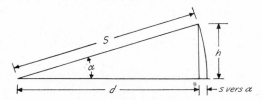

Fig. 7-5. Measurement on slope.

distance equal to the difference between the hypotenuse s and the side d of a right triangle having its vertical side equal to h (Fig. 7-5).   Thus h is the difference in elevation of the two points between which measurement is made.

From Fig. 7-5,

$$s - d = s - \sqrt{s^2 - h^2} = s - (s^2 - h^2)^{1/2}$$

By expanding $(s^2 - h^2)^{1/2}$ by the binomial theorem,* taking the first three terms of the series and simplifying, one gets the correction for slope, $C_s = s - d$:

$$C_s = \frac{h^2}{2s} + \frac{h^4}{8s^3} \tag{7-6}$$

On slopes up to 14 per cent, i.e., a 14 ft drop per 100 ft horizontal, the first term of series given by Eq. (7-6) gives correct answer to hundredths of a foot for a 100 ft distance.   Both terms will take care of slopes up to about 30 per cent.   For slopes greater than 30 per cent, the vertical angle should be measured.   For computation purposes, Eq. (7-6)

* This operation is possible for fractional exponents if $s^2 > h^2$.   The result of expansion is an infinite convergent series.

may be simplified by setting $h^2/2s = k$. Then

$$C_s = k + \frac{k^2}{2s} \qquad (7\text{-}7)$$

The slope correction in Eqs. (7-6) and (7-7) is given with a plus sign because it was made equal to $s - d$. In other words, horizontal distance $d = s - C_s$. On some special problems it may be required to find slope distances from a given horizontal distance d and a drop in slope h. It may be easily derived that the difference $s - d$ in terms of d is

$$s - d = \frac{h^2}{2d} - \frac{h^4}{8d^3} \qquad (7\text{-}8)$$

When angle α is measured together with a slope measurement (Fig. 7-5), slope correction $s - d$ is

$$s - d = s \text{ vers } \alpha \qquad (7\text{-}9)$$

7-16. Correction for sag. A suspended tape assumes the form of a curve known as the catenary. In order to find the correction that must

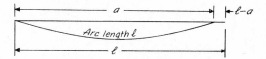

Fig. 7-6. Measurement with suspended tape.

be applied to a distance measured with a suspended length l of a tape when the length l is known for the tape supported throughout, it is necessary to find the difference between the length of curve l and the length of chord a (Fig. 7-6). This difference may be expressed in a series in terms involving the weight of tape per foot of length w, the chord a, and the pull p applied to the tape, so that

$$l - a = \frac{w^2 a^3}{24p^2} - \frac{w^4 a^5}{640p^4} + \cdots \qquad (7\text{-}10)$$

Since this correction is small in tape measurements and $a = l$ to about three significant figures, no error for the first three significant figures in a sag correction will result from the substitution of $l = a$, where l is the recorded distance. Equation (7-10) may be further simplified by neglecting the second term of the series, since its magnitude is negligible in taping problems. For instance, the second term is equal to 0.00008 ft for a 100 ft tape weighing 1.5 lb and suspended under 10 lb tension.

Accepting these approximations, the correction for sag C_a, for all practical purposes, is

$$C_a = \frac{w^2 l^3}{24p^2} \qquad (7\text{-}11)$$

The weight W of a *suspended length* l of tape may be substituted instead of wl, and Eq. (7-11) may be written as

$$C_a = \frac{W^2 l}{24p^2} \qquad (7\text{-}12)$$

Example 7-1. A distance was measured with a 100 ft steel tape weighing 1.75 lb and having its actual length equal to 100.009 ft at 68°F, 10 lb pull, supported throughout. The recorded length was 875.31 ft. The conditions of measurements were as follows: The first eight 100 ft spans and the last span were suspended, under 20 lb pull, between the stakes having elevation, from the first to the last one, as follows: 352.7, 347.3, 354.5, 359.0, 340.7, 330.8, 325.1, 325.8, 325.6, 325.4. The temperature during measurements was 42°F. Apply corrections to all systematic errors.

Solution:

Equation   Correction

           Tape correction $= 0.009 \times 8.753 = 0.079$

(7-1)   Temperature correction $= 0.00000645(42 - 68)875.3$

                         $= -0.147$

(7-5)   Pull correction $= \dfrac{10 \times 875.3}{8.82 \times 10^4 \times 1.75} = 0.057$

(7-6)   Slope correction. Difference in elevation between stakes of each successive span is

$h =$ 5.4,   7.2,   4.5,   18.3,   9.9,   5.7,   0.7, 0.2, 0.2

$\dfrac{h^2}{2s} = 0.146, 0.258, 0.101, 1.674, 0.488, 0.163, 0.002, \quad 0, \quad 0$

$\dfrac{h^4}{8s^3} = \quad 0, \quad\quad 0, \quad\quad 0, 0.014, 0.001, \quad\quad 0, \quad\quad 0, \quad 0, \quad 0.$

Total correction for slope $= -\left(\dfrac{h^2}{2s} + \dfrac{h^4}{8s^3}\right) = -2.847$

(7-11)   Correction for sag.

On first 8 spans, $- \dfrac{0.0175^2 \times 100^3}{24 \times 20^2} \times 8 = -0.255$

On last span, $- \dfrac{0.0175^2 \times 75.3^3}{24 \times 20^2} = -0.014$

Total negative corrections $= -3.263$

Total positive corrections $= \underline{0.136}$

Difference $= -3.127$

Corrected distance $= 875.31 - 3.13 = 872.18$ ft

7-17. Normal tension. The cross-sectional area of a 100 ft steel tape is given by Eq. (7-4). For any length of tape l weighing W lb, the equation becomes $A = 0.294(W/l)$.   By substituting this value of A in Eq. (7-3) when $L = l$, the correction for a pull of P lb becomes

$$C_p = \frac{(P - P_0)l^2}{0.294WE}$$ (7-13)

By equating Eqs. (7-12) and (7-13), one obtains the expression which may be solved for P, i.e., for the amount of pull necessary to apply to a suspended span, l, in order to eliminate corrections for both the pull and the sag.   Such pull is called *normal tension.*

By substituting in the expression for normal tension, $E = 30,000,000$, and simplifying, one obtains

$$P\sqrt{P - P_0} = 606W\sqrt{\frac{W}{l}}$$ (7-14)

In Eq. (7-14) W is the weight of suspended span l.   If a 100 ft tape weighing W_0 is used for measuring spans of length l, $W = \frac{W_0 l}{100}$.   When this value of W is substituted in Eq. (7-14) the equation becomes

$$P\sqrt{P - P_0} = 0.606lW_0\sqrt{W_0}$$ (7-15)

Equations (7-14) and (7-15) are cubic equations which may be easily solved by a cut-and-try method on the slide rule.

Example 7-2.   Find the normal tension for a 100 ft span weighing 1.50 lb, if $P_0 = 10$ lb.

Solution : Substituting given values in Eq. (7-14), one obtains $P\sqrt{P - 10}$ = 111.   Move the hairline of the slide rule runner to 111 on D-scale. Assume some value for $P - 10$, such as 20, and move the slide till 20 on the right side of B scale is under the hairline.   If the guess is correct, then $P = 30$ should be on D-scale at the right index.   In this case the right index falls near 25 on D-scale.   Move the slide right or left until $P - 10$ on B-scale corresponds to P on D-scale at the right index.   One soon finds that setting 17.0 on B-scale under the hairline gives 27.0 on D-scale at the right index. Thus $P = 27.0$ lb.

The use of normal tension may be preferred to making sag corrections when suspended spans are measured with the standard tension.   In precise surveying the normal tension is applied with an accurate spring balance and other equipment that help to control proper tension.

7-18. Planning a tape survey.   Measurements must be made to an accuracy prescribed by specifications.   Knowing the required accuracy, one may find it necessary to do a few simple computations to decide upon the type of equipment to be used and upon the necessary care to be exercised during measurements on a given project.

Table 7-2 shows approximate magnitudes of various random errors and also magnitudes for arbitrarily selected systematic errors on various taping operations. The last column in Table 7-2 shows also to what extent the accuracy of measurements may be affected by neglecting various errors in measuring 100 ft. For instance, if a measurement is made on a 5 per cent slope without making slope correction and assuming that no other errors are present, the resulting accuracy of the measurement is 1:800. In case of systematic errors the accuracy does not change with any number of measured tape lengths.

TABLE 7-2. THE EFFECT OF VARIOUS ERRORS ON ACCURACY

Type of Error	Conditions Causing the Error	Assumed Magnitude of Maximum Error (ft)	Effect on Accuracy in Measuring 100 ft
Random errors	(a) Swinging of one plumb bob	±0.030	1:2000
	(b) Reading tape to the nearest 0.01	±0.005	1:20,000
	(c) Error in sag correction due to 1 lb error in reading spring balance scale and using 1.25 lb tape at 10 lb pull	±0.015	1:6700
	(d) Same as (c) but with 2 lb error in reading scale	±0.037	1:2700
Systematic errors	(e) Tape too long or too short	0.005	1:20,000
	(f) 1 ft error in alignment	0.005	1:20,000
	(g) Sag of 1.25 lb tape at 10 lb pull	0.065	1:1500
	(h) Correction for 5% slope	0.125	1:800
	(i) Correction for 10% slope	0.500	1:200
	(j) Correction for 10°F difference in temperature	0.0065	1:15,000

Example 7-3. Determine the order of accuracy in measuring 272.35 ft under the following conditions: horizontal measurement with a light tape using 13 short spans, with the tape suspended, and with plumb bob at one end of each span. Assume that all corrections for systematic errors are being applied. The tape was read to the nearest 0.01 ft.

Solution: Assuming that the values of maximum random errors given in Table 7-2 are fair estimates for the given measurement, the evaluation of the total error may be computed as follows:

±0.03 error in swinging plumb bob occurs 13 times;

±0.005 error in reading tape occurs 13 times.

The total error E, using Eq. (5-14), is

$$E = \sqrt{13 \times 0.03^2 + 13 \times 0.005^2} = \pm 0.11$$

Approximate order of accuracy is $0.11/272 = \frac{1}{2500}$.

Example 7-4. A distance of 500 ft was measured by a 100 ft tape between the stakes set at the same elevation 100 ft apart. A tape weighing 1.25 lb was used with an ordinary spring balance at 10 lb tension. (a) Assuming that all systematic errors are being taken care of, estimate the approximate accuracy of the measurement resulting from 1 lb of random error in reading the spring balance scale and in reading the tape to the nearest 0.01 ft. (b) Compute the approximate accuracy if no correction for sag is made.

Solution: Using the errors shown in Table 7-2 for estimation of accuracy obtained in measurements, one may compute the evaluation of total error as follows:

(a) 0.005 error in reading the tape occurs five times,

0.015 error in sag due to assumed 1 lb of error in reading the scale of spring balance occurs five times;

$$\text{total error} = \sqrt{5(0.005^2 + 0.015^2)} = \pm 0.035$$

$$\text{Estimated order of accuracy} = \frac{0.035}{500} = \frac{1}{14,000}$$

(b) 0.065 ft in sag correction occurs 5 times;

$$\text{total error due to sag} = 0.065 \times 5 = 0.325$$

Accuracy by reason of neglect of sag correction,

$$\frac{0.325}{500} = \frac{1}{1500}$$

This accuracy may be further lowered by the presence of accidental errors assumed in part (a). Since accidental errors may occur with either plus or minus signs, and since the correction for sag is always negative, the presence of accidental errors may either increase or decrease the accuracy computed on the basis of neglecting correction for sag. In the worst case the order of accuracy will be equal to the sum of the accuracies computed above, or will be equal to

$$\frac{1}{14,000} + \frac{1}{1500} = \frac{1}{1350}$$

7-19. Measurement of inaccessible distances. A distance may not always be measured directly. Measurement of a distance across a river or a ravine, such as distance BC in Fig. 7-7, may require an indirect method. Referring to the same figure, the simplest way to measure distance BC is to measure a base line AB and the angles at A, B, and C. Then the side BC of the triangle ABC may be computed by the sine law, so that

$$BC = AB \frac{\sin A}{\sin C} \tag{7-16}$$

This method of measuring an inaccessible distance may result in a low degree of accuracy unless certain conditions of measurements are satisfied. Assume, for instance, that AB = 300 ft, BC is approximately 1000 ft, and the angle at B is close to 90°. Let the error in measuring angle B be 1′, then a distance ab, subtended by a 1′ angle 1000 ft away, is 1000 tan 1′ = 0.291 ft, and the error x in computing the side BC is $x = 0.291 \frac{1000}{300} = 1.0$ ft (approximately). This gives 1:1000 accuracy in measuring distance BC.

The accuracy of measuring distance BC by the above method may be improved by measuring the base line AB and the angles very accurately.

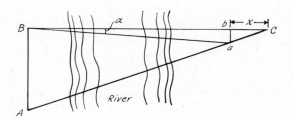

Fig. 7-7. Measuring inaccessible distance.

It is also important that in planning base line measurement, the angles at A and C should not be made smaller than about 30°. The reason is that these two angles enter Eq. (7-16) as sine functions. The sine function varies most rapidly near 0° and 180°. Thus a considerable error in the sine of an angle may be introduced owing to a small error in a measured angle if it falls between 0° and about 30°, or between 150° and 180°.

For information on measuring long, inaccessible distances one should consult the chapters on "triangulation" in advanced surveying textbooks.

PROBLEMS

In the following tape-correction problems use as the coefficient of expansion of steel 0.00000645 per degree F, and the modulus of elasticity of steel 30,000,000 lb per sq in., except where noted.

7-1. A 100 ft tape is X ft long at 68°F, 10 lb pull, supported throughout. This tape was used in measuring a distance at $t°$F, other conditions being equal. The measured distance was recorded in the field notebook as being D ft long. Correct it for systematic errors if

(A) X = 100.025, t = 90, D = 532.75.   *Ans.* 532.96 ft

(B) X = 99.982, t = 42, D = 786.32.

(C) X = 99.987, t = 85, D = 1237.4.

7-2. A distance was measured downhill and recorded to be 543.24 ft by field measurements. Measurements were made between stakes set at 100 ft intervals, on slopes, except for the last two stakes between which the measurement was 43.24 ft, also on slope. Reduce recorded distance to the horizontal by applying slope corrections for measured spans if the differences in elevation between stakes on six measured spans, in feet, were as follows:

(A) 7.3, 15.0, 25.7, 17.2, 9.4, 3.8.   *Ans.* 536.39 ft
(B) 19.0, 16.3, 6.8, 1.5, 18.3, 4.9.
(C) 14.1, 18.0, 22.3, 10.6, 8.7, 2.4.

7-3. If in making horizontal measurements with a 100 ft tape one end of the tape was held z ft below the other and y ft out of alignment, compute (a) the error due to holding one end z ft down; (b) the error due to y ft in misalignment; (c) the accuracy of measurement if corrections are not applied to measured 100 ft.

(A) $z = 2.5$, $y = 1.2$.   *Ans.* (a) 0.031 ft, (b) 0.007 ft, (c) 1:2600
(B) $z = 3.7$, $y = 2.1$.
(C) $z = 2.9$, $y = 0.8$.

7-4. The elevations of three points A, B, and C, set along a straight line, are 325.4, 293.5, and 314.9 ft respectively. Find horizontal distance AC if measurements AB and BC, made on respective constant slopes, were as follows:

(A) 357.60 ft and 254.72 ft.   *Ans.* 610.00 ft
(B) 571.32 ft and 215.41 ft.
(C) 472.35 ft and 245.72 ft.

7-5. The calibration certificate for a 100 ft steel tape shows that it is 100.000 ft long at 68°F and 17 lb pull when supported at the 0 and 100 ft points only. The tape weighs 2.25 lb. A distance was measured with this tape at t°F, on level ground with 17 lb pull and with the tape supported throughout. Correct recorded distance D for systematic errors, if

(A) $t = 47°$, $D = 592.57$ ft.   *Ans.* 592.92 ft
(B) $t = 81°$, $D = 479.35$ ft.
(C) $t = 75°$, $D = 687.91$ ft.

7-6. The Navy had to measure a length equal exactly to one U.S. nautical mile, for speed tests. They used a 300 ft tape weighing 5.25 lb. At the time of measurement the temperature was 75°F, and it was found that at that temperature the tape was 300.000 ft long at 15 lb pull when supported throughout. Consequently, 15 lb pull was used in measurements but each tape length was supported at footmarks shown below. The last odd length was supported at the ends only. All stakes were set at the same elevation. Find what must be the recorded field measurement for measuring the nautical mile (6076.10 ft).

(A) Tape supports at 0, 100, 200, 300 footmarks.   *Ans.* 6079.53 ft
(B) Tape supports at each 50 ft interval.
(C) Tape supports at 0, 150, 300 footmarks.

7-7. A 100 ft tape is 100.000 ft long at 68°F and 27 lb pull when supported at the ends only. It weighs 0.0150 lb per ft and has a cross-sectional area equal to 0.00440 sq in. A line was measured with this tape under the following conditions: t°F temperature, P lb pull, and on a slope having h ft rise for 100 ft on slope. The tape was supported throughout, and the recorded field measurement was D ft. Compute the actual horizontal length of the line measured if

    (A) $t = 92, P = 10, h = 5, D = 618.45.$ *Ans.* 617.77 ft
    (B) $t = 52, P = 12, h = 8, D = 486.35.$
    (C) $t = 84, P = 15, h = 10, D = 852.49.$

7-8. A tape approximately 100 ft long is used in measuring a distance on a slope having h ft drop per tape length on slope. Find the limits between which the actual length of the tape may fall in order that the slope correction computed by formula $h^2/2s$ will differ by ± 0.0005 ft from the slope correction computed by the same formula, but for a tape exactly 100.00 ft in length.

    (A) $h = 5.0.$ *Ans.* 99.60 ft and 100.40 ft
    (B) $h = 3.0.$
    (C) $h = 4.0.$

7-9. A 300 ft steel tape, weighing 7.50 lb, was used in measuring a line. A 10 lb pull was used in measurement, and the recorded length was 1828.73 ft. If the length of tape is L ft under a pull of P lb, correct the measured length for indicated systematic errors if

    (A) $L = 300.016, P = 15.$ *Ans.* 1828.79 ft
    (B) $L = 300.005, P = 16.$
    (C) $L = 299.984, P = 7.$

7-10. A line was measured by setting stakes 100 ft apart and measuring between the stakes without using plumb bobs. A spring balance was used on all measured spans, and proper corrections for temperature, pull, sag, and slope were applied to the measured distances. The tape was suspended on all spans. The sources of errors may be estimated as follows: No correction was applied for incorrect length of 100 ft tape which was actually X ft long; estimated error in reading spring balance was ± 1 lb under 10 lb pull used in measurement; tape readings were to the nearest 0.01 ft. Compute the magnitude of total maximum expected error that should result from these sources and also the resulting accuracy, if the number, n, of spans measured and the length, X, of the tape used were as shown below. The weight of tape used was 1.25 lb. [*Hint:* Use Table 7-2 to estimate errors.]

    (A) $n = 10, X = 100.005.$ *Ans.* 0.10 ft, 1:10,000
    (B) $n = 16, X = 99.993.$
    (C) $n = 20, X = 99.997.$

7-11. It is necessary to stretch a cable between the tops of two columns having elevations of 325.2 ft and 307.0 ft. The weight of the cable is 0.125 lb per ft, and the horizontal distance between the cable supports is X ft.

If required tension in the cable is P lb, find the actual length of cable between the supports, neglecting stretching of the cable.

(A) $X = 250.0, P = 30.$ *Ans.* 262.0 ft

(B) $X = 175.0, P = 20.$

(C) $X = 300.0, P = 40.$

7-12. Find in Problem 7-11 (a) the cross-sectional area of the cable in square inches if the steel of which the cable is made weighs 490 lb per cu ft; (b) total elongation of the cable in feet if the modulus of elasticity of its material is 28,000,000 lb per sq in.   *Ans.* (A) (a) 0.0367 sq in., (b) 0.0077 ft

7-13. A wire is L ft long at 65°F. The electric current in the wire may heat it to t°F. Find elongation of the wire due to thermal expansion if the coefficient of expansion of wire material is 0.0000125 per 1°F.

(A) $L = 150.0, t = 250.$ *Ans.* 0.35 ft

(B) $L = 235.7, t = 175.$

(C) $L = 268.0, t = 212.$

7-14. Compute normal tension for $P_0 = 10$ lb and for the weight W of the suspended length l of tape.

(A) $W = 0.75$ lb, $l = 50$ ft.   *Ans.* 18.8 lb

(B) $W = 1.75$ lb, $l = 100$ ft.

(C) $W = 0.938$ lb, $l = 75$ ft.

CHAPTER **8**

Field Instructions—Tape Traverses

8-1. Definitions. Various methods of tying significant objects to a transit line have been discussed in Chapter 6. This chapter is concerned with running the transit line itself. A *transit line* is a line staked on the ground by sighting along the line with the transit telescope. When the staking of one line is completed the transit is moved to the point at the far end of the line, where a horizontal angle is measured in order to establish a new direction in which to stake out a new line. While the lines are being staked, the horizontal distances are measured between the points of the transit's set-ups. This process of staking out and measuring the lines is called *traversing,* and the lines so established on the ground constitute a *traverse.*

The traverses may be run for many purposes: to establish the boundary lines of a property, to stake out the center line of a highway, to mark the building lines of a proposed structure, to determine the topographic features of an area, and so on. When a traverse closes on the point of beginning, as in surveying the boundaries of a property, the traverse is called a *closed traverse;* and when a traverse does not close on the point of beginning, as in surveying the center line of a highway, the traverse is called an *open traverse.*

8-2. Boundary surveys. When a new engineering project is contemplated it is necessary first of all to choose a suitable site for the location of proposed structures. Thus a reconnaissance survey of several possible alternate locations may be required. Such a survey must consider the size of an area, its suitability for proposed structures, the economic

100

factors involved, the availability of water supply, and numerous other factors. Aerial photographs, when available, offer excellent aid in the study of various sites.

After a site is selected, the boundaries of the real estate property must be surveyed by a professional engineer or a licensed land surveyor. The surveyor draws a plan, showing all essential features of the real estate, according to the existing laws and regulations. At the time of purchase of the land the plan is registered at the county clerk's office.

Many municipalities in the United States require that a surveyed property be tied to the national net of horizontal controls. Such a procedure, when feasible, must be a recommended practice on any property survey, since the boundaries tied to a national net may be re-established in their original location even if all monuments defining such boundaries become obliterated.*

8-3. Tying traverses to the national control nets. One of the best ways to tie a parcel of real estate to the national net of horizontal control is to run a traverse from a corner of the property to the nearest U.S. Coast and Geodetic Survey marker, called a *station*. Information about the coordinates of such stations is available without charge either from the Washington office or from a regional office of the USC&GS. Each station is identified by a name. The location of a station is specified not only by the latitude and longitude but also by the x and y coordinates in the plane coordinate system of the state in which the station is located.

The *State System of Plane Coordinates,* described in more detail in Chapter 13, has been established by the USC&GS in every state to give control points of known location, as defined by their x and y coordinates, to local engineers and surveyors. The plane coordinate system is possible on a spherical surface only within certain limits. By dividing the whole area of the United States into certain areas, called **zones,** of such size within which a spherical surface projected on a plane surface does not produce a scale distortion greater than about 1:10,000, it is possible to do plane surveying work of a third order accuracy within a zone (see Table 7-1). All points of horizontal control within a zone have their x and y coordinates computed in reference to a single pair of rectangular coordinate axes. The y-axis for each zone runs parallel to the central meridian for a given zone and the x-axis in a direction perpendicular to the y-axis. The origin of these axes is so located that the coordinates of all points within a zone are positive. It has been found that the area covered by a single zone need not be smaller than the area of such states as New Jersey or North Carolina. Larger states may have several zones, with a certain amount of overlap between them, so that the points near

---

* See Appendix D for certain details of property surveys.

border lines may have their coordinates transferred from one zone to another. The above type of coordinate system in a state is known as the *state grid.*

All of the states except the thirteen original states and Texas, Kentucky, and Tennessee have also been surveyed by a Federal agency now called the Bureau of Land Management. These surveys constitute an independent net known as the *United States System of Public Land Surveys.* This system divides the land into townships approximately six miles wide in east-west direction and six miles long in north-south direction. Each regular township is divided into 36 sections approximately one mile wide and one mile long. Each section is divided into quarter sections, each equal to about 160 acres. Each section corner and quarter-section corner is marked by a stone monument or some other marker. In populated centers most of these original corner monuments have been replaced by local surveying markers when subdivision of land into smaller parcels has taken place.

The Federal system of public land surveys offers a means of tying traverses to section corners in cases where the stations of the state coordinate system may not be available in the vicinity of a traverse. This system is described in more detail in Appendix C.

8-4. Stations of the U.S. Coast Survey.* The stations of the U.S. Coast and Geodetic Survey are irregularly scattered throughout the

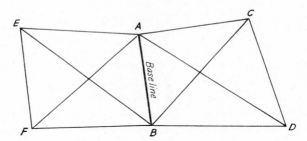

Fig. 8-1. Typical triangulation net.

country. The lack of systematic regularity in locating the stations results from the necessity of conducting surveys by the **triangulation method.** In this method an accurately measured selected distance, called a **base line,** serves as one side of several triangles formed by a number of selected distant points, as shown in Fig. 8-1. These distant points are of necessity selected for visibility on high hills or on elevated plateaus. The lengths of all unmeasured sides of these triangles are

---

* Information on the USC&GS stations in a given region may be obtained by writing to the Director of the USC&GS, Washington 25, D.C.

computed from the measured length of the base line and the measured angles at the vertices of the triangles.

A continuous series of figures extending over a considerable distance constitutes a **triangulation arc.** The basic, first order net of such arcs covers the area of the United States in all directions. The stations of first order triangulation are usually situated many miles apart. It is not unusual for these stations to be 20, 50, or 100 and more miles apart. Thus a second order triangulation net is run to connect the first order stations. It is planned that eventually the stations of the second order will be placed about seven miles apart throughout the country.

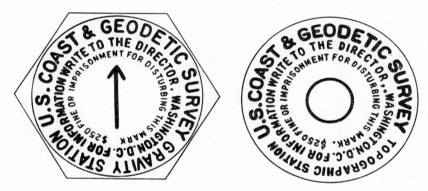

Fig. 8-2. Standard marks of the U. S. Coast and Geodetic Survey.
(Courtesy U. S. Coast & Geodetic Survey.)

Not all triangulation stations are ground stations. In many cases such points as the top of a water tank, a church steeple, or a radio tower serve as triangulation stations. Although such stations, because of their inaccessibility, cannot be used directly for tying traverses, they often have so-called *eccentric ground stations* near-by. The distance and the direction from a main station to the eccentric station are known and are available with the rest of the station data.

Accessible triangulation stations of the Coast Survey are concrete monuments set in the ground. A brass disc with a proper inscription is imbedded in the top of each monument. Figure 8-2 shows discs with inscriptions from which the type of the marker can be identified.

8-5. Acquisition of right-of-way. For the purpose of constructing such public facilities as highways, railroads, and canals, the necessary strip of land is acquired by **easement titles.** An easement title is a document transferring the rights to use the land to the company holding such a title. Although the original owners are compensated for the use of their properties, the companies acquiring easement titles do not buy the land but buy a **right-of-way,** that is, the right to use the land as long as the constructed facility is used to provide a specific service to the public. Should the land under the easement be abandoned by the company using it, the right to use the land reverts to the original owners.

When a right-of-way is acquired, the strip of land must be of sufficient width for all cut and fill slopes, for any side structures, for telegraph poles, and so forth. Due consideration should also be given to the economic

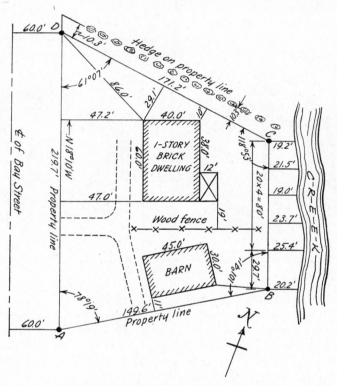

Fig. 8-3. Sketch of a traverse and details.

factors favoring acquisition of a right-of-way for future expansion and improvements. A right-of-way strip of land is a logical place for the installation of additional ground control stations. When improvements contemplated within a right-of-way require removal of existing monuments, the monuments must be carefully relocated and the relocation data sent to the agency responsible for setting those monuments.

8-6. Closed traverses. Aside from the establishment of boundary lines, a closed traverse may be run within a property area for the purpose of locating on a map the various physical features on that area, and to determine elevations of points for plotting contours. A complete map of the existing ground is necessary before the engineers may proceed with a design.

Figure 8-3 shows the sketch of a traverse which locates both the property boundaries and the details. Such sketches are drawn in the field notebook. They are usually made freehand and not to scale. The plans are plotted from these sketches and from other data found in the field notebook.

Line	Meas. Length Forw'd Ft.	Temp. Pull °F. Lb.	Diff. in Elevat. or Vertical Angle	Conditions of Support	TAPING TRAVERSE ABCDE PROJECT No. 328 x							
					Tape: 100.015 Ft. long at 68°F., 10 lb. pull supported throughout. W = 1.50 lb.							
					CORRECTIONS FOR						
					Tape	Temp.	Pull	Slope	Sag	Total	Corrected Distance
A-1	100.00	85 10	7.2 Ft.	At ends only				-0.259	-0.094		
1-2	56.73	" "	O	" " "				O	-0.017		
2-B	32.50	" "	1.5 ft.	Throughout				-0.035	O		
AB	189.23	85 10			0.028	0.021	O	-0.294	-0.111	-0.356	188.87
BC	74.35	" "	20°15'	At ends only	0.011	0.008	O	-0.460	-0.039	-0.480	73.87
CD etc.											

June 6, 1958   ⊼ A.Jones   9.
Clear, Calm   Head Tapeman D. Black
Tape No. 15   Rear Tapeman M. Gay
Notes   R. Smith

Fig. 8-4. Recording of tape measurements.

Since the members of a party making field measurements do not normally plot field data on paper, it is important that all field recordings be neat, complete, and clear to any draftsman doing the plotting.

Figure 8-4 shows how tape measurements should be recorded in a field notebook. The left-hand page shows the same data appearing in Fig. 4-2. The right-hand page shows all taping corrections and the corrected measurements.

Corrected distances, shown in the last column of the right-hand page on Fig. 8-4, are transferred to a new page in the field notebook (Fig. 8-5). It should be noted that in this figure the column headed by "Difference" shows the estimated error of each measurement by taking the difference between the rounded-off average value and a measurement which gives the greatest difference. Such an estimation of error is based on the assumption that the average measurement is a correct measurement, which may or may not be true. However, for practical purposes such estimation of errors provides a check on measurements. A further check on the accuracy of measurements in a closed traverse is obtained from the error of closure of the whole traverse as described in Chapter 15.

The sketch of a traverse, such as shown in Fig. 8-3, should be drawn on the right-hand page of Fig. 8-5. The angles measured on a closed traverse are recorded on a separate page as described in Chapter 12 (see Figs. 12-2 to 12-5). The adjusted angles and the bearings of lines should be shown on the sketch drawn in the notebook.

PROJECT No. 35 TAPE TRAVERSE ABCDE (SEE p.9)						June 9, 1958 Distances from p.9 Tape No.15	π A.Jones H.Tapeman D.Black R.Tapeman M.Gay Notes R.Smith /2.
Distance	Forw'd. Ft.	Back Ft.	Avg. Ft.	Diff.	Approx. Relat. Error	Remarks	
AB	188.87	188.81	188.84	0.03	1:6300	✓	
BC	73.87	73.84	73.86	0.02	1:3700	To be remeas.	
CD	472.52	472.57	472.55	0.03	1:15,700	✓	
DE	287.31	287.30	287.31	0.01	1:28,700	✓	
EA							

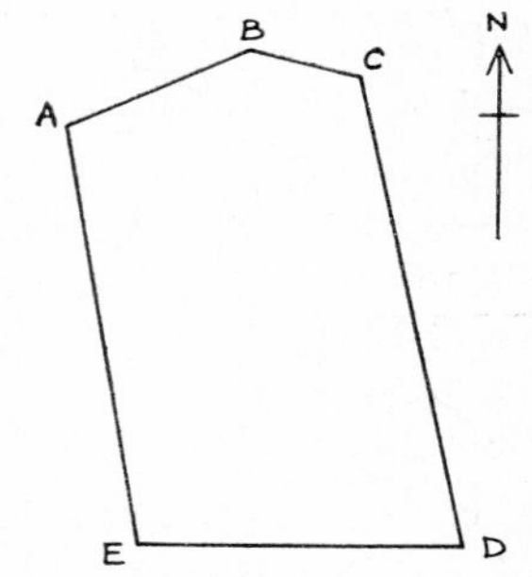

Fig. 8-5. Field notebook recording of distances.

In a third order traverse any distance measurement having an estimated relative error greater than 1:5000 should be remeasured. When the required accuracy in a traverse is such that no tape corrections are necessary, and where all measurements are made horizontally, the measured distances may be recorded directly as shown in Fig. 8-5. For instance, such recordings may be satisfactory on many building construction jobs where the required order of accuracy is 1:3000 or lower.

8-7. Open traverses. The open traverses are run mostly on route surveys. The word *route* is used in surveying in a broad sense, including not only railroads and highways but also canals, transmission lines, pipe lines, or any other long and relatively narrow strip of land needed for transportation or communication.

The surveying for a route may be divided into three stages: the *reconnaissance,* the *preliminary,* and the *location surveys.* The reconnaissance survey consists of a general study of the area in a search for a feasible and economic location of a route. Such a survey includes studies of the existing topography, soil conditions, drainage, river crossings, accessibility, route interconnections, existing land use, and so on. These studies, formerly made by a locating engineer in the field, are now conducted primarily by means of aerial photographs.

After the general location for a route has been decided upon, a surveying field party runs on the ground what is known as the ***preliminary line***. Running the preliminary traverse line is only a part of the preliminary survey. It includes also the determination of elevations along the transit line, and at a right angle to the line. The elevation along the transit line is known as the ***ground profile***, and the elevations at right angles to the line are known as ***cross sections***. The latter are used mainly for drawing ground contours and for computing the quantities of earthwork on a given route.

The preliminary line is run as an open traverse. Starting at the point of beginning, usually designated as Station 0+00, a series of straight lines are staked out on the ground in the direction of a proposed route. The lines are called ***tangents***, and the *points of intersection* of tangent lines are usually designated as P.I. stations. The angles between tangent lines are measured with a transit and all hubs set at P.I. points are referenced by one of the methods described in Chapter 6. The intermediate points are marked by stakes usually set 100 ft apart. Distances are measured continuously along the tangents from the first to the last stake of the entire traverse. The points staked on the ground are called ***stations*** and are designated by the number of 100 ft tape lengths plus the number of feet less than one hundred that have been measured up to the station involved. For instance, a stake set 2753.7 ft from the point of beginning is marked as Sta. 27+53.7.

The preliminary line is plotted on paper with the profile of the ground shown under the plan view. This arrangement of plan and profile constitutes a working drawing on which engineers design horizontal and vertical curves, grades and superelevations, and also determine the location of bridges and all other structures necessary for the construction of a route. When the design is completed, a complete set of blueprints of final drawings is made available to contractors interested in submitting bids for construction.

The final ***location survey*** of a route is staked out on the ground by field parties which set stakes along the adopted center line of the route, determine the limits of slopes for cuts and fills, and set at such limits what are known as ***slope stakes***. The stationing on location surveys follows all horizontal curves. The accuracy of location surveys varies with the type of route being constructed. Like any other engineering survey, the location of a route must be tied to the national net of horizontal controls.

On preliminary surveys the measured distances are recorded as stations in the first column of the left-hand page, and the angles measured at P.I. points are recorded in the second column. The stationing runs up the page on route surveys in order to correspond with the sketch of the center line and with the details shown on the right-hand page when looking ahead, that is in the direction of increasing stations. The red line of the field notebook running at the center of the right-hand page is used in sketches as the surveyed transit line. A complete set of field notes for the preliminary survey of a route is shown in Fig. 12-4 (p. 206).

8-8. Staking out a building. The location of a building on construction plans is usually shown in relation to property lines, from which

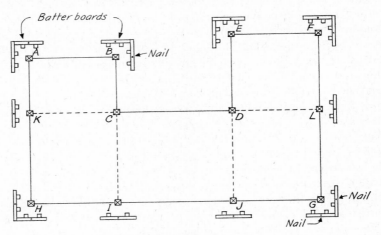

Fig. 8-6. Staking a building.

measurements for proper location of a building on the ground must be made. If a building is facing a street, the property line along the street may be established by measurements made from the center line of the street.

All corners of a building are staked out by running a transit-tape traverse around the building. Normally the face lines of building walls are staked on the ground. If the plans show that the walls are offset with respect to the face of the foundation, it is important to make clear to the building contractor which lines of the building are being staked out.

Figure 8-6 shows building lines *ABCDEFGH* with the stakes set at each corner and also at points *I* and *J* along the line *GH* and points *K* and *L* on line *CD*. These points are set for the purpose of making diagonal measurements as a check for staking any rectangular part of the building such as *ABIH* or *EFGJ*. After the face of the building has been staked, all lines are offset about 3 or 4 feet from the surveyed lines. These offset lines are marked by *batter boards*.

8-9. Batter boards.   Batter boards are boards about 1 in. by 6 in. which are nailed horizontally to two posts driven into the ground on the offset lines (Fig. 8-7).   The posts may be 2 by 4 in. scantlings, long enough to permit the top of the boards to be set at the elevation of a definite part of the building.   The boards are usually set at the elevation of the ground floor.   Either the engineer's level or the builder's level (Fig. 9-10) and a leveling rod are used to set the boards at desired elevations.   The leveling operations are described in Chapter 9.

After the boards are nailed to the posts, other nails are partly driven along the top edges of boards in order to mark the lines corresponding to the face of building walls, already staked on the ground (Fig. 8-6).   A

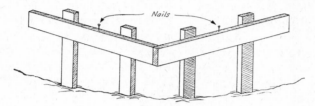

Nails

Fig. 8-7. Batter boards.

string stretched between two nails along the face of a wall gives not only the alignment for the walls but also a line of definite elevation from which it is possible to measure a vertical distance to any part of the building.

Where the irregularities of the ground surface do not permit all batter boards to be set at desired elevations, some boards are set a whole number of feet above or below a given elevation.   This must be plainly marked on the boards with a crayon.   The batter boards secure the alignments during construction, since the original stakes marking the faces of building walls are removed by the foundation excavation.

FIELD EXERCISES

8-1. Making ties and sketches; measurement of grades by clinometer

Party: Four men.

Equipment: Cloth tape, one level rod, one clinometer.

Object: To learn how to tie established points to trees, buildings, and other objects, and how to record these ties in the field notebook; also to gain experience in the use of the clinometer for measuring grades.

Procedure: The instructor will require each party to set four hubs on sloping ground, making an irregular quadrilateral figure, and to tie those hubs to near-by objects.   In making the ties, measure three distances from each hub to the near-by trees, fence posts, or any other substantial objects. Try to select objects that can be identified by a person unfamiliar with the given locality. Describe the objects and make sketches in the notebook showing measured ties. Draw on the sketch also an arrow showing approximate north-south direction.

After setting the hubs each man will proceed to pace the distances between them and to record the measurements in the field notebook (see Fig. 8-5). Pace each distance twice, once in each direction, and take the average of the two values. In pacing a distance on slope, one may expect to count fewer paces going down the hill than coming up. Convert the measured distances into feet, by using the pacing factor found in Field Exercise 6-1, and then measure paced distances with a cloth tape. Determine the difference between the taped horizontal values and the average paced values of distances. Express the accuracy of each measured distance as one part per so many measured parts.

Next, determine the grades between the hubs by using a clinometer. A *grade* is the rate of slope, normally expressed in per cent; that is, so many feet of drop or rise per 100 ft of horizontal distance. Upgrades are considered positive and downgrades negative. Some clinometers have scales that will read grades in per cent directly. On others it may be necessary to read vertical angles in degrees, and to compute the grades using measured horizontal distances.

When using the clinometer, stand over the point at one end of a sloping distance and determine the height of your eyes by holding the leveling rod directly in front. Sight with clinometer on the same point on the rod when the rod is held at the other end of slope (see Fig. 4-3). Read the grade or the vertical angle on the clinometer's arc.

8-2. Accurate measurements with steel tape

Party: Four men.

Equipment: Tape, tally pins, two range poles, two plumb bobs for taping, 1 spring balance, 1 thermometer.

Object: To gain experience in taping short distances with an accuracy of 1:5000. This exercise may be performed as part of a larger project, that is, making a complete survey of a parcel of land and drawing a finished map of the surveyed area. The measurements obtained in this exercise may also be used in Field Exercise 16-2 for computation of the area.

Procedure: The instructor will assign a general area to be surveyed. Each party may be required to stake out original corners of an area or to find already set corner-hubs from sketches showing ties to near-by objects. The ties must be verified. A neat sketch of the assigned polygon should be drawn on the right-hand page of the field notebook. See Fig. 8-4 for the proper way of recording field measurements. A closed tape-traverse will be run by each party around the polygon's perimeter. The aimed accuracy of measurements is 1:5000.

It may be assumed that the project engineer has estimated that in order to achieve the required accuracy in taping, it will be necessary to tape each distance twice, once in each direction; to read the tape to the nearest hundredth of a foot; and to make corrections for all systematic errors incurred in taping.

After completion of field work make all necessary corrections to the measured distances. Refer to Figs. 8-4 and 8-5.

Measurement of distances in this exercise may be also extended to diagonals connecting various vertices of the polygon, so as to divide the polygon into a number of triangles. Knowing three sides of each triangle, one can compute the angles in each triangle. Then, by adding proper angles at each corner of the polygon, one can find the angular closure for the interior angles of the polygon. This may serve as another demonstration of how the angles in a closed figure may be found by using tape measurements.

CHAPTER 9

Determination of Elevations

Leveling Procedure

9-1. Mean sea level. The elevations of points are normally referred to the mean sea level, which is considered to be at zero elevation. Points above mean sea level have positive elevations and points below mean sea level have negative elevations.

By definition, a level surface is the surface which is at any point perpendicular to the direction of gravity. The direction of gravity depends to some extent on the distribution of the earth's masses and on their densities. For instance, a plumb bob held vertically at the foot of a mountain will deflect toward the mountain. Such deflections are small, seldom exceeding 1'; nevertheless they make a level surface slightly irregular. Thus a surface of zero elevation around the earth is a curved, slightly irregular surface. The shape which this surface makes is called the **geoid.**

The elevations of points which are determined on the surface of the earth with reference to the mean sea level are affected by slight upheavals and settlements taking place in the earth's crust. In the areas unaffected by earthquakes and having stable rocky soil, such changes in elevation may be hardly discernible through many years, but in places of active disturbances the elevations may change considerably overnight. The mean sea level itself is not a steady frame of reference. Its changes depend on the melting of polar ice, the accretion of volcanically derived water, and many other factors.

112

9-2. The U.S. Coast and Geodetic Survey level net. The USC&GS establishes throughout the United States the points of known elevation called the **bench marks**. The net of such bench marks constitutes a system of **vertical control** in this country. The elevations of bench marks are referred to the geoid of some particular year. For instance, the level net throughout the United States was adjusted in the year 1929, and since that time the elevations have been referred to the so-called "1929 datum." The elevations of bench marks and their complete descriptions are published by the USC&GS in pamphlet form for a given region. These publications are available from the USC&GS.

A constant check on the changes in elevation of established bench marks is carried out by the USC&GS. Corrections to the elevation of points, still referred to the 1929 datum, are available from the offices of the USC&GS in various supplementary publications. The 1929 datum provides a fairly constant frame of reference for the elevations on the North American Continent.

Fig. 9-1. Standard Bench Mark. (Courtesy U. S. Coast and Geodetic Survey.)

As it was pointed out in Art. 1-7, some arbitrarily chosen datum may be used in surveying work. Some cities, for instance, are using arbitrarily chosen datum selected before any elevations referred to the mean sea level were locally available. Also on minor surveys an **assumed datum** is sometimes used for determining the difference in elevation of points.

9-3. The bench marks. A typical USC&GS bench mark is a concrete monument with an imbedded brass disc such as the one shown in Fig. 9-1. Many other bench marks have been established by engineers from those set by the USC&GS.

On engineering projects some bench marks are established on the proposed site of construction, usually during preliminary surveys, so that their established elevations can be used in design, and later in construction of designed structures. Such bench marks must be located close to construction sites in places where they are not likely to be disturbed. Any identifiable mark set on a firm existing object may serve as a bench mark. Crosses chiseled on rocks or concrete slabs, nails driven into the roots of trees, or just ordinary stakes firmly driven into the ground are among the bench marks most commonly used on construction sites. When permanent bench marks are established in the form of concrete monuments, the bottom of the monument must be extended well below the frost line so that the monument will not be disturbed by changes of ground elevations resulting from freezing and thawing.

9-4. Differential leveling. The surveying procedure employed in determining the elevation of new points—by finding the difference

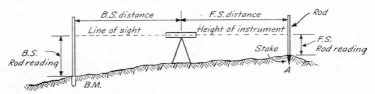

Fig. 9-2. Backsight and Foresight in leveling.

between their elevation and those of points of known elevation—is called *differential leveling.* The equipment needed in differential leveling consists of a leveling rod (Fig. 9-15) and a leveling instrument. The most commonly used levels are the engineer's levels shown in Figs. 9-3 and 9-4, although a transit (Fig. 2-18) may also be used as a level. In essence, a

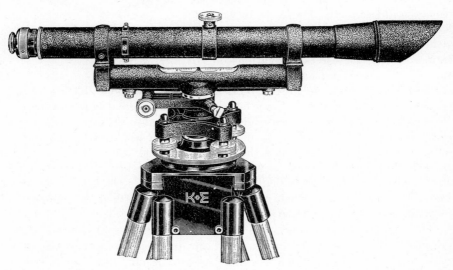

Fig. 9-3. Dumpy level.   (Courtesy Keuffel & Esser Co.)

level consists of a spirit level attached to a telescope producing the line of sight, so that when the bubble of the spirit level is centered, the line of sight assumes a horizontal position. When in use, the leveling instrument is mounted on a tripod.

In leveling of low order of accuracy a hand level (Fig. 2-15) may be used. Although it is important to choose instruments and equipment that will produce the required accuracy in the determination of the elevation of points, it is a bit extravagant to use instruments capable of producing accuracies far beyond those required.

The principles involved in a leveling operation will be first described for two points and then extended to a distance with many points, comprising what is known as a *differential leveling circuit*.

Fig. 9-4. Wye level.   (Courtesy Keuffel & Esser Co.)

Referring to Fig. 9-2, let it be required to measure, with a hand level and a leveling rod, the difference in elevation between a bench mark and a near-by point A.   The man holding the level takes his position at some convenient location from which he can see the rod when it is held on either point.   Normally, he tries to make distances to both points approximately equal, but his position need not be on the line joining the points.   He takes a sight on the rod held vertically on the bench mark. By definition, *a sight taken on a point of known elevation is called a backsight and is designated as B.S.*   Let the reading of the rod on this backsight be 6.3 ft.   Next, the man with the hand level takes a sight on the rod held vertically on point A.   This is a sight taken on a point of unknown elevation.   By definition, *a sight taken on a point of unknown elevation is called a foresight and is designated as F.S.* Let the reading of the rod on this foresight be 1.7 ft.   Then the difference in elevation between the bench mark and point A is $6.3 - 1.7 = 4.6$ ft.

If the elevation of the bench mark in the above example is, say, 638.4, to the nearest tenth of a foot, the elevation of point A is 638.4

+ 4.6 = 643.0. In a notebook, this computation is performed in two steps. First, the B.S. reading is added to the elevation of the bench mark, thus giving what is known as the *height of instrument* (H.I.), that is, the elevation of the line of sight; and second, the F.S. reading is subtracted from the height of the instrument, thus giving the elevation that is being determined. In the example above, H.I. = 638.4 + 6.3 = 644.7 and the elevation of point A is 644.7 − 1.7 = 643.0. Since in such operations the backsight reading is used with a plus sign and the foresight reading with a minus sign, the former is often referred to as the *plus sight* and the latter as the *minus sight*.

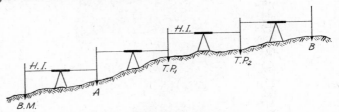

Fig. 9-5. Differential leveling.

The above example shows that a differential leveling is nothing but a measurement of distances in a vertical direction. Since such measurements cannot be made directly with a graduated rod alone, an instrument producing a horizontal line of sight is used to establish a reference line from which vertical distances are measured on a leveling rod.

The procedure of finding the difference in elevation of two points has certain limitations. If the length of a leveling rod is h and the difference in elevation of two points is greater than h, the difference in elevation cannot be found from measurements made at a single set-up of the instrument. The distance from the instrument to the rod must also be restricted to certain limits, depending upon the type of instrument used. The reading of the rod with a hand level, for instance, becomes difficult at distances exceeding 45 or 50 ft. When telescopic instruments are used, the corrections in rod readings, due to the curvature of the earth and the refraction of the atmosphere, should be made for sight distances exceeding 200 ft. The random errors in rod readings also increase with the increase in sight distance.

Differential leveling between widely separated points is normally accomplished in the series of steps described above for two points. For instance, the leveling shown in Fig. 9-2 may be carried beyond point A to some distant point B, as is shown in Fig. 9-5. After finding the elevation of point A the level is moved to a new position, in the general direction of point B. A backsight is then taken on point A and a foresight on some new point marked by T.P.₁ in the figure. The designation T.P.

stands for a *turning point,* since the rod is "turned" to face a new direction on such points when a sight is taken from the new set-up of the instrument.

In order to obtain a check on leveling operations, the differential leveling must be carried back to the point of beginning, thus effecting what is known as the *closure.* A closure may be also made on any other bench mark. The line of levels carried from the point of beginning to the point of closure constitutes a *differential leveling circuit,* and the

Sta.	B.S.	H.I.	F.S.	Elevat.	Adjust. Elevat.	B.S. and F.S. Distances	Description of Points
							LEVELING. DETERMINING APPROX. ELEVATION OF POINTS "A" AND "B" — Feb. 10, 1960 Clear, cold Level No. 12 — 𝕏 D.A. Adams Rod – K. Rust Notes – J.M. Bell 7.
B.M.₁	6.3	644.7		638.36			Brass disc on front steps of Administration Bldg.
A	8.1	651.1	1.7	643.0	643.0		A – iron stake, N.E. corner
T.P₁	5.8	654.6	2.3	648.8			
T.P₂	4.9	655.3	4.2	650.4			
B	5.7	658.0	3.0	652.3	652.2		Concrete Monument at Gates
T.P₃	3.2	656.0	5.2	652.8			
T.P₄	2.7	652.3	6.4	649.6			
T.P₅	0.5	645.7	7.1	645.2			
B.M.₁			7.1	638.6			
Σ	37.2		37.0				
	37.0			638.4			
DIFF.	0.2 ← Check →			0.2			

Fig. 9-6. Leveling notes.

difference between the known and closing elevation of a bench mark determines the *error of closure* in a given leveling circuit.

9-5. Recording of data. There is a standard way of recording leveling notes. Figure 9-6 shows recordings for the leveling shown in part in Fig. 9-5. The standard headings for five columns on the left-hand page are: *Station, B.S., H.I., F.S.,* and *Elevation.* The station is *not* the point occupied by the leveling instrument, but the point on which the rod is held.

In the example given in Art. 9-4, the first sight was taken on the bench mark, thus B.M. is entered on the first line in the station column. Also the known elevation of the bench mark is entered on the same line in the elevation column. The backsight on the bench mark is entered in the B.S. column opposite B.M., and the foresight on point A is entered in the F.S. column opposite A shown in the station column. The B.S. reading is added to the elevation of the point on which the backsight is taken, in order to obtain the height of the instrument in the H.I. column, and the F.S. reading on a point is subtracted from the height of instrument in order to obtain the elevation of that point.

All leveling notes must show a check of the arithmetic described above. The check consists of taking the difference between the sum of the backsights and the sum of the foresights, and comparing this difference with the error of closure. Any discrepancy between the two numbers indicates that an arithmetical error exists in the notes. Figure 9-6 shows that the error of closure, 0.2 ft, checks the difference between the Σ B.S. and Σ F.S.

The right-hand page of leveling notes must contain description of locations of bench marks and of all other points which may be useful in subsequent field operations.

9-6. Accuracy in leveling. If a random error in running 1 mile of levels is n ft, the random error in running a leveling circuit of D miles is $n \sqrt{D}$ ft. Assuming that the error of closure, e, in a circuit is due entirely to the accumulation of accidental errors, it may be written that

$$e = n \sqrt{D} \qquad (9\text{-}1)$$

where e is in feet. Thus

$$n = \frac{e}{\sqrt{D}} \qquad (9\text{-}2)$$

The accuracy of leveling is classified according to certain values assigned to n in Eqs. (9-1) and (9-2). Table 9-1 shows the maximum allowable values for n in leveling of *first, second,* and ***third orders*** and in ***ordinary leveling.***

TABLE 9-1. VALUES OF n IN LEVELING
(IN FEET PER MILE)

	First Order	Second Order	Third Order	Ordinary Leveling
n	0.012	0.025	0.05	0.1

First and second order leveling may be classified as precise and semi-precise levelings respectively. Accordingly, precise and semi-precise levels should be used for this type of work. The engineer's levels shown in Figs. 9-3 and 9-4 may be described as standard leveling instruments. Standard engineer's levels are used extensively on engineering surveys and may be expected to produce third order accuracy. Various types of levels are described below.

Precise levels and some standard levels have stadia hairs on their cross-hair rings for estimation of horizontal sight distances in leveling.

Using such instruments, one may estimate the length of a leveling circuit by adding all backsight and foresight distances in the circuit. If a level does not have stadia hairs, the sight distances may be measured by pacing; or the length of a circuit may be estimated by multiplying the estimated average length of a sight by the number of sights taken in a given circuit. For instance, the leveling notes shown in Fig. 9-6 are given for leveling operations performed with a hand level. Assuming that the average length of sight was about 40 ft, and observing that there were eight backsights and eight foresights, one may estimate the length of the circuit as $40 \times 16 = 640$ ft or 0.12 miles. This length of circuit substituted for D in Eq. (9-2), with $e = 0.2$ ft (from Fig. 9-6), gives the value of n equal to 0.58. Thus it is apparent that the leveling recorded in Fig. 9-6 was quite inaccurate. In fact, a hand level should be used only in cases where a rough approximation of elevations is satisfactory. Measurements taken for the computation of quantities of earthwork on engineering projects sometimes fall into this class of work.

9-7. Adjustment of observed elevations. Equation (5-8) shows that accidental errors accumulate in direct proportion to the square root of the number of observations. Thus, assuming that the accumulation of accidental errors at the end of 1 mile is equal to E, the error must be $E \sqrt{2}$ at the end of 2 miles, and so on. Equation (5-14), however, shows that corrections applied to observed values must be directly proportional to the square of accidental errors. Thus if $E \sqrt{2}$ is the correction that must be applied to the observed elevation of a point at the end of 2 miles of leveling and E is the accidental error at the end of 1 mile of leveling, the correction that must be applied to the elevation of a point at the end of 1 mile must be $(E)^2/(E \sqrt{2})^2 = \frac{1}{2}$ of that at the end of two miles.

In general, if E is the error of closure at the end of D miles, the correction, C, that must be applied to the observed elevation of a point at the end of d miles of leveling must be

$$C = E \frac{d}{D} \qquad (9\text{-}3)$$

Equation 9-3 shows that *corrections in a leveling circuit are applied in direct proportion to the distances.* This statement assumes that the number of observations, i.e., the number of rod readings, is directly proportional to the distances, which is generally true in leveling, especially on fairly uniform terrain.

If the distances in a leveling circuit are not known, it may be assumed that the number of set-ups of the instrument is proportional to the horizontal distances. Thus the error of closure may be distributed in direct proportion to the number of the set-ups of the leveling instrument.

It may be observed, for instance, that the number of set-ups in the leveling circuit shown in Fig. 9-6 is 8 and that there was one set-up to point A and four to point B.   This means that $\frac{1}{8}$ of the error of closure should be applied to the observed elevation of point A and $\frac{1}{2}$ to point B.   The adjusted elevations of these points are shown in the last column of the left-hand page in the notebook shown in Fig. 9-6.

   9-8. The spirit level tube, or level vial.   Every leveling instrument, with the exception of the self-leveling level (Fig. 9-14), has a spirit level tube, also called *level vial*, that is used in leveling the instrument. In its longitudinal section the top of the vial is shaped inside to conform to the arc of a circle of radius R, as shown in Fig. 9-7.   The movement of

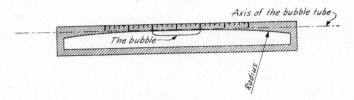

Fig. 9-7. Spirit level tube, or vial.

the air bubble of the tube in response to the angular motion of the vial in a vertical plane depends on the radius of the tube; that is, the greater the radius, the greater the sensitivity of the bubble and consequently the sensitivity of the instrument itself.

   The graduations along the top of the tube (Figs. 9-3 and 9-4) serve the purpose of centering the bubble in leveling operations.   The air bubble expands and contracts with changes in temperature so that its central position may be judged when the bubble extends the same number of divisions on each side of the center mark.   Each graduation of the tube is equal either to 0.1 in. or, more commonly, to 2 mm (0.1 in. = 2.54 mm).

   A line tangent to the radius of curvature of the vial at its central mark is called the ***axis of the vial*** or the axis of the spirit level.   When the bubble is centered, the axis is in a horizontal position.   ***The sensitivity of a leveling instrument is defined as the vertical angle of rotation of the axis of the vial that moves the bubble through one division marked on the tube.***

   The sensitivity of an instrument may be determined experimentally by taking two rod readings on a leveling rod held some distance D ft from the instrument (Fig. 9-8).   One reading is taken when the bubble is $n/2$ divisions to the left and another when the bubble is $n/2$ divisions to the right of central position.   The sensitivity, expressed as the angle α subtended by one division of the tube, is the angle having its tangent

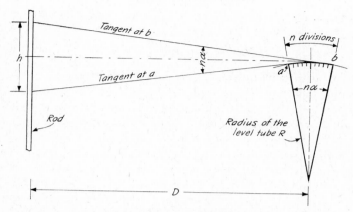

Fig. 9-8. Rod measurements to determine level's sensitivity.

equal to the difference h ft in rod readings divided by nD.   Or in seconds,

$$\alpha = \frac{h}{nD}\frac{180}{\pi} 3600 = \frac{206{,}265h}{nD} \tag{9-4}$$

Example 9-1.   When the bubble was 5 divisions left of center, the rod reading was 5.571 ft; and when the bubble was placed 5 divisions to the right of center the rod reading was 5.280.   Determine the sensitivity of the instrument if the distance between the rod and the instrument was 200 ft.

Solution: $n = 10$, $D = 200$ ft, $h = 5.571 - 5.280 = 0.291$ ft

$$\alpha = \frac{0.291}{200 \times 10} \times \frac{180}{\pi} \times 3600 = 30 \text{ sec}$$

9-9. What sensitivity should a level have?   Equation (9-1) shows the expression $e = n\sqrt{D}$ for the error of closure in a circuit of D miles. Also, Table 9-1 shows maximum values of n on leveling operations of various orders of accuracy.   A level used for certain types of leveling must have the sensitivity capable of producing the error of closure within allowable limits.   Also the leveling operations must be carried out in such a way as to produce required results.

Assume that a maximum random error in taking a sight at a distance of l ft is E ft.   Then, since one backsight and one foresight are taken at each set-up of the instrument, the maximum random error for each set-up must be $E\sqrt{2}$.   Also, assuming all sight distances equal to l ft, the number of set-ups in a leveling circuit of L ft is $L/2l$, so that accumulated random error at the end of the circuit is $E\sqrt{2}\sqrt{L/2l} = E\sqrt{L/l}$. This expression may be written as $E\sqrt{(D \times 5280)/l}$, where D is the length of a leveling circuit in miles.   Equating this to the error of closure given by Eq. (9-1), solving it for E and simplifying, the following expression for E is obtained:

$$E = 0.0138n \sqrt{l} \qquad (9\text{-}5)$$

The value of n in Eq. (9-5) may be obtained from Table 9-1 for any type of leveling, and the value of E may be determined experimentally as follows: Repeated rod readings may be taken at any convenient distance equal to s ft, recentering the bubble at each reading. This should give sufficient data to determine the average deviation in rod readings and to compute the probable error for a single reading by using Eq. (5-2). Also, maximum random error E_s for a single reading may be obtained by multiplying probable error by 3 as explained in Art. 5-9. The value of E in Eq. (9-5) is then equal to $E_s(l/s)$. Substituting this value in Eq. (9-5) and solving it for l,

$$l = \left(\frac{0.0138ns}{E_s} \right)^2 \qquad (9\text{-}6)$$

It should be noted that the value of E_s in Eq. (9-6) may vary not only with the sensitivity of various instruments but also with different instrumentmen, rodmen, and various atmospheric conditions under which the repeated rod readings are taken. However, for given conditions of leveling operations, Eq. (9-6) gives the maximum length of sights l that should be taken in the leveling circuit in order to meet the requirement of a given order of accuracy.

Example 9-2. It has been determined experimentally for a given instrument that under certain conditions the maximum random error E_s for a sight of 100 ft is ± 0.0053 ft. Determine the maximum sight distance for a leveling circuit in order to meet the requirements for third order accuracy.

Solution: $E_s = 0.0053$, $s = 100$ ft, and $n = 0.05$ from Table 9-1. Substituting these values in Eq. (9-6), $l = 170$ ft.

Levels and Rods

9-10. The engineer's dumpy and wye levels. Figure 9-9 shows the main features of a dumpy level. The name "dumpy" was originally applied to levels having an inverting eyepiece and having the telescope rigidly attached to the supporting *level bar* (1), shown in Fig. 9-9. Such levels had shorter telescopes than the levels with detachable telescopes and erecting eyepieces, called *wye levels.* At the present time, however, either a dumpy level or a wye level may be made with either type of an eyepiece. The only distinct difference between the two types of levels remains in the way their telescopes are attached to the supporting level bar.

In contrast with the dumpy level shown in Fig. 9-3, the wye level, shown in Fig. 9-4, has its telescope supported by Y-shaped bearings called the **wyes.** The telescope is locked in place by semicircular hinged clips attached to the wyes. The clips may be opened and the telescope may then be reversed end-for-end in its bearings. Such an arrangement makes for more component parts in wye levels and consequently for

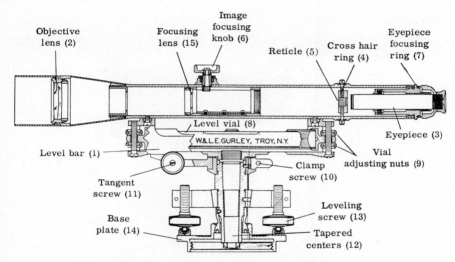

Fig. 9-9. Main parts of a level. (Courtesy W. & L. E. Gurley.)

more parts that potentially may get out of adjustment. For this reason wye levels are not as widely used as dumpy levels. In other respects the two types of levels have similar features.

Certain features of a level should be noted. The telescope (see Fig. 9-9) has at one end the **objective lens** (2) and at another end the **eyepiece** (3). An erecting eyepiece requires two additional lenses for turning the image right-side up. Since any additional parts may be potential sources of error, precise levels have, as a rule, inverting eyepieces. An ordinary level may have either an erecting or an inverting eyepiece. The erecting telescopes seem to be more popular. The power of the telescopes varies with make, type, and model of the instrument, from about 20 to 40 diameters. Some instruments, like the one shown in Fig. 9-9, have a variable-power eyepiece.

Other parts of a telescope include the **cross-hair ring** (4), which holds the **glass reticle** (5) on which the cross hairs are etched, and the **image focusing knob** (6). The cross hairs are brought into focus by a

focusing ring (7) at the eyepiece end.   The *line of sight* of a telescope
is an imaginary line passing through the intersection of the cross hairs
and the optical center of the objective lens.   A *level vial* (8) is attached
underneath the telescope and serves for leveling the instrument by means
of *leveling screws* (13).   The vial is attached to the level bar (1) in
dumpy levels and to the telescope in wye levels.   At one end of the vial
are *vial adjusting nuts* (9) by means of which one end of the vial may

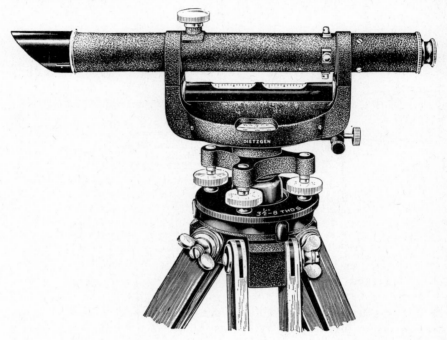

Fig. 9-10. Builders' level.   (Courtesy Eugene Dietzgen Co.)

be raised or lowered in order to make the axis of the tube perpendicular
to the vertical axis of the level.

The telescope, with the vial and the level bar, has a rotational motion
around an imaginary vertical axis passing through the middle of the
tapered center (12) which rotates with the telescope in an accurately
fitted socket in the leveling head of the instrument.   The rotational
motion may be arrested by means of a *clamp screw* (10).   When this
screw is clamped, the *tangent screw* (11) may be used to effect slow
rotational motion.

The leveling head contains *leveling screws* (13) which rest on the
base plate (14).   The base plate has standard threads, inside, for
attaching the instrument to a *tripod*.   The standard levels of American

manufacture have four leveling screws, but precise levels and most European instruments normally have only three screws in order to have as uniform bearing pressure on leveling screws as possible.

The tripods usually used with levels are non-extending in order to provide as solid a support as possible for the instrument.

9-11. Builder's level. A builder's level (Fig. 9-10) is less sensitive than an engineer's level. The special feature of a builder's level is the horizontal circle between the vial and the leveling head of the instrument. The horizontal circle is used in measuring horizontal angles. The circle

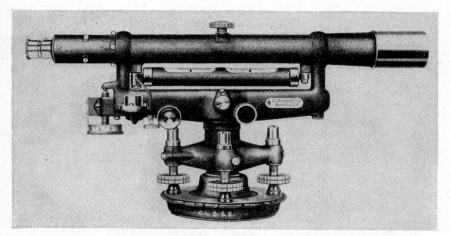

Fig. 9-11. Engineers tilting dumpy level. (Courtesy C. L. Berger & Sons, Inc.)

is divided normally from zero to 90° in each quadrant so that, besides measuring the angles, the bearings of lines could also be set on the circle after the instrument is oriented in a known direction. Angles and directions can be read on the horizontal scale within 5′.

Builder's levels are used mostly in building construction where the required accuracies are consistent with the level's sensitivity. Builder's levels are not used in the construction of large buildings or on engineering projects of any importance.

9-12. Tilting levels. The characteristic features of a tilting level (Fig. 9-11) consist of a *fulcrum,* on which the telescope and the vial may be tilted in a vertical plane; *a tilting screw with a graduated drum;* and some reflecting arrangement for the vial, enabling the instrumentman to see the level bubble as he looks through the telescope.

The tilting arrangement facilitates the centering of the bubble just prior to reading the rod. By means of an attached side mirror (not shown in Fig. 9-11) the instrumentman is able to view the rod and the vial bubble simultaneously.

Other models of tilting levels may incorporate a special prism arrangement by means of which the centering of the bubble may be accomplished by the coincidence of two halves of a *split bubble* (Fig. 9-12). Actually, the two halves of the apparent bubble are really the two opposite half-ends of the bubble, which coincide when the bubble is centered.

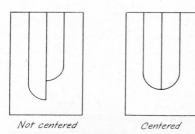

Not centered   *Centered*

Fig. 9-12. Split bubble.

A tilting arrangement and other features designed for accurate operation of leveling instruments are usually incorporated in instruments built for precise and semi-precise work.

Figure 9-13 shows a precise dumpy level of USC&GS type. The sensitivity of this instrument is 2″ per 2 mm division.

9-13. Self-leveling level. Figure 9-14 shows Carl Zeiss Ni2 self-leveling level, employing inside the telescope a suspended prism, called

Fig. 9-13. Precise dumpy level (U. S. Coast and Geodetic Survey type). (Courtesy C. L. Berger & Sons, Inc.)

the *compensator,* which produces a horizontal line of sight. This pendulum arrangement eliminates the spirit level entirely. Only a circular level is used to bring the telescope to approximately level position. When this is done, the compensator levels the line of sight accurately and automatically. Precise work can be done with this instrument.

9-14. Leveling rods. Leveling rods, used in the United States on engineering surveys and on land surveys, are graduated into feet, tenths and hundredths of a foot.   There are several patterns of such graduations on the rods.   One rod, called the ***Philadelphia rod,*** has widespread use throughout the United States.

The so-called ***tape rods*** require a slight modification in leveling procedure.   The use of this rod is described in Art. 9-16.   Another rod

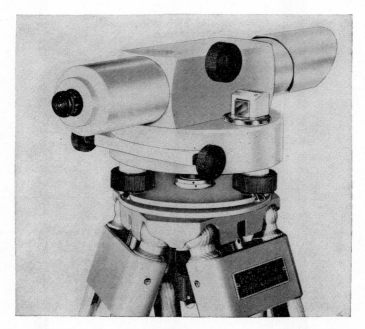

Fig. 9-14. Carl Ziess Ni2 self-leveling level.   (Courtesy Keuffel & Esser Co.)

used in precise surveying work is the ***geodetic rod,*** described briefly in Art. 9-17.

9-15. The Philadelphia rod. Figure 9-15a shows the extension-type Philadelphia rod with a sliding target.   This rod consists of two sliding sections which allow a $6\frac{1}{2}$ ft rod to be extended to 12 ft, and a 7 ft rod to 13 ft.   The graduations run upward from zero at the bottom. The footmarks are shown in red numbers, the tenths in black numbers, and the hundredths are shown by alternate black and white horizontal bars.

Rods of this type may be read on most sights directly by the instrumentman, and thus are called ***self-reading rods.***   When needed, the thousandths may be also estimated on these rods.   Thus as a rule these

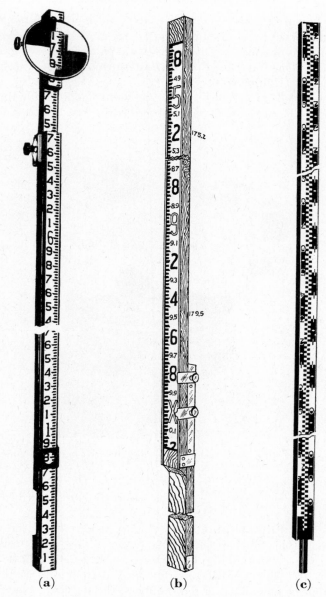

Fig. 9-15. Leveling rods: (a) Philadelphia rod (W. & L. E. Gurley.), (b) Tape rod (Lenker Mfg. Co.), (c) Geodetic rod (W. & L. E. Gurley.).

rods are used without a target. Experience shows that leveling done by reading the rod directly is practically as accurate as that done by reading the rod with the aid of a target, even though the target has a *vernier* scale that reads graduations to thousandths. However, the target is useful when difficulties are encountered in reading the rod directly— when the rod is held in poorly lighted places, when the sights are obscured by foliage, or when extra-long sights are necessary. The target is also useful in setting a line of stakes at the same elevation.

Since leveling rods are made of wood, temperature variations do not appreciably affect the lengths of rods, but varying humidity may produce as much as about 0.01 ft error in the length of a rod. For this reason, the best rods are those which have a metal strip, on which graduations are marked, attached to the face of a rod in such a way that the swelling and shrinking of the rod does not affect the length of the attached strip. If wooden rods without the metal strip are used in accurate leveling operations, their lengths must be frequently checked by a steel tape. The use of leveling rods in leveling is described in more detail in Chapter 10.

9-16. The tape rod. A tape rod (Fig. 9-15b) usually has the same type of graduations as the Philadelphia rod, except that the scale runs in the opposite direction; that is, from the top downward. The graduations are made on a steel tape supported at the top and bottom on rollers. The tape runs in a continuous loop from zero to 10 ft, so that the place on the tape marked by X serves for both the zero and the 10 ft mark. With this arrangement only about one-half of the tape is exposed to view, but the tape may be rolled and clamped in any desired position. The part of the rod on which the tape and the rollers are mounted can be moved up or down very much in the same way as the movable section of the extension rod.

In order to show how a tape rod works, assume that a tape rod is held on a point having an elevation of 327.25 ft. Then the rodman moves the tape until the line of sight of the level falls on 7.25 ft on the rod and clamps the tape in this position. Next, when he holds the rod on a foresight point, and the instrument reads, say, 5.71 ft, the elevation of the foresight point is recorded as being 325.71. If this point is used as a turning point, then, with the new set-up of the level, the tape is moved till the line of sight falls on 5.71. On the next foresight point the rod is read directly as in the preceding set-up and so on. It seems that the name "self-reading" could have been more appropriately applied to tape rods, had it not already been used on standard leveling rods.

The use of tape rods is not as widespread as might be expected. This is due to the following disadvantages: (a) a definite reading must be set on the rod on each backsight; on a windy day and on long sights this requires the instrumentman and the rodman to use sign language for numbers; it is also time-consuming; (b) it is easy to confuse the zero mark with the 10 ft mark, creating a potential source of a 10 ft error in reading the rod; and (c) the work with the tape rod places on the rodman the responsibility of keeping clamp screws securely clamped between the backsight and foresight.

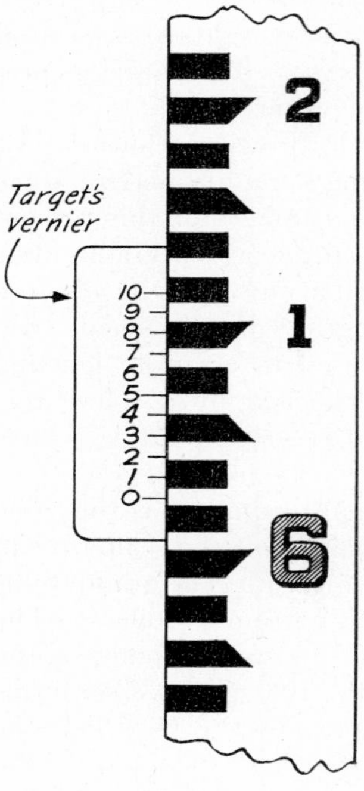

It must be pointed out that on relatively level terrain, when a number of foresight readings may be taken from the same position of the instrument, as in taking cross sections or running profile leveling, the tape rod may be employed to good advantage.

9-17. The geodetic rod. The type of geodetic rod shown in Fig. 9-15c is used by the USC&GS for precise leveling. This rod is made of one solid piece of wood about 3 in. by 1 in. in cross section. It has a *nilvar* metal strip attached to the face of the rod in such a way that the length of the strip is unaffected by slight expansions or contractions of the rod itself. Nilvar is a metal alloy which has a very low coefficient of expansion. Graduations are in meters, decimeters, and centimeters, with the numbers painted upside down for use with inverting telescopes. The back of the rod is divided into feet and tenths of a foot. A centigrade thermometer and a circular spirit level, for holding the rod in a vertical position, are attached to the back of the rod. There are also geodetic rods graduated in yards, tenths, and hundredths of a yard.

Fig. 9-16. Rod and target's vernier.

9-18. Theory of verniers. *A vernier is an auxiliary scale attached to a given scale in order to increase the precision of reading the given scale.* Figure 9-16 shows a vernier scale of a rod target, designed for reading the leveling rod to thousandths of a foot. Verniers are also used on the horizontal and vertical circles of transits and on a variety of other instruments.

A vernier may be *direct* or *retrograde,* although the latter is used very seldom. In the design of a direct vernier a certain length of a given scale, containing $n - 1$ least divisions, is divided into n divisions of the vernier. Thus if the smallest division on a given scale (call it *main scale*) represents the value of d measuring units, the $n - 1$ divisions must contain $d(n-1)$ units. Then, one division on the vernier will be equal to $d(n-1)/n$ units.

The difference between the value of one division on the main scale and the value of one division on the vernier scale represents the least precision, or the **least count**, as it is called, of the vernier. Thus the least count (l.c.) of a vernier is $d - \dfrac{d(n-1)}{n}$. Simplifying this expression,

$$\text{l.c.} = \frac{d}{n} \tag{9-7}$$

In a retrograde vernier the length of $n+1$ divisions on the main scale is divided into n divisions on the vernier. Retrograde verniers are not used on surveying instruments.

Figure 9-16 shows a section of a leveling rod with the target vernier. It may be observed on the figure that the length of 9 smallest divisions on the rod is divided into 10 divisions on the vernier. Thus $n = 10$ for this vernier, and since the smallest division on the rod $d = 0.01$ ft, the least count of the vernier is 0.001 ft from Eq. (9-7). The rod reading at the zero mark of the vernier on Fig. 9-16 is slightly over 6.02 ft. The excess over 6.02 ft is read on the vernier scale as 4, i.e. 0.004, since the vernier line opposite 4 coincides with a line on the main scale. No other line on the vernier can be in coincidence with any other line on the rod; thus the reading of the rod is 6.024 ft.

Example 9-3. The scale of a balance is divided into pounds and half-pounds. Design a vernier to read the scale to the nearest ounce.

Solution:
l.c. $= 1$ oz., $d = 8$ oz.
From Eq. (9-7), $n = 8$ divisions. Also $n - 1 = 7$ divisions. Thus the length of 7 half-pound divisions on the main scale must be divided into 8 divisions on the vernier.

Instrumental Errors in Leveling and Adjustment of Levels

9-19. Rod errors. Barring personal errors, rod errors may be either accidental or systematic in nature. Accidental errors arise from conditions which limit the accuracy of rod reading. The vibration of the air plainly seen through level telescopes on a hot day, poor visibility, the necessity to estimate thousandths—all these may increase the magnitude of accidental errors in rod readings. On the other hand, systematic errors may come from two sources. One is incorrect length of rod and another, the rod being held out of plumb.

If a rod is too long or too short, all rod readings will be consistently too small in the first case or too great in the second. Some of these errors are eliminated by the fact that the B.S. readings are used with a plus sign in leveling operations and the F.S. readings with a minus sign. Thus in leveling up or down a hill only the difference between the sum of the plus sights and the sum of the minus sights contributes to the errors in elevation of points caused by the incorrect length of rod.

If in leveling of second or higher order of accuracy a precise rod is not available, the error in rod length may be determined with a steel tape, and corresponding corrections to the determined elevations of points may be applied at the end of leveling operations. Since the measurement of the difference in elevation of points is a linear measurement in a vertical direction, the same theory that was used in making corrections for incorrect length of tape in horizontal measurements applies to measurements of difference in elevation with an incorrect rod. For instance, if a rod is too long, the measured difference in elevation of points will be too small. Normally, no corrections for incorrect length of rod need be applied in leveling of the third order.

Fig. 9-17. Rod level. (Courtesy   Keuffel   & Esser Co.)

Unlike the errors due to incorrect length of rod, errors due to a rod held out of plumb cannot be corrected, since if the rodman had known that he was not holding the rod straight, he would have tried to correct that situation in the first place. A rod reading at the top of a 12 ft rod held 1 ft out of plumb is in error by 0.042 ft. Thus in first and second order leveling a *rod level* must be used. A typical rod level with a circular spirit level is shown in Fig. 9-17.

Since all errors in reading inclined rods are plus errors, a slow waving of the rod when taking readings is sometimes recommended. A reasonable assumption here is that since the smallest reading of the rod is observed when the rod passes through its vertical position, that reading is the one that should be recorded. However, experience shows that waving the rod is more likely to be a source of errors in reading the rod than a method of eliminating them. If a rodman has difficulty in keeping the rod plumbed, he should use a rod level. This type of error tends to accumulate with the increase in the difference of elevation of points.

9-20. Errors and adjustment of dumpy levels. A level may be represented diagrammatically by three lines as shown in Fig. 9-18. The top horizontal line represents the line of sight of the telescope, the lower horizontal line represents the axis of the spirit level tube, and the vertical line represents the vertical axis passing through the tapered center (12) shown in Fig. 9-9. In a properly adjusted instrument the line of sight is parallel to the axis of the level tube, and both are at right angles to the vertical axis of the level.

Even if a level has no perceptible errors when it is checked, a change in temperature may cause non-uniform expansion or contraction of various parts, resulting in maladjustments. For instance, when exposed to the sunshine a telescope will develop a slight curvature. For this reason, in precise leveling the instrument must be protected from sunshine by a parasol. Although no such protection is necessary in ordinary leveling operations, the instrumentman should be constantly aware of

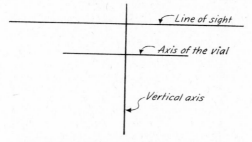

Fig. 9-18. Schematic diagram of a level.

possible accumulation of errors, and he should do his work in the manner that will minimize those errors.

The instrumental errors of a level that may be eliminated by adjustment in the field are: (1) the axis of the spirit level tube is not perpendicular to the vertical axis of the instrument, (2) the horizontal cross hair is not in a plane perpendicular to the vertical axis, and (3) the line of sight is not parallel to the axis of the spirit level tube. The presence of these conditions in a dumpy level, their effect on leveling operations, and the methods of adjusting the instrument are considered below.

9-21. (1) *The axis of the spirit level tube (vial) is not perpendicular to the vertical axis of the instrument.* When this condition exists, the centering of the bubble does not put the vertical axis in a truly vertical position. By referring to Fig. 9-19 it may be observed that if the axis of the vial deviates from the perpendicular to the vertical axis by an angle α, the vertical axis itself will be inclined to the true vertical direction by the same angle α when the bubble is centered.

Designating the smaller angle between the axis of the vial and the vertical axis by β, it may be seen in the figure that $\beta = 90° - \alpha$. By turning the telescope through 180°, the angle β will also rotate through 180° about the vertical axis of the instrument. This will cause the axis of the vial to move away from its original horizontal position through the angle 2α.   Consequently, the bubble will move off center a distance corresponding to twice the error of the level tube.   Thus in order to correct the error, it is necessary to raise or lower one end of the level tube, using adjusting nuts [shown in Fig. 9-9 (9)] until the bubble moves half-way toward the center.   After this is done, the releveling of the instrument by leveling screws [Fig. 9-9 (13)] will center the bubble and at the same time will put the vertical axis in a truly vertical position.

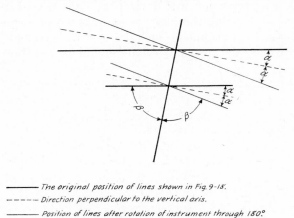

——————— The original position of lines shown in Fig. 9-18.
— — — — — Direction perpendicular to the vertical axis.
——————— Position of lines after rotation of instrument through 180°.

Fig. 9-19. Diagram showing level's vial not perpendicular to the vertical axis.

The effect of the vial being in error by angle α, on leveling operations, is such that if the line of sight is parallel to the axis of the vial and a backsight is taken with the bubble centered, the line of sight will be inclined to the horizontal through angle 2α on a foresight taken in the opposite direction, if the bubble is not recentered.   In order to eliminate this instrumental error, **the bubble must be centered each time a rod reading is taken.**

9-22. (2) *The horizontal cross hair is not in a plane perpendicular to the vertical axis of the instrument.* When the cross-hair ring is not properly adjusted it may be rotated clockwise or counter-clockwise by means of adjusting screws holding the ring in place [Fig. 9-9 (4)], until the horizontal hair does fall in a plane perpendicular to the vertical axis.   In order to check the adjustment of the cross-hair ring, a sight is taken on some well-defined point and the telescope is rotated by means of the tangent screw [Fig. 9-9 (11)].   If the point sighted on does not stay on the horizontal hair, the ring needs adjustment.   If the ring is in good adjustment, the point will remain on the horizontal hair regardless whether or not the instrument is leveled.

In order to adjust the cross-hair ring, it is necessary to loosen slightly the two adjacent screws holding the ring.   The slots through which the adjusting screws are inserted will allow a slight rotational motion of the ring. By the trial-and-error method the ring is rotated until the point sighted on does stay on the horizontal hair. The adjustment is completed by tightening the adjusting screws. The turning of the adjusting screws is accomplished by special adjusting pins which fit the holes in the capstan-head adjusting screws.

When the cross-hair ring is out of adjustment, the horizontal hair crosses the rod at an angle. This may cause small errors in reading the rod. In order to eliminate this type of error, one should read the rod at the intersection of cross hairs.

9-23. (3) *The line of sight is not parallel to the axis of the vial.* The line of sight is an imaginary line passing through the optical center of the objective lens and the intersection of the cross hairs. If the line of sight is not parallel to the axis of the vial, the cross-hair ring may be moved up or down until the line of sight is made parallel to the axis of the vial. A slight shifting of the cross-hair ring may be effected by tightening a proper adjusting screw on one side of the ring and loosening another screw on the opposite side. These are the same adjusting screws used in rotating the ring in number (2) adjustment; rotation of the ring, however, may be prevented by not permitting the ring to become loose. In order to determine the error of the line of sight and consequently the required extent of adjustment of the cross-hair ring, it is necessary to perform what is known as the *two-peg test.*

Two stakes (pegs) are set in the ground about 120 ft apart and the level to be adjusted is set up near one stake for the first set of rod readings and near the other stake for the second set. The locations of the set-up of the level must be chosen so that it would be possible to take a reading on the rod held at either stake.

Let one stake be designated by A and another by B. The level may be set up first close to either stake. Figure 9-20 shows two set-ups of the instrument. The points of set-up need not be in line with the stakes, although such an arrangement may be preferred. The desired distances between the instrument and the stakes may be measured approximately by a cloth tape. The distance to the near stake should be about 15 ft since with some instruments it is not possible to read the rod through the telescope at much closer range. Rod readings are taken on each stake for each set-up of the instrument, so that a complete set of two-peg test data should include the following:

	Instrument Set-ups	
	First	Second
Rod reading on stake A	R_A'	R_A
Rod reading on stake B	R_B'	R_B
Distance between instrument and stake A	D_A'	D_A
Distance between instrument and stake B	D_B'	D_B

Assume that because of the inclination of the line of sight, the error in reading the rod at a distance equal to 1 ft is e. This can be either positive or negative. Then, for the first set-up of the instrument, the error in reading the rod at A must be eD_A' and the error in reading the rod at B must be eD_B'. Correcting respective rod readings for these

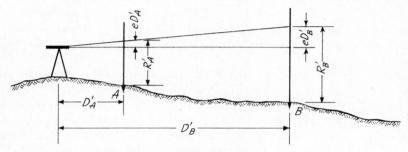

(a) The first set-up of the instrument.

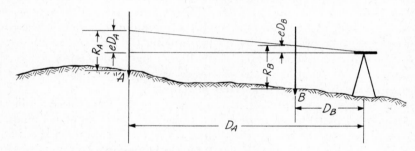

(b) The second set-up of the instrument.

Fig. 9-20. The two-peg test.

errors and subtracting rod reading at B from rod reading at A, the correct difference in elevation (C.D.E.) between A and B is found as

$$\text{C.D.E.} = (R_A' - eD_A') - (R_B' - eD_B') \qquad (9\text{-}8)$$

Similarly for the second set-up of the instrument,

$$\text{C.D.E.} = (R_A - eD_A) - (R_B - eD_B) \qquad (9\text{-}9)$$

Equating right sides of Eqs. (9-8) and (9-9), simplifying, and solving for e,

$$e = \frac{(R_A' - R_B') - (R_A - R_B)}{(D_A' - D_B') - (D_A - D_B)} \qquad (9\text{-}10)$$

In order to find the errors in rod readings at A and B for the second set-up of the instrument, the value of e in Eq. (9-10) must be multiplied by the distances to points A and B, respectively. Designating by E_A the error in rod reading at A and by E_B the error in rod reading at B, it may be written that

$$E_A = D_A \frac{(R'_A - R'_B) - (R_A - R_B)}{(D'_A - D'_B) - (D_A - D_B)} \tag{9-11}$$

$$E_B = D_B \frac{(R'_A - R'_B) - (R_A - R_B)}{(D'_A - D'_B) - (D_A - D_B)} \tag{9-12}$$

When distances to the near stakes and to the far stakes in both set-ups are made equal, Eqs. (9-11) and (9-12) may be simplified by the substitution of D_A for D'_B and D_B for D'_A (see Fig. 9-20). Eqs. (9-11) and (9-12) then assume the form shown by Eqs. (9-13) and (9-14).

$$E_A = D_A \frac{(R'_A - R'_B) - (R_A - R_B)}{-2(D_A - D_B)} \tag{9-13}$$

$$E_B = D_B \frac{(R'_A - R'_B) - (R_A - R_B)}{-2(D_A - D_B)} \tag{9-14}$$

When the values of E_A and E_B in all above equations [and that of e in Eq. (9-10)] are positive, the line of sight is inclined upward; and when those values are negative, the line of sight is inclined downward. In either case the values of E must be subtracted from the respective rod readings at A and B in order to obtain correct rod readings C_A and C_B, respectively, for the horizontal line of sight in the second set-up. Thus

$$C_A = R_A - E_A \tag{9-15}$$

and

$$C_B = R_B - E_B \tag{9-16}$$

After finding the correct rod readings at A and B by Eqs. (9-15) and (9-16), the cross-hair ring is moved either up or down, as the case may be, until the intersection of cross hairs falls on the correct rod reading on the far stake when the bubble is centered. This should place the line of sight parallel to the axis of the vial. A check should be made on the rod held on the near stake. The reading should check the correct rod computed for that stake. If no check is obtained, errors in computation may be suspected.

The most convenient way of measuring equal distances to the near stakes and to the far stakes in both set-ups is to make measurements in line with the two stakes. This would make the instrument set-ups either along the continuation of line AB, as is shown in Fig. 9-20, or between the two stakes. It should be noted that it is quite immaterial which of the two schemes is followed and also which of the two stakes is designated by A or by B.

Equations (9-13) through (9-16) can also be applied to a case when the first set-up is made right at one stake and the second set-up right at another stake rather than near those stakes. In such a case all distances in Eqs. (9-13) and (9-14) cancel out and do not have to be measured in the field at all. The apparent simplification of computation procedure for such set-ups involves certain complications in reading the rod at the stake at which the instrument is setup.

In setting the instrument "at a stake" the telescope eyepiece should be about $\frac{1}{2}$ in. from the rod held on that stake. If one looks through the *wrong end* of the telescope, only a small circle on the rod is visible. It is easy to spot the center of this circle with a pencil. The rod then can be read within about ± 0.002 ft. This is an accidental error in reading the rod, which has nothing to do with the inclination of the line of sight for which the two-peg test is made. For all practical purposes the distance between the instrument and the stake at which the instrument is set up is considered to be equal to zero. Therefore, the error E in rod reading at that stake, owing to the inclination of the line of sight, must also be equal to zero. This is obvious from Eqs. (9-13) and (9-14) since either D_A or D_B, entering those equations as factors, is considered equal to zero. One of the equations, which is not reduced to zero, gives the error in rod reading at the far stake. This method does not produce a check on the near stake.

The method of setting the instrument at the stakes may be followed, if desired, in the adjustment of ordinary levels but it should not be used in the adjustment of precise levels.

It may be advisable to check the instrument used in third order leveling about once a month. Precise levels should be checked at the beginning of each day's work.

In order to avoid the accumulation of systematic errors in leveling owing to the inclination of the line of sight, the sum of backsight distances and the sum of foresight distances must be balanced up to those points, in a leveling circuit, the elevations of which are being determined.

Example 9-4. The following two-peg test data are given for a level:

	Instrument at Point M	Instrument at Point N
Rod reading on M	4.372	2.105
Rod reading on N	6.945	4.728

The instrument was set up *at* the points. Determine (a) correct rod reading on point M when the instrument was at N, (b) whether the inclination of the line of sight is up or down, (c) the difference in elevation between M and N.

Solution: Assume one point to be A and another B. For instance, let point M be B and point N be A. The data given above can then be rewritten as follows:

	Instrument at B	*Instrument at A*
Rod on B	$R_B' = 4.372$	$R_B = 2.105$
Rod on A	$R_A' = 6.945$	$R_A = 4.728$

Since the instrument was set up the second time at point A, the distance from the instrument to point A in the second set-up must be equal to zero, that is, $D_A = 0$ in Eqs. (9-13) and (9-14). This gives $E_A = 0$ from Eq. (9-13), but Eq. (9-14) reduces to the following form:

$$E_B = \frac{(R_A' - R_B') - (R_A - R_B)}{2}$$

Substituting numerical values in this equation,

$$E_B = \frac{(6.945 - 4.372) - (4.728 - 2.105)}{2} = -0.025$$

Also from Eqs. (9-15) and (9-16),

$$C_A = 4.728 - 0 = 4.728$$

$$C_B = 2.105 - (-0.025) = 2.130$$

(a) The correct rod on B (i.e., on M) is 2.130.

(b) The line of sight is inclined downward, since E_B is negative.

(c) The difference in elevation between points M and N is $2.130 - 4.728 = -2.598$ ft.

Example 9-5. In making a two-peg test for a level on two stakes set 160 ft apart, the following data are obtained:

	First Set-up	*Second Set-up*
Rod reading on near stake (20 ft)	3.972	4.843
Rod reading on far stake (180 ft)	3.960	4.780

Determine (a) rod readings on the far and on the near stakes for the horizontal line of sight on second set-up of the instrument, (b) the inclination of the line of sight, (c) the difference in elevation of the two stakes.

Solution: The given data may be rewritten as follows:

	Instrument at A	*Instrument at B*
Data for point A:	$R_A' = 3.972, D_A' = 20$	$R_A = 4.780, D_A = 180$
Data for point B:	$R_B' = 3.960, D_B' = 180$	$R_B = 4.843, D_B = 20$

Substituting these values in Eqs. (9-13) and (9-14), the following results are obtained:

$$E_A = 180\,\frac{(3.972 - 3.960) - (4.780 - 4.843)}{-2(180 - 20)} = -180\,\frac{0.075}{320} = -0.042$$

$$E_B = -20\,\frac{0.075}{320} = -0.005$$

Also from Eqs. (9-15) and (9-16),

$$C_A = 4.780 - (-0.042) = 4.822$$

$$C_B = 4.843 - (-0.005) = 4.848$$

(a) The correct rod reading on far stake is 4.822; the correct rod reading on near stake is 4.848.

(b) The line of sight is inclined downward, since E_A and E_B are negative.

(c) The difference in elevation of points is $4.822 - 4.848 = -0.026$

9-24. Adjustment of wye levels. A different procedure of adjustments than that outlined above is normally prescribed for wye levels, since these levels have additional parts, such as wyes, to be checked and adjusted. However, if the wyes holding the telescope are not loose and if the telescope is well secured in position by the clips holding it, wye levels may be adjusted exactly the same way as described for dumpy levels in Arts. 9-21 through 9-23.

Other Methods of Determining Elevations

9-25. Trigonometric leveling. The process involved in determining elevations through trigonometric leveling has been mentioned in Chapter 4 in connection with measuring distances on a slope. It may be seen from Fig. 4-4 that by measuring slope distance s between two points and the vertical angle α, it is possible to compute not only the horizontal distance between the points but also the difference in elevation $h = s \sin \alpha$. This method of measuring the difference in elevation of points is called *trigonometric leveling.* The method of measuring the hypotenuse and the vertical angle α is called the *sine method* in order to differentiate it from the *tangent method* in which horizontal distance d and the vertical angle α are measured to give $h = d \tan \alpha$. A transit should be used for measuring angle α.

Unless the vertical angle is measured with a good precision, the elevations determined by the trigonometric method are only approximate. For instance, assuming that $1'$ error is made in measuring a vertical angle $\alpha = 20°$, the error in determining the difference in elevation of points 500 ft apart is

$$e = 500(\tan 20°01' - \tan 20°) = 0.17 \text{ ft}$$

Although this is a very rough leveling by most leveling standards, there are occasions, such as map making, when trigonometric leveling is fully justified. The accuracy of trigonometric leveling may be improved by using precise optical theodolites, which measure angles to seconds.

9-26. Reciprocal leveling. The method of reciprocal leveling is based on the theory employed in the two-peg test. If in Fig. 9-20 $D'_A = D_B$ and $D'_B = D_A$, the errors in rod readings entering Eqs. (9-8) and (9-9) may be eliminated by adding those two equations together. The left side of the new equation is then 2(C.D.E.), or twice the correct difference in elevation between the two points on which rod readings were taken. Dividing both sides of the equation by 2, one gets

$$\text{C.D.E.} = \frac{(R'_A - R'_B) + (R_A - R_B)}{2} \tag{9-17}$$

Equation (9-17) shows that in order to obtain a correct difference in elevation between two points, when backsight and foresight distances cannot be balanced, two sets of rod readings should be taken on those points—one set with the instrument close to one point and another with the instrument close to the other point. The average of the differences in rod readings obtained in each set of readings gives, theoretically, the correct difference in elevation between the points.

This method of leveling may be employed in determining the elevation of points across a river or a ravine. On long sights, targets may be used on leveling rods. This method eliminates the errors resulting from the curvature of the earth and the refraction of the atmosphere, provided that atmospheric conditions remain unchanged throughout leveling. If the time interval between readings taken at the two points is short, it may be reasonably assumed that atmospheric conditions have not affected the accuracy of the results.

If best results are desired, however, two levels may be used simultaneously at the two points. By taking two sets of simultaneous readings, and then interchanging levels and taking two more sets of simultaneous readings, the computed average of the results should give quite accurately the difference in elevations of the two points.

9-27. Stadia method. The measurement of distances by the stadia method has been briefly described in Art. 7-4. The stadia method can also be used to measure differences in elevation. The method is described in detail in Chapter 17. Suffice it to say here that the differences in elevation of points, as determined by the stadia method, are computed from measured vertical angles and from observed rod intercepts between the two stadia hairs of the transit, the instrument used in making stadia measurements.

The use of the parameters described above in determining the difference in elevation of points produces a low degree of accuracy. However, this method is quite useful in making topographic maps and plans, and in making quick measurements for estimation purposes. Standard transits are usually employed in stadia measurements.

9-28. Barometric leveling.   Aneroid barometers, popularly called *altimeters*, are used in approximate measurement of elevations.   The instrument consists of a chamber (box) made of thin metal which flexes in response to changes in atmospheric pressure.   The air is partially

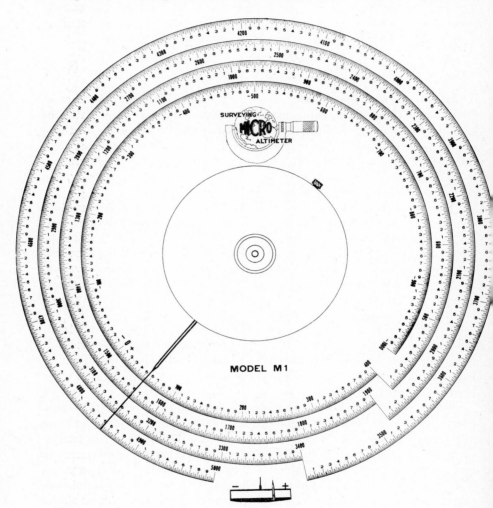

Fig. 9-21. Altimeter.   (Courtesy American Paulin System.)

evacuated from the chamber.   A system of springs and chains transfers the deflection of the chamber walls to a shaft in the middle of a dial shown in Fig. 9-21.   Depending on the model of the altimeter, each graduation on the dial may correspond to 1, 2, 5, 10, or more feet.   Thus the elevations of points are read directly in feet. A special knob is provided to set the indicator at a chosen elevation when the instrument is held on the point of known elevation.

Many altimeters are marked "compensated," which means that a change of temperature does not affect the altimeter's performance. However, the pressure of the atmosphere changes not only with the elevation but also, to a small degree, with the temperature and the humidity of the air. Thus in taking altimeter readings, the temperature and the time are also recorded and the readings are later adjusted for variations in atmospheric conditions that have occurred during barometric leveling.

Certain altimeters are sensitive to very small variations in the atmospheric pressure and may perform with a probable error of about ±2 ft. The smallest division on the dial of the altimeter shown in Fig. 9-21 is equal to 1 ft.

Altimeters are small, light, and easily portable; thus the approximate elevations on a large area may be determined in a short time. Altimeters are used in ground reconnaissance for engineering projects, in the approximate ground control in photogrammetry, and in other applications where an altimeter's accuracy is consistent with allowable errors in measured elevations.

9-29. Photogrammetry. Measurement of ground elevations by means of photographs taken from the air has been mentioned in Art. 7-6 in connection with topographic mapping. This application of photogrammetry is discussed in more detail in Chapter 17. Other uses of aerial photographs on engineering projects include ground reconnaissance, planning, and studies involving land use, soil conditions, availability of construction materials, and drainage conditions. These studies require not only qualitative evaluation of the ground areas considered for proposed construction but also actual measurements of distances, differences in elevation, acreage, and sometimes an approximate estimation of the volume of earthwork involved in proposed construction.

A stereoscopic pair of photographs, which can be viewed in three dimensions under a stereoscope, are required for measurement of differences in elevation of ground points. Relatively inexpensive laboratory equipment consisting of a *stereoscope* and a *parallax bar* (Fig. 9-22) may be employed to determine the difference in elevation of points. The accuracy of such measurements is greatly dependent upon the scale and quality of photographs, precision of aerial cameras, the aircraft used in taking pictures, weather conditions, and many other factors. A high degree of accuracy requires precise cameras, expensive equipment, and skilled workmanship. If necessary, photographs can be made from which elevations may be measured within a fraction of a foot. All of the above factors, together with measuring techniques and the use of meas-

Fig. 9-22. Pocket stereoscope with parallax bar. (Courtesy Abrams Instrument Corporation.)

uring instruments, constitute a special course of study usually called *photogrammetry*.

PROBLEMS

9-1. The notes shown below have entries made in the field for a leveling circuit from B.M.$_1$ to a given point and back. (a) Fill in all missing data, (b) show customary check for the arithmetic, (c) compute the order of accuracy of the work.

(A)

Sta.	B.S.	H.I.	F.S.	Elev. (ft)	B.S. dist. (ft)	F.S. dist. (ft)
B.M.$_1$	10.731	*436.661*		425.930	105	
T.P.$_1$	7.322		2.791		95	120
T.P.$_2$	6.597		1.234		110	65
T.P.$_3$	6.431		0.840		100	150
N	4.395		8.597	*443.549*	160	70
T.P.$_4$	3.682		11.785		120	180
T.P.$_5$	2.157		12.302		140	110
B.M.$_1$			3.785			60

Ans. (c) Third order

(B)

Sta.	B.S.	H.I.	F.S.	Elev. (Ft)	B.S. Dist. (Ft)	F.S. Dist. (Ft)
B.M.$_1$	3.725			632.754	150	
T.P.$_1$	2.138		9.372		170	160
T.P.$_2$	0.025		10.591		140	150
M	3.721		8.318		90	150
T.P.$_3$	8.920		5.240		100	120
T.P.$_4$	10.715		2.197		110	105
T.P.$_5$	7.350		0.372		120	90
B.M.$_1$			0.504			105

(C)

Sta.	B.S.	H.I.	F.S.	Elev. (Ft)	B.S. Dist. (Ft)	F.S. Dist. (Ft)
B.M.$_1$	5.372			571.038	120	
T.P.$_1$	4.890		9.130		100	110
T.P.$_2$	3.524		10.652		90	80
T.P.$_3$	4.718		11.127		100	60
T.P.$_4$	3.242		8.431		125	160
K	8.371		7.113		120	130
T.P.$_5$	10.621		4.259		90	110
T.P.$_6$	12.145		0.137		110	100
B.M.$_1$			2.059			95

9-2. (A) Adjust the elevation of point N in problem 9-1(A). *Ans.* 443.559 ft

(B) Adjust the elevation of point M in problem 9-1(B).

(C) Adjust the elevation of point K in problem 9-1(C).

9-3. A leveling circuit was run to establish the elevation of a new bench mark, B.M.$_2$. The leveling started from an established bench mark B.M.$_1$ and and the field notes show that the difference in elevation between B.M.$_1$ and B.M.$_2$ is H ft. When the rod used in this leveling was checked by a steel tape, it was found that the distance between the zero mark and the 13 ft mark at the top was X ft, the error being distributed uniformly throughout the rod. Correct the difference in elevation between the two B.M.'s for the discrepancy in the rod's length, if

(A) $H = 137.52$, $X = 13.006$.   *Ans.* 137.58 ft

(B) $H = 275.46$, $X = 12.995$.

(C) $H = 315.89$, $X = 13.004$.

9-4. A leveling circuit of X miles between two established bench marks has the error of closure equal to E ft. This leveling was done with a rod which had its base plate missing, making the rod shorter by 0.05 ft. There were 15 set-ups of the level between the two bench marks. (a) Determine how much of the closing error is due to the missing base plate, (b) find n, using Eq. (9-2), and state what order of accuracy this survey has, and (c) find correction for the elevation of a point to which five set-ups of the instrument were made from the beginning of leveling, if
(A) $X = 2.5$, $E = -0.077$.   *Ans.* (b) 0.05, third order, (c) 0.026
(B) $X = 3.5$, $E = 0.06$.
(C) $X = 2.1$, $E = -0.08$.

9-5. Assume that, in leveling, the random errors of a single sight in rod recording are ± 0.003 ft because of difficulty to read the rod exactly, and ± 0.005 ft because of difficulty to center the bubble exactly. Estimate the total error due to other causes, such as not balancing B.S. and F.S. distances, in a leveling circuit in which X set-ups were made and for which the error of closure E is as shown below.
(A) $X = 15$, $E = -0.042$ ft.   *Ans.* -0.010 ft
(B) $X = 20$, $E = 0.067$ ft.
(C) $X = 27$, $E = -0.095$ ft.

9-6. If a 13 ft high rod is held out of plumb at the top by 1.50 ft horizontally, and in the vertical plane of the line of sight, correct the following rod readings due to this cause:
(A) 11.374 ft.   *Ans.* 11.298 ft
(B) 10.925 ft.
(C) 9.638 ft.

9-7. One division on the vial of a level is equal to 2 mm. A rod was held 100 ft from the instrument and two readings of the rod were taken, as is shown below, before and after the bubble was moved x divisions between the two readings. Determine (a) the sensitivity of the level in seconds, and (b) the inside radius of the vial in feet.
(A) 2.437 ft and 2.514 ft, $x = 8$ divisions.   *Ans.* (a) 20 sec, (b) 68 ft
(B) 4.747 ft and 4.602 ft, $x = 10$ divisions.
(C) 5.395 ft and 5.440 ft, $x = 6$ divisions.

9-8. Determine the number of divisions on the main scale that must be divided into a certain number of divisions on a direct vernier, in order for the vernier to have the least count, as indicated below, if the smallest division on the main scale is d units.
(A) $d = 1$ cm, l.c. of the vernier 1 mm.   *Ans.* 9 on scale, 10 on vernier
(B) $d = 1$ lb, l.c. of the vernier 1 oz.
(C) $d = \frac{1}{8}$ in., l.c. of the vernier $\frac{1}{64}$ in.

9-9. In a two-peg test for a level the distance between the stakes is 200 ft, and the level was set up 18 ft from the near stake and 182 ft from the far stake in both set-ups. Rod readings were as shown below. For the second set-up of the instrument, at point B, find (a) correct rod on the far stake, (b) correct rod on the near stake, (c) correct difference in elevation between points A and B, (d) the inclination of the line of sight in feet per 100 ft distance.

(A)

	Level near A	Level near B
Rod read. on A	5.726	7.693
Rod read. on B	3.571	5.516

Ans. (a) 7.681 ft, (b) 5.515 ft, (c) 2.166 ft, (d) 0.0067 ft up

(B)

	Level near A	Level near B
Rod read. on A	4.192	5.372
Rod read. on B	4.166	5.390

(C)

	Level near A	Level near B
Rod read. on A	4.526	4.078
Rod read. on B	5.730	5.315

9-10. In a two-peg test of a level the instrument was set up at point C first and then at point D. The distance to the near points was zero in both set-ups. For the instrument at point D, determine (a) correct rod at C, (b) correct difference in elevation between C and D, and (c) by how many feet the line of sight is inclined up or down in a distance of 100 ft if $CD = 150$ ft and the rod readings were:

(A)

	Instrument at C	Instrument at D
Rod read. on C	5.672	5.766
Rod read. on D	5.691	5.738

Ans. (a) 5.742 ft, (b) 0.004 ft, (c) 0.016 ft up

(B)

	Instrument at C	Instrument at D
Rod read. on C	4.731	4.557
Rod read. on D	5.612	5.489

(C)

	Instrument at C	Instrument at D
Rod read. on C	4.832	4.882
Rod read. on D	4.759	4.975

9-11. The elevation of B.M.$_1$ is 432.737 ft. In establishing a new bench mark B.M.$_2$, three leveling circuits were run between B.M.$_1$ and B.M.$_2$. The lengths of these three circuits X_1, X_2, and X_3 are given below. The elevations of B.M.$_2$ as determined from each circuit were E_1, E_2, and E_3. Determine (a) the most probable value of the elevation of B.M.$_2$, and (b) the order of accuracy of each leveling circuit. Arrange all computations in tabular form. The values are:

(A) $X_1 = 17$ miles, $X_2 = 11$ miles, $X_3 = 19$ miles, $E_1 = 371.506$, $E_2 = 371.579$, $E_3 = 371.592$ ft. *Ans.* (a) 371.561 ft, (b) second, first, first

(B) $X_1 = 6$ miles, $X_2 = 13$ miles, $X_3 = 9$ miles. $E_1 = 537.360$, $E_2 = 536.122$, $E_3 = 538.290$ ft.

(C) $X_1 = 12$ miles, $X_2 = 18$ miles, $X_3 = 25$ miles. $E_1 = 491.235$, $E_2 = 491.785$, $E_3 = 490.135$ ft.

9-12. The elevations of B.M.$_1$ and of point A, also B.S. and F.S. distances, as recorded in a leveling circuit, are shown below. If the line of sight of the level used in the leveling circuit was inclined downward 0.042 ft in 100 ft, as it was determined by the two-peg test after completion of the leveling, find (a) elevation of point A adjusted for systematic errors, (b) elevation of point A adjusted for both systematic and random errors, (c) the order of accuracy of the survey (after it is adjusted for systematic errors).

(A)

Point	B.S. Distance (Ft)	F.S. Distance (Ft)	Elevation (Ft)
B.M.$_1$	210		734.395
T.P.$_1$	185	53	
T.P.$_2$	170	72	
T.P.$_3$	150	60	
A	70	50	756.526
T.P.$_4$	80	200	
T.P.$_5$	100	190	
T.P.$_6$	50	145	
B.M.$_1$		150	734.330

Ans. (a) 756.728 ft, (b) 756.740 ft, (c) third

(B)

Point	B.S. Distance (Ft)	F.S. Distance (Ft)	Elevation (Ft)
B.M.$_1$	60		379.526
T.P.$_1$	75	100	
T.P.$_2$	40	150	
T.P.$_3$	60	120	
A	100	130	362.731
T.P.$_4$	110	60	
T.P.$_5$	90	70	
T.P.$_6$	100	50	
B.M.$_1$		90	379.627

(C)

Point	B.S. Distance (Ft)	F.S. Distance (Ft)	Elevation (Ft)
B.M.$_1$	100		452.357
T.P.$_1$	90	150	
T.P.$_2$	80	120	
T.P.$_3$	70	90	
A	100	80	431.528
T.P.$_4$	90	70	
T.P.$_5$	80	70	
T.P.$_6$	110	60	
B.M.$_1$		80	452.367

CHAPTER **10**

Field Instructions—Use of
Leveling Rod and Level
Leveling on Engineering Projects

10-1. Various types of rods. Three distinct types of leveling rods—the Philadelphia rod, the tape rod, and the geodetic rod (Fig. 9-15)—have been briefly described in Chapter 9. The rod most commonly used on engineering surveys is either the Philadelphia rod or a rod similar to it, but differing from it, perhaps, by the manner in which the face of the rod is graduated.

Non-extensible rods are 12 or 13 ft long, and are awkward to handle and to transport; for this reason they are not as popular as extensible rods.

Extensible rods are made in two or three sections. Two-section rods are usually either $6\frac{1}{2}$ or 7 ft long when closed. They extend respectively to 12 and 13 ft lengths. Three-section rods are $4\frac{1}{2}$ ft long, and extend to 12 ft. The two-section rods seem to have the widest distribution of any type.

10-2. How to hold a rod. When a rod is held on a point for a sight to be taken on it, the rodman faces the leveling instrument and holds the rod vertically, directly in front of himself. The rod is held lightly between the fingers of both hands. Such handling enables the rodman to balance the rod to keep it in a vertical position.

If the rod is not held truly vertical, the instrumentman may call,

150

"Plumb the rod," or he may give a signal for plumbing the rod by extending one arm straight up and then moving it slowly in the direction in which the top of the rod should be moved. The rodman never holds his fingers on the face of the rod because he might thus obstruct the view of the rod's graduations.

10-3. High rod. When the height of instrument (H.I.) is higher than the top of a folded rod held on a point, the instrumentman calls to the rodman "High rod," and the rodman extends the rod all the way up so the instrumentman may read the rod directly. Care must be exercised by the rodman to make certain that the rod is fully extended and that the clamp screw is tight enough to prevent the extension from sliding slowly downward. If, on the other hand, the instrumentman wants the rodman to read the high rod, he calls to the rodman, "Set the target for a high rod." The rodman then observes the reading of the vernier on the back of the closed rod and sets the target to read the same number on the face of the rod. For instance, if the back vernier reads 7.002 ft, the rodman sets the target on 7.002 ft. Then he extends the rod only high enough for the line of sight to hit the target, and he clamps the rod in that position. Next, he holds the rod for a check sight by the instrumentman. The instrumentman may signal for whatever slight correction may be required, or, when the line of sight is on the horizontal line of the target, he calls, "All right." The rodman then reads the back vernier. He may read, for instance, 9.347, which means that the rod was extended from 7.002 ft, on which the target was set, to 9.347 ft; that is, 2.345 ft up. The increased reading of 9.347 ft at the back vernier is possible because the graduations on the back of the rod increase from the top downward, starting with 7.000 ft or 6.500 ft, depending on the height of the folded rod.

10-4. Rod at close range. If the rod must be read at close range, only a short section of the rod appears in the field of view of the telescope. Thus it often happens that no red number, marking an integral footmark, is visible. The instrumentman then observes the number of tenths at the intersection of the cross hairs, guesses the number of feet, and asks the rodman to hold his finger on a certain division. For instance, the instrumentman may call, "Hold your finger on four point six." If he sees no finger appearing in the field of view, he calls, "Hold on three point six," or, "Hold on five point six," till he ascertains the number of integral feet for his rod reading.

Another method of ascertaining the number of feet requires the rodman to raise the rod slowly until the instrumentman observes a red number. For this procedure the instrumentman calls, "Raise for red," followed by, "All right," after a red number has appeared in the field of view. He proceeds then to read the rod in the usual manner.

10-5. Use of rod levels. A typical rod level is shown in Fig. 9-17. Rod levels are generally not used in third order leveling. However, if leveling must be done with an inexperienced rodman, it is better to use a rod level rather than to run the risk that the survey may fall short of required accuracy.

A rod level is held firmly against the back corner of a rod without obstructing rod graduations. On precise rods the rod level is permanently attached to the back of the rod.

10-6. Use of target. As has been mentioned in Chapter 9, the leveling rods of the type shown in Fig. 9-15a are called self-reading rods, because in most cases they can be read directly by the instrumentman with about the same accuracy as by the rodman with the use of the target. For this reason a target is seldom used on ordinary or third order leveling operations.

On certain occasions, however, the target may be employed to good advantage. One such case was described above (reading high rod by the rodman). This may occur when it is necessary to take a sight on some distant point. The target may also be used when the view of the rod is partially obscured by foliage or when rod graduations are dimmed by poor lighting. Other occasions which require the use of the target may become apparent from the nature of special leveling operations. For instance, it may be necessary on some engineering surveys to set a line of stakes on a constant grade. By measuring the distance between the stakes, the rod readings corresponding to the required elevation of stakes may be easily calculated. The target is then set on the calculated rod reading for a given stake. As the stake is driven into the ground, frequent checks are made for the elevation of the top of the stake until the line of sight of the level falls on the horizontal line of the target.

10-7. Hand signals. On windy days or when long sights must be taken, it may be necessary for the instrumentman and the rodman to use sign language. A few of the most common hand signals are:

Give a sight. A hand is raised up and is held for a moment in a vertical position.

Set a turning point. The instrumentman raises his hand up, as for a signal, "Give a sight," and describes a small circle over his head.

This is B.M. or T.P. The rodman raises the rod and holds it in a horizontal position over his head. Then he lowers the rod and holds it on the point.

High rod. The instrumentman holds both hands extended sideways in a horizontal position, then brings them together over his head.

Kill the brass. The sliding section of the extension rod is attached to the rod at the bottom by means of a brass sleeve which obstructs the view of about two inches of rod graduations. When the line of sight strikes this brass piece, it is necessary to raise slightly the sliding section of the rod. The signal for this is the same as for a high rod. The rodman must use his judgment as to which meaning of the signal is being conveyed.

Move the target. The instrumentman extends one hand horizontally and moves it either above or below the shoulder, depending on whether he wants the target to be moved up or down.

Clamp the target. As the target gets into a proper position for the line of sight, the instrumentman describes a vertical circle with his extended arm for the target to be clamped in the desired position. If on checking the target position it is necessary to move it just slightly up or down, the instrumentman makes quick short motion of the extended arm up or down. Such a motion may be emphasized by holding a handkerchief in the hand.

All right. The instrumentman shows the palms of both hands, or waves them left and right.

Pick up the level. This signal may be given by a chief of party when a new set-up of the instrument is desired. Both hands are raised quickly up from downward position, as though lifting an imaginary object.

10-8. Keeping level in adjustment. Each level comes with a box especially made for a certain given type of level. The instrument is kept in the box between specially made pads that hold the instrument firmly during transportation. For this reason it is important to keep the box in good repair. With proper handling, an instrument will stay in good adjustment for many days. However, an instrument must be checked periodically or when maladjustment is either obvious or suspected.

In precise leveling the two-peg test must be made before the start of each day's work. The inclination of the line of sight, computed in the two-peg test, is entered in the field notebook, and the elevations of those points for which the sum of backsight distances is not equal to the sum of foresight distances are adjusted for the errors caused by the inclination of the line of sight.

In second order leveling the two-peg test should also be made at the beginning of each day's work. However, if proper care is taken in field work to keep the backsight and foresight distances balanced, it may not be necessary to check the instrument more often than about once a week.

Third order leveling is by far the most extensive leveling operation on engineering projects. On such work, when the level is in more or less constant use, it should be checked and, if necessary, adjusted about once a month.

When a wye level is being adjusted as though it were a dumpy level, it is important to check it for any loose parts, such as wye clamps, and to see that the telescope is firmly secured in the wyes.

10-9. Carrying the level. When not in use the level is usually kept in its box, and it is often carried in the box to the site of work. During leveling operations, however, the instrument is carried around

on the tripod. It may be carried on the shoulder in open spaces, but if there are trees or other obstructions, the tripod should be carried under the arm, so as to have the instrument in full view of the carrier (Fig. 10-1).

The clamp screw, which arrests the rotational motion of the telescope, should be just tight enough for the moving parts to yield on possible collision with a firm object.

10-10. Setting up the instrument. Two types of tripod may be used with a level—the fixed-leg tripod or the extension tripod. If the tripod legs are made of a solid piece of wood the tripod is called a *fixed-leg tripod;* if the legs have a sliding section, the tripod is an *extension tripod.* All tripods have a pointed metal piece called a *shoe* at the end of each tripod leg. The shoes usually have a metal projection, called a *spur,* for pressing the tripod legs into the ground. On

Fig. 10-1. Carrying an instrument among obstructions.

many American-made tripods the legs are attached to the tripod head by wing-nut screws. After the legs of a tripod have been firmly set in the ground, in preparation for leveling operations, the wing-nuts must be tightened.

In setting the instrument along a slope, one leg of the tripod is always directed uphill. When the legs are being spread on the ground, it is essential to keep the foot plate of the instrument as horizontal as possible. This may sometimes be done by comparing the foot plate with a building in the background, or with any object having some defined horizontal lines. A horizontally placed foot plate assures quicker and easier leveling of the instrument.

It is a good practice for the instrumentman to carry a hand level. The hand level is used to find the approximate height at which the instrument must be set up in order to be able to see the rod. If there is no hand level, the instrumentman may select a proper place for a set-up by holding the tripod legs together on the ground and by looking at the rod alongside of the telescope barrel, when the bubble is approximately centered. This precaution should eliminate aggravating situations in which one sets the instrument up only to discover that the rod cannot be brought into the field of view of the leveled telescope.

10-11. How to level the instrument. The standard instruments of American manufacture have four leveling screws (Fig. 9-3). In leveling an instrument the telescope is placed first over one pair of diagonally opposite screws for centering the vial's bubble, and next over the other pair. Since all screws have exactly the same threads, it is necessary to turn them in opposite directions (Fig. 10-2) in order to extend one screw and to shorten another. Thus the screws may be kept in bearing while the instrument is being leveled. The bearing pressure of all screws should be kept about the same. The screws should not be set too tight, but should yield to a turn when held between thumb and forefinger.

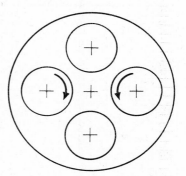

Fig. 10-2. Turning of leveling screws.

When the leveling screws are turned, the bubble moves in the direction of motion of the left thumb. First the bubble is centered only approximately over each pair of diagonally opposite screws; then the operation is repeated one or more times until the bubble stays centered in both directions. Next, the telescope is turned through 180° in order to check the adjustment of the vial. If the vial is in adjustment, the bubble will stay centered, because with a properly adjusted vial the vertical axis of the level assumes a truly vertical position when the bubble is centered. A slight maladjustment of the vial may be expected to appear even from changes of temperature. Such maladjustment, however, should not impair the accuracy of leveling operations if the bubble is centered each time the rod is read, and if backsight and foresight distances are balanced.

10-12. Leveling on engineering projects. It has been pointed out in Chapter 9 that ground elevations are required on almost every engineering project. It has also been pointed out that ground elevations may be determined by various methods, depending on the accuracy required in measured elevations. In fact, several methods may be used on the same project. For instance, the elevations of reference points, set as bench marks on a construction job, may be determined quite accurately, using an engineer's level, but the elevations of some ground points needed to compute the amount of earthwork may be determined by using a hand level. Several leveling operations on engineering construction jobs are briefly discussed below.

10-13. Profile leveling. Profile leveling is usually run along the transit line on route surveys, sewer surveys, surveys for water supply lines, and for other construction projects. The determined ground elevations along the transit line are plotted on paper to specified vertical

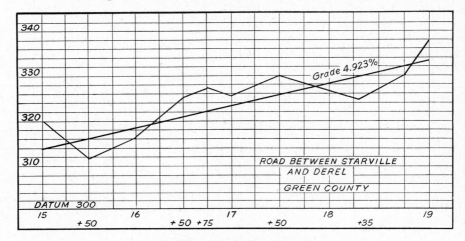

Fig. 10-3. Typical road profile.

and horizontal scales. Such a vertical section of the ground constitutes a *profile drawing.* Figure 10-3 shows a typical profile drawing. The vertical scale on such drawings is usually exaggerated; it is often made from about five to ten times greater than the horizontal scale in order to emphasize ground irregularities which otherwise might be overlooked. The designers use profiles for designing the grades and for locating various structures such as bridges, culverts, and water inlets. A special graph paper called *profile paper* is often used for plotting profiles.

A profile drawing must contain the following information: (a) stationing along the line, including all points at which ground elevations were taken, (b) the horizontal and vertical scales of the drawing, (c) the elevation of the datum from which the ground points were plotted, and (d) the title describing the line and the job.

Since the elevations of ground points are usually taken at places that show breaks in the ground surface, the points plotted on the profile are often connected by straight lines, which normally give fairly good representation of the existing ground configurations.

The elevations of ground points in profile leveling are usually required only to the nearest tenth of a foot—accuracy of a fairly low order. However, it will be later required to measure the final elevations for structures, along the same lines, to about third order accuracy. Thus in running profiles two distinct leveling operations may be simultaneously involved. One is to run accurate leveling ahead and to set bench marks in the vicinity of the line to be used in future construction, another is to take what is known as **side shots** to determine approximate elevations of ground points. These latter elevations are used in plotting profiles.

Sta.	B.S.	H.I.	F.S.	Ground Sights	Elevat.	Elev. of Flow Line	Cut or Fill	Description of Points

GRADE STAKES FOR STORM SEWER Sta. 0+00 to 10+22.7	March 22, 1958 Cool, windy Level No 27 Rod No.9	Party No.3 K - T.C.Adams Rod - K.L.Greene Notes - C.N.James	14.

Sta.	B.S.	H.I.	F.S.	Ground Sights	Elevat.	Elev. of Flow Line	Cut or Fill	Description of Points
B.M₂	3.25	735.22			731.97			Nail in root of 12" Red Oak
T.P₁	7.20	738.50	3.92		731.30			
T.P₂	6.74	742.99	2.25		736.25			
0+00				3.9	739.1	734.83	c 4.3	Stk.
+50				6.2	736.8	733.25	c 3.5	"
1+00				7.3	735.7	731.67	c 4.0	"
+50	3.82	742.76	4.05		738.94	730.09	c 8.9	"
2+00				3.7	739.1	728.51	c 10.6	"
+50				2.4	740.4	726.93	c 13.5	"
3+00			5.27		737.49	725.35	c 12.1	"
etc.								

Fig. 10-4. Leveling notes for grade stakes.

When profile leveling is done in the manner described above, two columns are used for recording foresights in the field notebook. One column is used for recording foresights on turning points and the other for recording side shots. The foresights on turning points are usually recorded to the nearest hundredth of a foot, but the side shots, or the **ground sights,** are recorded only to the nearest tenth of a foot. Figure 10-4 shows such recording of foresights in leveling operations for a storm sewer discussed below.

10-14. Grade stakes for a storm sewer. The transit line for a storm sewer is run along the center line of the proposed drain pipe. The stakes are set at more or less regular intervals, about 50 or 25 ft, and are marked by stations, which show the distances from the point of beginning of a survey. Since the center line stakes will be lost during excavation of the ditch for the proposed pipe line, another line of stakes, called the *offset line,* is set in the ground about 6 ft right or left from the center line stakes. A guard stake (see Fig. 10-5) is set alongside each line stake, and the same stations as those marked on the center line stakes are marked on the guard stakes, together with the number of feet that the line stake is offset from the center line. For instance, a stake mark 3+75.3 L4, means that the line stake is 4 ft left of center line at station 3+75.3. The left or right side is determined by looking ahead in the direction of increasing stations.

The offset line stakes may also serve as the **grade stakes.** The figures for the grade stakes, which are marked on the same guard stake, represent the number of feet to be cut or filled vertically from the elevation of the top of stake to the flow line of the sewer pipe at the center line station shown on the line stake. For instance C4.6 means, "cut 4.6 ft," and F5.2 means, "fill 5.2 ft." Figure 10-5 shows a section of an excavated ditch with a grade line stake and a guard stake, offset from the center line of pipe. On some jobs there may be a separate line of grade stakes and line stakes. In such cases the grade stakes are set alongside the line stakes.

In order to determine the cut or the fill at a station, a line of levels is run along the proposed direction of a pipe line, and the elevations of grade stakes are determined from the side shots taken in that leveling operation. The elevation of grade stakes is usually measured to the nearest hundredth of a foot. The elevation of the sewer flow line, at the same stations at which the grade stakes are set, is read off or computed from the final construction plans. The difference between the grade stake elevation and the flow line elevation is the cut or fill at the station in question. The plus sign for the difference means "cut" and the minus sign means "fill."

Figure 10-4 shows two columns added on the right-hand page for recording the elevation of the flow line and the cuts or fills at various stations. It may be noted that the line of levels was run from some bench mark, B.M.$_1$, set in the vicinity of construction probably during the preliminary survey. The line of levels must be closed either on the starting bench mark or on some other convenient bench mark in the vicinity of survey lines.

10-15. Setting batter boards. Ditch excavations are often performed by machines moving along the staked center line. The required depth of excavation is measured approximately during machine excavation and then finished by hand shovels to insure a smooth grade. These final measurements are made from the batter boards set across the ditch at grade stake stations.

A batter board may be nailed to 2 by 4 in. posts set on each side of the ditch, or the board may be fastened by C-clamps to iron stakes, as shown in Fig. 10-5. The top of the board is set a certain number of integral feet above the sewer flow line. This vertical distance is called a **pole,** because it is measured by a pole, graduated into feet. The pole has at its bottom end a metal bracket which fits into the pipe's invert. A chalk line is stretched between batter boards directly above the center line of the pipe, so that pole distance to the invert of any pipe section can be measured from the chalk line.

The vertical distance above the grade line stake at which the top of a batter board should be set, at a given station, is obtained by subtracting the cut at that station from the "pole." For instance, if the pole is 8 ft and the cut is 5.72 ft, the top of the batter board must be set 8.00 − 5.72 = 2.28 ft above the grade stake.

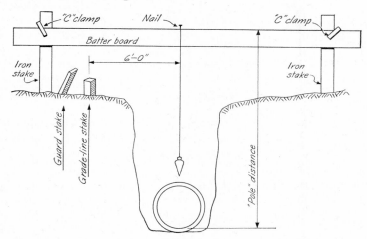

Fig. 10-5. Batter board over a pipe ditch.

First two batter boards are set up as soon as machine excavation permits. In this way the depth of ditch excavation at the machine can be controlled by the pole by sighting along the top edge of boards before other batter boards are set up.

10-16. Cross sections. The name *cross section* is applied to a line of levels run perpendicular to the transit line. On route surveys the cross sections are run at established center line stations and at plus stations where noticeable breaks in the ground profile occur.

If the elevations along the transit line have already been determined by the leveling parties, these elevations are used in carrying leveling along cross section lines. However, if center line elevations are not known at the time cross sections are taken, the center line elevation at each station is assumed to be at zero elevation; and the elevations of all points along a given cross section are referred to that zero elevation. Later, when the center line elevation for a given section has been ascertained, that elevation is added algebraically to the respective relative elevations of all points along the cross section.

The leveling operation along a cross section may be done partly by an engineer's level and partly by a hand level as shown in Fig. 10-6. Assume, for instance, that a backsight of 5.3 ft is taken with the engineer's level on center line, assumed to be at zero elevation. A foresight taken on a point 30 ft left of center line might be 7.5 ft. The difference

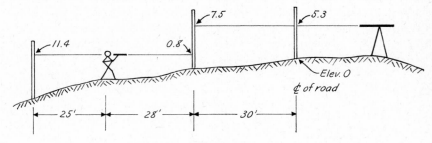

Fig. 10-6. Cross section leveling.

in elevation between the backsight point and foresight point is then $-7.5 + 5.3 = -2.2$ ft. This difference is recorded for the foresight point, 30 ft left of center line in this case, in the form of a fraction $\dfrac{-2.2}{30}$ as is shown on the right-hand page of Fig. 10-7 opposite station 12+00, recorded on the left-hand page. Actually the recorded fraction is

						March 3, 1959 K–K.D.Jones 19.			
CROSS SECTIONS *ROUTE 52 SEC.3*						Rod – T.E.Black *Clear, Warm* Notes – M. Harvey			
STA.	B.S.	H.I.	F.S.	ELEV.		LT.	₵	RT.	
12+00	2.31	375.03		372.72		52.4 59.9 70.5 372.7 77.9 79.9 84.6 92.9 −20.3 −12.8 −2.2 0 5.2 7.2 11.9 20.2 105 83 30 0 30 50 75 105			
13+00			5.72	369.31		61.5 63.6 67.0 70.3 369.3 72.4 75.3 78.5 79.8 −7.8 −5.7 −2.3 1.0 0 3.1 6.0 9.2 10.5 95 80 36 15 0 25 47 67 82			

Fig. 10-7. Cross section notes.

nothing but two recordings separated by a horizontal line. The figure above the line is the elevation of a point referred to the assumed zero elevation at the center line, and the figure below the line is the distance from the center line to the point on which the foresight reading was taken.

If the rod held on the next point, along the same cross section, is too low to be read by the instrument, the cross sectioning may be continued with the hand level. The instrumentman takes a cloth tape, gives the zero end of tape to the rodman, and proceeds with the hand level along the cross section line. He stops at some convenient distance from the rod, say 28 ft, and takes backsight reading on the rod with the hand level (Fig. 10-6). Let this reading be 0.8 ft. Next, he motions to the rodman to move still further from the center line, say another 25 ft, where there appears to be a break in the slope of the ground. The rodman carries the zero end of the tape ahead so that a 25 ft distance is read by the instrumentman operating the hand level and holding the reel of cloth tape. The instrumentman then takes foresight reading on the rod. Let this reading be 11.4 ft. This makes the difference in elevation between the backsight point and foresight point equal to $-11.4 + 0.8 = -10.6$ ft. However, the difference in elevation between the last foresight point, which is $25 + 28 + 30 = 83$ ft left of center line, and the center line point is $-10.6 - 2.2 = -12.8$ ft. Thus the notebook recording for the last point is made as $\dfrac{-12.8}{83}$.

The leveling operation described above is continued to a distance of about 100 or 150 ft on each side of the center line. Whether or not such distances are sufficient depends on the amount of cut or fill at a given station. This, however, is not known to the field parties at the time the preliminary survey is made.

Figure 10-7 shows one type of note used in recording cross section data. The data for leveling shown in Fig. 10-6 are recorded opposite station 12+00. Distances are usually measured to the nearest foot. If the same party runs both the profile and the cross sections, the left-hand page is used for recording profile leveling. The figures shown above the cross section data in Fig. 10-7 are elevations of ground points reduced to the same datum as the leveling shown on the left-hand page.

The elevations determined by cross section leveling are plotted on sheets of graph paper divided into squares. The same vertical and horizontal scales are used in plotting. The cross section of the designed road, for the station at which a ground cross section was taken, is also plotted on the same cross section paper. The result, such as shown in Fig. 10-8, gives the area of cut or fill at a given station. These areas are usually measured by a planimeter (see Fig. 15-10) and are recorded on cross section sheets. The areas are used in computation of the volume of earthwork on a given project.

Cross sections may be run on construction projects other than route surveys. For instance, before excavation has begun for a building or a *borrow pit*, ground cross sections are often taken at regular intervals as determined by the stakes set outside the excavation area. After the excavation has been completed, a new set of cross sections is run along the same lines. The two sets of cross sections give sufficient data for computation of the volume of excavated material.

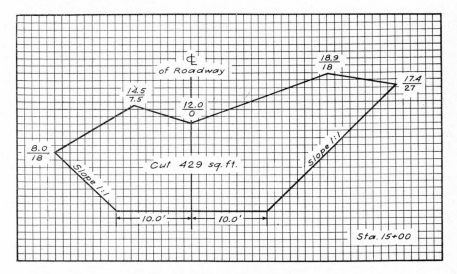

Fig. 10-8. Typical cross section.

A *borrow pit* is a place where suitable fill material is excavated by the contractor who buys it from the owners of land adjacent to construction projects. This is done when the contractor needs more fill than is available from a project's earthwork, or when hauling of free fill material becomes uneconomical.

FIELD EXERCISES

10-1. Practice exercise in leveling

Party: Three men.

Equipment: Standard engineer's level and leveling rod.

Object: To gain experience in setting up the engineer's level, taking rod readings, holding the rod properly, reading the rod verniers, and recording the data properly.

Procedure: Each person should try to set up the instrument and to level it. If the instrument must be set up on a hillside, one leg of the tripod must be directed up the hill. Set up the instrument so that the foot plate is approximately level; then press on the tripod legs to set them firmly on the ground, tighten the wing nuts, and center the bubble over the two diagonally opposite leveling screws. Repeat the leveling process over the other pair of screws. Turn the instrument 180° in azimuth and see whether the bubble remains centered. If it moves, the vertical axis of the instrument is not truly vertical. Nevertheless, when reading the rod the bubble must be centered each time the reading is made.

In leveling, try to obtain as nearly as possible an even bearing pressure on all foot screws and avoid making the screws too tight. They should turn readily when held between the thumb and the forefinger.

If the line of sight of the instrument is not truly horizontal when the bubble is centered, balanced backsight and foresight distances will help to eliminate the errors in rod readings caused by an inclination of the line of sight.

Focus the telescope on the rod, held about 100 ft from the instrument; then adjust the eyepiece until the cross hairs appear sharp and distinct. Repeat the procedure until the object and the cross hairs are both in focus. Read the rod, estimating the thousandths, then set the target on the rod for the same sight and see if the rodman will check your readings.

Learn how to hold the rod directly in front while balancing it in a vertical position between the fingers. Also practice reading high rod directly and by setting the target.

Having learned how to set up the level and to take rod readings, run a small differential leveling circuit starting with some definite point. Assign to this point an arbitrary elevation of 100.00 ft. After making about four set-ups, see how well you close on the starting point. The difference between the initial and final elevation of the starting point is the error of closure of the circuit. If it does not exceed $\pm 0.01 \sqrt{N}$, where N is the number of set-ups in the circuit, the error of closure may be due entirely to the accumulation of random errors. If the error of closure is greater than the above amount, it is most likely that some mistakes have been made in reading the rod or in setting up the instrument. Follow a standard form in recording the data (see Fig. 9-6), reading the rod to the nearest hundredth of a foot.

10-2. Running a third order leveling circuit

Party: Four men.

Equipment: Standard engineer's level and leveling rod.

Object: To establish the elevations of four corners of the lot that was used for taping. These elevations will serve later as bench marks for the topographic survey of the lot.

Procedure: The instructor will assign the initial bench mark and all points where elevations will have to be determined.

Each party will run an independent circuit of levels from the initial bench mark and back. In order to achieve a satisfactory result in this exercise, the following procedures should be observed:

(a) Rod readings are to be made to thousandths, either directly or by using the target.
(b) Backsight and foresight distances are to be paced, in order to keep them closely balanced. These distances must be recorded in feet in the last column of the left page of the field book.
(c) Sight distances must not exceed 200 ft.
(d) Instrument set-ups are to be on firm ground. (Note that a road pavement will vibrate with passing automobiles.)
(e) Turning points are to be taken on well-defined points of solid objects such as stones or steps.
(f) The bubble must be carefully centered just before reading the rod.
(g) The rod must be held vertically at the time of reading.

It may be estimated that if the above precautions are observed, the error of closure may be well within $\pm 0.05 \sqrt{D}$, where D is the length of circuit in miles.

Distribution of the error of closure. When one is satisfied that the error of closure (that is, the difference between the actual and closing elevation of the initial bench mark) is due only to random errors, this error of closure, E, must be distributed to those points in the circuit the elevations of which are being determined. The error distributed to a point A, C_a, must be proportional to the length, a, of the circuit to point A. Thus if L is the length of the whole circuit,

$$C_a = E \frac{a}{L}$$

These corrections can be readily computed on the slide rule. Use standard type notes in this exercise with an extra column for sight distances. Show the customary check for the arithmetic. The right-hand page must contain descriptions of bench marks and their locations on the same line on which the elevations of these bench marks are shown on the left page.

CHAPTER 11

Measurement of Angles

11-1. Various units for measuring angles. There are several systems of units used for measuring angles. The angular system of units used in the United States and in many other parts of the world is the *sexagesimal system.* In this system the circumference of the circle is divided into 360 equal parts. The central angle subtended by one such division is equal to 1 *degree.* There are 60 *minutes* in one degree and 60 *seconds* in one minute. Fractions of a second are measured as decimal parts.

Another system of angular units, which is widely used in Europe at the present time, is the *centesimal system.* In this system one complete revolution encompasses 400 *grads.* 1 grad (g) is equal to 100 *centigrads* (c), and 1 centigrad is equal to 100 *centi-centigrads* (cc).

Still another system of angular units divides the circumference of the circle into 6400 parts. One such angular unit is called a *mil.* Thus 6400 mils are equal to 360 degrees. This system of angle measurement is used principally by military men.

It is often convenient to express an angle in a form that may be readily used in equations expressed in linear units. For instance, when one expresses the area of a sector as $R^2\theta/2$, where R is the radius and θ is the central angle, this angle must be expressed in *radians.* The angle equal to one radian is the angle subtended by the circular arc equal in length to its radius. Since the size of such an angle is constant for any radius, the angle equal to one radian may be used as a measuring unit. Being a ratio of the length of arc to the length of its radius, an angle expressed in radians is dimensionless.

By drawing an arc $l = AB$ of radius r for the angle $\alpha = AOB$, as shown in Fig. 11-1, it is evident that angle α expressed in radians must be l/r.   It may also be seen from the figure that $\sin \alpha = s/r$ and $\tan \alpha = t/r$, where $s = AD$ and $t = CB$, both lines being perpendicular to the radius OB. Since $s < r < t$ for any angle, it may be concluded that the numerical value of an angle expressed in radians must be always greater than the sine and smaller than the tangent of the angle. Thus

$$\sin \alpha < \alpha < \tan \alpha \qquad (11\text{-}1)$$

As a variable angle becomes smaller, the difference between the sine and the tangent is also getting smaller, so that for small angles $\sin \alpha = \tan \alpha$ to a certain number of significant figures. For instance, $\sin 2° = 0.03490$ and $\tan 2° = 0.03492$. Since these two functions are equal to each other to three significant figures, it can be said that to the same number of significant figures $\sin \alpha = \alpha = \tan \alpha$ for a 2° or smaller angle.

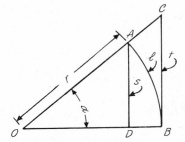

Fig. 11-1. Angle in radians

$$\alpha = \frac{l}{r}$$

Another practical deduction pertaining to small angles is that the angles are proportional to their sines or tangents to a certain number of significant figures. For instance, if computations are carried only to three significant figures and it is required to find sine of 20″, then, remembering that $\sin 1' = 0.000291$, $\sin 20''$ must be one-third of that, or 0.0000970. The angle of 20″, expressed in radians, is also equal to 0.0000970. To express large angles in radians it is necessary to use either special convergence tables or to use the equation, 1 radian = $180/\pi$ deg, where $\pi = 3.1416$ to five significant figures. Some engineers prefer to remember that 1 radian = 206,265 sec.

11-2. The transit. Figure 11-2 shows a typical engineer's transit, the instrument used principally for measuring horizontal and vertical angles. Other uses of a transit include such operations as prolongation of a straight line, measurement of distances and differences of elevation by the stadia method, astronomical observations for the true direction of lines, leveling operations similar to those made with the engineer's level, projection of points along vertical lines, alignment of jigs in aircraft industry, and many other uses on various engineering projects and in land surveying work.

In many of the operations described above the work with transit may require a high degree of accuracy. Thus it is important to know not only the general functions of various parts of the instrument but

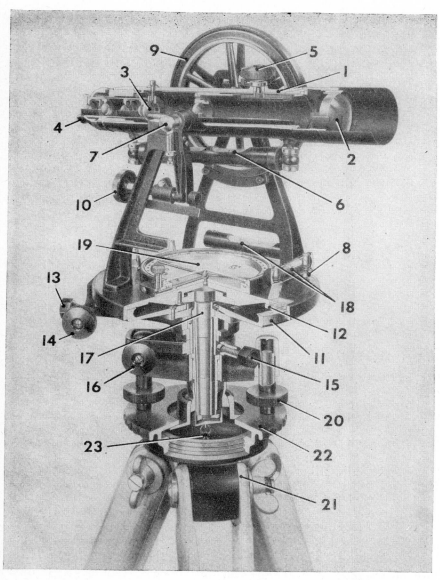

Fig. 11-2. Main functional parts of engineer's transit. (Courtesy W. & L. E. Gurley.)

167

also how to operate the transit to reduce possible instrumental errors to a minimum.

Various parts of a transit are shown in Fig. 11-2. The **telescope** (1), used for viewing the objects, contains the **objective lens** (2), the **cross-hair ring** (3), the **eye piece** (4), adjustable for focusing the cross hairs, and the object *focusing knob* (5). The **telescope level** (6) is attached under the telescope for the purpose of using the transit in leveling operations. The telescope is mounted on the **horizontal axis** (7), which is supported by two upright **standards** (8). The **vertical circle** (9) is also mounted on the horizontal axis, so that rotation of the telescope through a certain angle may be read on the vertical-circle vernier attached to the standard. There is a vertical circle clamp screw (not shown), which is used for arresting rotational motion of the telescope; the **vertical circle tangent screw** (10) is used for fine motion of the telescope.

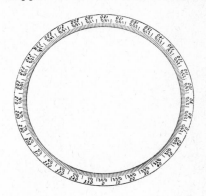

Fig. 11-3. Horizontal circle graduated 0°–360° both ways. (Courtesy Keuffel & Esser Co.)

The standards are supported by a metal plate which encloses the lower and the upper limbs used for measuring horizontal angles. The lower limb, also called the **lower plate** (11), is graduated into degrees and parts thereof and the upper limb, also called the **upper plate** (12), contains two verniers for reading horizontal angles. The upper plate fits inside the lower plate. Two verniers marked by letters *A* and *B* are attached to the upper plate 180° apart, so that vernier *B* always reads 180° more than vernier *A*. Figure 11-3 shows the horizontal circle, and Fig. 11-4 shows the enlarged view of a part of the horizontal circle and the vernier *B*.

The two plates may be clamped together by the **upper motion clamp screw** (13). The accurate setting of an angle on the horizontal circle is made with the **upper motion tangent screw** (14). When the upper motion clamp screw is clamped and the **lower motion clamp screw** (15) is loose, the two plates may be rotated together. The **lower motion tangent screw** (16) provides fine rotational motion for the lower plate.

Two **plate levels** (18) are attached to the plate supporting the standards. The plate levels are used for leveling the instrument. Many transits have also a **compass** (19) affixed to the top of the horizontal plates. The compass is used on engineering surveys for rough checks on measured angles. Some transits have no compass.

The upper plate is supported by the **tapered center** (17), which turns inside the tapered center of the lower plate.   Both centers must be concentric to insure proper functioning of the upper and the lower motions of the transit.   The centers fit inside the leveling head of the instrument.   The leveling head holds four **leveling screws** (20), which are used for leveling the instrument by the plate levels.   Precise transits have only three leveling screws.   This provides more uniform distribution of bearing pressure among leveling screws.   The leveling screws rest on the **foot plate** (22), which has standard threads for attaching the instrument to a **tripod** (21).

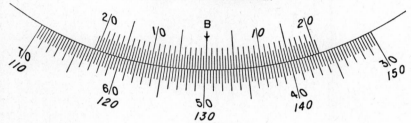

GRADUATED 20 MINUTES READING TO 30 SECONDS
DOUBLE DIRECT VERNIER

Fig. 11-4. Horizontal circle with vernier plate.   (Courtesy Keuffel & Esser Co.)

A **chain** (23) with a hook is suspended from the cover cup at the bottom of the transit.   The chain hangs between the tripod legs and is used for attaching a plumb bob so that a transit may be set over a point.

A transit may be visualized as having three main parts—the upper part or the alidade, the middle part or the horizontal circle, and the lower part or the leveling head.   The exploded view of these three parts is shown in Fig. 11-5.

11-3. Various types of transits.   Transits vary in size, weight, and number of parts, depending upon the purpose for which the instruments are intended.   For instance, the vertical circle and the telescope level may be lacking in a transit used only for measuring horizontal angles.

Lightweight transits, such as the mountain transit (so called because it is often used for work in a rugged terrain), weighs about $9\frac{1}{2}$ lb, whereas a standard engineer's transit weighs close to 16 lb.

There are also transits designed for a special type of work such as mine surveying.   Figure 11-6 shows a typical mining transit.   Its special feature is the auxiliary telescope, used for measuring vertical angles greater than $\pm 60°$ since such angles cannot be measured with the transit's telescope.

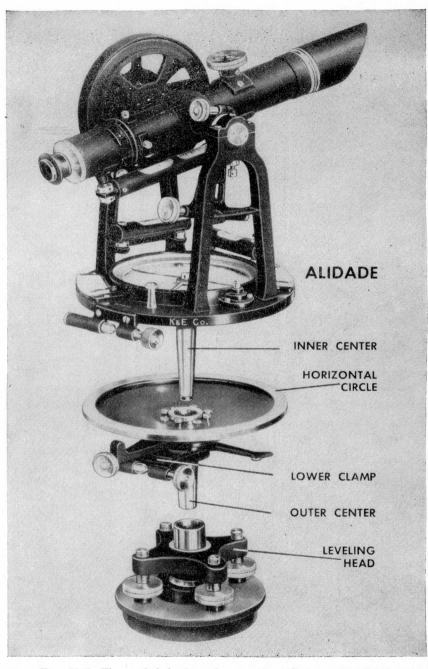

Fig. 11-5. The exploded view of a transit. (Courtesy Keuffel & Esser Co.)

170

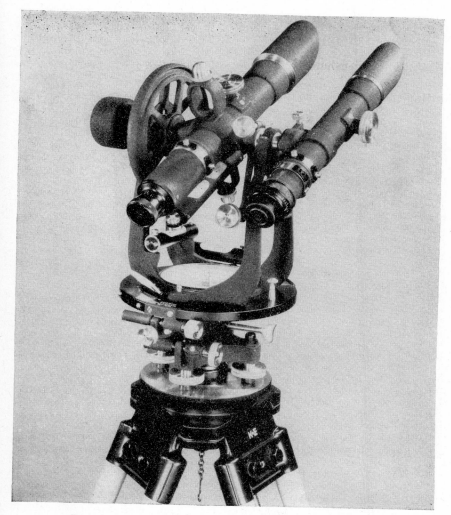

Fig. 11-6. Mining transit. (Courtesy Keuffel & Esser Co.)

The transit's horizontal circles and the verniers, used for measuring horizontal angles, are constructed with precisions varying from about 1′ to 5″. Since measurement of horizontal angles is by far a more common and more important operation on most engineering projects than the measurement of vertical angles, the horizontal circle scale is often constructed to read the angles with a greater precision than the vertical circle scale on the same instrument. When a transit is spoken of as a

1 min, 30 sec, 20 sec, 10 sec, or a 5 sec transit, it means that horizontal angles can be read directly with those respective precisions.

11-4. Builders' transit-level. Figure 11-7 shows a builder's transit-level which has the horizontal circle and an arc of the vertical circle for measuring vertical angles. A builder's transit-level is a useful instrument on building construction jobs where the angles and directions need not be measured with a greater accuracy than about 5'.

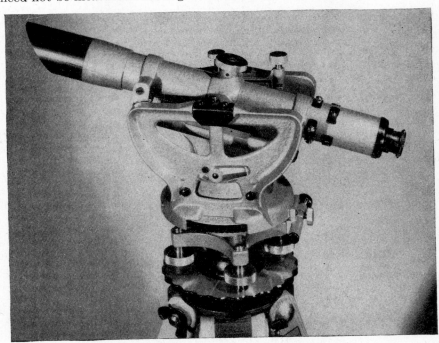

Fig. 11-7. Builders' transit-level. (Courtesy Keuffel & Esser Co.)

11-5. The theodolite. Like a transit, the theodolite is an instrument used for measuring horizontal and vertical angles. Originally all surveying instruments built for such a purpose were called theodolites. They had long telescopes that could not be rotated through 360° about the horizontal axis. Later some theodolites were designed to allow a complete rotation of the telescope about the horizontal axis. Since these telescopes could "transit" through the zenith, they became known as *transits*.

Most surveying instruments intended for measuring angles are designed nowadays so that their telescopes can be rotated through 360°. Thus the original distinction between a theodolite and a transit has lost its meaning and whether an instrument should be called a *transit* or a *theodolite* has, to some extent, become a matter of choice or local usage. For instance, the precise optical instruments for measuring horizontal and vertical angles, largely of European manufacture, came to be known in this country as optical theodolites. Figure 11-8 shows a Wild T-2 theodolite of Swiss manufacture—an instrument used for precise work.

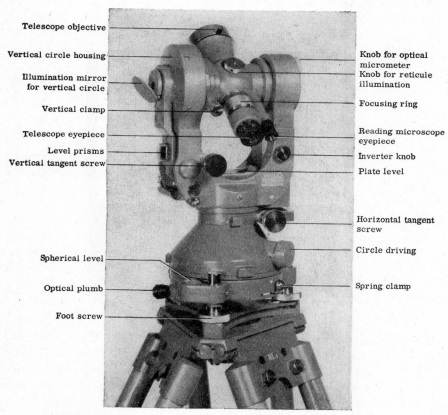

Telescope objective

Vertical circle housing

Illumination mirror
for vertical circle

Vertical clamp

Telescope eyepiece

Level prisms

Vertical tangent screw

Spherical level

Optical plumb

Foot screw

Knob for optical
micrometer
Knob for reticule
illumination

Focusing ring

Reading microscope
eyepiece

Inverter knob

Plate level

Horizontal tangent
screw

Circle driving

Spring clamp

Fig. 11-8. Wild T-2 theodolite. (Courtesy Wild Heerbrugg Instruments, Inc.)

The same figure also includes a brief description of the various operational parts used in measuring horizontal and vertical angles.

Certain distinct features of optical theodolites are: completely enclosed optical system for reading horizontal and vertical angles; micrometer microscope attachment for reading the scales; micrometer vernier scale turned by a special knob for bringing horizontal or vertical scales into coincidence (Fig. 11-9); split bubble for a level attached to the vertical circle for minimizing instrumental errors in measuring vertical angles; optical system for setting the instrument over a point; light-reflecting mirrors for reading the scales; internal wiring for artificial lighting of scales and cross hairs; three leveling screws; absence of the telescope level and compass.

Some optical theodolites are so-called *repeating instruments,* which can measure horizontal angles by accumulation of readings on the horizontal circle, that is, by repetition, very much in the same way as on transits. The horizontal scales on such theodolites may read

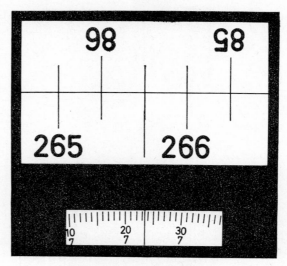

Fig. 11-9. Wild T-2 theodolite horizontal scale, reading 265°47′23″.5.

horizontal angles directly to 10 or 20″. More precise theodolites may read the scales directly to 1″ or a fraction of a second. In these theodolites the lower motion, which permits measurement of angles by repetition in a repeating instrument, is lacking. The reason is that repeated sighting on points may introduce a greater error in a measured angle than the error in reading the scales. Non-repeating instruments are called *direction instruments.* The Wild T-2 theodolite shown in Fig. 11-8 is a direction instrument—its scales read to the nearest second directly.

11-6. Three types of horizontal angle. Barring instrumental errors the angles recorded on the horizontal circle of a transit are *horizontal angles,* i.e., projections of sighted angles on a horizontal plane. There are three types of horizontal angle that may be measured at a point in order to fix the direction of one line with respect to another. They are: *direct angles, deflection angles,* and *azimuth angles.*

11-7. Direct angles. A direct angle is the angle that is measured directly from one line to another at the point of intersection of two lines.

a definite angle, the sighting must be done first and then the horizontal circle may be rotated and set to read any desired angle.

Assuming that a direction theodolite reading the angles directly to 1" is used in measuring an angle six times, the maximum random error of the mean of six measurements may be estimated as follows:

Vernier reading............   0.2", occurs 12 times
Pointing..................   1", occurs 12 times
Error of circle graduation... 2", occurs 12 times

$$E_{max} = \frac{1}{\sqrt{6}} \sqrt{12 \times 0.2^2 + 12 \times 1^2 + 12 \times 2^2} = \pm 3.2'' \qquad (11\text{-}10)$$

It is interesting to note that as far as the magnitude of random errors is concerned, the result of measuring an angle by a 30 sec transit with

T̄ S'ght at pt.	S'ght on pt.	T E L.	No. of Meas.	Vernier A	Vernier B	Mean	Measur. Direct Angle	Computations
B	A	D		0°20'30"	180°21'00"	0°20'45"		
	C	D	1	120°33'00"	300°33'00"			1°36'15" + 720° − 0°20'45" = 721°15'30"
	C	D	3	0°59'30"	181°00'00"			
	C	R	6	1°36'00" Lt.	181°36'30"	1°36'15"	120°12'35" Lt.	$\dfrac{721°15'30''}{6} = 120°12'35''$

(Table header block:)

MEASUREMENT OF HORIZONTAL ANGLES

May 20, 1959   C. B. Clark   17.
Cloudy, Warm   M. D. Byrd
Transit No. 5   K. C. Dixon

Fig. 11-16. Recording of measured direct angles, reading both verniers.

six repetitions, as is shown by Eq. (11-9), is about the same as measuring the angle six times by a 1 sec theodolite, provided of course that the random errors behave strictly according to the theory of probability. However, this is not likely to occur in a few observations. Thus unexpected deviations from the computed values of errors may be expected in Eqs. (11-9) and (11-10).

It is important to point out that certain variations of random errors in pointing are likely to occur under different working conditions. For instance, other conditions being equal, pointing may be done more accurately on longer sights. Random errors in circle graduations may also be subject to variation in different instruments.

Another interesting thing about the result shown by Eq. (11-10) is that if the same angle were measured by the same 1 sec theodolite only once or twice, the maximum random error, theoretically, would stay the same. Actually, however, better accuracy should be expected from increased number of observations up to the point when random errors begin to behave according to the theory of probability. After this, no further increase in accuracy should be expected from additional measurements.

Instrumental Errors in Measured Angles

11-15. Transit's schematic diagram.   Figure 11-17 presents a schematic diagram of a transit showing the horizontal and vertical axes,

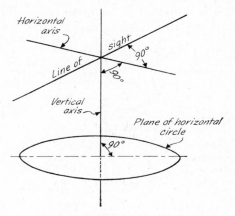

Fig. 11-17. Transit's schematic diagram.

the line of sight, and the plane of the horizontal circle.   The instrumental errors of a transit may be largely eliminated if in setting up the instrument one may be certain that the vertical axis of the instrument is truly vertical, that the horizontal axis is perpendicular to the vertical axis, and that the line of sight is perpendicular to the horizontal axis, as is shown in Fig. 11-17.   Since no instrument is perfect and some instrumental errors are liable to cause a certain amount of error in measured angles, a transit should be used in a manner that will eliminate as much as possible the errors of its maladjustment.   Various sources of errors and the methods to eliminate them are discussed below.

11-16. Inclination of the vertical axis.   When a transit is set up, it is leveled by means of plate levels [Fig. 11-2(18)].   If the axes of plate levels are perpendicular to the vertical axis of the instrument, then by leveling the instrument the vertical axis is put in a truly vertical position. There are two plate levels on a transit—a longitudinal level which is parallel to the vertical plane containing the telescope, and a transverse level, at a right angle to the telescope.   The sensitivity of these levels on a standard engineer's transit is about 2′. Thus if a transit is leveled within one-half of one division of a plate level, the angle of maximum inclination of the vertical axis may be expected to be 1′. In order to set the vertical axis in as truly a vertical position as possible, one may use the telescope level in leveling a transit. The sensitivity of the telescope level is about 30″ on the same type of instrument.

11-17. Errors in horizontal angles. The inclination of the vertical axis may affect the measurement of horizontal angles. As the horizontal axis of a transit is rotated about the inclined vertical axis, the horizontal

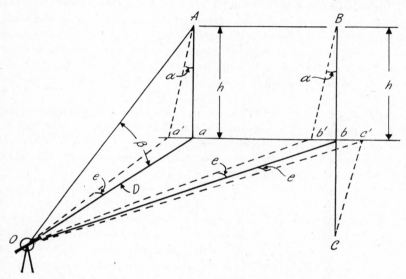

Fig. 11-18. Errors in measuring horizontal angles.

axis describes a plane inclined to the horizontal. Depending on the position of the horizontal axis with respect to the inclined vertical axis, the angle of inclination of the horizontal axis to the horizontal will vary from zero to the angle by which the vertical axis itself is out of plumb. Thus the error in pointing and consequently in reading the horizontal circle will vary from zero to some maximum value when the inclination of the horizontal axis is the greatest.

Assuming, however, that a vertical axis is in a truly vertical position, the inclination of the horizontal axis to the horizontal may be caused by the condition that horizontal axis is not at a right angle to the vertical axis. In this case, the error of inclination of the horizontal axis will be constant in all directions of sighting. Assume, for instance, that the horizontal axis is inclined through angle α to the horizontal, and also that a backsight in measuring a horizontal angle is taken on a point A elevated through angle β, as shown in Fig. 11-18.

The inclination of the horizontal axis to the horizontal will cause the line of sight to move in an inclined plane when the telescope is lowered. Assume that the trace of such inclined plane is represented by the line Aa' shown on the figure. Then the horizontal angle $a'oa = e$ must be the error in the horizontal angle aob measured between points A and B which are assumed to be at the same elevation. Similarly there will be error $b'ob = -e$ in the same horizontal angle aob when foresight is taken on point B. Since the two errors in angle aob are the same in magnitude and opposite in sign, they will cancel each other, and the measured horizontal angle between points A and B will be free of errors caused by the inclination of the horizontal axis. However, should the horizontal angle be measured between points A and C, where direction to point C is inclined to the horizontal through angle $-\beta$, the horizontal angle aoc will have error e with the same sign on both the backsight and the foresight. This makes the total error in measured horizontal angle aoc equal to $2e$.

If the angle of inclination of the horizontal axis is $\alpha = a'Aa$ and if the elevation of point A is h ft, distance $a'a = h\alpha$; and the error, $e = aa'/D$, because of elevation of one sight through angle β, is $e = h\alpha/D$, where D is the horizontal distance between the instrument and point A. Also, since $h = D \tan \beta$, from Fig. 11-18,

$$e = \alpha \tan \beta \qquad (11\text{-}11)$$

The horizontal axis may be inclined to the horizontal either because of its own maladjustment, which occurs when the horizontal axis is not perpendicular to the vertical axis, or because the vertical axis is out of plumb. In the first case, the errors in measured horizontal angles may be eliminated by measuring the angles the same number of times with the telescope in direct position as with the telescope in reversed position, since on reversal of the telescope the errors in horizontal angles change sign. Thus accumulated measurements on the horizontal circle divided by the number of repetitions should give the horizontal angle free of errors arising from maladjustment of the horizontal axis. However, *if the reason for the inclination of the horizontal axis is that the vertical axis is not truly vertical, the reversal of the telescope does not eliminate errors in horizontal angles resulting from the inclination of the horizontal axis to the horizontal.* On many precise instruments special levels are used for leveling the horizontal axis and keeping it level during measurements.

An error in a measured horizontal angle may also result from the line of sight of a transit not being at right angle to the horizontal axis of the instrument, provided that the points sighted on are at different elevations. Figure 11-19 shows a sight taken on point A with a vertical angle equal to β. Assuming that the line of sight is off from being perpendicular to the horizontal axis by angle $e = ABA'$, in which the side BA' is at right angle to the horizontal axis, the horizontal projection of angle ABA' is angle $DBD' = DD'/BD$, approximately. Designating this angle by e_h and noting that $DD' = AA'$ and $BD = BA \cos \beta$, $e_h = AA'/(BA \cos \beta)$. Also since $AA'/BA = e$ (approximately),

$$e_h = e \sec \beta \qquad (11\text{-}12)$$

Thus the error in horizontal angle when one sight is elevated through angle β and another sight is horizontal is $e_h - e = e(\sec \beta - 1)$ or,

$$e_h - e = e \operatorname{exsec} \beta \qquad (11\text{-}13)$$

Errors in measured horizontal angles may also result from lack of care in setting the transit over a point. The magnitude of such errors

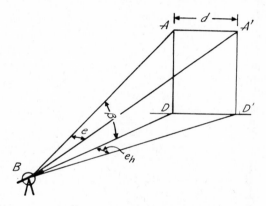

Fig. 11-19. Error in direction on elevated sight.

varies with the length of sight, the size of a measured angle, and the relative horizontal position of the center of transit with respect to the point over which it is set up. Such errors are equal to zero for any size of angle if the point, the center of the transit, and the points sighted on in measuring an angle project on the circumference of the same circle. However, speaking of maximum possible errors, the errors are negligible for very small measured angles and are largest for angles close to 180°.

Assuming, for instance, that the center of a transit is offset with respect to the point over which the transit is set up by $\frac{1}{8}$ in. horizontally, and that a backsight is taken in the right angle direction to this offset, the error in direction for a 100 ft sight is then $\sin^{-1}[1/(8 \times 12 \times 100)] = 21''$. This also will be the maximum error in measuring a 90° angle. In measuring an angle equal to 180°, the error will be twice the above computed value, or $42''$, if the foresight distance is also equal to 100 ft.

For longer sights and smaller offset errors in setting up a transit, the errors in measured angles will be proportionately smaller.

11-18. Errors in vertical angles. The vertical circle of American-made transits is graduated from 0° to 90° in each of the four quadrants (Fig. 11-20). This arrangement of graduations and the lack of a double center in vertical motion make it impossible to measure vertical angles by repetition as may be done in measurement of horizontal angles. How-

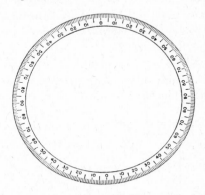

ever, the vertical angles seldom need to be measured as accurately as horizontal angles. The greatest use of vertical angles on engineering projects is in making topographic maps and plans, where scale limitations make it unnecessary to measure vertical angles very accurately. Special precautions necessary in measuring vertical angles in astronomical observations are discussed below.

When a transit's telescope is in a horizontal position, the vertical circle vernier should read zero. A sight taken on some elevated point would turn the telescope, the horizontal axis,

Fig. 11-20. Transit's vertical circle graduated in quadrants. (Courtesy Keuffel & Esser Co.)

and the vertical circle through the angle of elevation of the sighted point. Such an angle is read on the vertical circle vernier. There are two things that may introduce errors in the measured vertical angle. First, the vertical circle vernier may be out of adjustment, and second, the vertical axis of the instrument may be inclined in the same plane in which the elevated sight is taken.

The inclination of the vertical axis of the instrument through angle α in the direction of sighting will introduce error in measured vertical angle equal to α. For a given set-up of the transit, the error α will be the same in magnitude and in sign in a vertical angle measured with the telescope either in direct position or in reversed position. Thus the only way to eliminate the errors resulting from inclination of the vertical axis is to level the instrument as carefully as possible if there is no spirit level attached to the vertical circle vernier. If the transit has such a level, it must be in proper adjustment so that the vernier will read correct vertical angle when the bubble of the level is centered. The reason why many transits do not have a spirit level attached to the vertical circle vernier is that unless such level is in proper adjustment, it will introduce, rather than eliminate, the errors in measured vertical angles.

Unlike the errors caused by the inclination of the vertical axis, the errors in vertical angles caused by the maladjustment of the vertical circle vernier plate can be eliminated by taking the average of angles measured with the telescope in direct and in reversed position.   In fact, measurement of vertical angles once direct and once reversed is a standard procedure in measuring vertical angles when accurate results are required, such as in astronomical observations.   In such measurements it may also be prudent to level the transit by using the telescope spirit level since it has greater sensitivity than plate levels.

11-19. Index correction.   Since the discrepancy in a vertical angle measured with the telescope in direct position and with the telescope in reversed position may be caused only by the vernier of the vertical circle being out of adjustment, the difference between the direct and the reverse value of an angle divided by 2 must give the value of the error due to maladjustment of the vertical circle vernier.

Assume, for instance, that a vertical angle measured with the telescope in direct position was recorded as 12°15′ and the same angle measured with the telescope in reversed position was recorded as 12°17′.   Since both readings must contain the error equal in magnitude and opposite in sign, the error v in the position of the vertical circle vernier plate may be found as follows:

$$v = \frac{12°15′ - 12°17′}{2} = -1′$$

The error subtracted from the direct reading of the angle must give the most probable value of the angle measured.   Thus the vertical angle must be 12°15′ − (−1′) = 12°16′.   The error v taken with opposite sign is known as the *Index Correction* (I.C.).   Thus in the example given above the I.C. = 1′.   The index correction added to the angles measured with the telescope in direct position gives the value of angles corrected for the error of the vertical circle vernier.   The angle so corrected may still contain the error resulting from inclination of the vertical axis.

In transits having a small spirit level attached to the vertical circle vernier, the vernier must read zero when the bubble of the level is centered and when the line of sight of the transit is horizontal.   Only under these conditions will the errors in vertical angles caused by the inclination of the vertical axis be eliminated within the sensitivity of the spirit level. Thus the sensitivity of the vernier level should be greater than that of plate levels, in order to be useful in the measurement of vertical angles. All precise theodolites have a vertical circle spirit level for measuring vertical angles.

11-20. Prolongation of a straight line.   A proper way to prolong a horizontal straight line AB is to set the transit at B, backsight on A and plunge the telescope, i.e., turn the telescope through 180° around the

horizontal axis. This procedure places the line of sight along the prolongation of line AB, provided that the line of sight is perpendicular to
the horizontal axis.

Figure 11-21 shows plan view of prolonging the line AB with the
transit set up at point B. The line DE shows the position of the horizontal axis at right angle to line AB. Thus if the line of sight is perpendicular to the horizontal axis, the plunging of the telescope, after
taking backsight on point A, should place the line of sight along BC,
which is a true prolongation of the line AB.

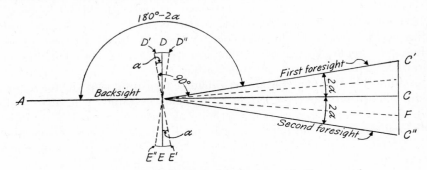

Fig. 11-21. Prolongation of a straight line.

Assuming, however, that there is a small error α in the direction of
the line of sight, as shown in Fig. 11-21, the backsight taken on point A
must place the horizontal axis in position $D'E'$, so that upon plunging the
telescope the line of sight assumes direction BC', which is off from the
true prolongation of line AB by the angle 2α.

If one rotates the instrument through $180° - 2\alpha$ in azimuth, in order
to take another backsight on point A, the horizontal axis is placed in
position $D''E''$, since it must also rotate through angle $180° - 2\alpha$. Then,
if one plunges the telescope from the inverted to direct position, the line
of sight is made to fall along the line BC'', which direction is off from the
true prolongation of line AB by the angle 2α on the side opposite to line
BC'. In order to find a true prolongation of the line AB, two points C'
and C'' are set on the ground, one alongside the other, and the distance
$C'C''$ is measured and bisected in order to find point C. This method
of prolongation of a straight line is called *prolongation by double centering*.
Even if the line of sight is perpendicular to the horizontal axis, the procedure of double centering must be followed in prolongation of a straight
line to eliminate possible errors from inclination of the horizontal axis.

11-21. Required accuracy in measured angles. The accuracy
with which the angles should be measured depends on the type of survey.
Generally speaking, the accuracy of measured angles should be consistent with the accuracy of linear measurements. For instance, if the

required accuracy of linear measurements on a given survey is of the third order, i.e., $1:5000$, and it is required to compute the x and y coordinates of a point from the coordinates of another point 5000 ft away, the new point must be located within 1 ft of its true location in any direction. Thus the angle subtended by 1 ft of arc at a distance of 5000 ft must be the maximum allowable closing error per single angle measured for any length of sight distance. This closing error, δ, is

$$\delta = \frac{1}{5000} \times \frac{180}{\pi} \, 3600 = 41''$$

It is on the safe side to round this allowable error to $40''$ for convenience in computations. When there are n angles measured in a traverse, the angular closure may be expected to increase in direct proportion to the square root of the number of measured angles, so that the allowable angular closure at check points on a third order survey should be $40\sqrt{n}$ sec.

TABLE 11-2.   RECOMMENDED ANGULAR CLOSURES ON TRAVERSES

Type of Survey	Accuracy of Linear Measurements	Angular Closure at Check Points Not to Exceed* (Sec)	Number of Angles between Check Points Not to Exceed
First order	$1:25,000$	$3\sqrt{n}$	15
Second order	$1:10,000$	$15\sqrt{n}$	25
Third order	$1:5,000$	$40\sqrt{n}$	35

* Where n is the number of angles measured between check points.

Table 11-2 approximately conforms to the U.S. Coast and Geodetic Survey practice.

For surveys lower than the third order, the values shown in Table 11-2a may be used.

TABLE 11-2a.   RECOMMENDED ANGULAR CLOSURES ON TRAVERSES

Type of Survey	Accuracy of Linear Measurements	Angular Closure at Check Points Not to Exceed* (Sec)	Number of Angles between Check Points Not to Exceed
Ordinary	$1:3,000$	$70\sqrt{n}$	45
Low order	$1:1,000$	$200\sqrt{n}$	55

* Where n is the number of angles measured between check points.

It should be pointed out that if closing accuracies on traverses are required to be those shown in the second column of Tables 11-2 and 11-2a, the accuracy of linear measurements should be somewhat better than those shown in the tables.

11-22. Field adjustment of a transit. Various transit parts have adjusting screws which make it possible to adjust a transit in the field. There are five main operations or adjustments which should be performed in the order indicated below.

(1) *To make the vertical cross hair lie in a plane perpendicular to the horizontal axis of the transit.* To check this condition the transit is set up about 100 ft in front of some object on which a well-defined point may be sighted. The instrument does not need to be leveled in this test. If the point sighted on stays on the vertical cross hair as the telescope is rotated up and down, the cross-hair ring [Fig. 11-2(3)] is in proper adjustment as far as this test is concerned.

In order to adjust the ring, two adjacent screws holding the ring are loosened and the ring is rotated until the point sighted on does stay on the vertical hair. Several trials may be necessary to achieve a good result.

(2) *To make the axes of plate levels [Fig. 11-2(18)] coincide with a plane perpendicular to the vertical axis.* This test is similar to that of testing the spirit level of an engineer's level. The bubble of each plate level is centered over a diagonally opposite pair of leveling screws, the instrument is rotated through 180° in azimuth, and deviation of each bubble from the center is observed. The error of each plate level is corrected by lowering or raising one end of the level tube, by means of adjusting screws holding the tube, until the bubble is brought halfway back toward the center. After this, the instrument is releveled and the test is repeated until both bubbles remain in centered position.

Should it be desirable to set the vertical axis in a vertical position without adjusting plate levels, the bubbles are centered, the instrument is rotated through 180°, and each bubble is brought halfway back by leveling screws. This should be a standard procedure in all transit operations to eliminate the errors caused by maladjustment of plate levels.

(3) *To make the line of sight perpendicular to the horizontal axis.* The procedure in this test is the same as in prolongation of a line shown in Fig. 11-21 and described in Art. 11-20. It may be seen from the figure that if the line of sight is not perpendicular to the horizontal axis by angle α, the two points C' and C'', set on the ground, give a distance $C'C''$ which subtends the angle equal to 4α. Thus in order to correct the line of sight for its error, the cross-hair ring is moved, right or left as the case may be, until the line of sight moves from point C'' to F

a distance $C''F = C'C''/4$. This is accomplished by tightening the adjusting screw on one side of the ring and loosening the adjusting screw on the opposite side. In order to prevent a possible rotation of the cross-hair ring in this adjustment, the top and bottom adjusting screws should be loosened just enough to make it possible to move the ring without rotating it.

(4) *To make the horizontal axis perpendicular to the vertical axis.* If the horizontal axis is not at right angle to the vertical axis by

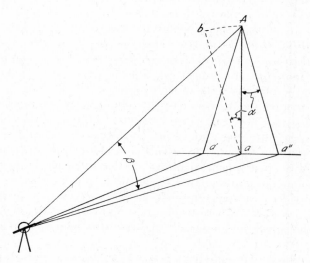

Fig. 11-22. Checking adjustment of the horizontal axis.

angle α, the rotation of the telescope causes the line of sight to describe an inclined plane. When a sight is taken on some high point, such as point A in Fig. 11-22, the trace of this inclined plane on a vertical plane is shown by the line Aa'. The angle $a'Aa$ is equal to the angle of inclination α of the horizontal axis.

Thus in order to test proper adjustment of the horizontal axis of the instrument, a transit is set up and leveled in front of some tall structure and the sight is taken on some well-defined point at the top of the structure. The telescope is then lowered to its horizontal position, and point a' is marked on the wall as shown in Fig. 11-22. Next, the telescope is plunged and the instrument is turned through 180° in azimuth for sighting point A with the reversed telescope. This operation changes the direction of the inclination of the horizontal axis so that in lowering the telescope the line of sight describes an inclined plane shown by the trace Aa'' on the figure. By marking point a'' on the wall and bisecting the distance $a'a''$, point a is found, which is the base of the perpendicular Aa to the line $a'a''$.

By taking sight on point a and raising the telescope, the line of sight will follow a line ab parallel to $a''A$, thus making angle baA equal to α. Then, by raising or lowering one end of the horizontal axis, the intersection of cross hairs is brought to point A. This procedure rotates the horizontal axis through angle α, thus making it perpendicular to the vertical axis of the instrument. The adjusting nuts at one end of the horizontal axis allow that end to be raised or lowered as required. Care must be exercised to make the final motion of the adjusting end of the axis directed up, so that the axis may not lose contact with its bearing.

(5) *To make the axis of the telescope level parallel to the line of sight and to make the vertical circle vernier read zero when the sight is horizontal.* In order to be able to adjust the telescope level, it is necessary to place the line of sight in a horizontal position. This is done by sighting on a computed correct rod in the two-peg test described in Art. 9-23(3) (see also Fig. 9-20). Briefly, a two-peg test consists of driving two pegs into the ground, about 150 ft apart, and setting the instrument first close to one stake and next close to another stake. In each set-up of the instrument, readings are taken on the rod held on each stake. If one stake is designated by letter A and another by letter B, the two sets of rod readings obtained on these stakes may be designated as R'_A, R'_B, R_A, and R_B, where primes designate rod readings in the first set-up and the subscripts designate the stakes on which the readings are taken.

It has also been pointed out in Art. 9-23 that although distances from the instrument to the near stakes and to the far stakes in both set-ups need not be equal, it simplifies the computations when they are made equal. In such a case only two distances need be used in computations, D_A and D_B, representing respectively distances from the instrument to stakes A and B in the second set-up of the instrument.

In order to facilitate the two-peg procedure in the field, the points of instrument set-ups are usually chosen in line with the two stakes, making the distances to the near stakes equal, and about 15 ft in length, in order to be able to read the rod at close range. In checking standard engineer's transits, some transitmen may prefer to make distances to the near stakes equal to zero, that is, to set the instrument first at one stake and next at another. This procedure is described in Art. 9-23(3) for a level.

Two expressions for the error E_A and E_B in rod readings on points A and B respectively, at the second set-up of the instrument, are given by Eqs. (9-13) and (9-14) for a case when distances to the near stakes and to the far stakes in both set-ups are equal.   These equations are also shown below as Eqs. (11-14) and (11-15).

$$E_A = D_A \frac{(R'_A - R'_B) - (R_A - R_B)}{-2(D_A - D_B)} \tag{11-14}$$

$$E_B = D_B \frac{(R'_A - R'_B) - (R_A - R_B)}{-2(D_A - D_B)} \tag{11-15}$$

For the case when the set-ups are made at the stakes, either D_A or D_B must be equal to zero, depending on whether the second set-up was at stake A or B.   In such a case all distances in Eqs. (11-14) and (11-15) cancel out and need not be measured in the field at all.   However, because of complications in reading the rods at the stakes where the instrument is set up, such procedure is not preferable.   Neither is it used with precision instruments.

It should be recalled that when E_A and E_B are positive, the line of sight is up, and when negative, the line of sight is down.   In either case, in order to compute correct rods C_A and C_B at A and B respectively, rod errors E_A and E_B must be subtracted from actual rod reading R_A and R_B in the second set-up.

$$C_A = R_A - E_A \tag{11-16}$$

and $$C_B = R_B - E_B \tag{11-17}$$

When one takes a sight on correct rod at the far stake, the line of sight is placed in horizontal position.   In order to make the axis of the telescope level parallel to the line of sight when it is in horizontal position, one end of the level tube is raised or lowered, by means of adjusting nuts, until the bubble is centered.   The telescope level is used only in leveling operations.   (Precise theodolites do not have telescope levels, and the horizontal line of sight is produced by setting 90 or 270° on the vertical circle.)

The vertical circle vernier is adjusted to read zero when the line of sight is made horizontal by sighting on "correct rod."   The vernier plate is held by two adjusting nuts.   When these are loosened, the plate may be moved right or left until the vernier is set on zero.   If there is a level attached to the vertical circle vernier, this level must be adjusted so that the bubble is centered when the vertical circle vernier reads zero.

PROBLEMS

11-1. A horizontal angle was measured by repetition with a transit ten times (10 D.R.).   The initial reading, the reading of horizontal circle after first measurement of the angle, and the final reading are as shown below. Only one vernier, A, was read. Find the angle measured.

	Initial	First	Final	
(A)	0°00′00″	30°15′30″	302°36′30″	Ans. 30°15′39″
(B)	0°00′00″	42°08′00″	61°21′30″	
(C)	0°00′00″	115°27′30″	74°33′30″	

11-2. A horizontal angle was measured by repetition with a 30 sec transit. The initial reading, the reading of the circle after first measurement, the final reading, and the number of measurements are as shown below. Only vernier A was read. Find the angle measured.

	Initial	First	Final	Number of Measurements	
(A)	0°05′30″	15°20′00″	122°02′00″	8 D.R.	Ans. 15°14′34″
(B)	0°01′00″	62°47′30″	16°39′00″	6 D.R.	
(C)	3°05′00″	120°18′00″	111°57′30″	4 D.R.	

11-3. A horizontal angle was measured by repetition with a 30 sec transit by reading both verniers A and B. The initial readings, the readings after first measurement, the final readings, and the number of measurements are as shown below. Find the angle measured.

	Number of Measurements	Vernier A	Vernier B	
(A)	0	0°00′00″	179°59′30″	
	1	132°17′30″	312°17′30″	
	4 D.R.	169°11′00″	349°11′00″	Ans. 132°17′49″
(B)	0	0°00′00″	179°59′30″	
	1	72°34′30″	252°34′00″	
	6 D.R.	75°28′00″	255°27′30″	
(C)	0	0°00′00″	180°00′30″	
	1	96°14′00″	276°14′00″	
	4 D.R.	24°56′30″	204°57′00″	

11-4. Using Table 11-1 determine maximum random error of measuring a horizontal angle by repetition, reading one vernier of a transit. The number of repetitions and the transit used are shown below.
(A) 4 D.R. 30 sec transit.　　　　　　　　　　Ans. ±4.8″
(B) 6 D.R. 1 min transit.
(C) 10 D.R. 20 sec transit.

11-5. It is required to measure horizontal angle with a transit with prescribed accuracy. Using Table 11-1 for estimating maximum random errors, determine the number of repetitions necessary to measure an angle with prescribed accuracy shown below.
(A) Within 3″ with 20 sec transit.　　　　　　Ans. 6 repetitions
(B) Within 5″ with 30 sec transit.
(C) Within 5″ with 1 min transit.

11-6. A horizontal angle was measured with a transit having one sight elevated through angle β. If the vertical axis of the instrument is out of plumb causing horizontal axis to be inclined by angle α to the horizontal on the elevated sight, determine the magnitude of error in a horizontal angle measured by double reversal of the telescope (2 D.R.).

(A) $\beta = 32°15'$, $\alpha = 1'$.   *Ans.* 37.9″

(B) $\beta = 40°20'$, $\alpha = 2'$.

(C) $\beta = 37°30'$, $\alpha = 1.5'$.

11-7. A horizontal angle was measured with a transit so that the backsight was elevated through angle β and the foresight was depressed through angle γ. Assuming that the vertical axis of the instrument was out of plumb by an angle which caused the horizontal axis to be inclined to the horizontal by angle α_b on backsight and α_f on foresight, determine the magnitude of error in measured horizontal angle by double reversal method (2 D.R.), if

(A) $\beta = 22°12'$, $\gamma = -37°10'$, $\alpha_b = 1'$, $\alpha_f = 40''$.   *Ans.* 54.8″

(B) $\beta = 31°40'$, $\gamma = -19°30''$, $\alpha_b = 30''$, $\alpha_f = 50''$.

(C) $\beta = 42°25'$, $\gamma = -30°17''$, $\alpha_b = 20''$, $\alpha_f = 1'$.

11-8. It is found that the line of sight of a transit is not perpendicular to the horizontal axis of the instrument. If the error is equal to e, and one sight is elevated through angle β and another sight is horizontal, determine the magnitude of error in measured horizontal angle when e and β values are as follows:

(A) $e = 3'$, $\beta = 33°34'$.   *Ans.* 36″

(B) $e = 5'$, $\beta = 28°15'$.

(C) $e = 4'$, $\beta = 25°10'$.

11-9. In an attempt to prolong a straight line AB the transit was set up at B, the sight was taken on A, the telescope was plunged, and point C was set on the ground. Then the transit was set up at C, the sight was taken on B, the telescope was plunged, and point D was set on the ground. The same procedure was used in setting points E and F. If the line of sight of the telescope was not at right angle to the horizontal axis by angle α find the following: (a) the angle that line EF makes with the line AB, (b) the offset by which point F is off from prolongation of line AB, if the distances in feet and the angle α are as shown below.

	AB	BC	CD	DE	EF	α
(A)	200	300	250	400	200	40″
(B)	300	250	300	200	350	1′
(C)	250	400	200	350	250	30″

Ans. (a) 5′20″, (b) 1.09 ft

11-10. To check the line of sight of a transit the instrument was set up at point B, backsight was taken on point A, the telescope was reversed, and point C was set on the ground. Then the instrument was turned in azimuth and the backsight was again taken on A, the telescope reversed to normal position, and point C' was set on the ground. Determine the angle by which the line of sight is off from being at right angle to the horizontal axis if all sights are level and the distances are as follows:

(A) BC = 200 ft, CC' = 0.214 ft.   *Ans. 55″*

(B) BC = 170 ft, CC' = 0.178 ft.

(C) BC = 250 ft, CC' = 0.372 ft.

11-11. Same as Problem 10 except that backsight on point A and the foresight on point C were at angles of elevation as is shown below. The distances were measured (horizontally) as follows:

(A) BC = 250 ft, CC' = 0.412 ft, backsight at 0°, foresight at +40°.

Ans. 1′05″

(B) AB = 300 ft, BC = 200 ft, CC' = 0.275 ft, backsight at +20°, and foresight at −30°.

(C) AB = 250 ft, BC = 300 ft, CC' = 0.321 ft, backsight at +25°, and foresight at +25°.

11-12. In the process of checking the horizontal axis of a transit, the transit was set up D ft from a tall building, and the sight was taken on a well-defined point at the top of the building. Then the telescope was lowered and point A was set on the wall of the building. After reversing the telescope the same point was sighted at the top of the building and point B was set alongside point A on the wall. Determine the angle of inclination of the horizontal axis to the horizontal if the vertical angle β and the measured distances were:

(A) AB = 0.152 ft, D = 65.0 ft, β = 33°15′.   *Ans. 6′08″*

(B) AB = 0.123 ft, D = 47.0 ft, β = 37°20′.

(C) AB = 0.215 ft, D = 52.0 ft, β = 42°35′.

11-13. The rod readings and the distances shown below were obtained in the two-peg test of a transit. Determine (a) the inclination of the line of sight in feet per 100 ft of horizontal distance, (b) the true difference in elevation of the two points A and B where the pegs were set, (c) reading of rod at A for the horizontal line of sight when the instrument was near B.

(A)

	Instrument near A	Instrument near B
Rod reading on A	5.317	6.415
Distance to A	20.0 ft	120.0 ft
Rod reading on B	4.713	5.833
Distance to B	120.0 ft	20.0 ft

Ans. (a) 0.011 ft down, (b) 0.593 ft, (c) 6.428 ft

(B)

	Instrument near A	Instrument near B
Rod reading on A	4.716	5.413
Distance to A	22.0 ft	153.0 ft
Rod reading on B	4.780	5.380
Distance to B	153.0 ft	22.0 ft

(C)

	Instrument near A	Instrument near B
Rod reading on A	4.372	5.681
Distance to A	25.0 ft	160.0 ft
Rod reading on B	5.176	6.545
Distance to B	160.0 ft	25.0 ft

11-14. A vertical angle was measured as α with the telescope in direct position and as α' with the telescope in reversed position. Find (a) the index error, (b) the index correction (I.C.), and (c) the angle α corrected for I.C.
(A) $\alpha = 13°15'$, $\alpha' = 13°16'$. *Ans.* (a) $-30''$, (b) $30''$, (c) $13°15'30''$
(B) $\alpha = 28°22'$, $\alpha' = 28°20'$.
(C) $\alpha = 33°07'$, $\alpha' = 39°10'$.

11-15. The location survey of a line was run for a highway. If the prescribed accuracy of this survey is $1:N$ and there are n angles measured between the check points, determine (a) the allowable angular closure at the check points, and (b) maximum possible correction per angle.
(A) $N = 3000$, $n = 20$. *Ans.* (a) $5'13''$, (b) $15.6''$
(B) $N = 5000$, $n = 14$.
(C) $N = 10,000$, $n = 12$.

11-16. In a closed traverse $ABCDE$ the deflection angles were measured as shown below. (a) Compute the error of closure for the angles. (b) Assuming that the error of closure was due to accidental errors, adjust measured angles. (c) Determine the order of accuracy of the survey, judging it by the angular closure.

Angles at:

A	B	C	D	E
(A) 22°15'30"L	36°42'00"R	97°05'30"R	152°17'30"R	96°13'00"R

Ans. (a) $2'30''$, (b) $30''$ added to A, subtracted from others, (c) ordinary

(B) 82°27'15"R	75°42'00"R	15°07'15"L	121°30'30"R	95°26'15"R
(C) 97°51'07"R	92°28'17"R	86°45'13"R	32°15'44"L	115°11'32"R

11-17. The interior angles of a closed traverse $ABCDE$ were measured as is shown below. (a) Compute the error of closure for the angles. (b) Assuming that the error of closure was due to accidental errors, adjust measured angles. (c) Determine the order of accuracy of the survey judging it by the angular closure.

Angles at:

A	B	C	D	E
(A) 200°10'30"	28°44'30"	145°19'00"	87°57'30"	77°47'00"

Ans. (a) $-1'30''$, (b) $18''$ added to each angle, (c) third

(B) 64°44'30"	194°47'15"	74°23'45"	106°23'00"	99°42'45"
(C) 91°04'38"	59°25'45"	211°14'34"	83°28'53"	94°45'50"

11-18. The P.C. point of a horizontal curve is at Sta. X, shown below, the radius
of the curve is R, and the central angle is I.   Find deflection angles to
all full stations on the curve, that is, all stations at even 100 ft distance.

(A) X is 17 + 32.45, $R = 752.30$, $I = 24°15'$.

Ans. 2°34′20″, 6°22′50″, 10°11′20″, 12°07′30″ (to the nearest 10″)

(B) X is 9 + 53.21, $R = 920.00$, $I = 15°10'$.

(C) X is 22 + 15.92, $R = 437.00$, $I = 12°40'$.

11-19. The length of a circular curve is given as L and the degree of the curve as D
(see below).   It is desired to lay out this curve in ten equal chord measurements.   Determine (a) the length of the chord between the points and
(b) deflection angles to all points to be staked out on the ground, if L and D
are as follows:

(A) $L = 423.75$ ft, $D = 15°30'$.

Ans. (a) 42.35 ft, (b) point number multiplied by 3°17′03″

(B) $L = 575.31$ ft, $D = 12°15'$.

(C) $L = 469.52$ ft, $D = 10°30'$.

CHAPTER **12**

Field Instructions—Work With Transit

12-1. Care of the transit. With proper care a transit will stay in good adjustment for a long time. However, a check-up of the instrument about once a month is advisable. When the transit is carried from place to place in its box, all clamp screws must be tightened or the telescope will hammer on the box walls.

It is a good practice to send a transit that is in constant use to a shop for cleaning and adjusting once a year.

12-2. Setting transit on the tripod. After the transit is taken out of the box it must be screwed onto its tripod. Almost all American-made transits of medium or large size have standard threads $3\frac{1}{2}$ in. in diameter, 8 threads per inch. The leveling head of the transit is set on the tripod while the transit is held in one hand by one of the upright standards. A slight counterclockwise turn of the leveling head will engage the transit threads with those on the tripod. Continuing to hold the transit in one hand, but turning the leveling head in a clockwise direction with the other hand, one can attach the instrument to the tripod. No force should be applied at the end of turning since this may make it difficult to unscrew the transit after the work is finished.

12-3. Setting transit over a point. When the transit is used for measuring horizontal or vertical angles, it may be set up over a point. The points on various surveying operations are usually hubs or stakes with a tack on top. On concrete slabs or rocks the points are often marked by chiseled cross marks.

When setting the transit up on a slope, one leg of the tripod should go up the slope and the other two down the slope.

The transit is set over a point first by eye. By looking at the foot plate against the background of some object like a building, with the eyes at the same elevation as the foot plate, one may judge whether the plate is approximately horizontal. If not, the tripod legs must be adjusted until the plate is approximately horizontal.

Next, the plumb bob is attached to the transit by suspending it from the chain hook that hangs at the bottom of the instrument. A sliding loop-knot is made with the free end of the plumb bob string so that the plumb bob may be raised or lowered by sliding the knot along the string. There must be no knot left on the string when the loop is pulled apart. If the position of the plumb bob indicates that the instrument is within about $\frac{1}{4}$ in. of the point, the legs of the tripod are pressed evenly into the ground, still keeping the plumb bob within about $\frac{1}{4}$ in. of the point. Then the wing nuts of the tripod legs are tightened, and the instrument is brought exactly over the point by sliding it along the foot plate. This may be done when the leveling screws are not tight. It is a good practice to do the last operation after leveling the instrument roughly with plate levels, since leveling may cause the plumb bob to move slightly off the point.

12-4. Leveling the transit. The next step after setting the transit over a point, is to level it carefully using the leveling screws. If there are four leveling screws, as on most American-made transits, the telescope of the transit is placed over an opposite pair of leveling screws. This places the longitudinal plate level (the one having its direction parallel to the telescope) parallel to the same pair of leveling screws, and places the transverse plate level (the one having its direction at right angle to the telescope) parallel to the other pair of diagonally opposite leveling screws.

When the plate levels are in positions described above, the turning of each diagonal pair of screws will affect principally only one plate level. In leveling, it is important that all foot screws bear evenly on the foot plate. If there is even pressure, all screws will turn with about the same ease. In order that the screws may bear evenly, opposite screws are turned in opposite directions as shown in Fig. 12-1. The bubble that is being centered will move in the direction of the motion of the left thumb.

If the plate levels are in good adjustment, the centering of each plate level bubble puts the transit into leveled position. However, a check must always be made by turning the transit through 180° in azimuth. If either or both bubbles move, the plate levels are not in good adjustment and consequently the vertical axis of the instrument is not truly vertical. The angle of inclination of the vertical axis in a vertical plane corresponding to the motion of a given bubble is equal to the angular error of the plate level in question. Thus in order to complete the leveling of the instrument it is sufficient to move each bubble halfway back toward the center by using leveling screws. After this the bubbles should not move when the instrument is rotated in azimuth.

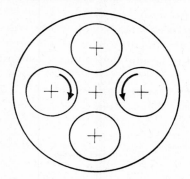

The sensitivity of plate levels in most transits is much lower than the sensitivity of the telescope level, since the telescope level exists for the purpose of using the transit in leveling operations. On a standard engineer's transit the sensitivity of plate levels may be expected to be about 2 minutes and the sensitivity of the telescope level about 30 seconds. Thus if it is desired to level the instrument quite accurately, the transit may be leveled with the telescope level, very

Fig. 12-1. Turning of leveling screws.

much in the same way as with plate levels. Such careful leveling may be necessary when measuring horizontal angles with the elevated or depressed sights. (See Art. 11-17.)

Most precise transits and theodolites have three leveling screws and only one plate level. In leveling such instruments, first centering of the plate level bubble is done over any two screws and then at right angle to them by moving the third screw alone.

12-5. Measuring direct horizontal angle. A direct horizontal angle (Fig. 11-10) may be measured either to the right or to the left. When the angle is measured to the right, clockwise horizontal scale graduations and the clockwise vernier are read, and when the angle is measured to the left the counterclockwise scale and vernier are read. Otherwise the field procedure in measuring angles either to the right or to the left is the same.

First, vernier A is set on zero and clamped; then the backsight is taken on a point in the direction from which the angle is being measured. This is done by using the lower motion of the transit and with the telescope in normal position. Then the lower motion is clamped and the foresight is taken on a point along the direction to which the angle is measured, using the upper motion of the transit. The horizontal circle shows the angle to the right on the clockwise scale and the angle to the left on the counterclockwise scale. These values of the angle, however, will contain the errors from possible maladjustment of the instrument, called *instrumental errors.* (See Art. 11-17.)

After the first measurement the upper motion is kept clamped, the telescope is reversed, and the backsight is taken using the lower motion of the instrument.. Then the lower motion is clamped and the foresight is taken using the upper motion, thus adding the second measurement to the first. The second measurement will contain the same instrumental errors as the first measurement except that they will occur with the opposite sign—making the registered double value of the angle free from instrumental errors. The final reading of the horizontal scale divided by the number of measurements gives the value of the measured angle.

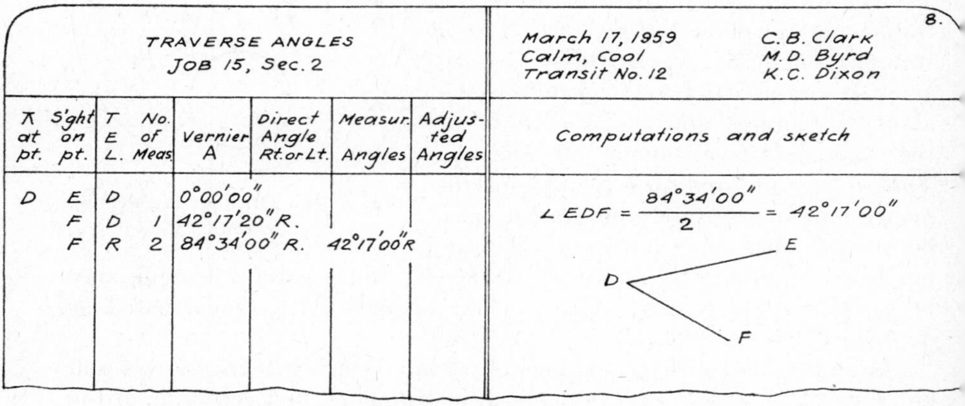

TRAVERSE ANGLES JOB 15, Sec. 2						March 17, 1959 C.B. Clark Calm, Cool M.D. Byrd Transit No. 12 K.C. Dixon	
Λ S'ght at on pt. pt.	T E L	No. of Meas	Vernier A	Direct Angle Rt.orLt.	Measur. Angles	Adjus-ted Angles	Computations and sketch
D E F F	D D R	1 2	0°00'00" 42°17'20"R. 84°34'00"R.		42°17'00"R		∠ EDF = 84°34'00" / 2 = 42°17'00" D E F

Fig. 12-2. Recording of measured direct angles.

If an angle is measured more than twice, it is measured the same number of times with the telescope in direct position as with the telescope in reversed position. Figure 12-2 shows field recordings of a direct angle measured twice (2 D.R.) using a 20 sec transit; Figure 11-14 shows recordings of a direct angle measured six times (6 D.R.). It should be noted that in the latter example the initial reading of the vernier is not equal to zero.

Figure 11-16 shows field recordings of the same angle shown in Fig. 11-14 except that readings of both verniers A and B are recorded. Direct angles are commonly measured on closed traverses.

12-6. Measuring the deflection angle. The procedure in measuring a deflection angle is similar to that described above for measuring a direct angle. After setting vernier A on zero, the backsight is taken with telescope in normal position on a previously established point, usually the point of the last set-up of the transit. The telescope is then plunged, thus setting the line of sight along the continuation of the previously established direction. With the lower motion clamped and the upper motion loose, the foresight is taken to a point along a new direction. The clamped horizontal circle now registers the deflection angle measured a single time.

Next, the backsight is taken with the lower motion and with telescope in reversed position. Then the lower motion is clamped, the telescope is plunged a second time, and the second measurement of the angle, using the upper motion of the instrument, is added to the first measurement. The final reading divided by 2 is the deflection angle measured.

If an angle is measured more than twice, it is measured the same number of times with the telescope in direct position as with the telescope in reversed position.

TRAVERS' HORIZONTAL ANGLES *ROUTE 17, SEC. 9*							*12.*
						April 25, 1960 Clear, Windy Transit No. 7	A.V. Brooks C.F. Starnes T. I. Miller
Sight at pt.	Sight on pt.	T E L. Meas	No. of Meas	Vernier A	Deflect. Angle Rt. or Lt.	Measur. Angles	Adjusted Angles	Computations and sketch
D	E F F	D R D	1 2	0°00'00" 15°10'30" R 30°21'30" R		15°10'45" R	

$$\angle \text{ at } D = \frac{30°21'30"}{2} = 15°10'45"$$

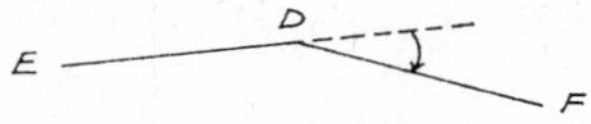

Fig. 12-3. Recording of measured deflection angles.

Figure 12-3 shows field recording of a measured deflection angle. Comparing this recording with the recording of a measured direct angle, as shown in Fig. 12-2, it may be seen that the recordings are quite similar. In order to avoid confusion as to what kind of angles were measured on a given traverse, the heading of the fourth column should show whether the measured angles were direct or deflection angles. In addition, the right-hand page must show the sketch of the traverse with the measured angles indicated on the sketch.

The measurement of deflection angles on route surveys is recorded on the same page with measured distances. (See Open Traverses, Art. 8-7.) Figure 12-4 shows recording of data for the preliminary location of the tangent lines on a proposed route. The measured distances are recorded as stations in the first column, and calculated tangent distances are often recorded in the last column. Deflection angles are recorded in the second column. However, it is a good practice to use two columns (the second and third) for recording deflection angles since otherwise the notes become crowded along the lines of P.I. points. Other recordings in Fig. 12-4 show calculated bearings computed from measured deflection angles. One of these bearings must have been determined by observations on the sun or on a star (described in Chapter 13). Under the heading "Magnetic Bearings" are recorded the readings of the transit compass. These readings are used only as a rough check on measured angles. The right-hand page shows the sketch of the surveyed transit line and accompanying details.

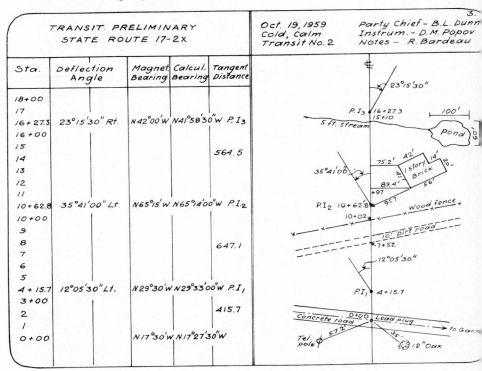

Sta.	Deflection Angle	Magnet. Bearing	Calcul. Bearing	Tangent Distance
18+00				
17				
16+27.3	23°15'30" Rt.	N42°00'W	N41°58'30"W P.I₃	
16+00				
15				
14				564.5
13				
12				
11				
10+62.8	35°41'00" Lt.	N65°15'W	N65°14'00"W P.I₂	
10+00				
9				
8				647.1
7				
6				
5				
4+15.7	12°05'30" Lt.	N29°30'W	N29°33'00"W P.I₁	
3+00				
2				415.7
1				
0+00		N17°30'W	N17°27'30"W	

TRANSIT. PRELIMINARY STATE ROUTE 17-2X

Oct. 19, 1959 Cold, Calm Transit No. 2
Party Chief – B.L. Dunn Instrum.– D.M. Popov Notes – R. Bardeau

Fig. 12-4. Preliminary transit survey for a route.

12-7. Measuring the vertical angle. As in measuring the horizontal angle, the vertical angle is usually measured once with the telescope in normal position and once in reversed position. Both measurements are made independently of each other since the vertical circle on transits is divided from 0° to 90° in each quadrant. With this arrangement it is not possible to accumulate measurements as is done in measuring horizontal angles. The average of measurements of vertical angles with telescope in direct position and with telescope in reversed position gives the best available value of the measured angle.

When a large number of vertical angles are to be measured, as in topographical mapping by the stadia method, the vertical angles are

measured only once, with the telescope in normal position.   The Index
Correction (Art. 11-19) is then applied to measured angles.

Many optical theodolites, especially those of foreign manufacture,
have vertical circles graduated from 0° to 360° so that the horizontal
position of the telescope corresponds to a reading of 90° with the telescope
in normal position.   Such theodolites also have a special level for the
vertical circle to eliminate errors in vertical angles owing to possible
inclination of the vertical axis of the instrument.   With the level bubble

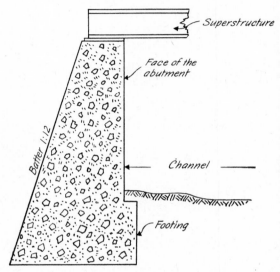

Fig. 12-5. Typical cross section of a bridge abutment.

centered each time the reading of the vertical circle is taken, the measured
angle is equal to the difference between the final reading and the respective graduation of the vertical circle corresponding to the horizontal
position of the telescope, such as 90° or 270°.

12-8. Staking out a bridge or a culvert.   Where a proposed highway crosses natural water channels, highway engineers design bridges
and culverts.   Small bridges of various types are quite numerous along
highways—reinforced concrete bridges, steel I-beam bridges, or sometimes wooden or steel truss bridges.

Every bridge has a substructure such as abutments and piers and a
superstructure, which is the structural part of a bridge that rests on piers
and abutments.   Figure 12-5 shows the cross section of a typical abutment.   The side of an abutment that provides channel walls for a stream
is called the *face* of the abutment.   The face is often made vertical, and
the back of the abutment is usually built on a slope.   This slope is called

a **batter;** for example, one might speak of a 1 to 12 batter, meaning a slope of 1 horizontal unit to 12 vertical units of length. At the top of the abutment, providing a bearing for the superstructure, is the **bridge seat.** A wing built at each end of an abutment prevents the dirt on roadway slopes from falling to the stream channel.

A structure completely covered by fill, and providing a channel for a stream or for drainage water, is called a **culvert.** Culverts are designed

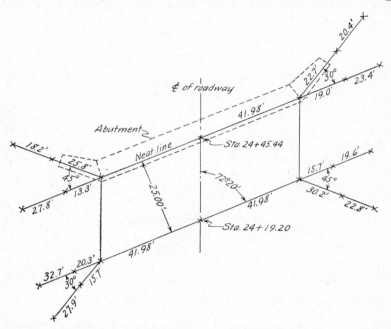

Fig. 12-6. Stake-out plan for a bridge or a culvert.

in many different shapes, those most commonly used are either a circular pipe, a box, or an arch culvert. Box culverts are made of concrete, whereas arches are made either of concrete or corrugated metal plates.

When bridge abutments or the barrel of a culvert is constructed at right angle to the center line of the roadway, it is said that the bridge, or culvert, has no **skew angle.** A skew angle is defined as the angle which the bridge abutment or the barrel of a culvert makes with a line perpendicular to the center line of the roadway. However, for convenience in staking out a bridge in the field, the complement angle to the skew angle is usually shown on plans and is referred to as skew angle. This angle is shown in Fig. 12-6.

When a bridge is to be staked out in the field, the center line of the roadway is located, and hubs are driven at the stations representing the

intersection of the center line of road with the face of abutments.   These
stations are shown in Fig. 12-6.   Then, the transit is set over these
station points and the skew angle is measured from the center line of the
roadway, thus determining the direction of the face of abutments.   The
length of the abutment is taped on each side of the center line and a hub
is driven at each end of the abutment, at the point of intersection of the
face of abutment with the face of the wing.   Next, the transit is set at
these points and wing angles, shown on construction plans, are turned
from the face of abutments.   Reinforced concrete arches and box culverts
are also constructed with wings at each end.

Figure 12-6 shows a stake-out plan for a bridge.   The outlines of one
abutment and two wings are shown on the figure to indicate position of
stakes and hubs relative to the proposed structure.   The line along the
face of the abutment is known as the **neat line.**   It may be observed
on the figure that the stakes are set along the prolongation of neat lines
so that the lines could be re-established at any time during construction.
The elevation of one of the hubs is normally determined by leveling and
is used as a bench mark during construction.   The neat lines of a culvert
are staked out very much in the same manner as those of bridges.

On preliminary surveys it is the responsibility of the engineer conducting surveys to choose suitable sites for bridge crossings, to determine
proper skew angles, to investigate soil conditions, and to survey the
gradient of the stream flow up and down the stream.   Any other data
pertinent to the location of a structure, such as the elevation of high
watermarks, must also be noted and recorded in the field notebook.

12-9. Staking out a circular curve.   A circular curve is normally
staked out from the point of curvature, or P.C. point (see Fig. 11-13).
However, if P.C. point is inaccessible, the curve may be staked out from
P.T. point or any intermediate point.   When transit is at the P.C.,
vernier A is set on zero and the backsight is taken on point C, the point
of intersection of tangent lines.   If that point is not visible, the backsight
may be taken on some point along the back tangent (such as point F in
Fig. 11-13) with the telescope reversed and with vernier A still reading
zero.   Then the lower motion is clamped, the telescope is plunged, and a
computed deflection angle [Eqs. (11-6) and (11-7)] to the first point to
be set on the curve is set on the clockwise scale if the curve is to the right,
or on the counterclockwise scale if the curve is to the left.

At the same time as the line of sight is being established in the direction of the point to be staked on the curve, the tape is stretched from the
transit point in the direction of the line of sight.   The rear tapeman
holds on the transit point some footmark corresponding to the length
of chord to be measured between the points [see Eq. (11-8)], while the
head tapeman holds his thumb on the fraction of a foot that must be

subtracted from the footmark that the rear tapeman is holding. This gives the length of chord being measured. The instrumentman aligns the tape with the line of sight, and at his signal a stake is driven at the mark held by the head tapeman. After this the tape is stretched a second time and a tack is driven on the stake.

For a second point, next deflection angle is set on the transit, but the second chord and all subsequent chords are measured between the last point set on the ground and the new point. In order to align the thumb held on some footmark with the line of sight, the head tapeman swings the tape right and left until the end of thumb is on the line of sight. The same procedure is followed until P.T. point is reached. The location of P.T. point should be checked by measuring the long chord between P.C. and P.T. points, or by measuring the length of tangent between P.I. and P.T. points.

The interval between the points on a curve depends on the sharpness of the curve and its length. Table 12-1 shows approximate degrees of curves for the points to be set at certain intervals along the curve.

TABLE 12-1. INTERVALS ON CURVES

Degree of Curve	Approximate Radius (Ft)	Interval (Ft)
0–3	down to 3000	100
3–10	3000–500	50
10–20	500–300	25
20–50	300–100	10

The intersecting tangent lines are normally established on the ground before a curve is staked out. Thus slight errors in staking out a curve by deflection angles do not affect the alignment of tangents. For this reason the deflection angles are usually measured with the telescope in direct position without reversal.

For the elements of a circular curve refer to Appendix A.

FIELD EXERCISES

12-1. Measurement of direct angles in a closed traverse
Party: Four men.
Equipment: Transit, two brass bobs.
Object: To gain experience in setting up the transit over a point, to read transit verniers, and to measure the interior angles of a closed traverse. The same traverse that was used in Exercise 8-2 may be used

in this exercise, so that measured distances and angles can be used later in computation of the area.

Procedure: Setting up the instrument. Set the tripod over the point so that the foot plate is approximately level. Attach the plumb bob by tying a sliding loop-knot. Observe how far the plumb bob is off the point horizontally; then lift the instrument as it is, with the legs of the tripod in spread position, and move it closer to the point, until the plumb bob is within about $\frac{1}{4}$ in. of the point. Press the legs of the tripod to set them firmly on the ground, tighten the wing nuts, and level the instrument, approximately, keeping the level screws fairly loose. Slide the instrument over the foot plate until the plumb bob is over the point, and about $\frac{1}{8}$ in. above the point. Turn the instrument in azimuth until each plate level is parallel to a diagonal pair of foot screws. Center each bubble, gradually tightening foot screws but not making them too tight. Try to secure an even bearing pressure on all four screws. Turn the instrument 180° in azimuth and if the bubbles move, bring them halfway back toward the center by means of the leveling screws. The bubbles then should not move when the instrument is turned in azimuth.

Measuring direct angle. Ordinarily only one vernier, A, is read and recorded. However, for practice, the recording of both verniers, A and B, is required in this exercise. Only minutes and seconds of vernier B need be recorded. For a backsight, set vernier A on zero and record the reading of both verniers A and B; then tighten the upper motion, loosen the lower motion of the instrument, and sight on the point to your left when facing the interior of the traverse. Use tangent screws for the final setting. For a foresight, tighten the lower motion, loosen the upper motion, and sight on the point to your right, thus measuring a direct angle clockwise, or "to the right." Record the readings, plunge the telescope, and backsight on the first point with lower motion and with the plates still showing the first measurement. Take the foresight on the second point with the upper motion, thus adding second measurement to the first. Obtain the mean values of the initial and final readings, subtract the initial reading from the final and divide by 2.

Normally, the error of closure should not exceed one-half the least count of the vernier times the square root of the number of angles measured. Check the sum of the measured angles against $180°(n - 2)$, where n is the number of sides of the traverse, and adjust the angles by applying equal corrections to each angle. Refer to Table 11-2 for the attained order of accuracy and to Fig. 11-16 for proper recording of field data.

12-2. Deflection angle transit-tape traverse

Party: Four men.

Equipment: Transit, 100 ft steel tape, three brass bobs, one hand level, one tape clamp, stakes (or tally pins), one hatchet.

Object: To gain experience in running transit-tape open traverses such as those used on route surveys.

Procedure: The aimed accuracy of linear measurement is 1:3000. It may be estimated that in order to achieve this accuracy (see Table 7-2), the measurements must be made with spring balance. Either the normal tension should be used or correction for sag must be applied. Corrections for temperature and for incorrect length of tape may be neglected. Check measurements must be made. Tape reading must be to the nearest hundredth of a foot.

Also referring to Table 11-2a, it may be seen that the angular closure at check points must not exceed $70 \sqrt{n}$ sec. It may be assumed that check points will be made every 2 miles by solar observations. If the average tangent length is about 1000 ft, there will be close to ten instrument set-ups in 2 miles. This makes the adjustment per angle not to exceed $70/\sqrt{n} = 22''$. This accuracy may be achieved by using a 1 min transit and by measuring angles by double reversal of the telescope.

Measuring a deflection angle. Set the instrument over the point and set vernier *A* on zero. Backsight along previously established direction using the lower motion of the instrument. Reverse the telescope and foresight along new direction. Backsight again with the telescope in reversed position, plunge the telescope, and measure the angle a second time. The second reading divided by 2 gives the angle that should be recorded.

Refer to Fig. 12-4 for proper recording of field data. Do not make recordings in the columns headed by "Magnetic Bearing" and "Calculated Bearing."

of observation must be subtracted from G.H.A. and the east longitude must be added to G.H.A.

The G.H.A. is given in ephemeris tables in degrees, minutes, and usually tenths of a minute, for certain instants of time on each day of a given year. Thus it is necessary to know the longitude of place of observation (see Art. 13-9) in order to find the L.H.A. and the meridian angle t, which is used in Eq. (13-3) in order to obtain the azimuth angle of Polaris.

13-12. Time of observation. When a sight is taken on Polaris with a transit, the time must be noted and recorded in the field notebook. In the United States the time of observation is normally standard time in the *time zone* of the place of observation. The whole area of the United States is divided into four time zones which use the following standard times: eastern standard time (E.S.T.), central (C.S.T.), mountain (M.S.T.), and Pacific (P.S.T.). These standard times are respectively the local mean solar times (watch times) of the following meridians: 75°W, 90°W, 105°W, and 120°W.

The difference during a year between the mean solar time (M.S.T.) and the time indicated by the real sun—the *apparent solar time* (A.S.T.)—varies with a maximum of about 16 min. Also the time interval of a mean solar day differs from the time interval of the sidereal day by about 4 min. However, the matter of time difference between mean solar time, apparent solar time, and sidereal time need not be confusing as far as obtaining proper data from the astronomical tables is concerned, since all table data are given for Greenwich civil time, which is the mean solar time (watch time) of 0° meridian, called the *prime meridian*.

Since 24 hours of mean solar time correspond to 360° rotation of the earth around its axis with respect to the mean sun, various mean solar time intervals correspond to certain differences in longitudes. These relations are shown in Table 13-1.

TABLE 13-1

Mean Solar Time Interval	Difference in Longitude
24 hours	360°
1 hour	15°
4 min	1°
1 min	15'
4 sec	01'

Since 15° difference in longitude corresponds to 1 hour mean solar time interval (Table 13-1), the difference in watch time between Greenwich time and the time of any other meridian may be easily computed. Also by adding such time differences to the watch time of west longitudes and subtracting the difference from the watch time of east longitudes, one obtains Greenwich civil time (G.C.T.).

13-13. Altitude of Polaris.   The altitude h of Polaris, in Eqs. (13-3) and (13-4), is the true vertical angle to that star.   This vertical angle may be measured directly by a transit, or it may be computed by Eq. (13-8).

$$h = \phi + p \cos t \qquad (13\text{-}8)$$

If a transit measures vertical angles directly to 1', a better value of the altitude of Polaris than that may be obtained by using Eq. (13-8). The small angle $p \cos t$, which must be added algebraically to the latitude ϕ of the place of observation to obtain h, is also given in the ephemeris tables.   When the vertical angle to a star is measured by the transit, the angle must be corrected for the refraction of the atmosphere.   These corrections are given in the ephemeris tables.

Equation (13-8) also shows that the latitude of the place of observation may be obtained from measured altitude of Polaris at any hour angle.

13-14. Bearing of a line from Polaris observations.   From the above discussion it is apparent that various data that may be required for computation of the bearing of a line from Polaris observations include: latitude and longitude of place of observation, time, horizontal angle from a reference stake to Polaris, and altitude and polar distance of Polaris.

Assume that the latitude of a place of observation is 37°24′50″N and the longitude is 79°12′32″W.   The field data, obtained from an observation on Polaris, are: time and date of observation, 8ʰ32ᵐ17ˢ P.M., E.S.T., Dec. 15, 1959; the horizontal angle measured from a reference stake (at point B) to Polaris, 31°09′30″ clockwise; vertical angle of the star, 38°20′. The transit, at the time of observation, was set up at point A. It is required to compute the bearing of the line AB.

Solution: The time of observation is 8ʰ32ᵐ17ˢ P.M., E.S.T., Dec. 15, 1959, or 20ʰ32ᵐ17ˢ E.S.T.

Since E.S.T. is the time of the 75th degree meridian, the difference between this time and the Greenwich civil time is 5 hours, from Table 13-1.   Also since the 75th meridian in question is west of Greenwich, the time difference must be added to the time of observation to obtain G.C.T. of observation.   Thus G.C.T. of observation is 25ʰ32ᵐ17ˢ, Dec. 15, 1959, which really is 1ʰ32ᵐ17ˢ, Dec. 16, 1959.

Knowing the G.C.T. of observation, the Greenwich hour angle of Polaris may be obtained from the ephemeris tables.   The tables give G.H.A. of Polaris at 0ʰ G.C.T. and the correction to G.H.A. for a given G.C.T.   These data for 1ʰ32ᵐ17ˢ G.C.T. are as follows:

G.H.A. for 0^h G.C.T. on Dec. 16, 1959 = 54°37.4 (from tables)
plus correction for $1^h32^m17^s$ G.C.T.   = 23°08.1 (from tables)
G.H.A. at time of observation   = 77°45.5
less longitude of place of observation = 79°12.5
Local hour angle (L.H.A.)   = $-1°27.0$

The negative sign for L.H.A. (see Fig. 13-7) means that Polaris was east of north at the time of observation. The meridian angle t that is used in Eq. (13-3) below is 1°27.0.

Polar distance of Polaris on Dec. 16, 1959 = 0°55.14 (from tables).

The altitude of Polaris from Eq. (13-8), $h = \phi + p \cos t$.

$$\text{latitude} = 37°24.8$$
$$0°55.14 \cos (1°27.0) = \underline{\quad 55.1}$$
$$h = 38°19.9$$

Azimuth angle of Polaris $Z = p \sin t \sec h$, by Eq. (13-3),

$$Z = 55.14 \times 0.02530 \times 1.2748 = 1.780 = 0°01'47''$$

Since Polaris was east of north and the horizontal angle was measured from reference stake to Polaris clockwise, the azimuth angle of Polaris must be subtracted from the measured horizontal angle in order to obtain the bearing angle of line AB. Thus

$$H = 31°09'30''$$
less $$Z = 0°01'47''$$
bearing angle $$= 31°07'43''$$

Bearing of line AB = N31°07'43''W

When the altitude of Polaris, h, is observed in the field, it needs be corrected only for refraction. Parallax correction for stars is negligible.

13-15. Solar observation. The apparent yearly path of the sun in the sky is known as the *ecliptic.* The plane of the ecliptic is inclined to the plane of the equator at 23°27' angle, very closely. . Because it is much farther from the pole than Polaris, the sun appears to move, in its daily path, much faster than Polaris. This makes accurate observation of the sun more difficult than that of Polaris. The size of the sun and its brightness add to this difficulty. Thus observations on Polaris for the bearing of a line are preferred. However, since solar observations can be made with a standard transit during usual working hours within about 01' accuracy, such observations have a place in engineering surveys. It is convenient, for instance, to make solar observations in route surveys at check points for closing errors in azimuths.

Equation (13-5) is used customarily for obtaining the azimuth of the sun by solar observation. This equation is also used in obtaining the azimuth of a star when observation is made on a star of low declination. Since this equation does not contain the hour angle, the time of observation need be known only within about 6 min. The time of observation is used only in obtaining the declination of the sun, δ, which varies from 0 to 01' per hour throughout the year, so that maximum error in declination, for 6 min of watch error, is only 0.'1. This amount of error in declination will produce a still smaller error in the sun's azimuth.

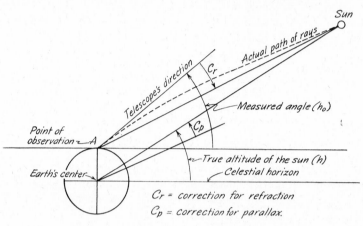

Fig. 13-8. Refraction and the sun's parallax.

Other quantities entering Eq. (13-5) include the latitude of the place of observation ϕ and the altitude of the sun h. The latitude need be known only within about 30''; thus it can be readily scaled from a USGS quadrangle sheet for the locality of a traverse. The altitude of the sun and the horizontal angle from a reference stake to the sun are measured in the field.

Two corrections must be applied to the measured altitude of the sun, h_0. One is a correction for the sun's parallax and another for the refraction of the atmosphere. Both are readily obtained from the ephemeris tables for the measured altitude of the sun. Figure 13-8 (greatly exaggerated) shows by the dotted line the curved path of the ray of light, coming from the sun or from a star, and entering the transit's telescope. The curvature is the result of refraction of the ray by the earth's atmosphere. Thus the transit, with its telescope directed along the tangent to the curve at the time of observation, measures the angle h_0 shown on the figure. The angle C_r is the correction for the refraction of the atmosphere, which is always negative. The measured angle, corrected for the refraction, must be reduced to the center of the earth. This is the parallax correction C_p, shown in the figure; it is always positive.

13-16. Bearing of a line from solar observations. Since the longitude of a place of observation is not needed for the evaluation of any quantities given in Eq. (13-5), only the latitude of the place must be known.

Assume that the latitude of a place of observation is $37°54'50''$N and that the field data obtained in a solar observation are as follows: the horizontal angle measured from a reference stake to the sun is $17°34'30''$ counterclockwise, the time of observation is 9^h32^m E.S.T. on June 20, 1959, and the vertical angle to the sun is $48°15'$. Let it be required to compute the bearing of the line CD from the transit at point C to the reference stake at point D.

Solution:

Time of observation	$= 9^h32^m$ E.S.T.
G.C.T. of observation ($+5$ hours)	$= 14^h32^m$ June 20, 1959
Sun's apparent declination at 0^hG.C.T.	$= N23°25'.6$ (ephemeris tables)
Difference in declination per hour $= 0'.03$	(ephemeris tables)
Correction for $14^h32^m = 0.03 \times 14.53$	$= \underline{\quad 0'.4}$
Declination of the sun	$\delta = N23°26'.0$ (positive)
Observed altitude of the sun	$h_0 = 48°15'$
Correction for refraction	$= -0'.85$ (ephemeris tables)
Correction for sun's parallax	$= \underline{+0'.09}$ (ephemeris tables)
Altitude of the sun	$h = 48°14'.2$

In order to evaluate Eq. (13-5), it is best to use logarithms if a computing machine is not available. Table 13-2 shows all necessary computations.

TABLE 13-2. AZIMUTH OF THE SUN BY EQUATION (13-5)

Symbol	Value	Logarithms	
δ	$23°26'.0$	log sin $= 9.599536$	
h	$48°14'.2$	log sec $= 0.176490$	log tan $= 0.049172$
ϕ	$37°54'50''$	log sec $= 0.102959$	log tan $= 9.891464$
1st term	0.756807	log $= 9.878985$	
2nd term	-0.872240		log $= 9.940636$
cos Z	-0.115433		
$180° - Z$	$83°22'17''$		
	Sun's bearing is S83°22'17''E		

In this example the cosine of the azimuth angle came out with minus sign, indicating that the angle is in the second quadrant. This, in fact, gives the azimuth angle ($180° - Z$) from south.

After finding the azimuth of the sun, it is a simple matter to find the azimuth or the bearing of a line using the measured horizontal angle. For the data given in the above problem, the computations are as follows:

Azimuth of the sun from south $= 83°22'17''$ counterclockwise
Horizontal angle from the stake to the sun $= 17°34'30''$ counterclockwise
Bearing angle of line $CD = \overline{65°47'47''}$

The bearing of line CD is S65°47'47''E.

State Grid System of Plane Coordinates

13-17. State grid. A brief description of a state grid, that is, the frame of reference for the points of horizontal control within a state,

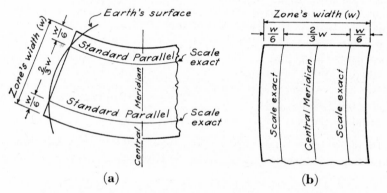

Fig. 13-9. Projecting surfaces. (a) The surface used in Lambert conformal projection. (b) The surface used in Transverse Mercator projection.

has been given in Art. 8-3. Every state in the United States has a frame of reference of this sort. The basic data and the tables for the use of state coordinates in various states are contained in Special Publications of the U.S. Coast and Geodetic Survey called "Plane Coordinate Projection Tables." These publications are available for each state from the Superintendent of Documents, Washington 25, D.C. for a small fee.

Figures 13-9a and 13-9b show respectively the Lambert and the transverse Mercator projection surfaces for a *zone*. Both projections are mathematical and conformal, meaning that the shape of projected areas remains undisturbed. There may be one or more zones in a state, each zone having a separate grid; that is, a system of parallel lines for the north-south grid directions and a system of parallel lines, perpendicular to north-south grid lines, for the west-east grid directions. Only the central north-south line in each zone, called a ***central meridian,*** coincides with a true north-south direction, and only at points along the central meridian do the grid's west-east lines coincide with true west-east directions. Figures 13-10 and 13-11 show by heavy lines the grid lines of a zone and by light lines the true meridians and parallels for state grids on the Lambert and on the transverse Mercator projection surfaces respectively.

13-18. Scales at various points of a grid zone. The grid lines of a zone may be drawn on maps constructed by various conventions, or "projections." Of these, only the *Lambert conformal conic projection*

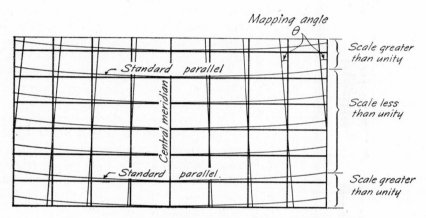

Fig. 13-10. True meridians and parallels on Lambert grid.

and the *transverse Mercator projection* are employed in connection with state grid systems. In the Lambert projection the points on the earth's surface are projected on a cone, the axis of which coincides with the axis of the earth and the surface of which intersects the surface of the earth, at the mean sea level, along two parallels of latitude. For a particular zone involved, these parallels are called ***standard parallels*** (Fig. 13-9a).

When a surface on which Lambert projection of a zone is made is developed, the true meridians appear as straight lines converging at a uniform rate. The lines of true parallels appear as arcs of concentric circles as shown in Fig. 13-10. The angle that a true meridian makes with the central meridian on a Lambert grid is called the ***mapping angle.*** This angle, designated by θ, can be obtained for any longitude from the Plane Coordinate Projection Tables of a zone. The mapping angle is the angle that must be applied to true bearings of lines in order to obtain their grid bearings and vice versa.

The Lambert projection is used for the states which have their greatest extent in west-east direction, thus the width of a zone is along north-south direction. Two-thirds of the width lies between two standard parallels of a zone and one-sixth of the width lies beyond each standard parallel along the north and south borders of a zone.

In the transverse Mercator projection the points on the earth's surfaces are projected mathematically on a cylindrical surface, much in the same way as is done for maps drawn on an ordinary Mercator projec-

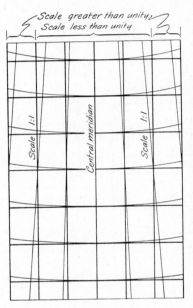

Fig. 13-11. True meridians and parallels on transverse Mercator grid.

tion surface, except that in case of the transverse projection the projection surface is placed in the "transverse" position; that is, it is turned through a 90° angle. The true meridians appear on the transverse Mercator grid as slightly curved lines, except the central meridian, which is shown by a straight line. The lines of parallels also appear as curved lines, but unlike the Lambert projection they are neither parallel nor circular.

The transverse Mercator projection is used for states which have their greatest extent in north-south direction; thus the width of a zone on the transverse Mercator grid is along west-east direction. The developed surface of this grid is shown in Fig. 13-11.

On either projection, the **grid scale factor** is the ratio of the scale of lines, drawn on respective projections, to the scale of corresponding lines on the surface of the earth at mean sea level. This ratio is equal to unity along the standard parallels on Lambert projection, since those parallels are the lines of intersection of a grid surface with the earth's surface at mean sea level. On the transverse Mercator projection the scale's ratio is made deliberately equal to unity along two grid meridians situated at one-third of a zone's width on each side of the central meridian. Everywhere else in a zone—on both grids—the scale varies, being slightly less than unity within the middle two-thirds of the width of a zone and slightly greater than unity outside these limits. Thus a grid scale factor is a number by which a distance measured on the surface of the earth (and reduced to mean sea level) must be multiplied in order to obtain the grid length of that distance.

Variation of grid scale factors from unity in a zone normally does not exceed 1:10,000. Thus if one is running a traverse by plane surveying methods, starting with a point of known grid coordinates in a zone and closing on another point in the same zone, the error of closure ascribable to the use of grid coordinates of those points will not exceed 1 : 10,000. If a closer check on such a survey is desirable, the surveyed distances must be reduced to grid lengths before making computations for the error of closure. The example of reduction of measured distances to grid lengths is shown in Art. 13-20 below.

Where surveyed distances are reduced to grid distances the directions of lines remain the same, since both projections, discussed above, are conformal. This means that the shape of a projected figure remains the same, and consequently, the size of angles does not change. Grid scale factors are given, with other data, in the Plane Coordinate Projection Tables mentioned in Art. 13-17.

13-19. State coordinate axes. The X and Y coordinate axes for a zone are so located that the whole zone is situated in the first quadrant. This makes both the x and y coordinates of any point in a zone positive. The direction of Y axis is made parallel to the central meridian and the direction of X axis is made perpendicular to the Y axis.

The width of a zone is made approximately equal to 160 miles, so that states the size of North Carolina or New Jersey have only one zone. The adjacent zones overlap each other, so that coordinates of marginal points are referred to the coordinate axes of both adjoining zones.

The *grid north* of a zone is the direction of the central meridian, and the grid west-east direction is the direction of the X axis of the grid. In order to obtain grid bearings of a line in any survey, the true bearing of the line, obtained by observation on the sun or a star, must be converted to grid bearing. The difference between the true bearing angle of a line and the grid bearing angle, on the Lambert grid, is the mapping angle θ. The same difference on the transverse Mercator projection is $\Delta\alpha = \Delta\lambda \sin \phi + g$, where $\Delta\lambda$ is the difference between the longitude of a point and that of the central meridian, shown in Plane Coordinate Projection Tables of a zone, ϕ is the latitude of the point in question, and g is a small correction, also obtained from the Projection Tables.

13-20. Advantages of state coordinate systems. There are many advantages that can be derived from the use of state coordinate systems on engineering surveys and on land surveys. A few of these are mentioned below.

(a) Any survey referred to the state coordinate axes may be conducted by plane surveying methods. Thus if the bearing of one line in a traverse is computed as a grid bearing, the bearings of all other lines computed from the plane angles measured in that traverse will be grid bearings.

(b) When x and y coordinates of a point are referred to the state coordinate axes, the point can be re-established in its original location by measurements from any other monuments tied to the state coordinate system.   This insures permanency of surveys and ties such surveys to the single net of national horizontal control.

(c) The geodetic markers of the U.S. Coast and Geodetic Survey may be used as control points.   The state grid coordinates of such markers are available from the Office of the Director of the Coast Survey.

(d) The state coordinate system is easy to use.   The reduction of distances to the mean sea level and to the state grid scale, when needed, requires only simple computations, as may be seen from Example 13-2 below.   Table 13-3 gives factors for reduction of distances to mean sea level datum.

TABLE 13-3.   SEA LEVEL REDUCTION FACTORS

Elevation (Ft)	Factor	Elevation (Ft)	Factor	Elevation (Ft)	Factor
Sea Level	1.0000000	3000	0.9998565	6000	0.9997131
500	0.9999761	3500	0.9998326	6500	0.9996892
1000	0.9999522	4000	0.9998087	7000	0.9996653
1500	0.9999283	4500	0.9997848	7500	0.9996414
2000	0.9999043	5000	0.9997609	8000	0.9996175
2500	0.9998804	5500	0.9997370	8500	0.9995936

Example 13-2.   A horizontal survey distance is 457.25 ft.   The survey was conducted at approximate elevation of 2300 ft above mean sea level. The state grid scale factor, as found in Plane Coordinate Projection Tables, is 1.000212.   It is required to reduce measured distance to the state grid scale.

Solution: By interpolation in Table 13-3, the sea level reduction factor for elevation 2300 is 0.9998900.

The measured distance, reduced to sea level, is

$$457.25 \times 0.9998900 = 457.25(1 - 0.0001100) = 457.25 - 0.05 = 457.20 \text{ ft}$$

This distance, reduced to the scale of state grid, is

$$457.20 \times 1.000212 = 457.20 + 0.10 = 457.30 \text{ ft}$$

It may be seen from this example that computations for the reduction of distances need not be more complicated than those in applying correction to a measured distance for the incorrect length of tape (see Art. 7-12).

Directions by a Compass

13-21.   Magnetic north.   The earth is a magnet with two magnetic poles inside the earth and a magnetic field around the earth.   The projections of magnetic poles on the earth's surface do not coincide with the geographic poles of the earth; neither do they have places of permanent location, but are constantly shifting around. At the time this chapter is written the location of the north magnetic pole is somewhere in the northern part of Baffin Island, Canada.

The direction to the magnetic north at any point on the earth's surface is the direction of the earth's magnetic lines at that point at a given time. This is the direction that a horizontally balanced magnetic needle assumes when there are no local attractions for the needle. The angular deviation of the needle, from the direction of a true meridian passing through the point of observation, constitutes the ***magnetic declination*** of the needle. Variations in magnetic declination are ascribed to both regular and irregular causes.

The earth's magnetic lines, except in the vicinity of the equator, are not parallel to a level line at a point on the earth's surface, but slope down in the direction of the north magnetic pole in the Northern Hemisphere and in the direction of the south magnetic pole in the Southern Hemisphere. This results in a corresponding ***dip*** of a magnetic needle balanced at its mid-point on a pivot support. In order to correct this dip, a counterbalance is attached to a proper half of the needle when it is used in compasses. The counterbalance normally consists of a few strands of wire wrapped around the needle.

13-22. Regular and irregular variations of declination. It is thought that the shift in position of magnetic poles follows a regular cycle of 300 years' duration. This is so-called *secular variation*. The observed regularity in this type of variation permits one to draw on the map of the United States the lines of constant westward and eastward changes in declination. Such lines are drawn for 0.5 increments in annual changes from the line having zero annual change. The charts showing these changes are published by the U.S. Coast and Geodetic Survey. The same agency also publishes ***isogonic charts,*** which show the lines of equal magnetic declination in the United States for a given year. Since the same changes in magnetic declination hold for a number of years, it is possible to compute magnetic declination of the needle at a given place even if an isogonic chart is several years old.

There are also small annual and daily regular variations in magnetic declination. The annual variation in the United States is less than $01'$, and the maximum amplitude of daily variation varies in different localities in the United States from about $03'$ to $12'$. These changes are too small to be considered in determining magnetic bearings of lines.

The irregular variations in the declination come from magnetic disturbances which are due to "magnetic storms." These variations may amount to one or more degrees.

13-23. Magnetic compass. The bearings of lines referred to the magnetic north-south meridians are called *magnetic bearings.* A *compass* is the instrument used to determine such bearings. The *surveyor's compass* (Fig. 13-12) has the magnetic needle balanced on a

Fig. 13-12. Surveyor's compass.   (Courtesy W. & L. E. Gurley.)

pivot in the center of a card marked with letters N, S, E, and W representing four cardinal compass directions. The two upright sights, attached to the compass box, where the letters N and S are marked on the card, serve for sighting in a desired direction. The SN line of the compass is oriented along the direction of a line the bearing of which is being determined, while the needle is allowed to rotate freely to assume the north-south magnetic direction.   The bearing of the line is read on the compass card at the north end of the magnetic needle.

The compass card is graduated into degrees, and usually into halves or quarters of a degree, from 0° to 90° in each quadrant.   The 0° mark is placed at the north (N) and south (S) markings and the 90° mark at the east (E) and west (W) markings on the card.   It may be easily seen

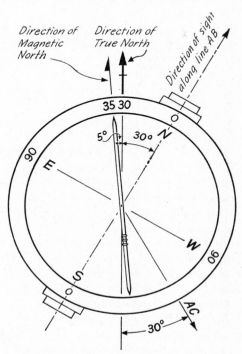

Fig. 13-13. True and magnetic bearings.

from Fig. 13-13 that in order to be able to read the proper direction of a line, the east and west markings on the compass card must be reversed.

13-24. True bearings.   Barring irregular variations of the needle's declination, the true bearing of a line, that is, the bearing referred to the geographic meridian, can be easily computed from the magnetic bearing if the declination of the needle is known.   The procedure in converting magnetic bearings to true bearings and vice versa is very simple.   The true north-south and east-west directions are drawn on paper and the declination of the needle is shown with reference to these directions as in Fig. 13-13.   Once this is done, the bearing of any line, such as *AB* on the figure, referred to the true north-south direction, is the true bearing of the line, and the bearing of the same line referred to the magnetic north-south line is the magnetic bearing of the line.   For instance, if the declination of the needle is 5°W, and the magnetic bearing of the line *AB* is N35°E, the true bearing of the line must be N30°E.   It should be noticed on the figure, however, that if the true bearing of the line *AC* is S30°E, its magnetic bearing, for the same declination of the needle, is S25°E.

13-25. Local attraction.   The compass needle deviates from its normal position owing to attraction of various iron and steel objects in the vicinity of the compass.   A pocket knife, parked automobiles, overhanging power lines, reinforcement in concrete structures, iron ore deposits in the ground—all these will exert their effects on the behavior of the needle.   Any deviation of the needle caused by local conditions is called a *local attraction.*

If a local attraction is of a more or less permanent nature, it may be determined by taking direct and reversed bearings of several lines, in a short compass traverse.   A line, the terminal points of which have no local attraction, will have its direct bearing correspond to its reversed bearing.   The local attraction of the needle at a point should be apparent from the discrepancy between the direct and reverse bearings of a line between the point in question and another point that is known to have no local attraction.   For instance, if *AB* has direct bearing N27°E and the reversed bearing S30°W, taken from point *B* which is known to have no local attraction, the local attraction at point *A* is 3°E.

Found for one line, the local attraction at a point is the same for the bearings of all other lines taken at that point.   To correct the bearing of a line for local attraction, the declination of the needle owing to local attraction should be treated in the same way as the declination owing to a regular variation described in Art. 13-24.   The position of the needle must be drawn on paper with reference to true north-south and east-west directions.   The bearings of lines with respect to the magnetic north-south direction, without the local attraction, are the normal magnetic bearings and those referred to the true north-south direction are the true bearings.

13-26. Application of magnetic bearings.   The compass has limited use in engineering surveys.   In fact, magnetic bearings are used only as a rough check on computed directions of lines and on the angles measured with a transit.   For instance, Fig. 12-4 demonstrates the use of compass bearings in the column headed by "Magnetic Bearings," in the sample of notes for a route survey.   The observed magnetic bearings of lines are recorded in this column as a check on the directions computed from measured deflection angles.   Should a deflection angle be recorded as being turned right instead of left, the error would become immediately apparent from recorded magnetic bearings.

Magnetic bearings were formerly used exclusively in land surveying.

The light, compact transit nowadays replaces the compass in all land surveys, except perhaps in those locations where the land is so cheap that a practicing land surveyor still gets by with a compass. The use of the compass on public land surveys conducted by the Bureau of Public Lands was discontinued in the year 1902.

The most useful application of the surveyor's compass at present is in retracing old property lines that were originally surveyed by means of such a compass. Where the old reference monuments mentioned in a deed are completely destroyed, the surveyor may have no other means available for re-establishing the lines in their original location, as is required by the law, except to retrace the lines with a surveyor's compass. In doing so he must find from the records and charts the magnetic declination of the needle in the year when the original survey was made to take that into account when retracing the lines.

PROBLEMS

13-1. A route survey is conducted in the neighborhood of the N-th degree parallel. The total extent of the survey at an azimuth check point is X miles west. The bearing of a line at the check point is N72°15'30"W. Correct this bearing for the convergence of meridians.
  (A) $N = 37.5°$, $X = 3.72$.   *Ans.* N72°17'59"W
  (B) $N = 43.2°$, $X = 4.27$.
  (C) $N = 48.6°$, $X = 3.18$ east, instead of west.

13-2. The adjusted deflection angles in a closed traverse $ABCDE$ are given as shown below. The bearing of the line AB, as determined by astronomical observations, is N15°27'15"W. Compute the bearings of other lines and obtain check on computed bearings by closing on the bearing of line AB.

Angles at:

	A	B	C	D	E
(A)	83°15'45"R	99°37'17"R	75°42'39"R	17°14'32"L	118°38'51"R
(B)	76°32'19"R	120°41'52"R	28°19'25"L	97°28'30"R	93°36'44"R
(C)	95°29'37"R	23°35'20"L	114°42'55"R	88°30'18"R	84°52'30"R

13-3. For the angles and the bearing of line AB given in Problem 13-2, compute azimuth angles from 0°N. Obtain check on azimuth angles by closing on the azimuth of line AB.

13-4. Compute interior angles of a closed traverse $ABCD$ from correct bearings of lines shown below and obtain check on angles by adding the angles together.

Bearings:

	AB	BC	CD	DA
(A)	S52°13'47"W	N27°38'15"W	N39°23'30"E	S42°50'23"E
(B)	N31°19'52"W	N28°42'30"E	S51°37'10"E	S38°25'57"W
(C)	S50°24'35"E	S41°19'45"W	N32°17'40"W	N28°37'23"E

13-5. The azimuth of Polaris, Z, from north, and the horizontal angle, H, as measured from the reference stake at B to Polaris, at the time of observation, are as given below. If the transit was at point A, determine the bearing of the line AB.

(A) $Z = 0°22'17''$ clockwise, $H = 125°37'15''$ to the left.

Ans. S54°00'28''E

(B) $Z = 0°47'25''$ counterclockwise, $H = 103°25'30''$ to the left.

(C) $Z = 1°02'13''$ clockwise, $H = 93°21'42''$ to the right.

13-6. Refer to Figs. 13-6 and 13-7 of the text. The polar distance of Polaris, p, the local hour angle, t, and the altitude of Polaris, h, necessary to solve PZS spherical triangle for the azimuth angle Z of the star, are given below. Determine the azimuth angle Z and the bearing of Polaris.

(A) $p = 0°55'.32$, $t = 72°15'27''$, $h = 37°43'15''$.

Ans. 1°06'.61, N1°06'37''W.

(B) $p = 0°55'.67$, $t = 203°18'40''$, $h = 32°25'04''$.

(C) $p = 0°55'.85$, $t = 300°53'32''$, $h = 43°17'31''$.

13-7. In making solar observation for the bearing of a line AB, the transit was set up at A and $17°29'15''$ horizontal angle was measured from point B to the sun clockwise. The latitude ϕ of the place of observation was found from a map as is shown below and the vertical angle h to the sun, corrected for the parallax and refraction, and the sun's declination δ are also shown below. Compute the bearing of the line AB. The sun was observed in the morning hours.

(A) $\phi = 35°42'20''N$, $h = 38°15'17''$, $\delta = -9°20'.2$. *Ans.* S52°17'29''E

(B) $\phi = 37°19'42''N$, $h = 39°52'25''$, $\delta = -7°13'.5$.

(C) $\phi = 42°31'19''N$, $h = 44°25'13''$, $\delta = +3°47'.3$.

13-8. A traverse was run at approximate elevation of h ft above mean sea level. The state grid scale factor, as found in Plane Coordinate Projection Tables, is S, and one of the distances measured in this traverse is X ft long. Reduce this distance to the state grid length, using the values given below.

(A) $h = 3250$ ft, $S = 0.999877$, $X = 532.74$ ft.   *Ans.* 532.59 ft

(B) $h = 4170$ ft, $S = 1.000176$, $X = 673.91$ ft.

(C) $h = 4730$ ft, $S = 0.999870$, $X = 725.30$ ft.

13-9. The central meridian of a state grid is $79°00'00''W$. A survey was conducted in the neighborhood of $X°$ west longitude. The mapping angle for this longitude is θ. The bearing of a line, as determined by astronomical observation, is given below. Reduce this bearing to that on the state grid.

(A) $X = 83°21'00''W$, $\theta = -2°30'39''$, the bearing is S15°27'15''W.

Ans. S17°57'54''W

(B) $X = 75°28'00''W$, $\theta = +2°02'22''$, the bearing is N59°32'27''E.

(C) $X = 81°43'00''W$, $\theta = -1°34'05''$, the bearing is S37°19'52''E.

13-10. An old deed shows that the original survey of a property was made in the year 1872 by a surveyor's compass. It was found that the declination D_0 of the needle in that year was as shown below. The present declination of the needle is D_x. The magnetic bearing of a line AB, as given in the deed, is also given below. In retracing the line AB, it is required to find (a) the true bearing of the line AB and (b) its present magnetic bearing.

(A) $D_0 = 5°30'E$, $D_x = 3°40'W$, old magnetic bearing is N32°15'W.

Ans. (a) N26°45'W, (b) N23°05'W

(B) $D_0 = 9°10'W$, $D_x = 6°25'W$, old magnetic bearing is S89°30'W.

(C) $D_0 = 7°15'W$, $D_x = 2°50'E$, old magnetic bearing is S88°50'E.

13-11. In order to find the local attraction of the compass needle at point B, a compass traverse was run from A to B to C and to D, and back. The result of compass readings taken on this traverse is shown below. Determine the local attraction at point B.

(A) AB — N13°45'E, BC — S72°15'E, CD — S13°30'E,
BA — S16°00'W, CB — N74°30'W, DC — N13°30'W. *Ans.* 2°15'W

(B) AB — S45°00'W, BC — N39°30'W, CD — S57°15'W,
BA — N43°00'E, CB — S37°00'E, DC — N57°15'E.

(C) AB — S52°30'E, BC — S2°00'E, CD — S40°30'E,
BA — N49°00'W, CB — N1°30'E, DC — N40°30'W.

CHAPTER **14**

Field Instructions—Observations
for Azimuth, Latitude and
Longitude

14-1. Reference points. True bearing of a line between any two points may be found by solar or stellar observations. However, if it is desired to establish such a true bearing for future reference, the points used in observations must be marked by substantial monuments.

The word *monument,* as it is used in property land surveys, describes any physical object that defines property lines. Objects such as trees or boulders are usually referred to as *natural monuments.* Stakes, fences, and other man-placed objects are referred to as *artificial monuments.* Artificial monuments placed to establish a permanent reference direction are usually square concrete posts having a side dimension varying from about 4 to 10 inches. The length of such posts depends on the depth of frost penetration in winter and on the stability of the topsoil. The monuments must be set so deep as not to be disturbed either by frost action or by soil movement due to hillside creep or flood waters. The usual length of monuments in the United States is from about 3 feet in the South to 4 feet in the North. A point on the top of a monument may be defined either by a carefully drilled small hole or by an iron or copper pin imbedded in concrete. A chiseled cross mark on the pin locates the point.

The monuments set by the U.S. Coast and Geodetic Survey have brass discs imbedded in concrete.   These discs have various markings corresponding to the type of point they represent.   Figure 14-1 shows some brass discs used by the Coast Survey.   Of particular interest to engineers and land surveyors are monuments showing the location of triangulation stations and azimuth stations.   The position of a triangulation station is fixed by its latitude and longitude and also by state grid

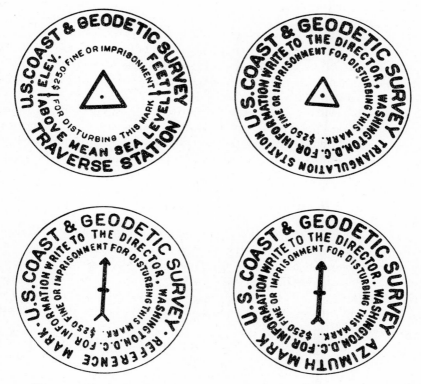

Fig. 14-1. Standard marks of the U. S. Coast and Geodetic Survey.
(Courtesy U. S. Coast & Geodetic Survey.)

coordinates.   Geodetic azimuths for such stations are computed relative to the near-by azimuth stations, to the monumented reference marks, and to other triangulation stations in the vicinity.   All the above-mentioned data are available either from Government publications describing the triangulation in a given state or from the regional offices of the U.S. Coast and Geodetic Survey.

Geodetic markers are often set within the rights-of-way of railroads and highways, because in these places the markers have a better chance for preservation.   In case of new construction which may require the removal of a monumented marker, the agency responsible for setting those markers must be notified. It is a punishable offense to disturb such monuments without proper authorization.

In order to set a new monument in place of a stake, four sturdy stakes are set criss-cross around a stake to be replaced by a monument. The distances to such stakes must be great enough so that the stakes will remain undisturbed during the excavation of a hole for the construction of the monument. Before the original stake is removed, the point on the stake is located by means of two cross strings stretched between nails driven on top of opposite auxiliary stakes. These strings are removed during the excavation and are used again in setting accurately the point on the newly placed monument. Concrete should be poured in the hole around the monument to insure its stability.

14-2. Observation on a star for azimuth. In northern latitudes Polaris is the star normally observed for the bearing of a line. Because of the proximity of Polaris to the celestial pole, accurate observations can be made on that star for both azimuth and latitude. The point of the instrument set-up and the reference point for establishing the bearing of a line should be situated so far apart as to make it unnecessary to change the telescope's focus between the sights taken on the reference stake and on the star.

It is possible to observe Polaris through the transit telescope during twilight. To get the star into the field of view in such observations, the approximate vertical angle from the pole to the star (see Art. 13-13) is applied to the latitude of the place of observation in order to obtain the altitude of the star. This angle is then set on the vertical circle and the star is brought into the field of view by using only the horizontal motion of the transit.

Precise theodolites are usually equipped with internal wiring for the illumination of the cross hairs and the verniers. However, ordinary transits do not have such illumination, so the observer must hold a flashlight close to one side of the objective end of the telescope to illuminate the cross hairs and at the same time to observe the star. One of many possible arrangements at the reference point is to support a tally pin in a vertical position over the reference point and to place a light behind it. An ordinary kerosene lantern will serve quite well, especially if its light is diffused through a screen of tracing cloth.

After the light is placed at the reference point, a sight is taken on the reference point with the transit set up at the other end of the line. This sight is taken with the instrument in normal position and with the vernier A set on zero, using the lower motion of the transit. The upper motion is used for all subsequent operations in star observation. The recording of readings taken during observation is shown in Fig. 14-2.

After the initial sighting on the reference point the sight is taken on the star. As it has been pointed out in Art. 13-7, either Eq. (13-5) or (13-6) may be employed in computation of the azimuth angle Z of a star. In Eq. (13-5) the altitude h of a star is used as a parameter, whereas in Eq. (13-6) the meridian angle t of a star must be known. When the

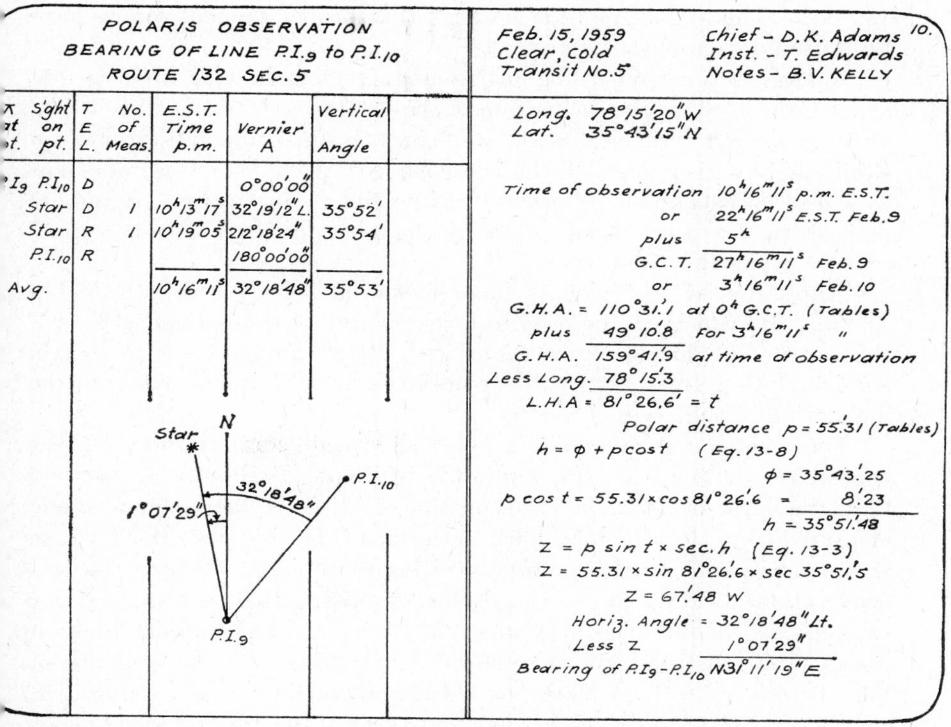

POLARIS OBSERVATION
BEARING OF LINE P.I.$_9$ to P.I.$_{10}$
ROUTE 132 SEC. 5

Feb. 15, 1959   Chief - D.K. Adams 10.
Clear, Cold   Inst. - T. Edwards
Transit No.5   Notes - B.V. KELLY

X S'ght at on pt. pt.	T E L.	No. of Meas.	E.S.T. Time p.m.	Vernier A	Vertical Angle
I$_9$ P.I$_{10}$	D			0°00'00"	
Star	D	1	10ʰ13ᵐ17ˢ	32°19'12"L	35°52'
Star	R	1	10ʰ19ᵐ05ˢ	212°18'24"	35°54'
P.I.$_{10}$	R			180°00'00"	
Avg.			10ʰ16ᵐ11ˢ	32°18'48"	35°53'

Long. 78°15'20"W
Lat. 35°43'15"N

Time of observation 10ʰ16ᵐ11ˢ p.m. E.S.T.
  or 22ʰ16ᵐ11ˢ E.S.T. Feb.9
  plus 5ʰ
  G.C.T. 27ʰ16ᵐ11ˢ Feb.9
  or 3ʰ16ᵐ11ˢ Feb.10
G.H.A. = 110°31'.1 at 0ʰ G.C.T. (Tables)
  plus 49°10'.8 for 3ʰ16ᵐ11ˢ "
G.H.A. 159°41'.9 at time of observation
Less Long. 78°15'.3
L.H.A = 81°26.6' = t
    Polar distance p = 55.31' (Tables)
$h = \phi + p \cos t$ (Eq. 13-8)
    $\phi = 35°43'.25$
$p \cos t = 55.31 \times \cos 81°26'.6 = 8'.23$
    $h = 35°51'.48$
$Z = p \sin t \times \sec h$ (Eq. 13-3)
$Z = 55.31 \times \sin 81°26'.6 \times \sec 35°51'.5$
    $Z = 67'.48$ W
Horiz. Angle = 32°18'48"Lt.
Less Z   1°07'29"
Bearing of P.I$_9$-P.I$_{10}$ N31°11'19"E

Star N   32°18'48"   P.I.$_{10}$ 1°07'29"   P.I.$_9$

Fig. 14-2. Recording of Polaris observations for azimuth.

altitude method is used, the vertical angle must be measured as accurately as possible, but when the hour angle method is used the accurate time of observation must be known. Although in the latter case the altitude of a star need not be known, it is a good practice in Polaris observations to record the vertical angle, since it serves as a check that the right star was observed. Equations (13-3) and (13-4) are used in Polaris observations.

The watch time is read at the instant when the star is placed at the intersection of cross hairs. The seconds are read first, then the minutes and the hour of observation. After this, the horizontal and vertical angles are read and recorded in the field notebook. Next, the telescope is reversed and a second sight is taken on the star, using the upper motion of the instrument. The time and the angles are recorded for this sighting in the same manner as before. After this, the sight is taken on the reference stake with the telescope still in reversed position. If the lower motion screw has not been accidentally turned during the observations, the final reading of the horizontal circle on the reference stake must be 180°00′. This should serve as a check that proper tangent screws have been used during observations.

A few cautions regarding instrumental errors in star observations are in order. Since the inclination of the vertical axis of the transit does affect measured horizontal angles and since this instrumental error is not eliminated by the reversal of the telescope (see Art. 11-17), it is important to level the instrument as carefully as possible. If accurate results are desired, the leveling must be done by the telescope level since it is more sensitive than the plate levels.

Many precise instruments have a special sensitive level called a *striding level* which can be used to level accurately the horizontal axis of the instrument during observations with elevated sights. Such a level eliminates to a great extent the errors in horizontal angles owing to the inclination of the vertical axis.

The right-hand page of Fig. 14-2 shows all computations for the bearing of the line from the point P.I$_9$ to P.I$_{10}$. It should be observed that the horizontal angle used in computation is the average angle measured from the reference mark to the star (Polaris), since this average angle corresponds to the average position of the star between the two observations. Thus the average time of observation is also used for computation of the local hour angle of the star. The vertical angle of Polaris was computed from Eq. (13-8), since this gives a better value of the altitude of Polaris than the measured vertical angle. However, even when Eq. (13-8) is used it is wise to record the vertical angle measured in the field as a check, showing that the right star was observed.

In order to make the time interval between the two sights taken on the star as short as possible, the vertical angle observed during the first sight is set on the vertical circle for the second sight with the telescope in reversed position; then it is easy to get the star into the field of view by using only the horizontal motion of the transit.

If it is desired to determine the bearing of the line within a few seconds of arc, several separate observations on Polaris are preferable to measurement of the horizontal angle several times by repetition. This is because in obtaining several separate answers for the bearing of a line, one has a reasonable check on the accuracy of each observation. If, for instance, four independent observations were made and it is found that one computed bearing of a line does not agree with the rest, the observation giving an odd answer should be rejected and only those answers which are in close agreement with each other should be averaged.

Observations for the bearing of a line on a circumpolar star such as Polaris give better results when the star is near one of its elongations, since at such a time the star moves practically in a vertical direction. A small error in the time of such an observation produces a least error in the star's azimuth. The time when the star is close to an elongation is easily obtained from the ephemeris tables. The tables show the Greenwich civil time of an elongation at Greenwich, but since the hour circle of a star rotates with the star, the *local mean time of star's elongation at any other meridian will not differ from the time of elongation shown in tables by more than* 4^m. A time interval, close to 4^m, is the time by which Polaris elongates earlier, each day, at a given place of observation. This difference in time of elongation is due to the difference between the sidereal (star's) day and the mean solar day.

Example 14-1. It is required to find the E.S.T. of the western elongation of Polaris, on a certain day, at a place of observation located at 78°20′W longitude and 30°00′N latitude.

Assume that the Greenwich civil time of western elongation at Greenwich, as is shown in the ephemeris tables for a particular day involved, is 19^{h}17.7^m. It should be observed that the time of elongation shown in the tables is given for 40°N latitude. If the stars moved westward at the same rate as the mean sun, Polaris would have reached its western elongation at 40°N latitude, at any meridian, at 19^{h}17.7^m by the mean solar time of the local meridian. The stars, however, move at a slightly faster rate than does the mean sun, gaining on the latter at the rate of 3.94^m per day or 0.011^m per degree of west longitude. This constitutes so-called **longitude correction** for the time schedules given in the tables.

Another correction which need be applied to the time of elongation, as given in the tables is the **latitude correction,** if the latitude of a place of observation is other than 40°N. This correction is given in the tables for various latitudes and a given elongation with a proper sign. The correction varies from about −2^m to +2^m, depending on the latitude.

Thus the computations of the local mean time of western elongation of Polaris at 78°20′W longitude and 30°00′N latitude may be arranged as follows:

G.C.T. of western elongation at Greenwich	19^{h}17.7^m
Longitude correction: −0.011 × 78.33 =	−0.9^m
Latitude correction (from tables) =	+1.0^m
Local mean time of western elongation	19^{h}17.8^m

The local mean time in this example is the mean time of the 78°20′W meridian. However, the local civil time at 78°20′W meridian in the United States is Eastern Standard Time, which is the mean time of the 75°00′W meridian. To compute the E.S.T. of western elongation at the place of observation a difference of 4^m per each degree of difference in longitude (see Table 13-1) should be applied to the local mean time if the standard time meridian is east of the place of observation, or -4^m for each degree of difference in longitude if the standard time meridian is west of the place of observation. In the example, here considered,

$$\text{correction to E.S.T.} = 4^m(78.33 - 75.00) = 13.3^m$$

Thus,   E.S.T. of western elongation $= 19^h17.8^m + 13.3^m = 19^h31.1^m$

When observations are made at an elongation, the transit must be set up and carefully leveled before the time of elongation. Then, allowing about 4^m between the sights on the star with the telescope in direct and in reversed positions, the first sight on the star should be made about 2^m before the elongation and the second, 2^m after the elongation.

The computation of the azimuth angle of Polaris by Eq. (13-4), $\sin Z = \sin p \sec \phi$, does not involve the star's altitude, thus no vertical angle really need be measured. When the star's vertical angle is not known some observers set an additional illuminated mark along the star's direction, in order to take sight at that point after the reversal of the telescope. This enables the observer to bring the star quickly into the field of view by using only the vertical motion of the telescope.

14-3. Solar observations for azimuth. Solar observations for the bearing of a line are in general less accurate than are stellar observations, especially those on a close circumpolar star. This is generally true if solar observations are made without a special attachment to the telescope, designed to produce about the same accuracy as that of star observations.

The difficulties encountered in solar observations result from the following three factors:

(a) The rapid rate of the apparent motion of the sun across the sky, since the sun is much closer to the equator than the circumpolar stars.

(b) The great apparent size of the sun, which makes it impossible to take accurate sights at the sun's center with a transit.

(c) The sun's extreme brightness, which precludes direct observations without special telescope attachments.

These difficulties in solar observations may be overcome, to a great extent, either by projecting the sun's rays through the telescope on a white card, held a few inches back of the eyepiece, or by using a special solar prism attachment at the objective end of the telescope.

The best time of the day for solar observations is before 10 A.M. and after 2 P.M. The recommended earliest and the latest hours of the day depend on the sun's altitude. Observations should be avoided when the sun's altitude is less than $20°$, since the correction of the observed vertical angle for the refraction of the atmosphere becomes large and relatively uncertain at low altitudes. Observations between the hours of 10 A.M. and 2 P.M. should be also avoided because between those hours the rate of change of altitude with lapse of time approaches zero, while small errors in the measured vertical angle cause relatively large errors in the azimuth angle Z.

The method of solar observations by projecting the sun's rays on a white card held a few inches back of the eyepiece produces the bearing

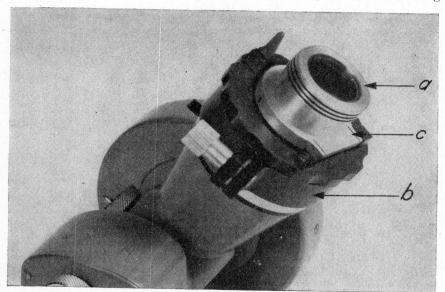

Fig. 14-3. Solar prism attachment. (Courtesy Wild Heerbrugg Instruments, Inc.)

of a line, computed from the data of a single observation, within the accuracy of about 02′. The average of about three or four observations should produce the results correct within about 01′. This may be satisfactory for surveys below third order accuracy. If better results are required, the sun must be observed through a special prism attachment (shown on Fig. 14-3) applied to the objective end of the telescope.

The collar b of this attachment fits over the objective end of the telescope. The front part a contains two prisms which are arranged in such a way as to produce simultaneously four images of the sun shown in Fig. 14-4. A dark filter placed inside the attachment allows direct observation of the sun. The overlapping four images of the sun allow accurate placing of the intersection of cross hairs in the center of the observed images. The bright cross shown by the unshaded portion of the figure makes the cross hairs plainly visible during an observation.

It is claimed that with this attachment the accuracy of solar observations for azimuth is comparable to that obtained in stellar observations.* This gives a maximum random error of the azimuth computed from a single set of observations equal to about $\pm 5''$ when a theodolite reading the angles directly to the nearest second is used.

This prism attachment must fit accurately over the objective end of the telescope. It is of European manufacture and if used on American-made transits, it must have a special adapter ring.

Fig. 14-4. Sun's images as seen through prism attachment.

The routine followed in solar observations with the prism attachment is the same as that in stellar observations. The transit is set up at a point, the vernier A is set on zero and a sight is taken on a reference point with the lower motion and with the telescope in normal position. In this sight the part a of the prism attachment, shown in Fig. 14-3, is kept off the line of sight by swinging it to a side about the hinge c which attaches part a to the collar b.

After the initial sight on the reference point, the part a containing the prisms is swung back in place and the sight is taken on the sun, using the upper motion. The following readings are recorded in this sight: the time, the horizontal angle, and the vertical angle. Next the telescope is reversed and the second sight is taken on the sun, making the same recordings as in first observation. After this, the prisms are swung aside and the final sight is taken on the reference stake, still using the upper motion of the transit. With this sight the reading of vernier A

* See the article "A New Device for Solar Observations" by R. Roelofs, *Surveying and Mapping*, Vol. VIII, No. 4, Oct.–Dec., 1948, p. 187.

must be 180°00′. This serves to check the fact that a wrong screw has not been turned during the observation.

Owing to unsymmetrical position of prisms in the attachment, certain corrections must be applied to measured horizontal and vertical angles. The correction applied to a horizontal angle is equal to one-half of the refracting angle of the prism divided by the cosine of the observed altitude. The correction applied to the vertical angle is equal to one-half of the refracting angle of the prism. For instance, if the refracting angle of the prism is equal to 23′10″ and the measured vertical angle is equal to 28°17′, the correction applied to the sun's azimuth must be 11′35″/cos 28°17′ = 40′24″ and the correction applied to the vertical angle must

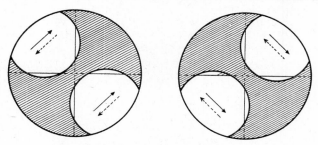

Fig. 14-5. Quadrants for solar observation.

be 11′35″. These corrections are independent of those made for the parallax and the refraction of the atmosphere.

When solar observations are made by holding a card a few inches from the eyepiece, a bright circular image of the sun appears on the card when the telescope is directed at the sun. By turning the focusing knob of the telescope and that of the eyepiece, the cross hairs are made plainly visible on the bright spot. Turning of the horizontal and the vertical tangent screws places the sun in one of the four quadrants, formed by the cross hairs, with the sun's limbs being nearly tangent to the horizontal and vertical hairs.

With the erecting eyepiece the sun appears to move on the card in the opposite direction to that in which it is actually moving, and with the inverting eyepiece both motions are in the same direction. A proper quadrant for observation is the one in which the sun appears to recede from one cross hair and to advance on the other, as shown in Fig. 14-5. This enables the observer to wait for one of the sun's limbs to become tangent to the hair from which it is receding while he keeps turning the tangent screw of a proper motion of the transit in order to keep the other hair tangent to the sun's other limb. This motion is arrested when the sun is tangent to both hairs, and the time and the measured horizontal and vertical angles are recorded in the notebook.

When the next observation is made with the telescope in reversed position, the sun is placed in the diagonally opposite quadrant, and the time and the measured angles are recorded as before. The initial and final sightings on the reference stake are made as with any other observation described above. The mean time of observation and the mean

SOLAR OBSERVATION
BEARING OF LINE AB

April 13, 1953 — Clear, Temp. 58°F. — Transit No. 27 — T. A. Burton, N. P. Carr, D. R. Simpson — 17.

⊼ at pt.	Sight on pt.	Tel.	P.S.T. p.m. Time	Vernier A	Vertical Angle
A	B	D		0°00'00"	
	☉	D	$3^h10^m15^s$	275°20'30" Rt.	39°40'
	☉	R	$3^h16^m07^s$	95°48'00"	37°20'
	B	R		180°00'00"	
Avg.			$3^h13^m11^s$	84°25'45" Lt	38°30'

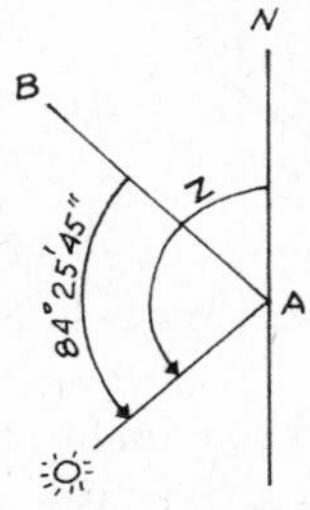

Lat. 34°04'26.4"

Computations:

Time of observation $15^h13^m11^s$ P.S.T.
plus 8^h
G.C.T. $23^h13^m11^s$ April 13

Declination $\delta = +9°13'.3$ April 14, 0^h G.C.T.
Correction for $47^m = -0'.7$
$\delta = +9°12'.6$

Observed altitude $h' = 38°3'.0$
Refraction $-1'.2$
Parallax $+0'.1$
$h = 38°28'.9$

$$\cos Z = \frac{\sin\delta}{\cos h \cos\phi} - \tan h \tan\phi \quad \text{Eq. 13-5}$$

$$= \frac{0.16004}{0.78280 \times 0.82832} - 0.79492 \times 0.67639$$

$\cos Z = -0.29086$
$Z = 106°54'33"$ from North
Less Hor. Angle 84°25'45"
Bearing angle = 22°28'48"

Bearing of AB N 22°28'48" W

Fig. 14-6. Recording of solar observations for azimuth.

value of the measured horizontal and vertical angles give the data corresponding to the mean position of the sun's center. Proper corrections for parallax and refraction must be applied to the measured vertical angle, as described in Art. 13-14.

Since it is difficult to set two cross hairs tangent to the sun's limbs exactly, one may expect a few minutes of error in the azimuth angles found by this method. Thus it is advisable to make several observations in order to ascertain the relative accuracy of observations. A complete recording of data and the computations of the sun's azimuth angle Z are shown in Fig. 14-6.

There are transits on the market equipped with a *solar attachment.* Such an attachment is an auxiliary telescope, similar to that shown on the mining transit (Fig. 11-6). Depending on the make of transit, a solar attachment is fixed on the side or on top of the transit telescope. In either case it serves the purpose of solving PZS triangle mechanically, so that while one is observing the sun with one telescope, the other is being automatically directed south. A solar attachment increases the number of moving parts in a transit, thus it also increases the sources of potential errors. For this reason it is questionable whether the results obtained with a solar attachment may be better than those obtained with a white card.

14-4. Observations for latitude. The latitude of a place of observation may be determined either by observing a circumpolar star at the time of its upper or lower culmination or by observing the sun at apparent noon (see Art. 13-9). The time of upper or lower culmination of a star is determined from the ephemeris tables, and the transit is set up on a point before the time of culmination. Then the star is followed with the horizontal hair until the star reaches its highest position at the time of upper culmination or its lowest position at the time of lower culmination. The observed vertical angle must be corrected for the index error of the transit and for the refraction of the atmosphere. The measured vertical angle and the time of observation are recorded in the field notebook. The polar distance of a star at the time of culmination is determined from the ephemeris tables. The polar distance subtracted from the corrected measured altitude of a star at the time of its upper culmination, or added to the altitude at lower culmination, gives the latitude of the place of observation.

When observations for latitude are made on Polaris, this star may be observed at any hour angle, since proper correction, equal to $\rho \cos t$ (see Eq. 13-8), to the true vertical angle to the star at the time of observation can be found in the ephemeris tables for obtaining the latitude of the place of observation.

Since the inclination of the vertical axis of the transit affects the measurement of vertical angles (see Art. 11-18), the instrument should be leveled, preferably with the telescope level. The index error of the vertical circle of the transit may be determined as described in Art. 11-19.

Observation on the sun at noon is similar to stellar observation except that either the upper or the lower limb of the sun is followed with the horizontal hair until the sun reaches its highest altitude at noon. The measured vertical angle at that time must be corrected for the semi-diameter of the sun, obtained from the ephemeris tables, for the index error of the vertical circle and for parallax and refraction. The correct altitude of the sun's center is used in Eq. (13-7) to obtain the latitude of the place.

When the sun's altitude at noon is greater than about 60°, it is necessary to have a small prism attachment for the eyepiece, with a dark filter, to be able to observe the sun with a transit. However, since the errors in azimuth angles vary as sec h [see Eq. (11-12)], observations at high altitude are not recommended.

The above-described methods of latitude determination should give sufficient accuracy for determining the bearing of a line on most engineering projects. For methods of precise determination of latitude, texts on advanced surveying should be consulted.

14-5. Observation for longitude. Observations for longitude should be made on a star of low declination for best results. The star should also bear either east or west. Since the arc of 15″ of longitude is equivalent to 1 second of time, the recorded time of observation must be extremely accurate. Figure 13-7 shows that the Greenwich hour angle of a star is equal to the local hour angle of the star plus west longitude (or minus east longitude) of the place of observation. Thus the equation for the longitude λ_w of a place west of Greenwich is,

$$\lambda_w = \text{G.H.A.} - \text{L.H.A.} \tag{14-1}$$

From the recorded time of observation the corresponding G.H.A. is obtained from the ephemeris tables, as is shown in the Example 14-2 below. Then the L.H.A. for the same instant may be obtained from the following solution of the *PZS* triangle for the meridian angle t:

$$\cos t = \frac{\sin h - \sin \delta \sin \phi}{\cos \delta \cos \phi} \tag{14-2}$$

Equation (14-2) shows that the altitude of the star h must be measured at the time of observation and that the latitude ϕ of the place of observation must be known. The declination δ is obtained from the ephemeris tables.

Example 14-2. Regulus was observed at $10^h47^m15^s$ P.M., E.S.T. (watch 1^m32^s fast) at 41°35′.3N latitude on April 29, 1959. Measured vertical angle is 38°15′.5. It is required to determine the longitude of the place of observation.

Solution:

Declination of Regulus = N12°09′.9 (tables)
Observed altitude   = 38°15′.5
Correction for refraction   −1′.2 (tables)
Correct altitude   = 38°14′.3

$$\cos t = \frac{\sin 38°14'.3 - \sin 12°09'.9 \sin 41°35'.3}{\cos 12°09'.9 \cos 41°35'.3}$$

$$= \frac{0.618934 - 0.210728 \times 0.663774}{0.977545 \times 0.747933} = 0.655222$$

or $t = 49°03'48''$, which is the same as L.H.A.

To compute the G.H.A. of the star, two angles given in the tables must be added together. One is the Greenwich hour angle of the vernal equinox, designated by G.H.A.♈, and the other is the sidereal hour angle (S.H.A.) of the star, which is defined as the angle measured westward from the vernal equinox to the star (see Fig. 14-7).

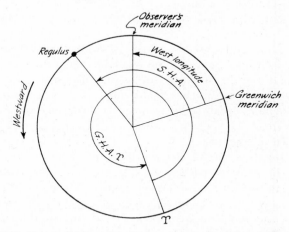

Fig. 14-7. Hour angles; measured in the direction of motion of stars.

The vernal equinox is the point of intersection of the ecliptic with the celestial equator, where the sun crosses the equator in the spring. The vernal equinox's hour circle serves as a reference circle for the hour circles of other celestial bodies.

In order to obtain G.H.A. from the tables, the Greenwich civil time of the time of observation is found as follows:

Recorded time of observation	$10^h47^m15^s$ P. M. E.S.T.
or	$22^h47^m15^s$ E.S.T.
Watch fast	1^m32^s
Correct time of observation	$22^h45^m43^s$ E.S.T.
plus 5^h difference with G.C.T.	5^h
G.C.T. of observation	$27^h45^m43^s$ April 29, 1959
which really is	$3^h45^m43^s$ April 30, 1959.

G.H.A.♈ at 0^h G.C.T., April 30	$= 217°11.'5$	(Tables)
correction for $3^h45^m43^s$	$= 56°35.'0$	
G.H.A.♈	$= 273°46.'5$	
plus S.H.A. of the star	$= 208°26.'7$	(Tables)
G.H.A. of the star	$= 482°13.'2$	
less 360°	$360°00'$	
G.H.A.	$= 122°13.'2$	
less L.H.A. (*t*)	$49°03.'8$	
Longitude of the place	$= 73°09.'4$ W	

FIELD EXERCISES

14-1. Solar Observations for Azimuth

Party: Three men.

Equipment: Transit, reading glass, and three hubs.

Object: To gain experience in solar observations for the bearing of a line.

Procedure: Three hubs are set in the ground about 200 ft apart, so as to form a triangular figure. The sun must be visible at each hub. With the tacks driven in the hubs, any point may serve as the point of the transit set-up and any other point may serve as a reference point from which the horizontal angle is measured to the sun. Follow the procedure described in Art. 14-3 for solar observation, and record the data as is shown in Fig. 14-6.

Make two separate sets of observations on the first stake and move the transit to the point which was used as the reference stake. In this set-up use the third hub as a reference point; then move the transit to the third hub using the first point as a reference point. Make two sets of observations at each point and compute the bearings of three sides of the triangle from the resulting data. This should give a closure for the computed bearings of lines. Using a standard transit for observations and the method of observation with a white card, the error of closure may be expected not to exceed about ±5 minutes.

If there are three field parties, each party may occupy a different stake and then move in a clockwise or counterclockwise direction to the next hub.

14-2. Star Observations for Azimuth

Party: Three men.

Equipment: Transit, reading glass, lantern, flashlight, and two hubs.

Object: To gain experience in observing a star for the bearing of a line.

Procedure: Two hubs are set about 800 ft apart, one serving as the point of transit set-up and the other as a reference point. Arrange a support for a tally pin or a plumb bob over the reference point and place the lantern behind it so that a sight can be taken on the point when the transit is set up at the other point.

Follow the procedure described in Art. 14-2 for observing Polaris and record the data in the field notebook as is shown in Fig. 14-2. Before going to the field, check the watch for correct time. This may be done by short-wave radio.

Make six independent sets of observations and compute the bearing of the line for each set. By using a 30 sec transit the computed bearings should agree within about 20″. Discard those observations which are obviously in error and average those which closely agree with each other.

CHAPTER 15

Methods of Area Computation

15-1. Land areas. On many engineering projects a determination of land area is needed for the transfer of title, for planning, design, construction, and many other purposes. For instance, in the design of a bridge or a culvert it is necessary to determine the watershed area and to compute the maximum anticipated discharge of water. It is necessary to find the area and the water-holding capacity of artificial lakes created by dam construction; to compute the areas allocated to street use and to rights-of-way; to find the areas of various parcels of land involved in a land subdivision, and so on. In property surveys, too, it is generally required to give the acreage of land and to show it on a map when a survey is recorded in a county official's office.

15-2. Regular and irregular areas. In some instances the area to be determined may be in the shape of some regular figure, such as a square, rectangle, or parallelogram. In such cases the area is best found by use of formulas of plane geometry. Geometrical methods of area computation are also applicable to any triangular area. Appendix A gives various formulas which are employed in the computation of areas of triangles, sectors, segments, and other regular figures.

In other instances an area to be determined may be quite irregular. Among irregular areas there are those which are bounded only by straight lines and those which are bounded either entirely or partially by curved boundaries. Methods of computing such areas are discussed in this chapter.

15-3. Areas bounded by straight lines. Determination of areas bounded by straight lines requires special methods of computation, not only because the process of breaking an area into a number of triangles and computing separately the area of each triangle involves additional field measurements of sides and angles but also because the process becomes extremely complicated when the number of sides is greater than three or four.   There exist two generally accepted, practical methods for the computation of areas bounded by straight lines.   One method is called the **double-meridian-distance method** and the other, the **coordinate method.**   Both of these methods require computation of *latitudes* and *departures* of the sides of a closed traverse, after the bearing and the length of each side have been determined.   Thus measurements of sides and angles, from which the bearings of lines can be computed, is a prerequisite for the application of these two methods.   Before the bearings are computed, the angular error of closure of the measured angles must be computed and the angles must be adjusted according to rules described in Chapter 5, Arts. 5-14 and 5-15.

It may be recalled from discussions in Chapter 5, that corrections applied to angles are inversely proportional to the weights assigned to the angles, and that the assigned weights must, other conditions being equal, be directly proportional to the number of repetitions in measurements.   (See Example 5-2.)   In a normally conducted survey, however, all angles are measured the same number of times, as is determined by a prescribed order of accuracy of a given survey (see Table 11-2, Art. 11-21). In such a case all angles have the same weight, so that the error of closure is equally distributed among the angles.

15-4. Latitudes and departures.   The latitude of a line (or a course) is its projection on the north-south line drawn through the point of beginning of the line.   The departure of a line is its projection on the west-east line drawn through the point of beginning of the line.   If a latitude extends north from the intersection of the cardinal directions drawn at the beginning of the line, the line is said to have **north latitude,** which is considered to be positive; if the latitude extends south, the line has **south latitude,** which is negative.   If a departure extends east from the intersection of cardinal directions, the line has **east departure,** which is considered to be positive; and if the departure extends west, the line has **west departure,** which is negative.

Figure 15-1 shows latitudes and departures of lines *AB* and *AC*. For practical applications the departure of a line is normally shown projected on the west-east line drawn through the end, rather than the beginning, of the line, as is shown in the figure.   This presentation allows one to think of the latitude and the departure of a line as of two successive distances that one must travel along two cardinal directions in order to get from the beginning to the end of the line.   For instance, if the bearing of the line *AB* is N62°15′E, as is shown in Fig. 15-1, one must go north a distance equal to AF and then east a distance equal to FB in order to get from A to B, AF and FB being, respectively, the latitude and the departure of line AB. Similarly, one may think of distances BH and HA, respectively, as of latitude and departure of the line BA, since one must go south and then west in order to get from B to A; or, as an alternative, one may go first west the distance BF and then south the distance FA. In either case the line BA, having bearing S62°15′W, has south latitude and west departure.

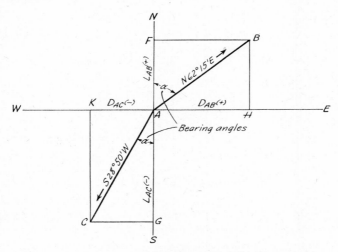

Fig. 15-1. Latitudes and departures of lines.

Figure 15-1 also shows bearing angle α of lines. It is easily seen from the geometry of the figure that in order to obtain the latitude of a line, its horizontal distance must be multiplied by the cosine of the bearing angle and in order to obtain the departure of a line its horizontal distance must be multiplied by the sine of the bearing angle. If the horizontal distance of a line is designated by s and its bearing angle by α the following equations may be obtained:

$$l = s \cos \alpha \qquad (15\text{-}1)$$

$$d = s \sin \alpha \qquad (15\text{-}2)$$

where l is the latitude and d is the departure of a line.

15-5. The error of closure. When a closed traverse is plotted on paper, the survey must close on a starting point. A closure must be effected not only graphically but also mathematically. This means that, numerically, the sum of all north latitudes in a closed traverse must be equal to the sum of all south latitudes, and the sum of all east departures must be equal to the sum of all west departures. The difference in the two sums of latitudes, designated here by ΔL, is the **error of closure in latitudes.** Similarly, the difference in the two sums of departures, designated here by ΔD, is the **error of closure in departures.** The values of ΔL and ΔD assume the sign which is obtained by adding algebraically all latitudes and all departures respectively. For instance, if the sum of north latitudes is 872.5 and the sum of south latitudes is -872.8, then $\Delta L = 872.5 - 872.8 = -0.3$.

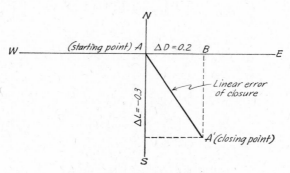

Fig. 15-2. The closing error.

The values of ΔL and ΔD, used as coordinates of the closing point in a traverse, may be plotted on paper in order to obtain the relative position of the starting and closing points. For instance, assuming that the starting point A is at the origin of X and Y coordinate axes and that $\Delta L = -0.3$ and $\Delta D = 0.2$, these errors of closure in latitudes and departures may be plotted respectively as the y and x coordinates of the closing point A'. Figure 15-2 shows the respective positions of A and A' for the errors of closure assumed above. The same figure shows that the **linear error of closure** E, for the traverse, may be obtained by solving the right-angled triangle ABA' for the hypotenuse AA'; thus

$$E = \sqrt{\Delta L^2 + \Delta D^2} \tag{15-3}$$

Table 15-1 shows distances and bearings of a closed traverse made with a 30 sec transit. It also shows computed latitudes and departures for the courses of this traverse. The table shows a customary arrangement of computations when a computing machine is used. It should be observed that the computed latitudes and departures [see Eqs. (15-1) and (15-2)] shown in the last two columns of the table are given with proper signs (Art. 15-4). Sometimes the latitudes are shown in two columns headed by N (north) and S (south) and the departures in two columns headed by E (east) and W (west).

Example 15-1. Compute the error of closure for the traverse shown in Table 15-1.

Solution: Table 15-1 shows that the error of closure ΔL in latitudes is -0.11 and that the error of closure ΔD in departures is 0.12. Thus the linear error of closure E, by Eq. (15-3), is

$$E = \sqrt{0.11^2 + 0.12^2} = 0.163$$

The accuracy achieved in a survey is equal to the error of closure divided by the sum of distances measured. Thus for the survey shown in Table 15-1 the accuracy is

$$\frac{E}{\Sigma\, s} = \frac{0.163}{799.8} = \frac{1}{4900} \qquad (15\text{-}4)$$

Since random errors in a survey exist not only in measured distances but also in measured angles, the relative accuracy computed by Eq. (15-4)

TABLE 15-1. COMPUTATION OF LATITUDES AND DEPARTURES

Line	Distance s (Ft)	Bearing	Cos α	Sin α	Latitude l	Departure d
AB	223.75	N48°59'47"E	0.656326	0.754668	146.85	168.86
BC	211.59	S40°27'12"E	0.760935	0.648828	−161.01	137.29
CD	46.20	S58°27'04"W	0.523226	0.852194	−24.17	−39.37
DE	111.55	S52°53'00"W	0.603440	0.797408	−67.31	−88.95
EA	206.68	N59°17'43"W	0.510614	0.859810	105.53	−177.71
Σ	799.77				−0.11	+0.12

reflects certain precisions that were used in the given survey in measuring both distances and angles. Thus a relative accuracy in the measurement of distances must be somewhat higher than the relative accuracy indicated by the ratio $E/\Sigma\, s$.

15-6. Adjustment of latitudes and departures. Since the closing error in a traverse is assumed to be caused entirely by the accumulation of random errors in measuring distances and angles, and since both the sign and the magnitude of closing errors in latitudes and departures are known, it is possible to find the corrections to the latitudes and departures of a traverse by applying the laws governing the behavior of accidental errors, discussed in Chapters 3 and 5 of this text. This process is called the adjustment, or the balancing, of latitudes and departures. The discussion of these adjustments is confined at first only to latitudes and then, by analogy, is extended to the adjustment of departures.

Equation 15-1 shows that the latitude of any line in a traverse is equal to $l = s \cos \alpha$. Thus a latitude is a product involving two quantities: one is the measured distance s, and the other is the cosine function of the bearing angle α computed from the angles measured in a traverse. According to Eq. (3-3) of Chapter 3, the relative error in the latitude of a line must be equal then to the sum of relative errors in the distance and in the cosine function of the bearing angle of the line. Or, expressing it in the form of an equation,

$$\frac{\Delta l}{l} = \frac{\Delta s}{s} + \frac{\Delta(\cos \alpha)}{\cos \alpha} \qquad (15\text{-}5)$$

The terms entering Eq. (15-5) are relative accuracies, which have no negative values, thus *all quantities entering the equation must be used with plus sign.*

Applying Eq. (15-5) to n courses of a traverse and designating the quantities pertaining to those courses by the subscripts corresponding to the course numbers 1, 2, 3, ... n, one obtains the following n equations:

$$\left.\begin{aligned}
\frac{\Delta l_1}{l_1} &= \frac{\Delta s_1}{s_1} + \frac{\Delta(\cos \alpha_1)}{\cos \alpha_1} \\[2mm]
\frac{\Delta l_2}{l_2} &= \frac{\Delta s_2}{s_2} + \frac{\Delta(\cos \alpha_2)}{\cos \alpha_2} \\[1mm]
&\;\;\vdots \\[1mm]
\frac{\Delta l_n}{l_n} &= \frac{\Delta s_n}{s_n} + \frac{\Delta(\cos \alpha_n)}{\cos \alpha_n}
\end{aligned}\right\} \qquad (15\text{-}6)$$

where Δl_1, Δl_2, ... Δl_n are the magnitudes of corrections that must be applied to corresponding latitudes of lines. The ratios $\Delta s/s$ on the right side of the equations show the accuracies attained in measuring various distances. These ratios may be assumed to be equal for all distances if reasonably good care is exercised in measuring those distances and if the same precision ratio is used in measurements. When all distance ratios in the right-hand side of Eqs. (15-6) are replaced by a single ratio $\Delta s/s$, and each equation is multiplied by its respective l value, the following set of equations results:

$$\left.\begin{aligned}
\Delta l_1 &= l_1 \frac{\Delta s}{s} + l_1 \frac{\Delta(\cos \alpha_1)}{\cos \alpha_1} \\[2mm]
\Delta l_2 &= l_2 \frac{\Delta s}{s} + l_2 \frac{\Delta(\cos \alpha_2)}{\cos \alpha_2} \\[1mm]
&\;\;\vdots \\[1mm]
\Delta l_n &= l_n \frac{\Delta s}{s} + l_n \frac{\Delta(\cos \alpha_n)}{\cos \alpha_n}
\end{aligned}\right\} \qquad (15\text{-}7)$$

Exactly the same reasoning can be applied to the departures of lines, which are expressed by a general equation $d = s \sin \alpha$. Thus a set of equations for departure corrections, Δd, corresponding to those obtained in Eq. (15-7) for latitudes of lines, can be analogously constructed:

$$\left.\begin{aligned}
\Delta d_1 &= d_1 \frac{\Delta s}{s} + d_1 \frac{\Delta(\sin \alpha_1)}{\sin \alpha_1} \\[2mm]
\Delta d_2 &= d_2 \frac{\Delta s}{s} + d_2 \frac{\Delta(\sin \alpha_2)}{\sin \alpha_2} \\[1mm]
&\quad \cdot \qquad\qquad \cdot \\
&\quad \cdot \qquad\qquad \cdot \\
&\quad \cdot \qquad\qquad \cdot \\
\Delta d_n &= d_n \frac{\Delta s}{s} + d_n \frac{\Delta(\sin \alpha_n)}{\sin \alpha_n}
\end{aligned}\right\} \qquad (15\text{-}8)$$

If Eqs. (15-7) are added, the sum of unknown corrections Δl on the left side of the equations is made equal to the absolute value $|\Delta L|$ of the total error of closure in latitudes. Similarly, the sum of the Δd terms on the left side of Eqs. (15-8) is the absolute value $|\Delta D|$ of the total error of closure in departures. The sums of Eqs. (15-7) and (15-8) are shown by Eqs. (15-9) and (15-10) below.

$$|\Delta L| = (l_1 + l_2 + \ldots + l_n)\frac{\Delta s}{s} + l_1 \frac{\Delta(\cos \alpha_1)}{\cos \alpha_1} + l_2 \frac{\Delta(\cos \alpha_2)}{\cos \alpha_2}$$
$$+ \ldots l_n \frac{\Delta(\cos \alpha_n)}{\cos \alpha_n} \quad (15\text{-}9)$$

$$|\Delta D| = (d_1 + d_2 + \ldots d_n)\frac{\Delta s}{s} + d_1 \frac{\Delta(\sin \alpha_1)}{\sin \alpha_1} + d_2 \frac{\Delta(\sin \alpha_2)}{\sin \alpha_2}$$
$$+ \ldots d_n \frac{\Delta(\sin \alpha_n)}{\sin \alpha_n} \quad (15\text{-}10)$$

If precision ratios for the cosine and sine functions in Eqs. (15-9) and (15-10) can be estimated, each equation will then contain only one unknown, the ratio $\Delta s/s$. Thus the respective equations may be solved for this ratio as is shown by Eqs. (15-11) and (15-12) in which abbreviation symbols are used for the sums of other terms.

$$\frac{\Delta s}{s} = \frac{1}{\Sigma\, l}\left[|\Delta L| - \sum l\, \frac{\Delta(\cos \alpha)}{\cos \alpha}\right] \qquad (15\text{-}11)$$

$$\frac{\Delta s}{s} = \frac{1}{\Sigma\, d}\left[|\Delta D| - \sum d\, \frac{\Delta(\sin \alpha)}{\sin \alpha}\right] \qquad (15\text{-}12)$$

where all latitudes and departures are used with plus sign.

In a traverse which has a great many courses, or, expressing it mathematically, when the number of courses $n \to \infty$, the distribution of random errors in measurements may be expected to be so well balanced that $\Delta s/s$ ratios, as computed by Eqs. (15-11) and (15-12), should closely approximate the actual accuracies attained in linear measurements of a given traverse. However, in a traverse having but a few courses the distribution of random errors is unpredictable, so that the numerical value of $\Delta s/s$ as computed from the latitude equation and from the departure equation may be quite different. In such traverses this ratio shows the accuracy attained in linear measurements only as far as its effect on the closing error in latitudes and departures is concerned. Thus in the balancing of latitudes and departures, $\Delta s/s$ must be computed independently from Eqs. (15-11) and (15-12) and then the respective values substituted in Eqs. (15-7) and (15-8) to obtain the magnitude of corrections Δl and Δd that must be applied to latitudes and departures in a given traverse.

In a limited number of courses in a traverse the $\Delta s/s$ ratio may also be unevenly affected by the precision ratios of cosine and sine functions in Eqs. (15-11) and (15-12). For instance, if bearing angles in a traverse are predominantly close to $0°$ or to $90°$, the precision ratios for cosine and sine function will show considerable variations. These variations not only affect the values of $\Delta s/s$ in Eqs. (15-11) and (15-12) but also reflect poorly the precisions that were actually used in measured angles.

Precision ratios for cosine and sine functions of bearing angles may be computed from the trigonometric tables of natural cosines and sines. For example, if a bearing angle is $27°14'$, which value is estimated to be known, say, within $30''$, one obtains from tables $\cos 27°14' = 0.88915$ and variation for $01'$ equal to 0.00013. Thus the precision ratio for the cosine of this angle is

$$\frac{\Delta(\cos \alpha)}{\cos \alpha} = \frac{0.00013}{2 \times 0.88915} = \frac{1}{13,700}$$

If the same angle were uncertain only by $\pm 15''$, the computed precision ratio would be twice as reliable, or $1/27,400$. When these ratios are obtained for substitution in Eqs. (15-11) and (15-12), it is usually sufficiently accurate to obtain them from the curves of Fig. 15-3. The number of seconds by which the curves are marked shows the corresponding magnitude of the uncertainty in measured angles.

The best way to estimate the magnitude of uncertainty in measured angles is to compute the amount of maximum random errors present in angles. When the angles are measured once direct, and once reversed, Table 11-1 may be used to compute maximum random errors, as was done in Eq. (11-9) (p. 181). Table 15-2 shows maximum errors computed for various transits, when the angles are measured once direct and once

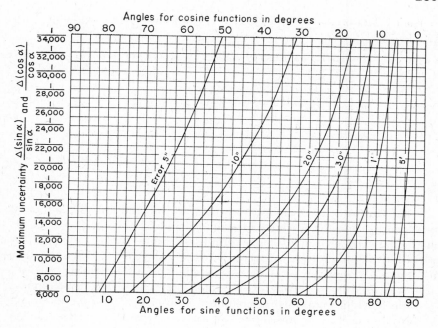

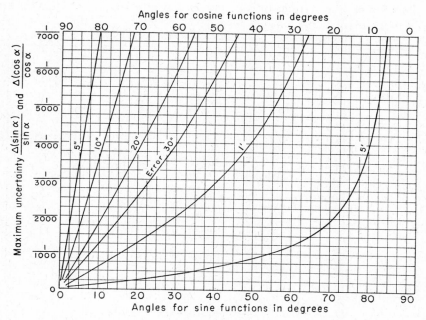

Fig. 15-3. Uncertainty ratios of sines and cosines for various angles. (For errors not shown by curves, proportion table ratios directly according to errors.)

reversed.　　The errors are computed from the data shown in Table 11-1 (Art. 11-12).

TABLE 15-2.　ESTIMATED ERRORS IN ANGLES

Transit's Least Count	Number of Measurements	Approximate Maximum Random Error
1′	2 D.R.	20″
30″	2 D.R.	10″
20″	2 D.R.	7″
10″	2 D.R.	4″

Computation of $\Delta s/s$ values from Eqs. (15-11) and (15-12), and of Δl and Δd corrections for latitudes and departures by Eqs. (15-7) and (15-8), may be best arranged in a tabular form as shown in Tables 15-3 and 15-4 for the latitudes and departures computed in Table 15-1.　Since the data in Table 15-1 are given for a traverse made with a 30″ transit, the 10″ curve was used in Fig. 15-3 for obtaining precision ratios in column 4. The sum of values obtained in column 5 is used in the equation shown at the foot of each table for computing the values of $\Delta s/s$.　This value is used then in column 6.　Column 7 gives the sum of values shown in columns 5 and 6, according to Eqs. (15-7) and (15-8).

TABLE 15-3.　ADJUSTMENT OF LATITUDES

1	2	3	4	5*	6	7	8	9
Line	Latitude l	Bearing Angle α	$\dfrac{\Delta(\cos \alpha)}{\cos \alpha}$	$\left\lvert l \right\rvert \dfrac{\Delta(\cos \alpha)}{\cos \alpha}$	$\left\lvert l \right\rvert \dfrac{\Delta s}{s}$	Δl	Used Δl	Adjusted l
AB	146.85	48°59′47″	$\dfrac{1}{18,000}$	0.008	0.023	0.031	0.03	146.88
BC	−161.01	40°27′12″	$\dfrac{1}{24,000}$	0.007	0.025	0.032	0.03	−160.98
CD	−24.17	58°27′04″	$\dfrac{1}{12,600}$	0.002	0.004	0.006	0.01	−24.16
DE	−67.31	52°53′00″	$\dfrac{1}{15,600}$	0.004	0.010	0.014	0.01	−67.30
EA	105.53	59°17′43″	$\dfrac{1}{12,000}$	0.009	0.016	0.025	0.03	105.56
Σ	| 504.87 |			0.030	0.078	0.108	0.11	0.00

$$* \frac{\Delta s}{s} = \frac{1}{\Sigma l}\left[\left\lvert \Delta L \right\rvert - \sum l \frac{\Delta(\cos \alpha)}{\cos \alpha} \right] = \frac{0.11 - 0.030}{504.9} = 0.000154 = \frac{1}{6300}$$

TABLE 15-4. ADJUSTMENT OF DEPARTURES

1	2	3	4	5*	6	7	8	9
Line	Departure d	Bearing Angle α	$\dfrac{\Delta(\sin\alpha)}{\sin\alpha}$	$\lvert d \rvert \dfrac{\Delta(\sin\alpha)}{\sin\alpha}$	$\lvert d \rvert \dfrac{\Delta s}{s}$	Δd	Used Δd	Adjusted d
AB	168.86	48°59'47"	$\dfrac{1}{25{,}500}$	0.007	0.027	0.034	−0.03	168.83
BC	137.29	40°27'12"	$\dfrac{1}{17{,}400}$	0.008	0.022	0.030	−0.03	137.26
CD	−39.37	58°27'04"	$\dfrac{1}{31{,}800}$	0.001	0.006	0.007	−0.01	−39.38
DE	−88.95	52°53'00"	$\dfrac{1}{28{,}000}$	0.003	0.014	0.017	−0.02	−88.97
EA	−177.71	59°17'43"	$\dfrac{1}{35{,}400}$	0.005	0.028	0.033	−0.03	−177.74
Σ	| 612.18 |			0.024	0.097	0.121	−0.12	0.00

$$* \frac{\Delta s}{s} = \frac{1}{\Sigma d}\left[\,\lvert \Delta D \rvert - \sum d\,\frac{\Delta(\sin\alpha)}{\sin\alpha}\right] = \frac{0.12 - 0.024}{612.2} = 0.000157 = \frac{1}{6400}$$

15-7. Explanation of Tables 15-3 and 15-4

Columns 1, 2, and 3 show the values transferred from a table in which latitudes and departures of a traverse are computed (see Table 15-1).

Column 4 shows the precision ratios for a proper function of bearing angle given in column 3. It is important to use an appropriate curve in Fig. 15-3 for obtaining these ratios. A proper curve is determined by the estimated or computed value of the maximum random error in measured angles. [See Tables 11-1 and 15-2, also Eq. (11-9), Art. 11-12].

Column 5 is obtained by multiplying the absolute values of latitudes and departures given in column 2 by the ratios shown in column 4. Before proceeding with column 6, $\Delta s/s$ ratio must be computed by the equations shown at the foot of each table. If $\Delta s/s$ comes out negative, a new estimate for the ratios shown in column 4 must be made, so that the sum of values given in column 5 does not exceed absolute values of ΔL or ΔD, computed for the latitudes and departures of a given traverse.

Column 6 shows the absolute values of latitudes and departures, in respective tables, multiplied by computed values of $\Delta s/s$.

Column 7 shows the sum of values shown in columns 5 and 6. The corrections for latitudes and departures, in respective tables, are computed to an extra decimal place as compared with those in latitudes and departures.

Column 8 shows the same numerical values, as those shown in column **7**, but rounded off to the same number of decimal figures as those in the latitudes and departures. Since corrections for latitudes and departures, computed in column 8, are, for simplicity of computations, added algebraically to the latitudes and departures given in column 2, the obtained corrections must be used with a sign opposite to those in the respective errors of closures ΔL and ΔD.

Column 9 shows the algebraic sum of columns 2 and 8. These are the adjusted latitudes and departures which must algebraically add up to zero. Normally, the absolute values of the sum of corrections applied to the positive and to the negative latitudes and departures, are equal. However, it may be expected that in some surveys the two sums may not be equal.

Since $\Delta s/s$ ratios obtained from the latitude and departure tables in this example are nearly equal, they show the actual accuracy attained in linear measurements in the given traverse. Thus in this example (angles having been measured as they were) it is possible to estimate the necessary increase in the accuracy of linear measurements over that shown by 1:4900 closure. The necessary increase in accuracy in per cent, in this example, is $[(6350 - 4900)/4900]100 = 30\%$. Thus precision ratio for linear measurements must be a better ratio than the required order of accuracy for the closure. For instance, in order to attain 1:5000 linear closure in a traverse, 1:7500 precision may be used in linear measurements, provided the angles are measured with a comparable precision.

15-8. Odd distribution of random errors. As it has been pointed out in Art. 15-6, if there are but few courses in a traverse, an odd distribution of random errors may be expected. As an example, one may think of a closed traverse in which all sides having east departures have random errors with minus sign and all sides having west departures have random errors with plus sign. The effect is that errors accumulate in departures much like systematic errors, but compensate to an unusual extent in latitudes. This case is shown in Table 15-5A.

The data shown in Table 15-5A are for a traverse made with 1 min transit. Each angle was measured twice (2 D.R.). The maximum random error in angles, according to Table 15-2, should be close to 20″. However, as it may be observed from the number of seconds in the bearings of lines, the angles in the traverse were adjusted only to the nearest 15″, thus the 30″ curve of Fig. 15-3 may give a better estimation of the magnitude of angular errors present in bearing angles of this traverse than the 20″ curve.

Table 15-5B shows the adjustment of latitudes. The crossed-out figures in column 5 show the values of angular errors estimated from the 30″ curve of errors. The sum of these errors is equal to 0.124, which value is greater than the error in latitudes 0.04. This gives negative

TABLE 15-5A. COMPUTATION OF LATITUDES AND DEPARTURES

Line	Distance s (Ft)	Bearing	Cos α	Sin α	Latitude l	Departure d
AB	420.7	N82°17′15″E	0.13420	0.99095	56.46	416.89
BC	271.8	S5°28′00″W	0.99548	0.095267	−270.57	−25.89
CD	62.46	S12°09′15″E	0.97758	0.21054	−61.06	13.15
DE	349.5	S67°45′00″W	0.37865	0.92554	−132.34	−323.48
EA	415.6	N11°17′45″W	0.98063	0.19587	407.55	−81.40
Σ	1520.0				+0.04	−0.73

$$E = \sqrt{0.04^2 + 0.73^2} = 0.73, \qquad \frac{E}{\Sigma s} = \frac{0.73}{1520} = \frac{1}{2080}$$

TABLE 15-5B. ADJUSTMENT OF LATITUDES

1	2	3	4	5*	6	7	8	9
Line	Latitude l	Bearing Angle α	$\dfrac{\Delta(\cos\alpha)}{\cos\alpha}$	$\lvert l \rvert \dfrac{\Delta(\cos\alpha)}{\cos\alpha}$	$\lvert l \rvert \dfrac{\Delta s}{s}$	Δl	Used Δl	Adjusted l
AB	56.46	82°17′15″	$\dfrac{1}{960}$	0.020 ~~−0.059~~	0	0.020	−0.02	56.44
BC	−270.57	5°28′00″	$\dfrac{1}{66,300}$	0.001 ~~−0.004~~	0	0.001	0.00	−270.57
CD	−61.06	12°09′15″	$\dfrac{1}{32,600}$	0.000 ~~−0.002~~	0	0.000	0.00	−61.06
DE	−132.34	67°45′00″	$\dfrac{1}{2800}$	0.016 ~~−0.047~~	0	0.016	−0.02	−132.36
EA	407.55	11°17′45″	$\dfrac{1}{32,700}$	0.004 ~~−0.012~~	0	0.004	0.00	407.55
Σ	∣927.98∣			0.041 ~~−0.124~~	0	0.041	−0.04	0.00

$$*\frac{\Delta s}{s} = \frac{0.04 - \overset{0.041}{\cancel{0.124}}}{928} = 0 = \frac{1}{\infty}$$

value for $\Delta s/s$. Therefore precision ratios for the angles were overestimated, since the sum of values in column 5 cannot exceed 0.04. Assuming in this case that all errors are due to errors in angles, the sum of precision ratios in column 5 must be equal to 0.04. This value may be approximated by dividing 0.124 by 3, which gives 0.041. Thus instead of the 30″ curve of errors the 10″ curve must be used in this adjustment.

The second set of figures in column 5 shows the values obtained from the 10″ curve of errors. This makes $\Delta s/s$ ratio equal to zero. In other words all errors in latitudes, in this example, must be due to the angular errors and, since the effect of linear errors on the closure of latitudes is nil, $\Delta s/s = 1/\infty = 0$.

In the adjustment of departures, shown in Table 15-5C, the originally estimated 30″ maximum random error in angles is used to obtain

TABLE 15-5C. ADJUSTMENT OF DEPARTURES

1	2	3	4	5*	6	7	8	9
Line	Departure d	Bearing Angle α	$\dfrac{\Delta(\sin\alpha)}{\sin\alpha}$	$\lvert d\rvert\,\dfrac{\Delta(\sin\alpha)}{\sin\alpha}$	$\lvert d\rvert\,\dfrac{\Delta s}{s}$	Δd	Used Δd	Adjusted d
AB	416.89	82°17′15″	$\dfrac{1}{49{,}500}$	0.008	0.288	0.296	0.30	417.19
BC	−25.89	5°28′00″	$\dfrac{1}{657}$	0.039	0.018	0.057	0.06	−25.83
CD	13.15	12°09′15″	$\dfrac{1}{1500}$	0.009	0.009	0.018	0.02	13.17
DE	−323.48	67°45′00″	$\dfrac{1}{16{,}800}$	0.019	0.224	0.243	0.24	−323.24
EA	−81.40	11°17′45″	$\dfrac{1}{1350}$	0.060	0.056	0.116	0.11	−81.29
Σ	| 860.81 |			0.135	0.595	0.730	0.73	0.00

$$* \ \frac{\Delta s}{s} = \frac{0.73 - 0.135}{861} = 0.000691 = \frac{1}{1450}$$

precision ratios in column 4. These precision ratios give 0.135 for the sum of values in column 5 and $\frac{1}{1450}$ for $\Delta s/s$, which is lower accuracy than $\frac{1}{2080}$ obtained for the linear error of closure. This may happen as the result of either one or both of two things—an odd distribution of random linear errors, and underestimation of precision ratios for the angles. In the example considered, it is likely to be the former.

Tables 15-5B and 15-5C show that even in the case of an odd distribution of random errors, it is possible to make a good adjustment of latitudes and departures if the data obtained in computations are properly analyzed.

15-9. Short cuts in adjustments. In the example of latitude and departure adjustments shown in Tables 15-3 and 15-4, it may be observed that 27%, [(0.030/0.11)(100)], of errors in latitudes and 20%, [(0.024/0.11)(100)], of errors in departures are attributed to angular measurements and the remaining 73% and 80%, respectively, are attributed to the linear measurements. In traverses in which the angles are measured with a much greater accuracy than the distances, precision ratios for angles may nearly become negligible.   Assuming, in such a case, that all $\Delta(\cos \alpha)/\cos \alpha$ ratios in Eq. (15-11) are equal to zero, $\Delta s/s = \Delta L/\Sigma\, l$. Substituting this value in Eqs. (15-7), one obtains the following general equation for a latitude correction:

$$\Delta l = \Delta L\, \frac{l}{\Sigma\, l} \tag{15-13}$$

Similarly for a departure correction,

$$\Delta d = \Delta D\, \frac{d}{\Sigma\, d} \tag{15-14}$$

Equations (15-13) and (15-14) show that, in special cases considered, the distribution of errors in latitudes and departures may be respectively carried out in proportion to the latitudes and departures themselves. This method of adjustment is known as the ***transit rule adjustment.***

TABLE 15-6.   ADJUSTMENT OF DEPARTURES BY THE TRANSIT RULE

Line	Departures		Correction Δd	Balanced Departure	
	E	W		E	W
AB	416.89		0.35	417.24	
BC		−25.89	0.02		−25.87
CD	13.15		0.01	13.16	
DE		−323.48	0.28		−323.20
EA		−81.40	0.07		−81.33
Σ	430.04	−430.77	0.73	430.40	−430.40

$$\Delta D = -0.73$$

The transit rule adjustment should also give good results in traverses in which the distribution of random errors is well balanced, unless some bearing angles come close to 0° or 90°.   A well-proportioned distribution of random errors may be judged by comparing $\Delta L/\Sigma\, l$ and $\Delta D/\Sigma\, d$ ratios. If they are nearly equal, the errors in a traverse are most likely evenly distributed.   It may be observed, for instance, in the example given in Tables 15-3 and 15-4 that

$$\frac{\Delta L}{\Sigma\, l} = \frac{0.11}{504.9} = 0.000218$$

and

$$\frac{\Delta D}{\Sigma\, d} = \frac{0.12}{612.2} = 0.000196.$$

The adjustment of latitudes and departures, given in these tables, by the transit rule gives nearly the same results as the adjustment by the method shown in Tables 15-3 and 15-4. The same thing cannot be said about the example given in Tables 15-5B and 15-5C. Table 15-6 shows the adjustment of departures, given in Table 15-5C, by the transit rule.

The discrepancies between the values of departure corrections as computed in Tables 15-5C and 15-6 are shown in per cent in Table 15-7.

TABLE 15-7

Line	Δd Values		Discrepancy in Per Cent
	Table 15-5C	Table 15-6	
AB	0.30	0.35	17
BC	0.06	0.02	67
CD	0.02	0.01	50
DE	0.24	0.28	17
EA	0.11	0.07	36

15-10. Bearings and distances from adjusted latitudes and departures. It is a good practice to complete the adjustment of a survey by computing distances and bearings from the adjusted latitudes and departures. Extreme caution must be exercised if the bearing angles of lines are close to 0° or to 90°, lest the computed distances and bearings introduce greater errors in distances and angles than what they were before the adjustment. The reason is that the rate of change of sine functions in small angles and of cosine functions in angles close to 90° is relatively large, while the random errors in measured angles are independent of the size of angles. Thus the use of sine functions of small angles and cosine functions of angles close to 90° may introduce relatively large errors in computed latitudes and departures. Although this factor is taken into consideration in the adjustment of latitudes and departures by the method shown in Tables 15-3 and 15-4, yet one may hesitate to use such latitudes and departures to compute distances and bearings.

The tangent of the bearing angle of a course is equal to the departure of the course divided by its latitude; or

$$\tan \alpha = \frac{\text{Dep.}}{\text{Lat.}} \tag{15-15}$$

Also the distance s of a course, from Eqs. (15-1) and (15-2), is

$$s = \text{Lat.} \times \sec \alpha = \text{Dep.} \times \csc \alpha \tag{15-16}$$

Or, from the right-angled triangle formed by the latitude l, departure d, and the distance s of a course,

$$s = \sqrt{l^2 + d^2} \qquad (15\text{-}17)$$

The bearings and distances, computed from the adjusted latitudes and departures in Tables 15-3 and 15-4, are shown in Table 15-8.

TABLE 15-8. ADJUSTED BEARINGS AND DISTANCES

Line	Latitude	Departure	Bearing	Distance
AB	146.88	168.83	N48°58′38″E	223.78
BC	−160.98	137.26	S40°27′10″E	211.55
CD	−24.16	−39.38	S58°28′18″W	46.20
DE	−67.30	−88.97	S52°53′42″W	111.56
EA	105.56	−177.74	N59°17′38″W	206.72

Comparing adjusted bearings shown in Table 15-8 with the originally computed bearings in Table 15-1, one may observe that some bearings hardly changed while others changed by about as much as 01′, as for instance the bearing of line AB. This means that the aggregation of random errors in measured distances and angles produced that much error in the direction of line AB. Thus distances and bearings computed from the adjusted latitudes and departures should be expected to be more nearly correct, than those the lines had before the adjustment of latitudes and departures.

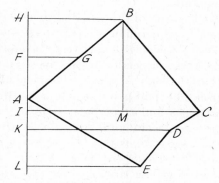

Fig. 15-4. Traverse points referred to a meridian.

If the bearing of one course in a traverse was accurately determined by astronomical observation, and after adjustment it is found that it has changed somewhat, one should further adjust the bearings of lines by rotating the whole traverse through an angle equal to the obvious angular error of the line of accurately known bearing.

15-11. Meridian distance of lines. A meridian, which gives north-south direction at a point, may be passed through any point of a traverse. Figure 15-4, for example, shows the meridian passed through point A of the traverse $ABCDE$. The expression *meridian distance*, as it is used in surveying, means the shortest distance from a line, or a point, to a particular meridian in question. Meridian distances east of the meridian are considered to be positive, and those west of the meridian, negative. In the case of a line, the meridian distance is the average distance of all the points on that line, which in fact is the meridian distance of the mid-point of the line. For instance, the meridian distance of line *AB* from the meridian passing through point *A* is the line *FG*, which is the perpendicular dropped from the mid-point *G* of the line to the meridian. It is positive because the line *FG* is east of the meridian.

A double meridian distance of a line is the meridian distance of the line multiplied by two. Double meridian distances, often abbreviated D.M.D., are used in computing the area of a field enclosed by a traverse, using a method known as the *double-meridian-distance method.*

15-12. Computation of an area by the double-meridian-distance method.* In computation of an area by this method it is customary to pass the reference meridian through the most westerly point of the traverse, as is shown in Fig. 15-4. The advantage of this is to assure that all meridian and double meridian distances of lines will be positive.

After a traverse is plotted, the double meridian distances of lines are computed in a consecutive order going around the traverse in clockwise or counterclockwise direction from the point lying on the reference meridian.

The sum of two perpendiculars dropped from the ends of a line on the reference meridian is equal to the double meridian distance of that line. The reason is that the two perpendiculars of a line, the line itself, and the meridian projection of the line form either a trapezoid or a triangle, so that the sum of the two perpendiculars is equal to twice the distance from the mid-point of a line to the meridian. The number of such triangles and trapezoids is equal to the number of courses in a given traverse, each figure having a separate course as its side. For instance, the course *BC* is the side of trapezoid *HBCI* and the course *EA* is the side of triangle *AEL* (Fig. 15-4).

Proceeding around this traverse in clockwise direction, one may observe that by adding the areas of those figures which have courses with south latitudes as sides, and subtracting from the sum thus obtained the sum of areas of those figures which have courses with north latitudes as sides, the result is the area enclosed by the traverse *ABCDE*. This operation may be expressed by an equation, in which each term represents an area, [Eq. (15-18)].

$$ABCDE = HBCI + ICDK + KDEL - (AEL + HBA) \quad (15\text{-}18)$$

The numerical value of each area on the right side of Eq. (15-18) may

* Laboratory exercise for area computation is given at the end of Chapter 16.

be obtained by multiplying one-half of the double meridian distance of the appropriate course by the latitude of that course. Also, since in Fig. 15-4 all D.M.D.'s are positive, the area of a figure comes out with minus sign if the course corresponding to that figure has south latitude and with plus sign if the course has north latitude. For instance, the area *ICDK* comes out with minus sign if $\frac{1}{2}$(D.M.D.) of the side *CD*—that is, $(IC + KD)/2$—is multiplied by the latitude of that side (equal to *IK*). Thus if each area on the right-hand side of Eq. (15-18) is expressed as $\frac{1}{2}$(D.M.D.) $\times$ Lat. for the appropriate courses, the first three areas come out with minus sign, and the last two with plus sign. The algebraic sum of these areas gives the correct numerical value for the area *ABCDE* but with minus sign. Since a negative area has no meaning, the minus sign in front of computed area must be disregarded.

The negative sign in the result of computing an area may be avoided if one chooses to proceed around a traverse in the counterclockwise direction. Then all latitudes of the courses assume opposite signs, thus reversing the sign in the result. When the areas on the right-hand side of Eq. (15-18) are expressed as $\frac{1}{2}$(D.M.D. $\times$ Lat.), every term contains $\frac{1}{2}$ as a factor. By factoring $\frac{1}{2}$, and expressing the sum of areas by the summation sign, it is possible to obtain the general expression for an area, A, enclosed by any traverse, in the following form:

$$A = \tfrac{1}{2}\Sigma \ (\text{D.M.D.} \times \text{Lat.}) \tag{15-19}$$

The right-hand side of Eq. (15-19) may be easily computed if the latitudes and D.M.D.'s for each course in a traverse are known. The computation of latitudes was demonstrated in Tables 15-1 and 15-5A above, and the rules for computing D.M.D.'s are given below.

15-13. The rules for computing D.M.D.'s

(1) *The D.M.D. of the first course is equal to the departure of the course.*

(2) *The D.M.D. of any course is equal to the D.M.D. of the preceding course, plus the departure of the preceding course, plus the departure of the course itself.*

(3) *The D.M.D. of the last course is equal to the departure of the course with opposite sign.*

These rules are so commonly employed in computation of areas that they should be memorized. Rule (3) is used only as a check on computations after the D.M.D. of the last course is computed by Rule (2). The first course in Rule (1) is the course that starts at the reference meridian. If the reference meridian is not the meridian passing through the most westerly point of the traverse, the D.M.D.'s west of the reference meridian will be negative. In any case proper signs must be observed when the products and the sums in Eq. (15-19) are computed.

A general proof of the above rules is not given here because their validity may be easily verified on any traverse. Taking, for example, the traverse shown on Fig. 15-4, one may easily see that if AB is taken as the first course, the D.M.D. of this course is the line HB which is also the departure of the course. Also the D.M.D. of the course BC is equal to

$$HB + IC = HB + IM + MC = HB + HB + MC$$

which is what Rule (2) says it should be, and so on.

The Table 15-9 shows computation of D.M.D.'s, and of the area by the D.M.D. method, using adjusted latitudes and departures given in Tables 15-3 and 15-4 for the traverse shown in Fig. 15-4.

TABLE 15-9. AREA BY THE D.M.D. METHOD

Line	Adjusted Latitude	Adjusted Departure	D.M.D.	Double Areas	
				+	−
AB	146.88	168.83	168.83	24,798	
BC	−160.98	137.26	474.92		76,453
CD	−24.16	−39.38	572.80		13,838
DE	−67.30	−88.97	444.45		29,911
EA	105.56	−177.74	177.74	18,762	
Σ				43,560	120,202

$$A = \tfrac{1}{2}(120{,}202 - 43{,}560) = 38{,}321 \text{ sq ft}$$

Instead of using a reference meridian in computing D.M.D.'s for a traverse, it is possible to use a reference parallel, and the double parallel distances (D.P.D.) computed by using the latitudes of a traverse. The result will be the same area as that computed by the D.M.D. method if one-half of the sum of the products of D.P.D.'s times the appropriate departures of courses is divided by 2. Such a method of area computation is known as the *double-parallel-distance method of area computation.*

The D.P.D. method of area computation is often recommended as a check on the area obtained by the D.M.D. method. It is a highly recommended practice to obtain a positive check on computed areas. However, instead of using the D.P.D. method for a check, many engineers and surveyors prefer to use the coordinate method of area computation discussed below. This method has the advantage that it requires computation of coordinates of traverse corners. These coordinates may be later used in obtaining the state grid coordinates of points if the bearings of lines used in computation of latitudes and departures are grid bearings.

15-14. Computation of an area by the method of coordinates. Figure 15-5 shows a traverse referred to the X and Y coordinate axes. For the purpose of computation of the area enclosed by a traverse, it is convenient to select the X and Y axes respectively along the west-east and north-south directions and also to pass the X axis through the most southerly point of the traverse and the Y axis through the most westerly point. In such an arrangement of the coordinate axes, the coordinates of all corners may be easily computed from the latitudes and departures

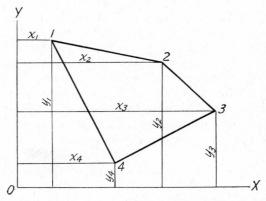

Fig. 15-5. Traverse corners referred to coordinate axes.

of courses in a traverse. However, for the purpose of demonstrating a general method of computation of an area, the X and Y coordinate axes are taken here entirely outside a traverse, and the traverse is placed entirely in the first quadrant which makes the coordinates of all points positive.

In Fig. 15-5 the points in a traverse are numbered consecutively, in clockwise direction, only for the purpose of better identification of coordinates of various points in the process of derivation of a general equation for the area. It is assumed that the x and y coordinates of all corners in a traverse are known, so that the area enclosed by the traverse may be computed by taking proper algebraic sum of the various trapezoids formed by Y axis, the sides of the traverse, and by the x coordinates of points shown on the figure. The process of derivation is similar to that used in computation of an area by the D.M.D. method. The algebraic sum of various trapezoids that gives the area A enclosed by the traverse is

$$A = \frac{x_1 + x_2}{2}(y_1 - y_2) + \frac{x_2 + x_3}{2}(y_2 - y_3) + \frac{x_3 + x_4}{2}(y_3 - y_4)$$

$$- \frac{x_1 + x_4}{2}(y_1 - y_4) \quad (15\text{-}20)$$

After the coordinates in Eq. (15-20) are multiplied out, the identical terms with opposite signs cancelled, and the terms rearranged, the expression for the area becomes

$$A = \tfrac{1}{2}(x_2y_1 - x_4y_1 + x_3y_2 - x_1y_2 + x_4y_3 - x_2y_3 + x_1y_4 - x_3y_4) \quad (15\text{-}21)$$

For convenience in computations, Eq. (15-21) may be presented in two different forms; one is shown by Eq. (15-22) and another by Eq. (15-23).

$$A = \tfrac{1}{2}[y_1(x_2 - x_4) + y_2(x_3 - x_1) + y_3(x_4 - x_2) + y_4(x_1 - x_3)] \quad (15\text{-}22)$$

It may be observed that each term in Eq. (15-22) shows the ordinate of a point multiplied by the difference between the abscissas of the following and preceding points (see Fig. 15-5). Thus the following rule for computation of areas by the method of coordinates may be stated:

An area is equal to one-half of the sum of products obtained by multiplying the ordinate of each point by the difference between the abscissas of the following and preceding points. Always subtract the preceding abscissa from the following or vice versa. If the area comes out with minus sign the sign must be disregarded.

Equation (15-21) may also be arranged in the form shown by Eq. (15-23).

$$A = \frac{1}{2}\left(\frac{x_1}{y_1} \diagdown \frac{x_2}{y_2} \diagdown \frac{x_3}{y_3} \diagdown \frac{x_4}{y_4} \diagdown \frac{x_1}{y_1}\right) \quad (15\text{-}23)$$

Equation (15-23) means that the area is equal to one-half of the sum of the products of coordinates joined by full lines minus one-half of the sum of the products of coordinates joined by dotted lines. Equation (15-23) has four more multiplications than Eq. (15-22) but only one sub-

TABLE 15-10. AREA BY THE METHOD OF COORDINATES

Point	Coordinates		$x_{\text{foll.}} - x_{\text{prec.}}$	$y(x_f - x_p)$
	x	y		
A	0	105.56	−8.91	−941
B	168.83	252.44	306.09	77,269
C	306.09	91.46	97.88	8,952
D	266.71	67.30	−128.35	−8,638
E	177.74	0	−266.71	0
Σ				76,642

$$A = \frac{76,642}{2} = 38,321 \text{ sq ft}$$

traction.   A reduction in the number of multiplications in either equation may be effected by passing the Y axis through the most westerly point and the X axis through the most southerly point of a traverse.   In the traverse shown in Fig. 15-5, this reduces the x_1 and y_4 coordinates to zero.

Table 15-10 shows computation of the area by Eq. (15-22) from the x and y coordinates of points obtained from the adjusted latitudes and departures shown in Tables 15-3 and 15-4.   These data are for the traverse shown in Fig. 15-4.   In computation of coordinates for this traverse x_a and y_e coordinates were made equal to zero by passing the Y coordinate axis through point A and the X axis through point E.

15-15. Areas with curved boundaries.   It is often required to compute areas that are bounded either totally or partially by curves. The curves may be regular or irregular.   For instance, a corner property in a city may have a circular curve along its property lines, or a property situated on the bank of a river may have an irregular curve for the property line along the river.   Figure 15-6 shows an area which has a circular boundary between the points D and E and an irregular boundary between B and C.

For the purpose of computation of the area shown in Fig. 15-6, a straight-line traverse $AFGCDE$ may be run by usual methods, the line GC

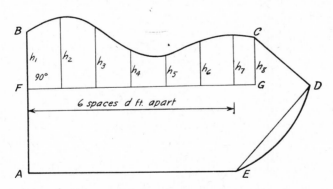

Fig. 15-6. Areas with curved boundaries.

being made parallel to the line FB.   The area enclosed by this traverse may be computed either by the D.M.D. or by the coordinates method. The remaining areas must be computed separately and then added to the area enclosed by straight boundaries.

The area of a circular segment between the points D and E may be computed by a formula which may be found in Appendix A for such a segment; but the area $FBCG$ may be computed by measuring offsets h_1, h_2, h_3, ... h_{n-1}, h_n from a selected base line (FG on Fig. 15-6) to the curve and then computing the area by one of the methods described below.

Several possibilities may arise in the measuring of these offsets. For instance, the base FG may be divided into equal parts or into parts of some convenient length, say 25 ft, leaving an odd length at one end of the base. Or in some cases it may be preferred to measure offsets at the curve's inflection points, making all intervals between the offsets unequal. The best way to measure the offsets may depend to a great extent on local conditions of the ground. After the offsets have been measured, the area is normally computed by either one of two methods, the *trapezoidal rule* or *Simpson's one-third rule*.

15-16. Trapezoidal rule. In the application of the trapezoidal rule to area computation, the points of intersection of the offsets with a curved boundary are connected by straight lines. This breaks the area between the base line and the curved boundary into a series of trapezoids having measured offsets h_1, h_2, ... h_n as their bases. The area is computed as the sum of these trapezoids. For equally spaced offsets, distance d apart, the area is equal to

$$\frac{h_1 + h_2}{2} d + \frac{h_2 + h_3}{2} d + \ldots + \frac{h_{n-1} + h_n}{2} d$$

In this series of terms only the first and the last offsets occur once and the rest of the offsets occur twice; also the interval d between the offsets occurs as a factor in every term. Thus by factoring d, and simplifying the above expression, one obtains the following equation for the area A:

$$A = d \left(\frac{h_1}{2} + h_2 + h_3 + \ldots + h_{n-1} + \frac{h_n}{2} \right) \qquad (15\text{-}24)$$

Equation (15-24) applies to n consecutive offsets spaced distance d apart. The areas of those trapezoids which have the interval between the offsets other than d must be computed separately and then added to the area computed by Eq. (15-24).

The accuracy of the trapezoidal formula varies with the shape of the curved boundary. If the curve has approximately equal lengths of convex and concave arcs, the plus and minus errors in the areas between the offsets may become well compensated. In general, the accuracy of the trapezoidal rule increases with the increased number of measured offsets; however, the measurement of too many offsets is time-consuming and may therefore be not practical. When the curved boundary is predominantly convex or concave, the application of the Simpson's one-third rule may be expected to give a more accurate value of the area.

15-17. Simpson's one-third rule. The application of Simpson's one-third rule is based on the assumption that the curved boundary consists of a series of parabolic arcs, each arc being continuous over two adjacent, equal intervals between the offsets. This assumption limits the application of the rule to an even number of equal intervals along the base. If there is an odd number of equal intervals, the area between the last two offsets must be computed separately by the trapezoidal rule. The trapezoidal rule must also be applied in the computation of the area between those end offsets which have a spacing different from the rest of the offsets.

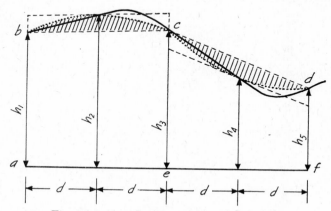

Fig. 15-7. Area by Simpson's one-third rule.

Figure 15-7 shows the first five offsets of Fig. 15-6. The dotted lines show two parabolic curves—one between h_1 and h_3 offsets and another between h_3 and h_5. The dashed lines show two parallelograms drawn around the respective parabolic arcs. The shaded area of each parallelogram is equal to two-thirds the area of the parallelogram. The application of Simpson's rule gives the area between the base line and the parabolas. First, the areas of trapezoids (such as $abce$ and $ecdf$) are computed, and then two-thirds of the respective parallelogram areas are added or subtracted, as the case may be, in order to obtain the desired area. These computations, for the first four sections shown in the figure, are as follows:

$$A = \frac{h_1 + h_3}{2} 2d + \frac{2}{3}\left(h_2 - \frac{h_1 + h_3}{2}\right) 2d + \frac{h_3 + h_5}{2} 2d$$
$$- \frac{2}{3}\left(\frac{h_3 + h_5}{2} - h_4\right) 2d$$

This equation, when simplified, shows the following pattern for the measured offsets $h_1, h_2, h_3, \ldots h_n$:

$$A = \frac{d}{3}\left(h_1 + 2h_3 + 2h_5 + \ldots + 4h_2 + 4h_4 + \ldots + h_n\right) \quad (15\text{-}25)$$

It may be observed that in Eq. (15-25) all offsets with odd subscripts, except the first and the last one, are multiplied by 2 and all offsets with even subscripts are multiplied by 4.   This allows the formulation of the Simpson's one-third rule in the form shown by Eq. (15-26).

$$A = \frac{d}{3}\left(h_1 + 2\sum h_{odd} + 4\sum h_{even} + h_n\right) \qquad (15\text{-}26)$$

Example 15-2.   The following offsets were measured from the base line to a curved boundary:

h_1	h_2	h_3	h_4	h_5	h_6	h_7	h_8
11.9	9.3	7.1	8.0	10.7	15.2	14.8	12.1

It is required to compute the area by the trapezoidal rule and by the Simpson's one-third rule if all offsets are spaced 15.0 ft apart.

Solution: By the trapezoidal rule,

$$A = 15.0\left(\frac{11.9}{2} + 9.3 + 7.1 + 8.0 + 10.7 + 15.2 + 14.8 + \frac{12.1}{2}\right) = 115\underline{7}$$

By the Simpson's one-third rule,

$$A_1 = \frac{15.0}{3}\,[11.9 + 2(7.1 + 10.7) + 4(9.3 + 8.0 + 15.2) + 14.8] = 961.5$$

To this must be added the area of the last odd section:

$$\frac{14.8 + 12.1}{2} \times 15.0 = 201.8$$

$$A_1 = 961.5 + 201.8 = 116\underline{3}$$

Should one obtain big differences in areas as computed by the two methods, it would mean that measured ordinates were spaced too far apart.

15-18. Subdivision of land.   Subdivision of large tracts of land into smaller parcels normally must be done according to the state, county, or city laws and regulations existing for land subdivisions in a given location.   If a tract of land is, for instance, within the limits of a city, the grades and curvatures of proposed streets, the easements for public utilities, provisions for proper drainage, lot sizes, and so on must be approved by the city.

When subdivision of land occurs in states in which the land was subdivided by the U.S. Bureau of Public Lands into townships and sections, Appendix C of this text should be consulted.

A subdivision often has the purpose of dividing an area into smaller parcels of a definite size.   Division of an area into certain proportional parts may be carried out by the use of special techniques in computations, which involve finding of missing bearings and distances of lines in traverses. The methods of finding missing data in traverses and proportional parts of an area are discussed in the following articles.

15-19. Missing data of lines. Missing survey data may consist of missing distances or bearings, or both. No more than two of these data may be missing in any closed traverse if they are to be found analytically. A problem may have the following three possibilities: (a) missing data are in one line, (b) missing data are in adjacent lines, (c) missing data are in non-adjacent lines.

(a) *Missing data are in one line.* When missing data are in one line, both the distance and the bearing of the line are unknown. Let it be

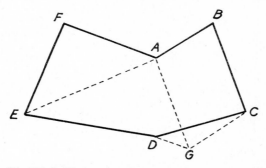

Fig. 15-8. Traverse with missing measurements.

assumed, for instance, that in the traverse *ABCDEF* (Fig. 15-8) the distance and the bearing of the line *DE* are unknown. First, it is necessary to compute the latitudes and departures of lines that have known bearings and distances. Since one latitude and one departure are missing, the excess in the sums of north or south latitudes and in the sums of east and west departures, taken with the opposite sign, must be respectively equal to the latitude and the departure of the line *DE*. Let the excess in computed latitudes be -314.7 and the excess in computed departures be $+1873.2$; then, the latitude of line *DE* must be 314.7 north and the departure 1873.2 west. The bearing angle of the line *DE* may be computed from Eq. (15-15),

$$\tan \alpha = \frac{1873.2}{314.7} = 5.9523, \qquad \text{or} \qquad \alpha = 80°27'48''$$

Thus, the bearing of line *DE* is N80°27'48''W. The distance, as computed from Eq. (15-16), is *DE* = 314.7 sec 80°27'48'' = 1899.5 ft.

(b) *Missing data in adjacent lines.* It may be assumed, in the traverse shown in Fig. 15-8, that the missing data occur in two adjacent lines, say *EF* and *FA*. In this case points *E* and *A* are connected by a straight line making the bearing and the length of line EA, in the traverse $ABCDE$, the unknown quantities. These missing data are determined by the method described under part (a) above, and then the triangle EFA is solved for the missing angles and distances of lines.

(c) *Missing data in non-adjacent sides.* In this case it may be assumed, for instance, that the missing data occur in lines AB and CD, shown in Fig. 15-8. The line BC, which has known bearing and distance, is moved parallel to itself until point B coincides with point A and point C comes to G. By connecting points D and G, one has a traverse $AGDEF$ in which the bearing and the length of line GD are unknown. These may be determined by the method described under part (a) above. Then in the triangle DCG, only one missing quantity occurs in the line CG and one in the line DC. These may be determined by solving triangle DCG. The missing quantity found in line CG is the same as that in line AB, since these are parallel lines.

15-20. How to run a line that cuts off a given area. It is often desired in a subdivision to divide the land into equal areas, or into areas bearing a certain proportion to each other. In all such cases it is required to run a new line or lines that would make the prescribed divisions. For the purpose of demonstrating the method it is sufficient to consider how to run just one line in order to cut off a certain area. In this operation the following two possibilities are considered: (a) the line must pass through a given point on a traverse, (b) the line must be run along a given direction.

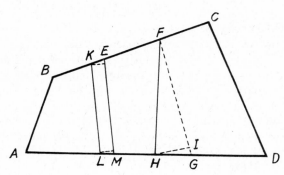

Fig. 15-9. Subdivision of an area.

(a) *Running a line through a given point.* Suppose it is required to run a line through point F of the traverse $ABCD$ shown in Fig. 15-9, in order to divide the area enclosed by the traverse in a given proportion. Since point F is a given point, the length BF may be measured. Next, the location of point G is estimated, so that the line FG will cut off the required area *FCDG*. In this traverse the distance *DG* is measured, thus leaving only the length and bearing of the line *FG* unknown. These may be determined by the method described in Art. 15-19(a). Then the area *ABFG* is computed and is compared with the area to be cut off. The difference between the two areas is the area of a triangle having line *FG* for its base, so that the altitude of the triangle may be computed. Let it be assumed, for example, that the area *ABFG* came out too large. Then the computed altitude of the correction triangle may be plotted as the line *HI* shown in the figure.

The triangle FGH may be solved for the sides *FH* and *GH*, so that in the traverse *ABFH*, which is equal to the area that it is desired to cut off, all bearings and distances become known.

(b) *Running a line in a given direction.* When the line that is supposed to cut off a certain area must be run in a given direction, say, *EM* shown in the figure, the length of line *BE* is first estimated to give the required size of the area *ABEM*. In the traverse *ABEM* the lengths of two adjacent lines *EM* and *MA* are unknown. These may be determined by the method of Art. 15-19(b). Then the area *ABEM* is computed and is compared with the area to be cut off. If the area *ABEM* is too large, the difference between the two areas gives the size of some trapezoid *KEML* in which the base *EM* and the angles are known. By the cut-and-try method the altitude of this trapezoid is estimated, and the length of line *KL* is computed by solving small triangles at each end of the trapezoid, until the computed length *KL* gives the area *KEML* equal to the above-determined difference between the two areas. This gives then the desired line *KL* in the area *ABKL* to be cut off.

Many other ramifications of the type of problems discussed in Arts. 15-19 and 15-20 may be met in actual practice. The solution of many such problems may largely depend on the ingenuity and the experience of the engineer doing the subdivision.

15-21. The planimeter. The planimeter is an instrument used for measurement of plotted areas—for instance, the areas of cross sections (see Fig. 10-8), the watershed areas shown on maps and needed for construction of bridges and culverts, the areas enclosed by construction contours, plotted on plans for computation of the amount of earthwork, and so on. In land surveying the areas adjacent to irregular boundaries along the water fronts, when plotted on paper, are often measured by a planimeter. The planimeter most commonly used in measuring such areas is the *polar planimeter*. One of its models is shown in Fig. 15-10.

The contact points that a polar planimeter makes with the working surface are (1) the *tracer point*, *A*, which is moved around the perimeter of an area being measured; (2) the bottom points of the *roller*, *B*; and (3) the needle point at the base of weight C. The last contact point is called the *anchor point*, or the *pole*, since it provides a fixed pivot contact for the instrument with the working surface.

The planimeter's *tracer arm F* is connected to the *polar arm E* by means of a free pivot at G. The roller B, graduated into 100 equal parts, is firmly attached to the tracer arm in such a way that the axis of the

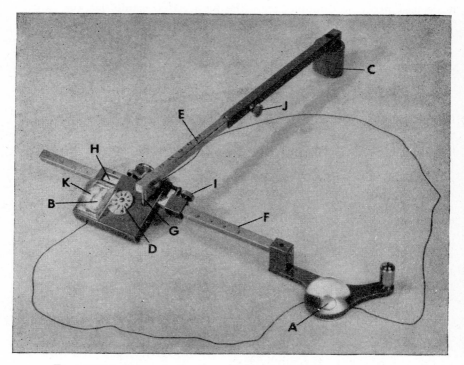

Fig. 15-10. Polar planimeter. (Courtesy Los Angeles Scientific Instrument Co.)

roller is parallel to the tracer arm. As the tracer point A is moved along the perimeter of the area being measured, the roller is dragged along the paper surface, partly rolling and partly slipping. The disk D, connected by a worm to the roller, records the number of complete revolutions of the roller. The number of drum divisions for the partial revolution of the roller is read at the index of vernier K. With the vernier reading, four significant figures are recorded for the number of revolutions of the roller.

By means of the clamp screw I, the tracer arm may be set at a desirable length indicated by the graduations read at the vernier H. The polar arm may have a fixed or an extensible length.   Figure 15-10 shows an extensible polar arm with a clamp screw J.

The size of an area traced completely around by the tracer point is proportional to the number of revolutions, n, of the roller, so that

$$\text{area} = cn \qquad (15\text{-}27)$$

where c is the measured area corresponding to one revolution of the roller. For a given setting of the planimeter's tracer arm, c is constant, so that various settings of the tracer arm correspond to various values of c. This c value, usually in square inches, is normally determined experimentally by tracing a known area of several square inches several times, taking the average of the resulting readings, and dividing the area traced by the number of revolutions of the roller.

When a measured area is plotted not to a natural scale, the results obtained by Eq. (15-27) must be multiplied by the number of square feet or inches in one square inch of plotted area.   For instance, if the horizontal scale of a figure is 1 in. = 500 ft and the vertical scale 1 in. = 50 ft, as is often the case in plotting a profile, there are 25,000 sq ft in 1 sq in. of plotted figure.

To obtain the number of revolutions of the roller, it is necessary to take the readings of the disc D and of the roller B before the tracing of the area and again after the tracer point is returned precisely to the starting point on the perimeter of measured area.   If the tracing is done in clockwise direction, with the anchor point outside the measured area, the final reading comes out greater than the initial reading.   If this is not the case, the zero index on the disc must have been passed during the operation, so that 10 must be added to the final reading.   The difference between the initial and the final readings gives the number n in Eq. (15-27).   If the area is traced in a counterclockwise direction, with the anchor point outside the measured area, the initial reading is greater than the final, but, numerically, the difference between the readings is the same, for a given area, in either case.   The accuracy of a planimeter varies with the size of a measured area; the relative random errors being greater in a relatively small area.   But ordinarily a polar planimeter is thought of as producing close to 0.1 per cent accuracy.   Some other types of planimeters, such as *rolling planimeters*, (not described in this volume) are more accurate than the polar type.

Example 15-3.   The initial reading of a planimeter is 3.725 and the final reading is 5.381, for the tracing done clockwise.   The measured area was plotted to a scale 1 in. = 50 ft; the constant c is 8.347 sq in.   It is required to determine the measured area.

Solution: One sq. in. of plotted area contains $50^2 = 2500$ sq ft, thus the measured area is

$$A = 2500 \times 8.347 \times (5.381 - 3.725) = 48,379 \text{ sq ft}$$

When it is required to measure an area so large that the anchor point cannot be kept outside the whole area, the area may be divided into a number of parts and each part may be measured separately. Another alternative is to place the anchor point inside the measured area and to trace the area completely around in one setting of the planimeter. When this is done, the area computed by Eq. (15-27) gives the measured area minus the area of the so-called *zero circle.* The zero circle is the circle described by the point of contact of the roller with the paper, when the tracer point is made to trace such a perimeter that the roller is kept, throughout the operation, in a plane passing through the anchor point. In such a tracing of an area the roller does not revolve and consequently the planimeter does not record any revolutions. Thus the area of the zero circle, when smaller than the measured area, must be added to the area computed by Eq. (15-27).

The area of the zero circle may be determined by measuring an area with the anchor point outside an area and then with the anchor point inside the same area. The difference between the two results gives the area of the zero circle.

PROBLEMS

15-1. Compute latitudes and departures for the traverses shown below, and determine closing errors in latitudes and departures. Traverses in parts (A) and (B) were made with a 30″ transit and in part (C) with 1′ transit. All angles were measured once direct, once reversed.

(A)

	Given Data		*Answers*	
Line	Distance (Feet)	Bearing	Lat.	Dep.
AB	199.79	N70°29′38″E	66.71	188.32
BC	144.06	S38°44′19″E	−112.37	90.15
CD	171.34	S29°55′06″W	−148.51	−85.46
DA	273.72	N44°47′34″W	194.25	−192.85

$$\Delta L = 0.08 \qquad \Delta D = 0.16$$

(B)

Line	Distance (Feet)	Bearing
PQ	543.90	N52°41′06″E
QR	650.13	S61°27′27″E
RS	522.91	S11°17′15″E
ST	885.32	S74°34′17″W
TP	772.17	N19°08′53″W

(C)

Line	Distance (Feet)	Bearing
CD	596.45	N82°07′23″E
DE	573.89	S7°21′12″E
EA	420.57	N77°19′41″W
AB	268.56	S78°00′14″W
BC	450.40	N1°09′19″E

15-2. From the computed latitudes and departures in Problem 15-1 above (a) find the linear error of closure, E, for the traverse, and (b) determine the relative error of closure $E/\Sigma s$; then (c) plot to approximate scale the obtained ΔL and ΔD values on coordinate axes and show the relative position of the closing point in the last course with respect to the beginning point in the first course, also compute the bearing of the line connecting the two points; (d) adjust latitudes and departures by the method shown in Tables 15-3 and 15-4, using Table 15-2 for the estimation of angular errors.

    (A) *Ans.* (a) 0.1775, (b) 1:4450, (c) N63°26′E, (d) Lat. 66.70, −112.39, −148.53, 194.22; Dep. 188.27, 90.12, −85.49, −192.90

15-3. Determine the corrections for the latitudes and departures computed in Problem 15-1 by the transit rule method. Compare these corrections with those obtained in Problem 15-2(d) by computing relative errors, in per cent, in corrections obtained by the transit rule. (See example in Table 15-7.)

    (A) *Ans.* Lat. 66.70, −112.39, −148.53, 194.22; Dep. 188.27, 90.12, −85.48, −192.91; per cent error: none in latitudes, 33% in Dep. of *CD*, 20% in Dep. of *DA*.

15-4. Compute bearings and distances from the adjusted latitudes and departures of Problem 15-2(d).

15-5. Use adjusted latitudes and departures of Problem 15-2(d) to compute the area of the traverse by the D.M.D. method. Use reference meridian through the most westerly point of the traverse. (A) *Ans.* 36,213 sq ft

15-6. Plot an assigned traverse of Problem 15-1, approximately to scale, using the computed latitudes and departures of the given courses.   (a) Using adjusted latitudes and departures of Problem 15-2(d), compute x and y coordinates of points referred to X axis through the most southerly point and Y axis through the most westerly point of the traverse.   (b) Compute the area by the method of coordinates.

(A) *Ans.* A(0, 194.22), B(188.27, 260.92), C(278.39, 148.53), D(192.90, 0); area = 36.21$\underline{3}$ sq ft

15-7. In the closed traverses shown below, the latitude and departure of one course are missing.   (a) Determine missing data from the given latitudes and departures of other courses, (b) compute distances and bearings of lines, (c) compute D.M.D.'s for the meridian through the most westerly point of traverses, (d) compute the area by the D.M.D. method.

(A)

Course	Given Data Latitude	Given Data Departure	*Answers* Dist.	*Answers* Bearing (to 30″)	*Answers* D.M.D.
A B	−163.7	−301.5	243.1	S61°30′W	301.5
B C	−247.0	145.2	286.5	S30°27′E	145.2
C D	183.4	125.3	222.1	N34°20′30″E	415.7
D E	49.1	259.9	264.5	N79°18′E	800.9
E A	178.2	−228.9	290.1	N52°06′W	831.9

area = 89,2$\underline{9}$0 sq ft

(B)

Course	Latitude	Departure
A B	−130.2	−225.6
B C	−493.5	−144.3
C D	190.7	270.2
D E	70.8	426.1
E F		
F A	229.4	−90.3

(C)

Course	Latitude	Departure
A B	−215.7	−250.3
B C		
C D	150.8	402.5
D E	297.2	−158.6
E A	104.7	−224.0

15-8. Plot the assigned traverse given in Problem 15-7 and compute the area by the method of coordinates, using X axis through the most southerly point and Y axis through the most westerly point of the given traverse.

(A) *Ans.* Area = 89,290 sq ft

15-9. In the traverses shown in Problem 15-7, it is required to run, through point B, a line that will divide total area into two equal parts. Determine the length and bearing of such a line. (A) *Ans.* 525.8 ft, S88°49′30″E

15-10. In the traverses shown in Problem 15-7, it is required to run a line MN that will divide the total area into two equal parts. Points M and N must be on the traverse and the bearing of line MN must be N68°50′E. Determine distance MN and the proportional parts of the two lines divided, respectively, by points M and N.

Ans. MN = 407.7 ft, $BM:MC$ = 95.8:190.7; $AN:NE$ = 161.4:128.7

15-11. A base line was measured on the ground a certain distance from a curved boundary. This base line was divided into ten sections. The first nine sections, from left to right, are each 25.0 ft long and the last section is 17.5 ft long. The points along the base were numbered from 1 to 11 from left to right and the right-angle offsets were measured from the base to the curved boundary, in feet, as is given below. Determine the area between the base and the curve by the trapezoidal rule.

(A)	h_1	h_2	h_3	h_4	h_5	h_6	h_7	h_8	h_9	h_{10}	h_{11}
	7.5	30.1	22.3	28.4	38.0	47.6	44.2	46.8	23.7	21.3	8.2

Ans. 7600 sq ft

(B) 5.9, 21.4, 28.3, 17.1, 9.7, 5.2, 13.5, 24.8, 17.0, 13.2, 9.5.
(C) 0 , 12.5, 27.3, 32.9, 21.4, 35.6, 31.0, 22.7, 13.4, 10.2, 7.3.

15-12. Determine the areas required in Problem 15-11 by Simpson's one-third rule. (A) *Ans.* 7900 sq ft

CHAPTER **16**

Underground Surveys

16-1. The purpose. Underground surveys are necessary either in tunneling operations, conducted for the establishment of transportation and communication routes, water conduits, pipe lines, and other such purposes, or in mine operations, conducted for the purpose of excavating organic and inorganic deposits such as coal and metal-bearing ores. These two types of operations are discussed in this chapter as *tunneling* and *mine surveys*, respectively.

Tunneling

16-2. Required surveys. The extent of the surveying work needed for tunneling naturally varies from one project to another, but, generally speaking, the planning, design, and construction of a tunnel require surveys of the same kind as are needed for any other structure. First, a *reconnaissance* survey is made of the terrain where the proposed facility is needed; second, *preliminary* surveys are conducted to obtain data for plotting various details and ground configurations on drawings that will be used in the design of the tunnel; and finally the *location* survey is made to establish exact grades and directions for the excavation and the construction of the tunnel.

If the proposed tunnel is a part of a transportation route or a pipe line, the reconnaissance survey is conducted largely by means of aerial photographs and small-scale topographic maps made from photographs.

The reconnaissance survey determines the location for the proposed structures, at which place the preliminary line is staked out on the ground.

The preliminary survey includes profile leveling, cross-sectioning, and other surveying operations needed for plotting elevations, ground contours, and various planimetric features in the vicinity of a proposed tunnel. Certain types of terrain, because of steep slopes, heavy vegetation, and rugged ground surface, may not be suitable for direct measurements along the proposed center line of a tunnel. In such places the distance and the direction along the center line of a route may be determined either as a missing line of a traverse run along a roundabout course, or by triangulation.

Figure 16-1 shows a traverse *ABCDEF* connecting two terminal points *A* and *F* of a route at the ends of a proposed tunnel. The closure on such a traverse is effected by running the traverse in both directions. If the location survey follows the preliminary alignment, the computed distance and the bearing of the closing line *AF* must check actual measurements made through the tunnel after completion of its excavation.

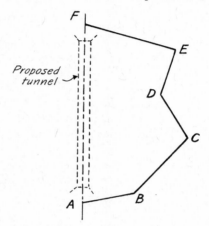

Fig. 16-1. A typical traverse for a tunnel.

On long tunnels the excavation normally proceeds from both ends. Such operations require not only accurate alignment but also accurate elevations and grades at both ends of the tunnel.

16-3. Traversing through a tunnel. The methods and the equipment used in running a traverse through a tunnel must conform to the limitations imposed by the narrow confines. Although in many cases the use of a standard engineer's transit may present no special difficulty, a smaller and lighter transit, known as a mining transit, is much easier to handle, especially in long narrow tunnels. Tripod legs of the transit must be adjustable, since a low height of the instrument may be necessary in some transit set-ups. The transit must have a point marked on the top of the telescope for setting the transit up under stations established on the tunnel roof. Telescopes on most transits have such a point, where the produced vertical axis of the leveled transit pierces the telescope barrel when the latter is in horizontal position. The transit should have a full vertical circle, preferably enclosed in a metal frame, in order to protect the scale from dripping water.

The station points along a tunnel traverse are often established on the roof of the tunnel, since here they are not likely to be disturbed.   In order to establish a station, a wooden plug is driven into a hole drilled in the roof; then a small hook, called a *spad*, is hammered or screwed into the plug.   The spads come in a variety of shapes but, in an emergency, even a bent nail will answer the purpose.   A plumb bob is hung from the spad when the sight is taken on that station with the instrument.

A rail spike, with a punched hole on top, may be used for a floor station.   This is especially convenient when there is a track on the floor, as is often the case in mines.   The stations are usually marked with a white ring painted around the station point, and the station identifications are marked on the tunnel walls.

A surveying party working in a tunnel, or in a mine, must be equipped with proper lamps and flashlights to provide illumination for the transit cross hairs and for the points sighted on.   A flashlight, held slightly to one side at the objective end of the telescope, provides satisfactory illumination for the cross hairs.   However, since the cross hairs are visible when a sight is taken on a brightly illuminated object, the string of the plumb bob, on which the sight is taken, may be silhouetted on a piece of white paper by means of a lamp held behind the paper.   This eliminates the necessity of illuminating the cross hairs, since the hairs and the plumb bob string both are made visible on the background of illuminated paper.

A distance in a tunnel is measured along a slope from the transit's horizontal axis to the point sighted on.   The vertical angle is also measured and the horizontal distance is computed by the formula

$$d = s - s \text{ vers } \alpha \tag{16-1}$$

where d is the horizontal distance, s is the correct slope distance, and α is the vertical angle.   In order to obtain the correct slope distance the measured distance must be corrected for the sag of the tape; for the incorrect length of tape at 68°F; for change in measured length due to temperature, if it is different from 68°F; and for change in length due to tension, if it is different from that at which the tape was standardized. The formulas for these systematic errors in taping are given in Chapter 7, Arts. 7-12 through 7-16.   Many engineers prefer to use the normal tension in taping, which eliminates corrections for both the sag and the pull (see Art. 7-17).   On minor jobs, where the required accuracy is lower than 1:3000, corrections for temperature and for the incorrect length of tape may be neglected.

Vertical angles must be measured once direct and once reversed, in order to eliminate the index error of the instrument.   This requires that the transits be equipped with a full vertical circle.   The instrument must be carefully leveled, preferably by the telescope level, in order to avoid errors due to the inclination of the transit's vertical axis (see Art. 11-18).

Horizontal angles in a tunnel are usually measured as direct angles to the right or to the left (see Art. 11-7). In measuring horizontal angles, one must exercise proper care in leveling the transit, because the inclination of the vertical axis affects measured angles when the backsight and foresight points are at different elevations (Art. 11-17). The greater is their difference in elevation the more carefully the transit should be leveled. It is best in such cases to level the instrument by using the telescope level since it has greater sensitivity than plate levels. All angles must be measured the same number of times with the telescope in direct and in reversed position.

16-4. Determination of elevation of points. The elevations of stations in a tunnel are found either by leveling operations, as on any other engineering project, or by measuring the height of the transit and the height of the point sighted on, at the time of measuring the slope distance. These data are used in combination with the measured slope distance and the vertical angle, to compute the difference in elevation of the stations involved.

The use of the engineer's level and the leveling rod normally yields more accurate results for the elevation of points than those obtained by the measurement of vertical angles. The reason is that a standard transit measures vertical angles only to the nearest minute. However, the use of vertical angles in finding the difference in elevation of points is accurate enough in most tunnel surveys.

If leveling is done with an engineer's level, or with a transit used as a level, the leveling rod must have three sliding sections. In closed position, such rods are $4\frac{1}{2}$ ft long. On roof stations the rod must be held upside down and must be illuminated by a lamp. A rod reading taken below a point is negative. Thus all rod readings on roof stations must be recorded with the minus sign. The procedures in computing the H.I. and the elevations of points are the same as with positive rod readings since all additions and subtractions must be performed algebraically. For instance, if the elevation of a station is, say, 520.32 ft and the backsight reading on a point is -2.10 ft, the height of instrument is $520.32 + (-2.10) = 518.22$ ft. (See Measurement of Elevations, Chapter 9.)

The method of finding the difference in elevation of two points by the use of a measured slope distance and the vertical angle is shown in Fig. 16-2. Let it be assumed that the correct slope distance between the instrument set up at Sta. A and the point sighted on at Sta. B is s, and that the vertical angle between those points is α. Then the vertical distance between these points is $s \sin \alpha$. This distance is positive if α is positive and negative if α is negative. In order to obtain the difference in elevation between the two roof stations A and B, shown on the figure, the height of transit (H.T.) must be added (algebraically) to the computed vertical distance (V.D.), and the height of point (H.P.) as read on the rod must be subtracted (algebraically) from the obtained sum.   However, since the height of point for a roof station is negative, and since subtraction of a negative quantity changes its sign to plus, it is customary in mine and tunnel surveying to regard the height of point below station as *positive* and to *add* it algebraically in finding the difference in elevation

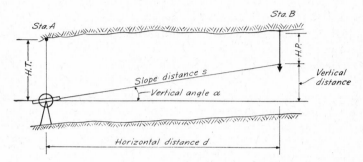

Fig. 16-2. Measurements in a tunnel.

between any two stations.   No such exception is made in the case of the height of transit.   Thus the following sign conventions for the H.T. and H.P. are used in the mine and tunnel surveying:

> H.T. is positive when measured above a station and negative when measured below a station.
>
> H.P. is positive when measured below a station and negative when measured above a station.

Under this sign convention the three quantities, V.D., H.T., and H.P., are always added algebraically in order to obtain the difference in elevation (D.E.) between the station on which the sight is taken and the station at which the transit is set up.   Thus

$$\text{D.E.} = \text{V.D.} + \text{H.T.} + \text{H.P.} \qquad (16\text{-}2)$$

Example 16-1.   The following data are recorded in a field notebook for measurements made in a tunnel between two Stas. A and B.   Transit is at Sta. A, having elevation 725.27 ft, H.T. $= -5.38$; H.P. $= 3.71$ at Sta. B; vertical angle $-7°21'$ with the telescope direct and $-7°22'$ with telescope reversed.   Slope distance between the points is $s = 82.45$ ft, measured under normal tension.   Neglecting corrections for tape and temperature, determine the horizontal distance and the difference in elevation between Stas. A and B.

Solution:

Mean vertical angle $= -7°21'30''$

horizontal distance $d = s - s$ vers $\alpha = 82.45 - 82.45$ vers $7°21'30''$

$$= 82.45 - 0.68 = 81.77$$

vertical distance V.D. $= s \sin \alpha = 82.45 \sin(-7°21'30'') = -10.56$

difference in elevation D.E. $=$ V.D. $+$ H.T. $+$ H.P. $= -10.56 - 5.38 + 3.71$
$$= -12.23 \text{ ft}$$

elevation of Sta. $B = 725.27 - 12.23 = 713.04$

It should be noted that the difference in the sines of small angles is equal to 0.000291 per 1' of change in angle. Thus if the value of the

Transit at Sta.	H.T.	H.P.	Vertical Angle	Slope Distan.	B.S. on Sta.	Direct Angle	Elev.	Remarks

TUNNEL TRAVERSE
Sta. 15+21 to 25+30

Sept. 15, 1959 — *H.C. Hale*
Transit No. 12 — *D.K. Long*
Tape No. 8 — *I.T. Black*
Rod No. 5 — *D.P. Green*

7.

Fig. 16-3. Notes for a tunnel traverse.

measured vertical angle is known to the nearest minute, the uncertainty in the sine function may vary from 0 to 0.000146, the last value being the sine of 30''. Thus in Example 16-1 the maximum error in the computed vertical distance, owing to 30'' uncertainty in the measured angle, may be as great as $82.45 \times 0.000146 = \pm 0.01$ ft. The accumulation of these errors should not greatly affect tunnel excavation. If more accurate leveling is required, the engineer's level and the leveling rod must be used.

16-5. Recording of data. As Example 16-1 shows, the recording of data in the field notebook, for a mine traverse, must combine the data needed for determining horizontal distances as well as the elevations of points. In addition, measured horizontal angles must be recorded in the field book. Thus the headings, extended across a double page of the notebook, should include those shown in Fig. 16-3.

In many tunnels, the dripping of underground water may soil the pages of a notebook, making the recorded data hard to read. For this reason, the recordings must be especially clear and distinct. If necessary, the pages should be rewritten at the end of a day's work.

Mine Surveying

16-6. Special considerations. Mine surveying differs from tunnel surveying in that the workings of a mine are far more irregular, since the excavations must follow underground deposits of ore, coal, or minerals. The purposes of mine surveying are to connect underground traverses to the property lines staked out on the surface; to determine the extent of excavations made at various levels; to determine the direction of tunneling when necessary; and to keep accurate records of underground workings for further planning and for making mine maps.

The subject of mine surveying includes also surface surveying for mining claims and surveying for a *patent*, both discussed at the end of this chapter.

16-7. Definitions. Definitions of some terms used in mining are given below.

Vein is a relatively thin stratum of mineral or ore deposits.

Lode is an ore-bearing rock-vein discovered on public lands.

Outcrop is the exposed section of a vein on the ground surface.

Strike is the line of intersection of the plane of a deposit with the horizontal plane; its direction is usually indicated as a bearing.

Dip is the vertical angle of inclination of a stratum relative to the horizontal. The angle is measured at right angle to the strike.

A *level,* designated as the first, second, and so on, determines the location of mine passageways in relation to ground surface. The first level is the one that is closest to the surface.

Stope is a room off a passageway, where the deposit is excavated.

Mill hole is the connection of a stope with the passageway.

Patent is a document, issued by the U.S. Government, granting to the owner of a claim exclusive rights to develop a lode.

16-8. Mine planning. It is relatively easy to determine the strike of a deposit from its outcrop. If the direction of the strike is known, the dip of the vein is calculated so that mine workings may be planned within the confines of the existing property lines. The mine's main passageway should be directly connected to the property line surveyed on the surface. If there are several mine entrances, the passageways leading from various entrances are eventually connected underground, thus making it possible to effect a closure for several traverses run from various entrances.

In most cases, however, mine planning is not as simple as it is when the outcrop occurs within the property lines of the owner planning a mining development. Many natural deposits occur deep underground and are discovered only by drilling holes in places where the deposits are suspected. Such deposits are often reached by excavating one or more vertical shafts.

16-9. Horizontal and vertical controls. It is important in mine surveying to tie underground traverses to the horizontal and vertical controls on the surface. When surface controls must be transferred underground through a shaft, special methods must be employed in order to do the work as accurately as possible. (See Arts. 16-11 and 16-12 below.)

16-10. Mining transit. The mining transit is shown in Fig. 11-6 (p. 171). One of its special features is an auxiliary telescope, attached at one end of the horizontal axis. Such transits are called *side telescope transits.* The side telescope may be used for any steep sight up to ±90°. The horizontal and vertical angles are measured with a side telescope in the same manner as with the main telescope. When the angles are measured the same number of times with the telescope in direct and in reversed positions, no correction for the *eccentricity* of the side telescope need be applied to measured horizontal angles. The reversal procedure also eliminates index errors in measured vertical angles.

Side telescopes are detachable and thus do not have to be on the transit when not needed. On some transits the auxiliary telescope may be attached either as a side telescope or on top of the main telescope. A transit with the latter arrangement is called a *top telescope transit.* The use of top telescope transit has at least the following three disadvantages as compared with the use of side telescope: (a) angles cannot be measured with the telescope in reversed position, (b) the top telescope uses extra head room which often cannot be spared in tunnel or mine surveying, (c) taking steep downward sights with the top telescope places the instrumentman in an extremely awkward position. For these reasons the use of the top telescope can not be recommended.

Since the auxiliary telescope is used primarily for measuring vertical and horizontal angles on steeply inclined lines of sight, the transit and the side telescope must be in good adjustment if accurate results in measurements are expected. (See Arts. 11-17 and 11-18 for systematic errors in measured angles.) The adjustment of the auxiliary telescope is discussed in Art. 16-16 below.

Mining transits are light instruments, weighing close to $9\frac{1}{2}$ lbs. They are built with a full vertical circle equipped with a light metal frame as protection from water drippings which are common in a mine. The tripod must be of the extension-leg type, on which the transit may be set with low height of instrument if necessary. A special short-leg tripod, called a *trivet*, that can be set on a mine's ledge, is a useful accessory to a mining transit. The optics of mining transits are such as to make it possible to focus objects at close range.

16-11. Transferring surface azimuth through a vertical shaft. A known azimuth of a line at the top of a vertical shaft is commonly transferred to the shaft's bottom by means of two piano wires suspended in the shaft. Weights are attached at the bottom ends of these wires in order to keep the wires taut and plumb. Good care must be observed in determining the azimuth of the vertical plane passing through the wires, since a slight error in the azimuth of two closely hung wires causes considerable errors at long traverse distances in the mine. For instance, a 2′ error in the azimuth of two wires, placed 5 ft apart, gives 0.00291 ft offset error at 5 ft and 2.91 ft error at 5000 ft.

The wires must be hung at the top of the shaft as far apart as possible without letting the wires touch any object along the shaft's framework. It is best to suspend the wires from pulleys fastened to a cross beam so that the transit may be set in line with the two wires on the ground surface. The weights suspended from the wires normally vary from about 20 lb to 50 lb, depending on the shaft's depth. A longer wire requires a greater weight to keep the wire plumb and straight. In order to reduce oscillations to a minimum, the weights are placed in oil-filled containers.

The azimuth of the vertical plane through the wires is determined at the ground surface by running a traverse to a line of known azimuth. The accuracy in determining the azimuth of the wires' plane is greatly dependent on the accuracy of the horizontal angle measured from the line of the wires to the first traverse point. In order to be able to measure such an angle, one must accurately set up the transit in line with the wires. For best results the angle must be measured by repetition, and measured the same number of times with the instrument in direct and in reversed position. If the alignment of the transit with the wires is not perfect after the reversal of the telescope, the instrument should be realigned with the wires before measuring the angle with the telescope in reversed position. The final reading of the horizontal circle, divided by the number of repetitions, gives the value of the measured angle. The accuracy of this measurement depends on the care exercised in lining up the transit and on the number of repetitions.

The same procedure of lining up the transit with two wires, and measuring the first horizontal angle in the underground traverse, is repeated at the shaft's bottom. Since certain oscillations of wires may be expected, caused by unavoidable air drafts, it is a good practice to fix a scale behind each wire and to notice through the telescope the amplitude of wire oscillations. The transit is then lined up with the amplitudes' mid-points marked on scales. After accurate measurement of the first angle, permanent markers are established, normally along the foresight direction of the measured angle, in order to fix a reference azimuth for mine traversing.

16-12. Transferring elevation through a vertical shaft. A leveling circuit is first run from a bench mark on the ground surface to some convenient point on a shaft's cross beam, from which a steel tape may be suspended, vertically, through the shaft.   A weight attached to the zero end of the tape is freely suspended near the bottom of the shaft while a certain footmark is held at the top at the point of known elevation.   The reading at the bottom end of tape is made by a transit or a level set as close to the tape as the telescope focusing permits.   The instrument is then carefully leveled and the tape is read at the intersection of the cross hairs.   Then a spike or a nail is driven in a solid timber at the elevation of the line of sight.   Such a point serves only as a temporary bench mark until a more permanent bench mark is established.

The weight attached at the bottom end of the tape, and the weight of tape itself, stretch the tape so that the difference between the tape readings at the top and at the bottom of the shaft must be corrected for the amount of tape elongation.   The average tension in a vertically suspended length L of a tape, owing to the weight W_L of this length, is $W_L/2$.   Thus with a weight Q attached to the lower end of tape, the total average tension in the tape is $Q + W_L/2$.   This value is substituted for P in Eq. (7-5), given in Chapter 7, in order to find correction C_p for the suspended length L of the tape.   A proportional amount C_v of this correction must be computed as the correction for the measured vertical length V.   By making the above-mentioned substitutions to Eq. (7-5), and using in that equation $100W_L/L$ instead of W_0, the following expression is obtained:

$$C_v = \frac{C_p V}{L} = \frac{V}{L}\,\frac{\left(Q + \dfrac{W_L}{2} - P_0\right)L}{8.82 \times 10^4\, W_L \dfrac{100}{L}} \tag{16-3}$$

When simplified, this expression reduces to the following form:

$$C_v = \frac{(2Q + W_L - 2P_0)VL}{1.764 \times 10^7 W_L} \tag{16-4}$$

In Eq. (16-4), W_L is the weight of the vertically suspended length L of the tape, Q is the weight attached to the tape, P_0 is the pull at which the tape was standardized, and V is the measured vertical distance.

The direct proportion $C_v = C_p V/L$, which is used in Eq. (16-3), is not strictly correct, since a vertically suspended tape does not stretch uniformly.   However, the amount of error is quite negligible, because the non-uniform stretching of the tape is due only to the weight of the tape, which is small, unless the tape is several hundred feet long.   But in the latter case the ratio V/L approaches unity thus making the error negligible in any case.

The actual lengths of tapes are made nowadays quite close to their nominal lengths, thus correction of a measured vertical distance for the incorrect length of tape should be in most cases quite negligible. The same thing applies to the correction for temperature.

Instead of using long tapes in deep shafts, a piano wire may be used to measure the vertical length. The ends of the measured length may be marked by pieces of adhesive tape wrapped around the wire. The wire is then stretched under the same tension on the ground and is measured by a steel tape.

16-13. Mines having two or more shafts. When a mine has two shafts, one wire is suspended in each shaft and a surface traverse is run

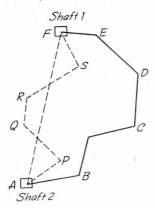

from one wire to another, closing back on the starting point. After the angles and the distances in this traverse are adjusted, the missing distance and the bearing of the line between the wires are determined by the latitude-and-departure method described in Art. 15-19. Figure 16-4 shows a surface traverse *ABCDE* between two mine shafts, from which the length and bearing of the line *AF* are computed.

Another traverse between the same wires is run through the mine with an assumed bearing of some line, possibly determined by a compass. From this assumed bearing and measured distances and angles, the length and bearing of the closing line *AF* are determined

Fig. 16-4. Mine traverses.

for the underground traverse. The difference between the bearing of the line *AF* as determined by underground traverse and the true bearing of the same line as determined by the surface traverse constitutes the correction that is applied to the courses in the mine traverse. One-half of the difference in lengths of the line *AF* as determined from the two traverses may be taken as the approximate error of closure in the mine traverse, thus giving an approximate idea of the accuracy attained in that survey.

Where there are more than two shafts, independent traverses may be run between the wires suspended in various shafts, thus affording more checks and a chance for better adjustment of the mine traverses.

16-14. Mine traversing. Mine traversing is quite similar to that described in Arts. 16-3 and 16-4 for tunnel surveying as far as the measurement of distances and the determination of elevations of points are concerned. There are more angles to be measured in a mine traverse, and many side measurements must be made off the main traverse courses. A good point to bear in mind in mine surveying is that the size, grade, direction, and relative location of all passages, mill holes, stopes, and other mine workings must be accurately recorded and later plotted on paper. Thus many offset measurements are made in a mine at various stations in order to obtain proper data for mine workings.

The mine surveyor should not forget that the success of a mine depends on the amount and the quality of excavated valuable materials and on the cost of their recovery. Thus it is important to record the quality and the amount of deposits excavated at various places; these data are necessary for proper planning and economical operation. In this respect, the duties of a surveyor overlap somewhat with those of other technical personnel connected with mine operations.

The type of notes shown in Fig. 16-3 are quite adequate for straight traversing in a mine. In addition, numerous sketches must show the location of various mine workings, so that a person unfamiliar with a given mine layout could, without difficulty, reproduce mine passages on drawings and on a model.

The solutions to many special surveying problems arising in mine operations, such as determining a proper grade and direction in connecting various mine passages, greatly depend upon the ingenuity and experience of the surveyor. The solutions to many such problems may be obtained relatively easily by computing the three rectangular coordinates of stations in space. If, for instance, a tunnel connection must be made between two points of known x, y, and z coordinates, it requires only simple computations to find the grade, distance, and the direction between the points.

16-15. Measurements with auxiliary telescopes. There is no difference in general procedure whether measurements of horizontal and vertical angles are made with the main telescope or with an auxiliary side telescope. Nor are any corrections required for the mean value of measured angles if the measurements are made the same number of times with the telescope in the direct and in the reversed positions. However, when the angles are measured with the top auxiliary telescope, no reversal of the telescope is possible. This is the main reason (see Art. 16-10) why the use of the auxiliary top telescope is not recommended. Only measurements with a side telescope are discussed below.

When vertical angles are measured with a side telescope that is in proper adjustment, the direct and the reversed readings of the vertical circle should be identical with those made by the main transit telescope, if steep sights with that telescope were possible. Thus the index errors in vertical angles measured with a side telescope are eliminated by taking the average of the direct and reversed readings of the vertical circle.

In the measurement of horizontal angles with a side telescope, the eccentricity affects the size of measured angles, as shown in Fig. 16-5. The horizontal angle between the points A and B, as measured by the side telescope, is angle $H' = AO'B$, if points C and D on the figure are respective positions of the side telescope when the backsight to point A and the foresight to point B are taken; $OC = OD = e$ being the eccentricity of the side telescope. The correct horizontal angle between A and B, for a given transit set-up at point O, is angle $H = AOB$. If one draws through O' the lines $O'A'$ and $O'B'$, parallel respectively to directions OA and OB, angle H is made equal to $A'O'B'$ with the vertex at O'.

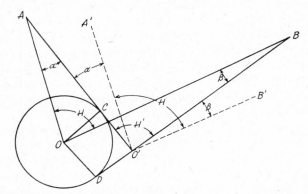

Fig. 16-5. Measurement of horizontal angle by side telescope.

Thus when it is necessary to obtain the value of angle H from the measured angle H', the angle α shown on the figure must be subtracted from H' and the angle β must be added to H'. Thus

$$H = H' - \alpha + \beta \qquad (16\text{-}5)$$

The angles α and β can be computed respectively from the triangles OAC and OBD as follows:

$$\alpha = \sin^{-1}\frac{e}{OA} = \tan^{-1}\frac{e}{CA} \qquad (16\text{-}6)$$

and
$$\beta = \sin^{-1}\frac{e}{OB} = \tan^{-1}\frac{e}{DB} \qquad (16\text{-}7)$$

After the reversal of the telescope the side telescope changes its position over to the opposite side of the main telescope. The effect is that the angle α has to be added to the measured angle H'' and the angle β has to be subtracted from H'' in order to obtain the correct horizontal angle H. Thus when the horizontal angle is measured between the same two points A and B with the side telescope in reversed position,

$$H = H'' + \alpha - \beta \qquad (16\text{-}8)$$

where α and β have the same values as in Eq. (16-5).

When Eq. (16-5) is added to Eq. (16-8) and the mean value of the accumulated angles $H' + H''$ on the horizontal circle is computed,

$$\frac{H' + H''}{2} = H \qquad (16\text{-}9)$$

In the narrow confines of mine workings, however, there may be situations when the points sighted with the side telescope in direct position become obstructed after the telescope is reversed. In such cases Eq. (16-5) must be used to compute the correct horizontal angle H.

16-16. Adjustment of a side telescope. On most mining transits the attached side telescope has no independent side motion. Thus the adjustment of the line of sight of a side telescope is made by moving the telescope's cross-hair ring. Before adjusting the side telescope, one must check the adjustments of other parts of the transit. Special care must be exercised in verifying the adjustments that the line of sight is perpendicular to the horizontal axis, and that the horizontal axis of the instrument is perpendicular to the vertical axis. (See adjustments 3 and 4, Art. 11-22.)

In the adjustment of the side telescope the following two conditions must be satisfied:

(1) That the horizontal cross hair lies in a plane perpendicular to the vertical axis, and

(2) That the vertical planes containing the lines of sight of the two telescopes are parallel.

In the first adjustment a well-defined point is sighted and is placed on the horizontal hair. The instrument is then slowly rotated in azimuth. If the point does not stay on the horizontal hair, adjust the cross-hair ring, by rotating it in a proper direction, until the sighted point does stay on the horizontal hair.

In the second adjustment (the line of sight of the main telescope already being in proper adjustment) the cross-hair ring of the auxiliary telescope is moved right or left until the line of sight of the auxiliary telescope becomes parallel to that of the main telescope. This adjustment may be accomplished in the following two ways:

(a) By sighting a distant point at least two miles away with the main telescope and then adjusting the vertical hair of the auxiliary telescope on the same point.

(b) By measuring the eccentricity of the side telescope and scaling this distance on a card. Two short vertical lines are then drawn through the end points of the line. The card is placed about 100 ft from the leveled transit and the left vertical line is sighted with the main telescope. The cross-hair ring of the side telescope is then adjusted on the right

vertical line. The adjustment may be double-checked by placing the
card 10 or 15 ft in front of the transit.

16-17. Mine maps and models. As on other engineering projects
the surveying data obtained in mine surveys must be plotted on paper
to form maps, plans, profiles, cross sections, and other drawings from
which a clear idea of the mine workings can be obtained.

Drawing of plans includes the *surface plan* and the *underground plan*.
The surface plan must show property boundaries, roads, buildings, mine
entrances, water lines, and all other features that are important to the
development of a mine. The topography of the ground surface should
also be shown on the surface plan by means of contours. Surface plans
are normally drawn to a scale varying from about 100 to 200 ft to an inch.

The underground plan must show the projection of all mine workings
on a horizontal plane. If there are several levels in a mine it is preferable
to have a separate plan for each level. If a single plan is made, the
various levels are shown in different colors. The underground plans
are usually drawn to a scale of about 40 or 50 ft to an inch.

A longitudinal section through the area of mine workings must be
drawn in order to show a profile view of all levels projected on a vertical
plane. The longitudinal section must show all workings indicated on
the underground plan, so that vertical distances between levels or other
workings could be obtained from the drawing.

Various cross sections, often drawn at right angle to the longitudinal
section, show the expansion of mine workings in lateral directions. The
required number of such sections depends on the size and the complexity
of the workings.

Separate maps showing the dimensions of each stope are important
drawings in mine operation. These maps must be kept up to date,
showing the progress made in removing mined deposits, and the thickness
and the angle of dip of such deposits. The notes accompanying each
such map should give information on the grade of the ore removed, the
waste material excavated, and other pertinent data.

Another important map that must be kept up to date in mine operations is the geological map. This map is often drawn for each level,
showing the thickness of deposits, the contours of a working bed, discovered faults, veins, and other geological data. Strikes and dips of
various strata are determined from the geological map. This map has
important bearing on the future planning of mine operations.

Plotting, in all such drawings, may be facilitated by determining the
coordinates of underground stations. If proper datum planes are chosen,
all coordinates may be made positive. When x, y, and z coordinates of
various stations are known, the plotting can be done easier, faster, and
with greater accuracy.

Known coordinates of underground stations are also extremely useful in making models of underground workings. Strips of glass, wood, and paint are commonly used, although various plastic materials are fast gaining popularity in the art of model making.

16-18. Staking a claim. When mineral deposits are discovered on public lands in the United States, the discoverer, usually a prospector, may file a claim to those deposits. The laws regulating such claims must be understood and strictly adhered to. The U.S. Government limits the surface area of a claim to 1500 ft in length and 300 ft on each side of the center line. The specified length may be along a straight course

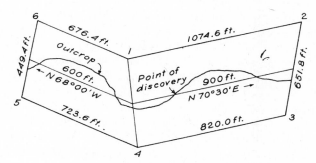

Fig. 16-6. Staking a claim.

or along any number and shape of courses. The end boundaries must be straight, parallel lines at any angle to the center line. Figure 16-6 shows 900 ft of a claim along a course of N70°30'E and 600 ft along a course of N68°00'W. The end lines marked by the corners 2, 3 and 5, 6 are parallel. The center line of a claim normally follows the approximate direction of the discovered outcrop of a deposit and passes through the point of discovery. Local state laws may further limit the extent of a claim but they cannot increase the above-specified limits of a claim.

After a claim is surveyed and is staked out on the ground, a metes-and-bounds description of it is recorded with the clerk of the county where the claim is located. This so-called *location certificate* must also include the name of the claimant, the date, and the description of the claim's location.

16-19. Surveying for a patent. Registering a claim does not secure for a claimant the right to mine the claimed deposits, but it is the first step in the process of obtaining a patent from the U.S. Government. The patent does convey such rights. Before applying for a patent the claimant must show the intention to develop his claim by making improvements estimated to be worth not less than $500 per claim. The claim must also be surveyed with about 1:1000 accuracy or better and reregistered with the county clerk, if the first survey in staking out a claim was only approximate.

When the application for patent is made, the Government appoints a surveyor, who has the title of United States Deputy Mineral Surveyor, to survey the claim for the patent. The deputy surveyor also secures an order from the Surveyor General of the state in which the claim is located to proceed with the patent survey.

The survey of a claim is made by the deputy surveyor like any property survey. The corners are monumented and the survey is tied to a section corner of the United States Public Land Survey or to a monument established by other government surveys.* After the patent is granted, the claimant has exclusive right to exploit the claimed deposits.

In development of a claim the extent of underground workings is limited by vertical planes passing through the end boundaries of the claim. However, in lateral directions the laws of the United States allow the mining to follow a bed of the deposits, for which the patent was issued, beyond the side boundaries of a claim, indefinitely. This constitutes what is known as the *extralateral rights* in mining. The law was enacted to encourage the development of natural resources. In other countries the extent of allowed mining is limited by the claim's boundaries on all sides.

FIELD EXERCISES

16-1. Computation of latitudes and departures and the area by the D.M.D. method. (This exercise involves computations which may be done in the drafting room on a rainy field period.)

Party: Each man should do the required set of computations.

Equipment: Pencil, paper, and five-place tables of logarithms.

Object: To compute the latitudes and departures of a closed traverse using five-place logarithms, to balance the obtained latitudes and departures by the transit rule (using a slide rule), and to compute the area by the D.M.D. method.

The instructor may assign any data suitable for this exercise. However, if the angles in Exercise 12-1 were measured on the same traverse on which distances were measured in Exercise 8-2, the field data of those exercises should be used here.

* Various details of the requirements for a patent survey are described in the "Manual of Instructions for the Survey of Public Lands." The book is published by the Bureau of Land Management and may be purchased from the Superintendent of Documents, Government Printing Office, Washington 25, D.C.

Underground Surveys

309

Procedure: The angles used in this exercise must be first checked for closure. If they do not close, the error should be distributed equally among the angles if the values of measured angles have equal weights. After the angles are adjusted, the bearings of lines are computed from the bearing of a line which had its true bearing determined by solar or stellar observations. If there is no line of known bearing, the instructor may assign an assumed bearing to a certain line.

Measured distances used in this exercise must be corrected for all systematic errors (see Systematic Errors in Taping, Arts. 7-11 through 7-16).

Make a table, with the headings shown in column 1 of Table 16-1, for the courses used in the exercise; then enter the distances and the bearings of lines on lines 2 and 3 of the table, respectively. Next, find the logarithms of distances and of sines and cosines of bearing angles. Enter them, respectively, on lines 7, 6, and 8. Add Log Dist. and Log Sin Bear. to obtain Log Dep. and enter the result on line 5. Similarly obtain Log Lat. and record the result on line 9. Next, find the antilogs for latitudes and departures and record them on lines 10 and 4 of the table.

TABLE 16-1. COMPUTATION OF LATITUDES AND DEPARTURES

Line	AB	ED	CD	DE	EA
Distance					
Bearing					
Departure					
Log Dep.					
Log Sin Bear.					
Log Dist.					
Log Cos Bear.					
Log Lat.					
Latitude					

The latitudes and departures of lines computed in Table 16-1 must be transferred to Table 16-2. Adjust the latitudes and departures in Table 16-2 by the transit rule, using proper sign for corrections which should be added algebraically to the latitudes and departures in order to obtain respective adjusted values in the last two columns of the table (see Table 15-6).

Compute also the error of closure e and the relative error of closure $e/\Sigma\ s$. Express this ratio as a fraction having the numerator equal to 1.

TABLE 16-2. ADJUSTMENT OF LATITUDES AND DEPARTURES

Line	Latitude		Departure		Corrections		Adjusted Lat.	Adjusted Dep.
	N	S	E	W	to Lat.	to Dep.		
$A\dot{B}$								
BC								
CD								
DE								
EA								
Σ								

$$\text{error of closure} = \sqrt{(\Delta L)^2 + (\Delta D)^2} = e$$

$$\text{Relative error of closure} = \frac{e}{\Sigma \text{ Dist.}} = \frac{1}{N}$$

Compute D.M.D.'s of the courses from their balanced departures and enter the results on line 2 of Table 16-3.   Follow the headings given in column 1 of the table to compute the area of the traverse.

TABLE 16-3. COMPUTATION OF AREA

Line	AB	BC	CD	DE	EA
D.M.D.					
Log D.M.D.					
Log Bal. Lat.					
Log $2A$					
$2A$					
A					

$$\text{Area} = \Sigma A$$

Exercise 16-1 may be extended to compute the coordinates of points and to compute the area by the method of coordinates.

16-2. Running a traverse with one missing line
Party: Four men.

Equipment: 100 ft tape, two plumb bobs, transit, reading glass, spring balance, two range poles, hatchet, hubs, and guard stakes.

Object: To run a traverse, of low degree of accuracy, similar to those used in the subdivision of large parcels of land.   It is assumed in this exercise that one line of the traverse is inaccessible, so that the distance and the bearing of the missing line must be determined from the missing latitude and departure of the line in the traverse.

Procedure: The instructor will assign a general area in which to run a traverse, one side of which is assumed to be inaccessible. Each party will measure the remaining distances, in both directions, and all angles except the two at the ends of the inaccessible line. The measured distances must be corrected for the sag and slope of the tape. The temperature, pull, and tape corrections may be neglected. Use 10 lb pull in measuring distances.

From an assigned or determined bearing of a line, compute bearings and latitudes and departures of measured courses. Then determine the latitude and departure of the missing course, and compute its bearing and distance (see Art. 15-19). Plot this traverse approximately to scale. Pass the Y-axis through the most westerly point and the X-axis through the most southerly point, and compute the area by the method of coordinates (see Art. 15-14).

CHAPTER 17

Topographic Surveys

17-1. Introduction. Topographic surveying was briefly mentioned in Art. 1-13. As the name implies, topographic surveys are conducted to secure data for drawing a map that will show ground relief in the included area. Three general methods are used to obtain topographic data. These are: the *transit-stadia method,* the *plane table method,* and the *photogrammetric method.*

In the transit-stadia method, the field data are recorded in a field notebook and later are plotted on paper in the office, for the purpose of drawing ground contours and various details. In the plane table method, the field technique is similar to that used in the transit-stadia method, but the plotting is done right in the field, on a paper attached to what is known as the plane table (see Fig. 17-8). In the photogrammetric method, briefly mentioned in Art. 9-29, the relative elevation of points is determined from photographs, usually taken from the air. Special cameras for taking photographs and special apparatus for plotting contours are needed in this method of topographic surveying. All three methods are discussed in this chapter.

It may be seen from the above description that the final result of a topographic survey is a map or a plan that shows ground configurations by means of ground contours. However, ground contours of an area, drawn on a map by themselves, hardly have any meaning unless they are shown in relation to the planimetric features of the same area. Thus the making of topographic maps and plans normally involves the delineation of both the planimetric and the topographic features of an area.

Various techniques employed in drafting a map are discussed in Chapter 18.

The stadia method and the plane table method involve measurement of distances and directions of lines as well as differences in elevation between various points. From these data the elevations and positions of points are computed and are plotted on paper before the contours are drawn. The elevations may be referred to any datum plane, but usually it is that of mean sea level. If a topographic map shows bench marks, the elevations of these bench marks are usually determined by leveling operations with an engineer's level and a leveling rod as described in Chapter 9.

In the photogrammetric method, contours are drawn from the negative or diapositive photographic plates and films by special plotting instruments.

The Transit-Stadia Method

17-2. Definitions. The word *stadia* is the plural of *stadium*. In ancient Greece stadium was the name applied to a foot-race course; the stadium was also a unit of length of about 600 ft. The word stadia, as it is used now in surveying, was derived from the latter. It means, in general, the measurement of distance as a function of a length of rod between two horizontal hairs in an instrument. Other words that are used sometimes to signify stadia measurements are *telemeter* measurements or *tacheometry*.

A brief account of measuring distances by stadia, with the telescope

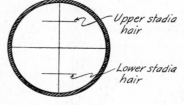

Fig. 17-1. Cross hair ring with stadia hairs.

of an instrument held in horizontal position, was given in Art. 7-4. However, it is not always possible to hold the telescope in horizontal position and still see the rod held at some distance from the instrument. If one must elevate or depress the telescope in order to see the rod, it is necessary to measure the vertical angle, in addition to taking appropriate rod readings, in order to be able to compute by trigonometry the horizontal distance and the difference in elevation between the points on which the transit is set up and on which the rod is held.

17-3. Stadia measurements with a horizontal sight. Figure 17-2 shows the transit, set up at point O, and rods held at points 1 and 2 on the ground; and Fig. 17-1 shows the cross-hair ring with the two stadia hairs. The upper stadia hair is shown in Fig. 17-2 at point a and the lower stadia hair at point *b*.   The objective lens of the telescope is shown at point *d*.   If the instrument has an inverting eyepiece, the instrument-man reads the rod at points *B*, *R*, and *A*, which are, respectively, the points where the lower stadia hair, the intersection of the cross hairs, and the upper stadia hair appear to cross the rod.

The instrument may have either an *external-focusing* telescope, in which case the focal plane of the objective lens is outside the instrument, passing through point *E*, or an *internal-focusing* telescope, in which arrangement the image-forming focal plane is located approximately at

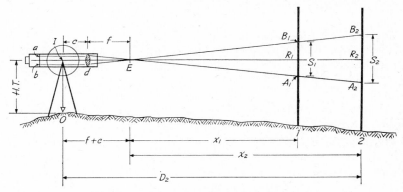

Fig. 17-2. Stadia measurements with horizontal sight.

the center of the telescope at point *I*.   In the external-focusing telescope the distance from the center of the instrument to the focal point at *E* is usually designated by $f + c$, where f is the focal length of the objective lens and c is the distance from the center of the instrument to the objective lens.   In the internal-focusing telescope $f + c = 0$, or nearly so, and in the external-focusing telescope $f + c$ is either equal to 1 ft or close to it.

The distance *AB*, read on the rod between the upper and the lower stadia hairs, is called the **stadia intercept** or **stadia interval**, while the reading of the height of rod, taken at the intersection of the cross hairs, is simply called the **rod reading.**

Figure 17-2 shows the line of sight of the instrument in its horizontal position.   From similar triangles EA_1B_1 and EA_2B_2 the following equation holds,

$$\frac{X_1}{A_1B_1} = \frac{X_2}{A_2B_2} = \frac{X_n}{A_nB_n} = K \text{ (constant)} \qquad (17\text{-}1)$$

where X is the horizontal distance from the focal point *E* to the rod, and where the subscript *n* denotes any point on the ground at which rod intercept A_nB_n is read with the leveled telescope.   For any rod intercept

S and the horizontal distance X from the focal point E of the objective lens to the rod, the **stadia constant,** K, shown by Eq. (17-1), may be expressed as X/S. This constant depends only on the spacing between the stadia hairs and is determined by the manufacturer of the instrument. In most American-made instruments $K = 100$.

If K is known, the equation $K = X/S$ may be solved for X. To this distance, X, must be added $C = f + c$ for the external-focusing telescope, in order to obtain the horizontal distance from the point of the instrument set-up to the point on which the rod is held. Thus a complete formula for a horizontal distance, H.D., obtained with a level sight, is

$$H.D. = SK + C \qquad (17\text{-}2)$$

For example, if $K = 100, f + c = 1$, and the stadia intercept $S = 1.34$, H.D. $= 134 + 1 = 135$ ft. The distance computed for the same stadia intercept reading with the internal-focusing instrument is 134 ft. In stadia measurements the stadia intercept is measured to hundredths, which are often estimated. This gives horizontal distances correct within about 1 or 2 ft.

Before one can compute the difference in elevation between a point of the instrument set-up and a point on which the rod is held, the following two measurements must be made: (1) the height of telescope, H.T., (see Fig. 17-2), above the point of the instrument set-up, and (2) the rod reading R at the intersection of the cross hairs. With a level sight, the H.T. serves as the backsight reading and R as the foresight reading. Thus the difference in elevation of points, D.E., is

$$D.E. = H.T. - R \qquad (17\text{-}3)$$

The elevation of the point on which the rod is held is found by adding, algebraically, the difference in elevation obtained by Eq. (17-3) to the elevation of the point on which the transit is set up. For example, if the elevation of the point on which the transit is set up is 327.4 ft above a datum plane, H.T. $= 5.2$ and $R = 7.0$ ft, then the elevation of the point on which the rod is held is $327.4 + 5.2 - 7.0 = 325.6$ ft. In measuring differences in elevation, the height of the transit and the rod reading are normally read to the nearest tenth of a foot. The resulting elevations are accurate enough for locating ground contours; moreover, substantially better accuracy is not attainable by the use of the stadia method.

Field technique used in stadia measurements includes also measurement of directions to the points sighted on. This is normally accomplished by orienting the horizontal circle of the instrument in such a way that when vernier A reads zero, the line of sight assumes a specified reference direction, with the telescope in its direct position. It is customary to orient the telescope south when vernier A reads zero. With the lower motion of the instrument clamped in oriented position of the horizontal circle, and with a sight taken on any point using the upper motion of the instrument, the vernier A reads the azimuth of the sighted direction on the clockwise scale of the horizontal circle. Thus all directions taken with such an orientation of the instrument must be recorded in a column headed by "Azimuth 0° South."

In order to orient a transit to read azimuths from south, the transit is set up at a point on a line of known bearing. Let the bearing of the line be, for example, S35°20'E. The azimuth of this direction from the south is 324°40'. Vernier A is set to read this angle on the clockwise scale of the horizontal circle and a sight is then taken along the line of known bearing, with the telescope in normal position, using the lower motion of the instrument. This orients the transit to read the azimuths from the south. In a similar way the transit may be oriented to read azimuths from the north

When stadia measurements are made, in topographic surveying, many sights may be taken in various directions from a given transit set-up. For efficiency of operation the readings must follow each other in a certain sequence. First, the transit is set up at a point of known elevation, and the H.T. of the instrument is measured. The H.T. of the instrument is the height of its horizontal axis above the point of the instrument set-up. This height is measured either by the rod held vertically close to the horizontal axis of the instrument, or by a pocket tape. Next, the instrument is oriented in azimuth, by the known bearing of the line on which the instrument is set up. After this, the lower motion is clamped and is not used again as long as stadia sights are taken at this set-up of the instrument.

The procedure of taking sights and rod readings is the same for each point. The telescope is leveled by the telescope level and the rod is read at the intersection of the cross hairs. Then the telescope is lowered, or raised, just enough for the lower stadia hair to fall on the closest integral footmark on the rod, and a rod reading is taken at the upper stadia hair. The rod reading on which the lower hair was placed is then subtracted from the rod reading at the upper stadia hair in order to obtain the required stadia intercept. For instance, let 3 ft be the footmark on which the lower stadia hair is placed and let the rod reading at the upper stadia hair be 4.25 ft. Then 1.25 is the stadia intercept, which is recorded in the field notebook in a proper column. Immediately after reading the intercept, the instrumentman waves to the rodman to proceed to a new point; then the instrumentman reads the azimuth of the sighted direction. This procedure is repeated when the sight is taken on each succeeding point. Field recording of stadia data is discussed in Art. 17-5 on page 319.

17-4. Stadia measurements with inclined sights. The process of obtaining distances and the elevations with a level line of sight is simpler than that involved in obtaining the same data with inclined line of sight. Thus in stadia measurements the level sight on the rod is tried first. If the readings cannot be taken with a level sight, the telescope is then raised or lowered in order to bring the rod into the field of view.

Figure 17-3 shows a transit set up at point O, and a rod held at point P. The stadia intercept, $S = AB$, for an inclined sight, is not at right angle

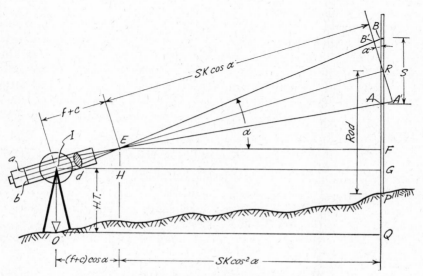

Fig. 17-3. Stadia measurements with inclined sight.

to the line of sight of the instrument. The angle of inclination of the rod to a line perpendicular to the line of sight is the same as the vertical angle of the transit's telescope. Thus by drawing through the point of intersection of the line of sight with the rod a line inclined to the rod by angle α, one obtains a stadia intercept $A'B'$ which is at right angle to the line of sight. If this perpendicular stadia intercept were known, the distance ER along the line of sight could be determined by multiplying $A'B'$ by the stadia constant K of the instrument. The instrument is assumed to have the external-focusing telescope in this example.

In the triangle $BB'R$ the angle $BB'R$ is greater than $90°$ by a small angle, which is equal to the angle $B'ER$. For $K = 100$ angle $B'ER = \tan^{-1} 0.5/100 = 17'$, very closely. Thus the angle $BB'R = 90°17'$. Within the accuracy of the stadia method, this angle may be taken as being 90°, so that

$$B'R = BR \cos \alpha \text{ approx.} \qquad (17\text{-}4)$$

Similarly,

$$A'R = AR \cos \alpha \text{ approx.} \qquad (17\text{-}5)$$

If one adds Eqs. (17-4) and (17-5) and substitutes $B'R + A'R = A'B'$ and $BR + AR = AB = S$, the following expression is obtained:

$$A'B' = S \cos \alpha \qquad (17\text{-}6)$$

Multiplying Eq. (17-6) by the stadia constant K, one obtains the distance ER along the inclined line of sight; so that $ER = SK \cos \alpha$. It may be observed from the geometry of Fig. 17-3 that ER is the hypotenuse of the right-angled triangle ERF, in which EF is the horizontal side. Therefore $EF = ER \cos \alpha$. Or, substituting $ER = SK \cos \alpha$ in this equation, one obtains $EF = SK \cos^2 \alpha$. In order to find the horizontal distance OQ from the point of transit set-up at O to the point where the rod is held, a small horizontal distance $(f + c) \cos \alpha = C \cos \alpha$, obtained from the right-angled triangle IEH, must be added to the distance EF obtained above. Thus

$$\text{H.D.} = SK \cos^2 \alpha + C \cos \alpha \qquad (17\text{-}7)$$

where the value of $(f + c) \cos \alpha$ is normally taken as 1 for an external-focusing telescope. In an internal-focusing telescope $(f + c) \cos \alpha = 0$. If in Eq. (17-7) $\alpha = 0$, as it is for a level sight, the equation reduces to Eq. (17-2) derived in Art. 17-3.

Since $\cos^2 \alpha = 1 - \sin^2 \alpha$, Eq. (17-7) may be given in the form shown by Eq. (17-8).

$$\text{H.D.} = SK - SK \sin^2 \alpha + (f + c) \cos \alpha \qquad (17\text{-}8)$$

The use of Eq. (17-8) is preferred to that of Eq. (17-7) when $K = 100$. Equation (17-8) is well adapted for slide-rule computations.

The difference in elevation between the points O, on which the instrument is set up, and P, on which the rod is held, is shown by the vertical distance PQ in Fig. 17-3. From the geometry of the figure, $PQ = RQ - RP$, where RP is equal to rod reading R, and $RQ = RF + FG + GQ$. Thus

$$\text{D.E.} = RF + FG + GQ - R \qquad (17\text{-}9)$$

The first two terms on the right side of Eq. (17-9) can be obtained from the triangles ERF and IEH.

From the triangle ERF, $RF = ER \sin \alpha = SK \cos \alpha \sin \alpha$. Also since $\sin 2\alpha = 2 \sin \alpha \cos \alpha$,

$$RF = SK \frac{\sin 2\alpha}{2} \qquad (17\text{-}10)$$

From the triangle IEH, $EH = (f + c) \sin \alpha = C \sin \alpha$ which is equal to FG; thus

$$FG = C \sin \alpha \qquad (17\text{-}11)$$

By substituting Eqs. (17-10) and (17-11) in Eq. (17-9), and noting that $GQ = IO = $ H.T., the height of the telescope, one obtains the following expression for the difference in elevation of the points:

$$\text{D.E.} = SK \frac{\sin 2\alpha}{2} + C \sin \alpha + \text{H.T.} - R \qquad (17\text{-}12)$$

If $\alpha = 0$, as it is for a level sight, Eq. (17-12) reduces to Eq. (17-3) derived for a level sight. It may also be observed that if a sight is taken on the rod at the height of instrument, in other words if R is made equal to H.T., these two terms cancel out in Eq. (17-12). For a depressed sight, α is negative, which makes the first two terms in Eq. (17-12) negative, but H.T. and R do not change their signs.

When stadia measurements are being made with inclined sights, the procedure is similar to that used with level sights. The transit is set up at a point, the H.T. is measured, and the transit is oriented in azimuth. Then the sight is taken on the rod at a point equal to H.T., if such a point on the rod is visible. After this, it is important that the vertical angle be read before the position of the telescope is slightly changed to read the stadia intercept. The azimuth is read last, while the rodman walks to a new point.

In the transit-stadia method the vertical angle is measured only once, with the telescope in direct position. However, the index correction (I.C.) of the transit should be determined (Art. 11-19) and recorded at the top of the page of stadia notes. This I.C. is then added, algebraically, to all recorded vertical angles when the stadia notes are reduced.

17-5. Field recording of data. Stadia data are recorded in the field notebook in the order in which the readings are made; however, the arrangement of columns in the notebook need not be in the same sequence. It is to some extent a matter of choice in what order to arrange recording columns.

Figure 17-4 shows a typical sample of stadia notes. The points on which the rod is held are identified in the first column, in the order in which they are observed. They are usually numbered consecutively. The next four columns are used to record various field measurements, and the last three columns are used to record computed distances and elevations. The remaining space in the notebook is used for brief descriptions of points. These descriptions are useful in plotting contours and planimetric features on plans.

Example 17-1. Let it be required to compute horizontal distances and the elevations of points 1 and 2 from the field data shown in Fig. 17-4.

TOPOGRAPHIC SURVEY GREENWOOD SUBDIVISION					Oct. 27, 1959 Transit No. 5		P. R. Dale T. N. Smith S. A. Popov	6.
Transit at point A, Elevation 476.39 K=100, f+c = 1, H.T. = 4.7 ft.								
Point	Azimuth 0°S.	Stadia Interc.	Vertical Angle	Rod	Horiz. Dist.	Diff. Elev.	Elev.	Description of points
1	30°15'	0.86	0	7.2				Top of slope
2	37°22'	0.72	-10°14'	H.T.				Low point
3	40°37'	1.25	5°26'	3.1				18" Oak tree

Fig. 17-4. Transit-stadia field recordings.

Solution: Equation (17-2) is used to compute horizontal distance to point 1, thus

$$\text{H.D.} = SK + C = 0.86 \times 100 + 1 = 87 \text{ ft}$$

Using Eq. (17-3) to find the difference in elevation,

$$\text{D.E.} = \text{H.T.} - R = 4.7 - 7.2 = -2.5 \text{ ft}$$

Thus the elevation of point 1 is,

$$\text{Elevation (1)} = 476.4 - 2.5 = 473.9 \text{ ft}$$

Since an inclined sight was used to obtain data for point 2, Eq. (17-8) must be used to determine distance to point 2. Thus,

$$\text{H.D.} = SK - SK \sin^2 \alpha + C \cos \alpha = 72 - 72 \times 0.178^2 + 1.0 = 71 \text{ ft}$$

Equation (17-12) is used to find the difference in elevations, so that

$$\text{D.E.} = SK \frac{\sin 2\alpha}{2} + C \sin \alpha = -0.72 \times 100 \frac{0.350}{2} - 0.18 = -12.8 \text{ ft}$$

Thus the elevation of point 2 is,

$$\text{Elevation (2)} = 476.4 - 12.8 = 463.6 \text{ ft}$$

17-6. How to use the stadia table. When a stadia table is available for computation of distances and the differences in elevation, the table offers a much more expedient method of computation than formulas. In surveying large areas, there may be thousands of points for which computations of distances and differences in elevation are required. Thus, in practice, stadia table and the slide rule are used in computations, and the results are entered directly in the field notebook.

The stadia table is given in Table VI, p. 522. The numerical values given in the table are for the following quantities: (a) $100 \cos^2 \alpha$—these values (given in the column headed by "Hor. Dist.") are used for computation of the horizontal distances by Eq. (17-7); (b) 100 sin$^2 \alpha$—these values (given in the column headed by "Hor. Corr.") are used for computation of horizontal distances by Eq. (17-8); and (c) $100 \dfrac{\sin 2\alpha}{2}$ and $C \sin \alpha$—these values (given in column headed by "Diff. in Elev.") are used in computation of difference in elevation by Eq. (17-12). All values except $C \sin \alpha$ are given for 2′ intervals of angle α. The values of $C \sin \alpha$ are given at the bottom of each difference-in-elevation column for the whole column, since this value is less than 1 and thus is needed only to one significant figure. Such a figure fits the whole set of values for 50 sin 2α that are included in a column. The tables are compiled for the stadia constant $K = 100$.

The answers to the Example 17-1, for point 2, are computed below by using the stadia table. No tables are needed for computations when $\alpha = 0$.

For point 2, 100 sin$^2 \alpha = 3.16$, from stadia table, for $\alpha = -10°14′$. Thus,

$$\text{H.D.} = 72 - 0.72 \times 3.16 + 1 = 71 \text{ ft}$$

Also 50 sin $2\alpha = -17.48$ from the difference-in-elevation column of the table; also $C \sin \alpha = 0.18$ at the bottom of the same column for $C = 1.0$. Thus

$$\text{D.E.} = -0.72 \times 17.48 - 0.18 = -12.8 \text{ ft}$$

For point 3 given in Fig. 17-4,

$$\text{H.D.} = 125 - 1.25 \times 0.90 + 1 = 125 \text{ ft}$$

$$\text{D.E.} = 1.25 \times 9.43 + 0.09 + 4.7 - 3.1 = 13.5 \text{ ft}$$

These computations can be made by the notekeeper on the slide rule, right in the field.

There are also stadia slide rules on the market. They are not as accurate as the tables, but are accurate enough for most topography work. A stadia slide rule has a slight advantage over the use of tables if computations are made in the field.

17-7. Stadia traverse. When a topographic survey is made of a relatively small area, one or two transit set-ups may be sufficient to cover the whole area. The number of points which should be observed on a given area, or for a certain set-up of the instrument, depends on the configuration of the ground surface being surveyed, on the contour interval, and on the scale used in plotting field data. Thus the number of points needed to be observed on an area of a certain size may vary considerably from one area to another.

The responsibility of deciding where to hold the rod rests largely with the rodman. The rod must be held at all changes in ground slopes. One must always remember the size of the contour interval to be used in the projected map. If, for instance, the contour interval is 5 ft, a few inches of irregularity in the ground surface will hardly affect contour plotting, while it may produce a noticeable contour error if plotted contours have 1 ft interval. It must be remembered, also, that in plotting

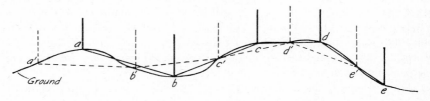

Fig. 17-5. Rod held at ground breaking points.

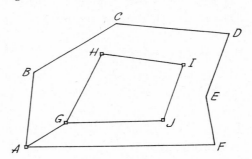

Fig. 17-6. Stadia traverse inside surveyed area.

contours the ground between the observed points is assumed to have a uniform slope.

Figure 17-5 shows a ground profile, the slope of which changes in several places. By holding the rod at the ground breaking points, as is shown by the solid vertical lines on the figure, and assuming that the ground has uniform slope between those points, one obtains a fairly accurate presentation of the actual ground configuration. However, if the rod were held at the same number of points, but in the places indicated by the dotted vertical lines, the ground configuration shown by the dashed lines between the rod points would give an entirely erroneous protrayal of the ground profile. Thus, it is of great advantage to have an experienced rodman.

Figure 17-6 shows a ground area *ABCDEF* which may cover many acres of land. If it is required to make a topographic survey of such an area, it may be necessary to run a stadia traverse such as *AGHIJ* in order to obtain enough stadia data on this area for plotting contours. Certain field procedures governing stadia traverses must be observed. Let it be assumed, for instance, that the elevation of corner A of this property is known; then, such a point would be a logical place to start a transit-stadia survey. When the transit is ready to be moved to another point, say point G, the rod is held at point G and stadia measurements are made on that point. After the transit is set up at G, it is oriented in azimuth by the line GA, since the azimuth of AG was determined when the transit was at A. Next, the readings are taken on the rod held at A, which still is the point of known elevation, and the distance GA and the elevation of point G are computed from these readings. The mean value of the distance AG and of the elevation of point G, as determined from both set-ups, gives the most probable value of the distance AG and of the elevation of point G. Point G then becomes the point of known elevation and stadia survey is made around point G until the transit is ready to be moved to the next point, and so on.

On a drawing, stadia stations are marked by a small square around the station point. Various details for plotting stadia measurements and drawing a topographic map are discussed in Chapter 18.

17-8. Stadia rods. On short stadia sights, up to about 250 ft, the Philadelphia rod, shown in Fig. 9-15a, gives best results. For longer sights special stadia rods must be used. Stadia rods vary in width from about $2\frac{1}{2}$ to $4\frac{1}{2}$ in. They are usually made in two sections, hinged together in the middle. The full length of a stadia rod is 12 ft, so that it folds to one-half this length. Some stadia rods are made in three sections. The design pattern of rod graduations varies considerably from one rod to another. Although a simple pattern consisting of black diamonds, squares, or wedges painted on white background gives best results for sights up to about 1000 ft, some special patterns designed for sights longer than 1000 ft are used in surveys of large areas. Figure 17-7 shows several patterns of stadia rods, which are in more or less common use. Most stadia rods are graduated in tenths of a foot, so that hundredths must be estimated in reading stadia intercepts.

17-9. Other applications of stadia measurements. Besides topographic surveying, the transit-stadia method is employed on other surveys for which the required accuracy is consistent with the precision of stadia measurements. For instance, stadia measurements may be employed in running rough traverses where the required accuracy of closure does not exceed about 1:500. Since the stadia method eliminates tape measurements, the work with stadia is extremely time-saving, especially in rough country where measurements with a tape may be difficult.

The transit-stadia method is also very useful in obtaining distance measurements to various planimetric features, for later use in plotting their positions on drawings. Thus, incidentally, stadia measurements may be successfully employed in conjunction with the tape and with other methods of measurement. The extent to which stadia measurements may be used in map plotting depends on the map's scale. For

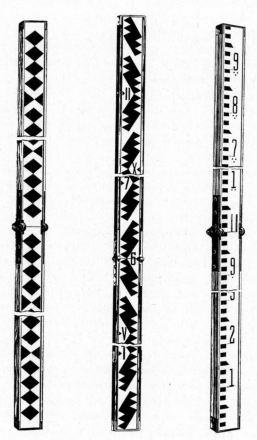

Fig. 17-7. Stadia rods. (Courtesy Eugene Dietzgen Co.)

instance, if a map is drawn to a scale 1 in. = 1000 ft, then 0.01 in., which is close to the thickness of a pencil point, is equal to 10 ft on the map. Assuming that stadia measurements can be made with 1:500 accuracy, or with 10 ft maximum error in measuring 5000 ft, this accuracy is close to that with which 5000 ft can be plotted on the map. Thus stadia measurements should be quite adequate for intermediate and small-scale map making.

Another variation of the stadia method, used mostly in making topographic and planimetric maps, consists of making measurements by means of a *plane table* and *alidade*. This method is described in the next section of this chapter.

Measurement of backsight and foresight distances by stadia, in direct leveling with a transit or a level, eliminates time-consuming pacing for balancing backsight and foresight distances. All precise and semi-precise levels are equipped with stadia hairs. A special technique called *three wire leveling* is usually employed in precise leveling. For details of such leveling operations a text on advanced surveying should be consulted.

Transit-stadia measurements may be used in low-order trigonometric leveling (see Art. 9-25). In order to find the difference in elevation between any two turning points, or between a bench mark and a turning point, the difference in elevation as computed by stadia formula from a backsight reading is subtracted from the difference in elevation computed from the foresight reading. For instance, if $(D.E.)_b$ is used to designate the difference in elevation between the point of transit set-up and the backsight point, and $(D.E.)_f$ is used to designate the difference in elevation between the point of transit set-up and the foresight point (also using corresponding subscripts for all measured quantities), the following two equations can be written [see Eq. (17-12)]:

$$(D.E.)_f = S_f \frac{K}{2} \sin 2\alpha_f + C \sin \alpha_f + H.T. - R_f \qquad (17\text{-}13)$$

$$(D.E.)_b = S_b \frac{K}{2} \sin 2\alpha_b + C \sin \alpha_b + H.T. - R_b \qquad (17\text{-}14)$$

By subtracting the second equation from the first, one obtains a difference in elevation which must be added, algebraically, to the elevation of the backsight point in order to obtain the elevation of the foresight point. It may be observed in this connection that if rod readings (R) are the same in both cases the last two terms in each question cancel out, so that neither the H.T. nor the rod readings need be recorded.

17-10. Errors in transit-stadia method. Although no special precautions in stadia measurements are needed in topographic work or in filling in planimetric details on maps, it may be desired to attain as accurate results as possible in running certain traverses by the transit-stadia method. It should be borne in mind that the horizontal angles in such traverses and consequently the directions of lines may be measured as accurately as in transit-tape surveys; thus, practically all errors contributing to the linear error of closure in a traverse come from the measurement of distances. The two parameters that are used in computation of horizontal distances by the stadia method are (1) the stadia intercept and (2) the vertical angle.

The errors in reading the stadia intercept naturally increase with longer sights.   Thus if accurate results are desired in measurement of distances the stadia sights must be as short as practicable.   Normally, no difficulty should be experienced in reading stadia intercepts to the nearest hundredth of a foot on sights up to 200 ft taken on a Philadelphia leveling rod.

Care must be exercised to hold the rod plumb, since a relatively small inclination of the rod may introduce an error of few hundredths of a foot in reading the stadia intercept.   For the same inclination of the rod this error increases with the magnitude of the vertical angle.   The best way to reduce this type of error is to use a rod level.

The effect of an error in a measured vertical angle on the computed horizontal distances is much smaller than that on the computed difference in elevation.   It takes almost a half-degree error in a measured 30° vertical angle to introduce a 1% error in the computed horizontal distance, while the same error in the vertical angle produces close to 0.4 ft error, per 100 ft of horizontal distance, in the difference in elevation of points.   Thus a small index correction that is applied to the measured vertical angles affects only the elevation of points, since it is negligible in computation of distances.

With due precaution in measuring the stadia intercept and by averaging distances as measured in both directions, the transit-stadia traverse may be expected to yield up to 1:1000 accuracy in distance measurements.   If better results are required, the distances must be measured by a steel tape.

The error of closure in elevation, in feet, should be expected not to exceed $\sqrt{D}$, where D is in miles.   Frequent checks on bench marks are recommended where they are available.

The Plane Table Method

17-11. General description of the method.   As in the transit-stadia method, stadia measurements are used in the plane table method; however, instead of a transit a special piece of equipment called a plane table and an instrument called an alidade are employed.

A *plane table* (Fig. 17-8) consists of a board attached to a tripod in such a way that it can be leveled or rotated in azimuth.   The board is used as a drafting table for plotting map details and ground contours right in the field, thus allowing the plotter to correlate his drawing with the visible territory reproduced in map form on that drawing.

An *alidade* (Fig. 17-9) consists of a straight edge which supports a device—usually a telescope—that is used to take sights. The line of sight in the alidade is parallel to the beveled edge of the straight edge, so that when a sight is taken with the alidade, a line drawn along the straight edge shows on the map the direction of that sight.   A telescopic alidade, such as shown in Fig. 17-9, has stadia hairs and vertical scales for determining distances and differences of elevation.

Fig. 17-8. Plane table.

Comparing horizontal motions of a transit with the method of operation of a plane table and alidade, one finds that the table performs the function of the horizontal circle of the transit, and the alidade performs the role of the transit's alidade (see Fig. 11-5).   The plane table can be oriented in the direction of a line drawn on the map and may be clamped in that position, just as is done with the lower motion of a transit when taking a backsight before measuring a horizontal angle.   Next, when a sight is taken on a point with the alidade, so that the straight edge passes through the plotted location of the plane table on the drawing, and when the direction of that sight is drawn on the map, the drawing shows an angle measured graphically from the previously drawn direction to the new direction.   Thus the plane table alidade in this operation performs the same functions as the transit's alidade when a foresight is taken on a point and the measured angle is read on the horizontal circle.

Besides graphically measuring angles, a plane table alidade, being equipped with certain vertical arc scales, is used to measure distances and the differences in elevation by the stadia method in a way similar to transit-stadia measurements.

The term "plane table" is often used to describe not only the table itself but also the whole plane table outfit, including the alidade.

Fig. 17-9. Telescopic alidade.   (Courtesy C. L. Berger & Sons, Inc.)

17-12. Uses of the plane table method.   The plane table method of drawing maps and plans is used in engineering, in geology, in landscape architecture, in forestry, and in other fields.   The method is especially suitable in those applications where, as in geology, it is important to have frequent verification of drawn features by field observations of ground formations and deposits.

In the not-so-distant past, the plane table method was the only method used in making planimetric, topographic, geologic, and other maps of large areas.   For example, the USGS quadrangle sheets were formerly made by the plane table method; but at present the method is being increasingly supplanted by the more efficient photogrammetric method.   Even in such fields as geology, pedology, and forestry, methods have been worked out that enable a photo-interpreter, in a given field, to identify on photographs various geological formations, the type of soil and vegetation, and many other features pertinent to a given field of study.   The plane table nowadays is confined mostly to mapping small areas for which the photogrammetric method may not be economical.

On small areas, plotted to a scale varying from about 1 in. = 20 ft to 1 in. = 500 ft, either the plane table method or the transit-stadia method is still being used quite effectively.   On construction projects the transit-stadia method may be preferred, whereas in other fields, such as in geology or forestry, the plane table may be employed to greater advantage.

17-13. The plane table.   The plane table board comes in various sizes, the largest being about 24 by 31 in.   The plane tables used by the U.S. Coast and Geodetic Survey are built with the board attached to a sturdy tripod through the tripod's leveling head, which has three leveling screws for leveling the table.   The leveling head has also a clamp and a tangent screw for controlling the rotational motion of the board in azimuth.

A table known as the *Johnson table* has a board either 24 by 31 in. or 18 by 24 in.   The board is attached to the tripod by means of a ball-and-socket joint.   Two clamp screws under the tripod head control the leveling and the rotation of the table.   The top screw is used for leveling the table and the lower screw for arresting the rotational motion.   A tangent screw provides slow rotational motion of the table for accurate orientation in azimuth.

A light plane table, sometimes known as the *traverse table*, has a 15 by 15 in. board attached to a light tripod by a single screw.   The board may be oriented and clamped in any desired position, but the leveling of the table must be done by adjusting the tripod legs.   The legs may be of a fixed or an extension type.   Since traverse tables are used sometimes for traversing with a *peep-sight alidade* (Art. 17-14), and also for sketching minor details in mapping, the board has a built-in compass, usually set flush with the board's surface, for quick orientation of the table.

In the field, a plane table is set successively over various points, which are already plotted or are being plotted on a sheet of drawing paper attached to the top of the plane table.   Waterproof plastic sheets, though more expensive, are now available for plane table work.   In small-scale mapping, the plane table is set over a point by eye.   With a larger plotting scale the setting over a point must be done more carefully, probably by dropping a pebble from under the table where the point is located, or by using a special bracket that fits around the edge of the table.   The top end of the bracket is placed on the plotted point while a plumb bob is suspended from the bracket's lower end.

17-14. The alidade.   The simplest type of alidade is the *peep-sight alidade* which has two upright sights attached to a straight edge about 12 in. long.   The sights are very much like those on a surveyor's compass, shown in Fig. 13-12.   Each sight has a longitudinal slot and usually a longitudinal hairline stretched through the middle of the slot in one of the sights.   The sights are hinged to the ends of the straight edge and can be folded when not in use.   The peep-sight alidade has limited application in engineering since it has no vertical arc scales for measuring distances and the differences in elevation.   When a peep-sight alidade is used in rough traversing with a plane table, the distances are usually measured by pacing.

The **telescopic alidade** (Fig. 17-9) has a telescope mounted on the straight edge.   It is the same type of telescope that is used in transits. The telescope has the cross-hair ring with stadia hairs and may have either external or internal focusing.   The telescope is held in place by a sleeve in which it can be rotated through 180° for the adjustment of its cross-hair ring.   The telescope is provided with a vertical motion for taking inclined sights but it is fixed in azimuth, so that the line of sight is always in a vertical plane parallel to the alidade's straight edge, when the instrument is in proper adjustment.

The straight edge is provided with a circular level, for leveling the plane table, and with a compass needle encased in a narrow rectangular box.   The needle has several degrees of freedom each side of the zero mark, so that the declination of the needle may be taken into account when drawing a true north direction on the map.

On each side of the sleeve that holds it, the telescope has two collars with a smooth surface for a striding level.   The level is detachable and is used to set the telescope, and consequently its line of sight, in horizontal position.   This setting is needed for level sights and for adjusting the verniers of the vertical arc scales attached to the telescope.

Several improvements in the design of alidades have recently been made by some manufacturers.   Figure 17-10, for instance, shows a Kern alidade, which has the following interesting features: a fixed eyepiece, inclined at a constant angle of $-30°$; a vertical arc scale read by a microscope mounted immediately above the telescope's eyepiece; the taking of inclined sights by tilting only the objective prism; stadia hairs designed as two pairs of curved lines, one pair being curved according to the formula for reading horizontal distances and another according to the formula for reading differences in elevation.   Work with this and other **optical alidades,** as they are called, is more efficient and less tiring.

A telescopic alidade normally has three vertical arc scales, all marked on the same arc mounted at one end of the horizontal axis. The arc rotates with the telescope and the scales are read at stationary indexes. One scale is divided into degrees; the other two, called *H* and *V* scales, are used for measuring (respectively) distances and differences in elevation. The *H* and *V* scales supplant the stadia tables. The original

Fig. 17-10. Kern RK optical alidade. (Courtesy Kern Instruments, Inc.)

design of these scales was devised by W. M. Beaman of the U.S. Geological Survey, so that the arc on which these scales are marked is called the ***Beaman stadia arc.*** Figure 17-9 shows one type of such arc. The *H* and *V* scales are sometimes shown also on the transit's vertical circle.

Many alidades have a vernier for reading fractions of a degree and a small level attached to the vernier arc; also a tangent screw by which the vernier can be set on zero. When the line of sight is made horizontal by the striding level, the alidade should have proper readings of vertical scales when the vernier level bubble is centered. If scales show incorrect readings, the alidade should be adjusted (Art. 17-20). The use of the vernier level eliminates errors in reading arc scales resulting from inclination of the plane table.

17-15. Beaman stadia arc. The construction of H and V scales was derived from stadia Eqs. (17-7) and (17-12), respectively, for the horizontal distances and the differences in elevation of points. In the derivation shown below, it is assumed that in all inclined sights the rod reading is made equal to the height of the alidade, so that H.T. and R terms in Eq. (17-12) are eliminated.

By factoring $K \cos^2 \alpha$ in Eq. (17-7) one obtains the following expression:

$$\text{H.D.} = \left(S + \frac{C}{K \cos \alpha} \right) K \cos^2 \alpha \qquad (17\text{-}15)$$

By factoring $K \dfrac{\sin 2\alpha}{2}$ in Eq. (17-12), and simplifying, one obtains the following expression:

$$\text{D.E.} = \left(S + \frac{C}{K \cos \alpha} \right) \frac{K \sin 2\alpha}{2} \qquad (17\text{-}16)$$

Assuming that $K = 100$, as is normally the case in instruments manufactured for the use in the United States, and taking $\cos \alpha = 1$, as it is for all sights up to 18° when taken to two significant figures, the terms given in parentheses in Eqs. (17-15) and (17-16) are reduced to $S + 0.01$ if the instrument has the external-focusing telescope and merely to S if the instrument has the internal-focusing telescope. On the Beaman arc, one vertical arc scale is constructed to read $100 \cos^2 \alpha$ values, and the scale is designated as H scale; another vertical arc scale is constructed to read $(K \sin 2\alpha)/2$ values, and the scale is designated as V scale. Thus Eqs. (17-15) and (17-16) are reduced to the following expressions:

$$\text{H.D.} = (S + 0.01)H \qquad (17\text{-}17)$$

$$\text{D.E.} = (S + 0.01)V \qquad (17\text{-}18)$$

where H and V are, respectively, the readings of the H and V scales on the Beaman arc.

On some alidades Beaman arcs are constructed according to Eqs. (17-17) and (17-18). For a level sight the H scale reads 100 and the V scale reads zero. The reading of each scale is multiplied by the stadia intercept S or $S + 0.01$, usually on the slide rule, in order to obtain the horizontal distance and the difference in elevation between the points.

On other alidades the H scale is constructed according to the following transformation: the $\cos^2 \alpha$ value in Eq. (17-15) is replaced by $1 - \sin^2 \alpha$. This reduces the equation to the following form:

$$\text{H.D.} = (S + 0.01)100 - (S + 0.01)100 \sin^2 \alpha \qquad (17\text{-}19)$$

Thus some H scales are constructed to read $100 \sin^2 \alpha$ values, which are really H-correction values (H_c) that must be subtracted from $(S + 0.01)$ 100. These H_c values are much smaller than H values and may be easily obtained from a single-page table (Table 17-1) as explained below. Besides, since H_c values are small, the addition of 0.01 to S in the second term of Eq. (17-19) may be neglected. It must be noted that the first term in Eq. (17-19) is not the slope distance, but an arbitrary term.

Since Eq. (17-18) yields either positive or negative values, depending on whether V readings are positive or negative, the V scale is so constructed, on many alidades, that the scale reads 50 with a level sight. This eliminates sign errors in recording V readings, since all of them come out positive. When these values are used in computations, 50 is subtracted from all recorded V values. Thus the alidades, which have modified H and V scales, have these scales constructed according to the following equations:

$$\text{H.D.} = (S + 0.01)100 - SH_c \qquad (17\text{-}20)$$

$$\text{D.E.} = (S + 0.01)(V - 50) \qquad (17\text{-}21)$$

Since H and V scales are constructed on the same arc, a given V reading corresponds to a definite H_c reading on the H scale. Thus instead of reading both, it is sufficient to read only the V scale and then to find the H_c value from Table 17-1, which is especially constructed for this purpose. An example will make this clear.

Example 17-1. The field notebook recordings shown below were taken with an alidade equipped with a Beaman stadia arc. It is required to find horizontal distances, to each point shown in this notebook, and also the elevation of points.

TOPOGRAPHIC SURVEY OF AREA X WITH PLANE TABLE AND ALIDADE						June 5, 1960 Clear Warm Alidade No.7		Inst. B.Gay *17.* Rod C.Andrews Notes T. Popov	
PLANE TABLE AT STA.F, ELEV. 327.4, H.T. = 3.5, f+c = 1.0									
POINT	V	V-50	S Hc	S+0.01	ROD	H.D.	D.E.	ELEV.	REMARKS
1	57	7	1	2.62	on H.T.	261	18.3	345.7	SW corner of build.
2	50	0	0	1.25	do	125	0	327.4	Point on slope
3	32	-18	13	3.86	do	373	-69.5	257.9	Bottom of slope
4	68	18	5	1.54	do	149	27.7	355.1	18" Oak

Solution: Horizontal distance for point 1 by Eq. (17-20) is H.D. = $262 - SH_c$. In order to find SH_c correction from Table 17-1, for $V = 7$, enter $(V - 50)$ column down to 7 and find, across, $SH_c = 1.0$ in 200 ft column and approximately 0.3 for 62 ft, which is between columns 50 and 75. Thus the total correction to the nearest foot is 1, so that

$$\text{H.D.}_1 = 262 - 1 = 261 \text{ ft}$$

Similarly one can find

$$\text{H.D.}_2 = 125 - 0 = 125 \text{ ft,}$$

$$\text{H.D.}_3 = 386 - 13 = 373 \text{ ft,}$$

where 13 is 10.2 + 3 (approx.) = 13;

$$\text{H.D.}_4 = 154 - 5 = 149 \text{ ft,}$$

where 5 = 3.4 + 1.7 = 5 (approx.).

For finding the differences in elevation, the slide rule is used to multiply $S + 0.01$ by $V - 50$. Thus,

$\text{D.E.}_1 = 2.62 \times 7 = 18.3$ and   Elev. (1) $= 327.4 + 18.3 = 345.7$

$\text{D.E.}_2 = 0$ Elev. (2) $= 327.4$

$\text{D.E.}_3 = 3.86 \times (-18) = -69.5$ Elev. (3) $= 327.4 - 69.5 = 257.9$

$\text{D.E.}_4 = 1.54 \times 18 = 27.7$ Elev. (4) $= 327.4 + 27.7 = 355.1$

All these values are entered directly in the notebook in the field and are also immediately plotted on the plane table map.

The details of plotting data and constructing a map are given in Chapter 18.

17-16. Field work. Since all angles in plane table work are measured graphically, they must be checked graphically wherever it is possible to do so. Also the closures on the starting point must be made graphically.

A topographic survey may include an area the boundaries of which may or may not be defined. For example, a topographic survey may be conducted for the purpose of finding a suitable bridge crossing over a river, or for finding a suitable site for a proposed dam or reservoir. On all such surveys the extent of the area to be surveyed may be defined only approximately. When, in any event, the work is to be done with a plane table, it may be necessary to traverse and compile details at the same time.

In plotting details from a plotted point of the plane table set-up, the sights are taken around on all significant objects and on breaks in ground surface. This method of plane table work is called *radiation.* As soon as the notekeeper gives the distance to a point sighted on, one

TABLE 17-1. HORIZONTAL CORRECTIONS SH_c TO $100S$, CORRESPONDING TO CERTAIN V-SCALE READINGS ON BEAMAN STADIA ARC

$V - 50$ (+) or (−)	100S						
	25	50	75	100	200	300	400
1							
2							
3	.05	.10	.15	0.2	0.4	0.6	0.8
4	.07	.15	.22	0.3	0.6	0.9	1.2
5	.07	.15	.22	0.3	0.6	0.9	1.2
6	.10	.20	.30	0.4	0.8	1.2	1.6
7	.12	.25	.37	0.5	1.0	1.5	2.0
8	.15	.30	.45	0.6	1.2	1.8	2.4
9	.20	.40	.60	0.8	1.6	2.4	3.2
10	.25	.50	.75	1.0	2.0	3.0	4.0
11	.3	.6	.9	1.2	2.4	3.6	4.8
12	.4	.8	1.1	1.5	3.0	4.5	6.0
13	.4	.9	1.3	1.7	3.2	5.1	6.8
14	.5	1.0	1.5	2.0	4.0	6.0	8.0
15	.6	1.2	1.7	2.3	4.6	6.9	9.2
16	.7	1.4	2.0	2.7	5.4	8.1	10.8
17	.8	1.5	2.3	3.0	6.0	9.0	12.0
18	.9	1.7	2.6	3.4	6.8	10.2	13.8
19	1.0	1.9	2.9	3.8	7.6	11.4	15.2
20	1.1	2.1	3.2	4.2	8.4	12.6	16.8
21	1.2	2.3	3.5	4.6	9.2	13.8	18.4
22	1.3	2.5	3.8	5.1	10.2	15.3	20.4
23	1.4	2.8	4.2	5.6	11.0	16.8	22.4
24	1.5	3.0	4.5	6.1	12.2	18.3	24.4
25	1.7	3.3	5.0	6.7	13.4	20.1	26.8
26	1.8	3.6	5.5	7.3	14.6	21.9	29.2
27	2.0	3.9	5.9	7.9	15.8	23.7	31.6
28	2.1	4.2	6.4	8.5	17.0	25.5	34.0
29	2.3	4.6	6.9	9.2	18.4	27.6	36.8
30	2.5	5.0	7.5	10.0	20.0	30.0	40.0
31	2.7	5.3	8.0	10.7	21.4	32.1	42.8
32	2.9	5.7	8.6	11.5	23.0	34.5	46.0
33	3.1	6.1	9.2	12.3	24.6	36.9	49.2
34	3.3	6.6	9.9	13.2	26.4	39.6	52.8
35	3.6	7.1	10.7	14.2	28.4	42.6	56.8
36	3.8	7.6	11.4	15.2	30.4	45.6	60.8
37	4.1	8.1	12.2	16.3	32.6	48.9	65.2
38	4.4	8.8	13.1	17.5	35.0	52.5	70.0
39	4.7	9.4	14.0	18.7	37.4	56.1	74.8
40	5.0	10.0	15.0	20.0	40.0	60.0	80.0

may plot the point on the map without drawing a line along the alidade's straight edge.   Such a procedure helps to keep the working map clean and unmarked by superfluous lines.   However, the number of a point, as it is recorded in the notebook, and the elevation, as soon as it is computed, are neatly lettered on the map.   It is helpful to keep the map covered with a sheet of paper with a circular hole centered around the map working area.

All lines of a traverse, however, must be drawn on the map, since a plotted traverse serves as a frame of reference to which all details are related.   The traverse itself must be tied to some monuments or permanent landmarks, so that plotted points can be checked from other locations and, if necessary, adjusted on the map.

The true north direction must be drawn on the map by an arrow.   On some topographic maps it is accurate enough to determine the true north direction by the compass if the declination of the needle is known for the location of the surveyed area.   If not, it can be found from magnetic charts and tables (Art. 13-22).   If geodetic stations or bench marks are located within the area being surveyed, the stations must be plotted on the map and used as reference points.

In setting the table over a point one must consider the scale of the map.   If the scale is, for instance, 1 in. = 100 ft, and the table is set up 1 ft off the point, the offset error of plotted points is 0.01 in. in the scale of the map.   This is a negligible error for the scale considered.   When the scale is about 1 in. = 500 ft or smaller, it is accurate enough to set the plane table, say, close to a tree, and to assume that the table occupies the station located on the map by that tree.

When the table is set up over a point on a line already plotted on the map, one orients the table by placing the straight edge of the alidade along that line and rotating the table until the line of sight falls on some ground point along the line.   The table is then clamped in that position.   Such a sight is called *backsight*.   It corresponds to taking a backsight with the lower motion of the transit in transit work.

When a new direction is plotted from a point, the alidade is rotated on the clamped table and a sight is taken along the new direction, while the beveled edge of the alidade is kept on the map-point over which the table is set up.   Such a sight is called *foresight*.   It corresponds to a foresight taken with the upper motion of the transit in transit work. When many radial sights are taken from a point, a fine needle is sometimes stuck at the point in order to keep the straight edge touching it while sights are being taken.

In traversing around an area, one should make checks on the plotted traverse points by graphical triangulation.   Graphical triangulation in ordinary traversing is accomplished either by *intersection* or *resection* of lines.

17-17. Intersection. Intersection, in plane table work, is the method of locating points on a map by intersecting lines, drawn from two or more points already plotted on the map. The lines are drawn from the points of known location when the plane table is set up over those points. Let it be required, for instance, to locate two trees shown in Fig. 17-11 at points C and D on the ground, if points A and B are already plotted on the drawing as a and b respectively.

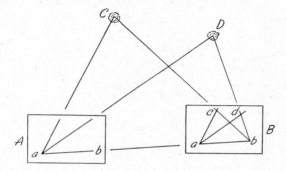

Fig. 17-11. Method of intersection.

When the plane table is set up at A and is oriented along the line AB, foresights are taken to points C and D and radial lines in the directions of those points are drawn through point a. Then the plane table is set up over point B, oriented by taking backsight on A, and two foresights are taken to the same points C and D. The intersection of corresponding lines drawn from points a and b locates the trees at c and d on the map. When several radial lines are drawn from the first point, the drawn rays must be labeled, so that proper lines can be identified at the set-up over the second point.

17-18. Resection. Resection is the method of locating the point of plane table set-up, on a plotted line, by taking a sight on some ground point already plotted on the map.

Figure 17-12 shows a plane table survey that was started by plotting the line AB as a base. While the table was at A a sight was taken on point C and that direction was plotted on the map. Then the table was set up at C and oriented by the drawn direction of the line from point A toward C. After this, the foresight was taken on point B by pivoting the straight edge around point b already plotted on the map. This foresight direction drawn through point b locates point c on the line drawn from a toward c.

17-19. Traversing. The plotting of lines shown in Fig. 17-12 can also be done by traversing. After orienting the table at A by backsighting on point B, one can determine the distance AC by stadia method, when the foresight was taken on C. When point c is located by this method and the table is set up at C, and is oriented by backsighting on A, the plotting of point c can be checked by resection through point b in the same way as it is shown in Fig. 17-12.

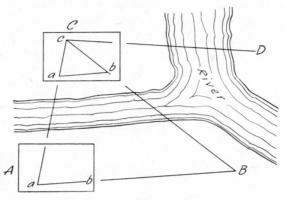

Fig. 17-12. Method of resection.

After foresight has been taken on D and point d has been plotted on the map, the plane table is set up at D and is oriented by backsight on point C. Then, the plotting of point d can be checked by resection through points a and b. Thus by taking advantage of available checks, one can detect any error in plotting early, without waiting for the last set-up in order to find out whether the traverse closes or not. Such checks by graphic triangulation constitute an important advantage of plane table work.

17-20. Adjustments of the alidade. The alidade's levels, the line of sight of the telescope, and the Beaman arc verniers must be in proper adjustment.

(a) *Adjustment of levels.* The alidade's straight edge has either a circular level or two level tubes placed at right angle to each other. A circular level is usually fixed and thus does not need the adjustment. But the tube levels are adjusted by setting the alidade on the plane table along a drawn line and centering the bubbles by leveling the table. The alidade is then turned through 180° in azimuth. If the bubbles move, they are brought halfway back by the level's adjusting screws.

The striding level is adjusted in a similar manner. First, it is set in its place on the telescope and the bubble is centered by leveling the telescope. Next, the level is reversed end-for-end. If the bubble moves, it is brought halfway back toward the center by the level's adjusting screws.

(b) *Adjustment of the line of sight.* The line of sight of the telescope must be concentric with the axis of the sleeve holding the telescope. A well-defined point is placed at the intersection of the cross hairs and the telescope is turned through 180° in the sleeve. If the intersection of the cross hairs moves off the point, the cross-hair ring is adjusted so that the intersection of the cross hairs is brought halfway back toward the sighted point. This adjustment is repeated until the intersection of cross hairs stays on the sighted point.

(c) *Adjustment of verniers.* The telescope is leveled by means of the striding level, and the zero indices on the vernier plate are set to read proper graduations on their respective scales. If there is no vernier level, the screws holding the vernier plate are loosened and the plate is adjusted to a proper position. But if there is a vernier level, there is also a tangent screw for moving the verniers, so that the verniers are set to read proper graduation by the vernier's tangent screw. If, after the verniers have been properly set, the vernier's level bubble is off the center, it is brought all the way back to center by the level's adjusting screws.

Once adjusted, the alidade does not easily get out of adjustment; thus frequent checks of the adjustment are not necessary.

The Photogrammetric Method

17-21. General. The science of photogrammetry deals with methods and techniques of making measurements by means of photographs. This science finds many applications not only in engineering but also in geology, botany, forestry, archeology, and in many other fields. Various uses of photogrammetry in engineering were mentioned in Arts. 1-15, 7-6, and 9-26. Because of its wide application in engineering, photogrammetry is taught now in many engineering schools as a special course of study. This chapter gives only a brief description of the photogrammetric method, as it applies to certain topographic surveys.

Photographs used in making topographic maps are aerial photographs, normally taken from an airplane. Photographs taken from the ground have very limited application in topographic surveying. The aerial photographs most widely used at the present time in topographic mapping are so-called *vertical photographs,* which are photographs taken with the camera axis held in a vertical position.

A complete photogrammetric survey, conducted for the purpose of making a topographic map, involves the following: flying, photography, ground control measurements, and map compilation.   Special apparatus and trained technical personnel are used in many phases of such work. Thus photogrammetric surveys are not economically suitable for topographic mapping of small areas.   On small areas, the transit-stadia and the plane table topographic methods remain the best methods now available.

In planning a photogrammetric survey, even of a large area, one must consider the limitations of the method.   Ground areas covered by snow or dense vegetation are not suitable for topographic survey by means of photographs unless such surveys are supplemented by ground surveys. Adverse weather conditions also play an important part in "flying" an area because weather affects the quality of photographs.   A certain amount of ground surveying is necessary in any photogrammetric survey in order to establish horizontal and vertical ground controls, which are used in checking the accuracy of compiled maps.

17-22. Required accuracies.   One of the important questions in planning a topographic survey by the photogrammetric method is, what accuracies can one expect from such surveys?   If it is assumed that good equipment and working personnel are available, the accuracy of photogrammetric surveys of unobscured areas comes close to matching the accuracy obtained by the transit-stadia and the plane table methods. In this connection the results of the widely different techniques employed in obtaining elevations by the ground and by the photogrammetric methods should be appreciated.   Although what is called the *point accuracy* in obtaining elevations may be better in ground surveys, it must be recalled (Art. 17-7) that slopes between the points of determined elevations, in ground surveys, are considered to be uniform when the contours are drawn on a map.   This method of mapping may result in considerable errors in the elevations of unobserved points.   A photogrammetric survey may not have as good point accuracy, but, on the other hand, in drawing contours the contact with the ground surface shown on photographs is constantly maintained.   Thus one must use a statistical approach in comparing relative accuracies of the two methods.

Another important difference between the ground and the photogrammetric methods of surveying is the difference in the rate of increase of cost with increased accuracy.   For instance, in order to double the accuracy of a ground survey, it may be necessary perhaps to double the number of sighted points and to increase the care exercised in taking various data, which altogether may increase the cost of a given survey by, say, 20 or 30 per cent.   However, doubling the accuracy of a photogrammetric survey may require not only an increase in the number of photographs for a given area but perhaps the use of better cameras and instruments and better working personnel.   All these may increase the cost of the new survey by considerably more than 20 or 30 per cent. Thus in planning a photogrammetric survey the pertinent question should be, what accuracy is required in the given application? Years of practice with maps made by the photogrammetric method have developed certain sets of standards, which are normally incorporated into specifications for photogrammetric surveys made for various purposes.

Highway engineering is one of many engineering fields in which the use of photographs and photogrammetric mapping in highway reconnaissance, location, and design is firmly established. When one compares the time required for a highway project to be completed by using the photogrammetric method with the time required when only ground surveying is used, the ground surveying begins to appear rather antiquated. The application of photogrammetry not only reduces the time required for a project to be completed, but also results in better and more economical highways.

The scale of topographic maps required on highway projects may vary from about 1 in. = 2000 ft with 5 ft contour intervals to 1 in. = 100 ft with 2 ft contours, or sometimes 1 in. = 40 ft with 1 ft contours. The cost increases with the increase in scale, varying from about $600 per mile of length to about $4000, at the time of this writing.

Generally accepted specifications for the accuracy of topographic maps made by the photogrammetric method are that 90 per cent of contours be plotted within the accuracy of $\frac{1}{2}$ contour interval and the remaining 10 per cent within the accuracy of a full contour interval. The horizontal accuracy that has been found to be practical in highway application is 1:200. This means the maximum 0.5 ft error in 100 ft, which in the scale 1 in. = 100 ft is 0.03 in.

It must be noted that the above-mentioned specifications for the accuracy of contours may include fairly large systematic errors. For instance, if 90 per cent of contour errors, on a map drawn with 2 ft contour intervals, are found to vary from 0 to +1 ft, a systematic error of +0.5 ft in map compilation may be suspected. The way to reduce systematic errors in plotting is to increase the amount of ground control used. This also increases the cost of the map.

17-23. Who makes photogrammetric surveys? The work of making photogrammetric surveys is often let by contract. Thus in order to be able to meet competition in this field one must be engaged in the business that specializes in this kind of work. Various aerial survey companies, some large, some small, are found nowadays in many parts of the world. Some are doing business on a global scale.

Many government agencies, as for instance the U.S. Geological Survey, do their own photogrammetric surveys. The tendency among the state highway departments at the present time is to set up their own photogrammetric laboratories.   It must be realized in this connection that the photographs and the apparatus used in compiling topographic maps may be used for other purposes, such as taking profiles or cross sections (see Arts. 10-13 and 10-16) along various routes or along several alternate locations of a route.   Such data may be either plotted on paper or fed to an electronic computer for estimation of the quantities of earth-work involved.   The application of electronic computers in highway work is still in its infancy.   Many new developments may be expected

Fig. 17-13. Fairchild's T-11 aerial mapping camera.   (Courtesy Fairchild Camera and Instrument Corporation.)

in the future from a combination of photogrammetry and electronic computing devices.

Other engineering projects such as construction of a dam or a hydro-electric power plant also warrant a special photogrammetric survey. On those projects on which it is uneconomical to "fly" the area, available photographs may be obtained from certain offices of the U.S. Geological Survey or from other government agencies.

17-24. The photographs. The art of producing suitable photographs plays an important part in a photogrammetric survey.   Special cameras and special installations in the airplanes for the cameras and other equipment, as well as competent working personnel, are necessary in order to produce good photographs.   Figure 17-13 shows one of the many types of cameras that are used in taking photographs for mapping purposes.   The magazine of such cameras is designed to carry roll films several hundred feet long.

The size of photographs most commonly used in the United States is 9 by 9 in. European-made cameras utilize mostly a size of 18 by 18 cm. The ground area is photographed from the airplane as it flies back and forth along parallel flight lines. The photographs taken in one flight line constitute a **strip**. These photographs are taken with a certain amount of overlap, usually 60 per cent, between any two adjacent photographs in a strip. This overlap is called the **end lap**. A certain amount of overlap, about 30 per cent, is also required between any two adjacent strips. This overlap is called the **side lap**.

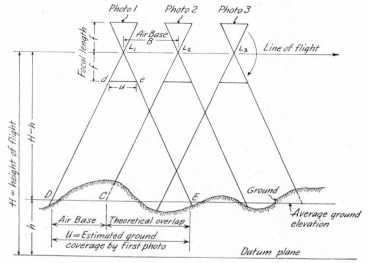

Fig. 17-14. Vertical profile through flight line.

17-25. Required number of photographs. Figure 17-14 shows a vertical profile through a flight line of the airplane taking vertical photographs. The points L_1, L_2, L_3, and so on along the flight line, at which camera exposures are made, are called the **exposure stations**. Various dimensions shown on the figure have the following meaning:

H—the height of flight above a datum plane (usually mean sea level).
h—the average elevation of the terrain above the datum plane.
f—the focal length of the camera lens.
u—side dimension of a square photograph.
U—theoretical ground distance covered by the width u of a photograph, computed from the average elevation of the terrain.
B—the distance between the exposure stations, called the **air base**.
W—the spacing between flight lines.

It may be seen from the figure that the actual ground distance covered by the width u of a photograph may be greater or less than the theoretical distance U shown on the figure for the average elevation of the terrain h above the datum plane. However, the estimated average elevation of the terrain above the mean sea level is normally used in computation of the number of photographs required in a strip and the number of strips required to cover a given area. For a rectangular area these computations are shown in Example 17-2 below.

It may be observed in Fig. 17-14 that a certain amount of end lap is shown for adjacent photographs. For instance, ground distance CE is the overlap that will appear on photographs 1 and 2. The remaining distance DC, covered by the photograph 1, is equal to the length of the air base B between the exposure stations L_1 and L_2.

If the theoretical ground distance covered by the width u of a photograph is U and the required end lap between the photographs is 60 per cent, then the overlap distance on the ground is $0.6U$. This leaves $0.4U$ for the ground distance which must be equal to the length B of the air base. In order to compute the number of photographs in a strip, $1.5B$ is usually added at each end of a strip for end coverage. The total length divided by the air base B gives the number of air bases in a strip. This number is rounded to the nearest integral number, and one is added to it, in order to obtain the number of photographs in the strip.

The number of strips for an area is computed in a similar manner. If the side lap between the strips is 30 per cent, $0.3U$ is the ground coverage that appears on two adjacent strips. Thus the distance W between the strip's flight lines must be $0.7U$. Because of possible deviation of the airplane from its flight lines, about $0.25W$ is added to the width of the area being surveyed, along each longitudinal border of the area. The total width is then divided by the spacing between the flight lines, and is rounded to the nearest integral number.

The above computations of the number of photographs in a strip, and of the number of flight lines, are derived from the theoretical ground distance U covered by one photograph. This distance varies with the height of flight, H, the average elevation h of the terrain, and the focal length f of the camera lens. If h and f are known, distance U can be computed from similar triangles dL_1e and DL_1E, shown in Fig. 17-14. From these triangles the following basic equation is derived:

$$\frac{f}{H - h} = \frac{u}{U} \qquad (17\text{-}22)$$

Equation (17-22) gives the average scale $f/(H - h)$ for a photograph, based on the average elevation of the terrain h. Since actual elevations vary from point to point, all photographs have variable scales throughout. However, as far as the estimation of the number of photographs is concerned, all computations are based on the average elevation of the terrain to be photographed. It may be observed that if f and u in Eq. (17-22) are in inches and the quantities shown in the denominators are in feet, no convergence of units is necessary in solving the equation for any quantity.

Example 17-2. It is required to estimate the number of photographs required for topographic mapping of an area 20 by 32 miles, based on the following data: focal length of the camera lens is 6 in., the average elevation of the terrain is 740 ft, the height of flight $H = 10,500$ ft, and the size of photographs is 9 by 9 in. Assume average end lap 60 per cent and average side lap 30 per cent.

Solution:
Ground coverage:

$$U = u \frac{H - h}{f} = 9 \frac{10,500 - 740}{6} = 14,640 \text{ ft}$$

The air base:

$$B = 0.4U = 0.4 \times 14,640 = 5856 \text{ ft}$$

The spacing between flight lines:

$$W = 0.7U = 0.7 \times 14,640 = 10,248 \text{ ft}$$

The length of one strip, assuming that flight lines are parallel to the longer border of the area:

$$32 \times 5280 + 3 \times 5856 = 186,528$$

The number of photographs in one strip:

$$\frac{186,528}{5856} + 1 = 31.8 + 1 = 33 \text{ photos}$$

The width of the area to be flown:

$$20 \times 5280 + 0.5 \times 10,248 = 110,724 \text{ ft}$$

The number of strips:

$$\frac{110,724}{10,248} = 10.8 = 11 \text{ strips}$$

The required number of photographs:

$$33 \times 11 = 363 \text{ photos}$$

An example how to estimate the height of flight H is given in Art. 17-29 below.

17-26. Photo-index. Vertical photographs obtained in a flight mission can be identified by the number of the photograph, the date when flown, and the project designation for which the prints are made. Other pertinent data, such as the scale, the focal length of the lens used, and so on, are normally shown on each photograph.

After the required area has been photographed, the prints are assembled in the manner shown in Fig. 17-15 and are photographed on a single

Fig. 17-15. Photo-index map.

sheet called the *photo-index*. The photo-index is used to identify photographs that show certain areas.

17-27. Stereoscopy. Any two adjacent photographs in a strip, having a certain overlap area, constitute a *stereoscopic pair* of photographs since the overlapping area can be viewed in three dimensions under a

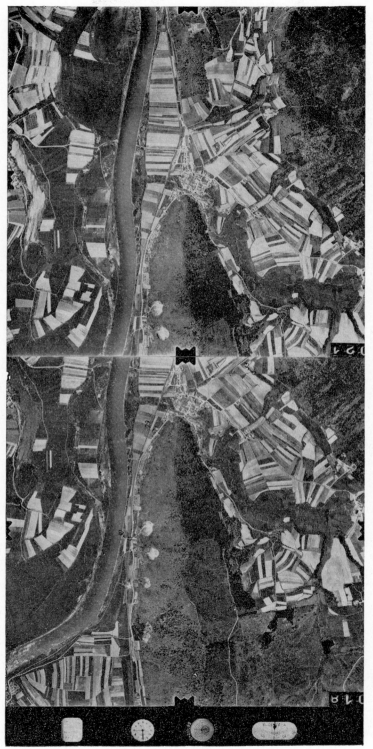

Fig. 17-16. Stereoscopic pair of photographs. (Taken with Zeiss RMK 21/18 aerial camera.) (Courtesy Zeiss Aerotopograph.)

stereoscope. A stereoscopic pair of photographs is also called a *stereogram* or a *stereopair.* Figure 17-16 shows a typical stereopair with about 60 per cent of overlap.

A pocket stereoscope (shown in Fig. 9-22) is often used in the field for identification of ground control points, property corners, and other points and objects requiring field inspection. Pocket stereoscopes are convenient for field work with photographs since they can be folded and carried

Fig. 17-17. Mirror stereoscope and parallax bar. (Courtesy Wild Heerbrugg Instruments, Inc.)

in a pocket. The stereoscopes that are used in the laboratory for studying photographs have reflecting mirrors which increase the viewing base. Some stereoscopes are also equipped with a pair of binoculars that have magnifying power of about 2, 3, or more diameters. Figure 17-17 shows a mirror stereoscope with binoculars.

Normal, unaided eyesight is capable of stereoscopic vision, which enables a person to view the objects in three dimensions. The reason is that the objects are viewed by each eye at a slightly different angle. The average interpupilary distance in people, called the *eye-base,* is about 2.63 in. Such an eye-base enables a person to have depth perception at distances up to about 2000 ft. This depth perception may be increased in two ways: by increasing the viewing base, and by magnification. If the viewing base is increased n times and the magnification is m diameters, the distance for depth perception is increased nm times. The viewing base in a stereopair taken from the air is equal to the length B of the air base. This explains why a stereopair may be viewed in three dimensions even though the photographs are taken at a distance of many thousands of feet.

Figure 17-18 shows a simple stereogram consisting of two cards on which four identical dots are marked. When viewed under a stereoscope, the dots a' and a'' may be fused together by adjustment of the distance between the cards. When this is done, the dots b' and b'' will also appear fused together, but the fused dot b will appear closer to the eyes than the fused dot a. The reason is that dots b' and b'' are viewed under a different angle than dots a' and a'', thus creating the illusion that the two fused dots are at different distances from the eyes. If the dots a' and a'' are moved to the positions shown by the circles, thus changing the parallactic angle at which the dots are viewed, the psychological effect is such that

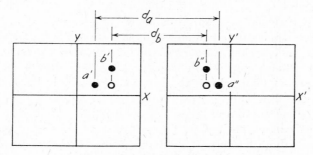

Fig. 17-18. A simple stereogram.

the fused dot appears to rise in the air, assuming the same elevation as the dot b, if the distance d_a between a-dots is made equal to distance d_b between b-dots.

The position of points shown in Fig. 17-18 may be fixed on each card by the x and y coordinates pertaining to the X and Y coordinate axes passing through the center of each card, as is shown on the figure. By the use of prime symbols to designate coordinates of points on the left card and double-prime symbols to designate coordinates on the right card, the coordinates of point b on the left and right cards may be respectively given as (x_b', y_b') and (x_b'', y_b'').

If y coordinates of a point shown on both cards are equal, the difference between its x coordinates, such as $x_b' - x_b''$, is called the **parallax** of that point and is designated by the letter p with a proper subscript for a given point. The difference of such values for any two points, for example $p_b - p_a$, is called the **difference of parallax** of those points.

It may be seen in Fig. 17-18 that $p_b - p_a = d_a - d_b$, where the difference on the right-hand side is the horizontal displacement of point a that causes the apparent rise of point a to the elevation of point b. Thus the difference of parallax of two points can be used to measure the difference in elevation between those points.

The example with the stereogram of two cards also explains the idea of a *floating mark* which is used in stereoplotting instruments mentioned below.   Two dots are placed on two pieces of glass and are moved along the surface of two photographs from one object to another.   If the objects are at different elevation the fused dot will appear to move either up or down, as the case may be.   By fastening the glasses to a worm and arranging a micrometer scale to measure horizontal displacement of the dots, one has what is known as a *parallax bar* for measuring the difference in elevation of points on stereoscopic photographs.   Figures 9-22 and 17-17 show parallax bars.   How closely the difference in elevation of points may be determined by the use of such equipment depends in large measure on the quality and the average scale of the photographs and on the experience and the visual acuity of the operator.

The difference in parallax measured by the micrometer scale of a parallax bar is a function not only of the difference in elevation of points but also of the focal length of the camera lens, the length of the air base, and the height of flight above the ground surface.   If these quantities are known, the difference in elevation of points on stereoscopic photographs can be measured and the elevation of points, referred to a certain datum plane, can be plotted on paper.   Such a process of plotting is, however, too elaborate to have much application in topographic mapping. For this reason the planimetric and topographic maps are normally made by so-called *automatic stereoscopic plotting instruments* (Figs. 17-19 and 17-20).

17-28. Stereoplotting instruments.   The stereoscopic plotting instruments, in which optical projection of photographs is used for measurements and for plotting, are widely used in the United States. In such instruments as the *multiplex* or the *Kelsh plotter* (Fig. 17-19), the projection of diapositive plates is made directly on the map compilation sheet placed on top of the working table.   If projection of one plate is made through a blue filter and projection of another plate through a red filter, one may view the projected model in three dimensions on the table by wearing complementary blue and red glasses, with a different color for each eye.   The projected model is called a *stereomodel* or a *spatial model.*

In such instruments the part of the floating mark is played by a lighted dot in the middle of the white platen of the *tracing table,* shown on the working table of Fig. 17-19.   The platen can be raised or lowered so that the dot may be made to touch the ground surface of the stereomodel at any point.   A pencil is attached to the underside of the platen right under the dot and may be lowered onto the map.   If the tracing table is moved around on the compilation sheet, the dot may be made to follow a certain elevation of the ground surface on the stereomodel, while the pencil draws a contour on the map.

A certain amount of ground control must be plotted on the compilation sheet for proper orientation of the stereomodel. Operation of stereoplotting instruments requires skilled workmanship and good knowledge of the working parts of the instrument.

Fig. 17-19. The Kelsh plotter (Model 5030).   (Courtesy The Kelsh Instrument Co., Inc.)

Zeiss' stereoplanigraph (Fig. 17-20) is another type of a stereoscopic plotting instrument.   In this instrument the three-dimensional effect is achieved with the diapositive plates by an optical binocular system which allows one eye to view one plate and the other eye another plate.   The system has a floating mark which can be moved in x, y, and z directions by various controls.   The x and y motions are transferred to a

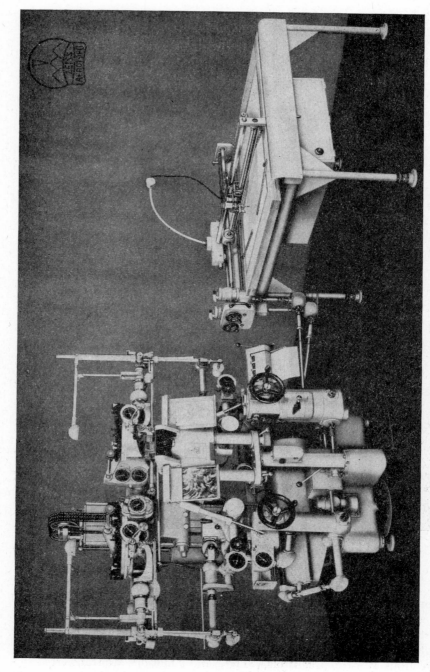

Fig. 17-20. Zeiss C-8 Stereoplanigraph. (Courtesy Zeiss Aerotopograph.)

table, called *coordinatograph,* on which the map compilation is made. It takes two men to operate the stereoplanigraph.

There are other stereoplotting instruments that use the principle of mechanical rather than optical projection; there are also instruments that utilize both. Textbooks on photogrammetry must be consulted for more detailed description of stereoplotting instruments.

17-29. Required scale of photographs. When estimates are made of the cost of a photogrammetric survey, it is necessary to estimate the number of photographs required for a given survey. However, as Example 17-2 shows, the computation of the number of photographs depends on the following factors: the focal length of the camera lens, the flying height of the airplane, the average elevation of the terrain, and the required end lap and side lap on photographs. An engineer making the estimates must know how to coordinate these factors. In order to do this effectively he must also know what kind of a stereoplotter will be used in map compilation. However, the estimated costs do not vary a great deal. Thus knowing how to make an estimate for one plotter should give one a fairly good idea of the cost involved.

Each stereoplotter has certain limitations for plotting contours. These limitations are sometimes expressed by a certain range of values of the *C-factor.* C-factor is defined as the ratio of the flying height above the ground, $H - h$, to the required contour interval on the map. The C-factor of a stereoplotting instrument varies somewhat, depending on the kind and scale of photographs used. However, there is a certain range of values for a given instrument which may be used in an estimate.

Many optical plotters are adapted to be used with a 6 in. focal length lens, which means that a 6 in. camera lens is often used on flying missions. Thus $f = 6$ in. may be used in making estimates. As far as the estimation of the over-all elevation of the terrain is concerned, it can be fairly well determined from any old topo-map. Certain limitations are often applied, by the people ordering topographic maps, to the maximum size of the stereomodel that can be used in plotting. For instance, some specifications limit model to photograph scales to 5-to-1 ratio.

Example 17-3. Let it be assumed that it is necessary to estimate the number of photographs for a map 1 in. = 100 ft with 2 ft contour intervals, for a certain area having an average elevation of 700 ft. Assuming that plotting will be done with a stereoplotting instrument with estimated C-factor equal to 1000, the greatest flying height H may be estimated from the definition of C-factor as follows:

$$1000 = \frac{H - 700}{2}, \text{ or } H = 2{,}700 \text{ ft}$$

Also assuming that the smallest allowable scale of the photograph should be $\frac{1}{5}$ of the plotting scale, the greatest allowable flying height can be computed as follows:

$$\frac{f}{H - h} = \frac{1}{5 \times 100}$$

For $f = 6$ in. and $h = 700$, $H = 3700$ ft.

Thus $H = 2700$ must be used in making an estimate. Knowing H, one may proceed to compute the number of photographs for a given area, as is shown in Example 17-2 above. A usual estimate for the end lap is about 60 per cent and for the side lap, 30 per cent.

PROBLEMS

17-1. From the stadia notes shown below, compute horizontal distances, differences in elevation, and the elevation of points, using formulas, and check the answers by using stadia table. See Table VI at the end of this text.

(A) Transit at Sta. A, Elev. 571.3, H.T. $= 5.0$, $K = 100$, $f + c = 0.85$.

Point	Stadia Intercept	Vertical Angle	Rod Reading	Answers		
				Hor. Dist.	Diff. Elev.	Elev.
1	0.73	6°13′	3.0	73	10.0	581.3
2	1.35	−8°42′	H.T.	133	−20.3	551.0
3	1.17	0	4.2	118	0.8	572.1
4	2.31	12°26′	H.T.	221	48.8	620.1

(B) Transit at Sta. B, Elev. 358.9, H.T. $= 4.6$, $K = 100$, $f + c = 0$.

Point	Stadia Intercept	Vertical Angle	Rod Reading
1	2.73	5°17′	H.T.
2	1.85	−9°12′	H.T.
3	3.46	−10°30′	7.3
4	0.87	4°42′	3.1

(C) Transit at Sta. C, Elev. 738.5, H.T. $= 3.7$, $K = 100$, $f + c = 1$.

Point	Stadia Intercept	Vertical Angle	Rod Reading
1	0.95	−7°12′	H.T.
2	2.72	8°52′	H.T.
3	1.86	−6°04′	H.T.
4	2.53	10°17′	5.7

17-2. A transit-stadia traverse was made along a polygon *ABCDE*. From the field notes shown below, (a) compute the average length for each distance, (b) assuming that the accuracy of this survey is 1:700 or better, find the maximum expected error of closure. The stadia constants of the instrument are: $K = 100$, $f + c = 0$.

(A)

Trans-it at	Backsight Readings			Foresight Readings		
	on Point	Rod Int.	Vert. Angle	on Point	Rod Int.	Vert. Angle
B	A	1.75	3°15′	C	2.38	2°40′
C	B	2.40	−2°34′	D	1.56	−4°28′
D	C	1.56	4°26′	E	3.24	−3°23′
E	D	3.20	3°30′	A	3.62	4°50′
A	E	3.58	−4°46′	B	1.76	−3°18′

Ans. (a) $AB = 174.9$, $BC = 238.5$, $CD = 155.1$, $DE = 320.8$, $EA = 357.5$, (b) 1.8 ft

(B)

Trans-it at	Backsight Readings			Foresight Readings		
	on Point	Rod Int.	Vert. Angle	on Point	Rod Int.	Vert. Angle
A	E	1.37	3°17′	B	2.52	2°50′
B	A	2.51	−2°52′	C	2.75	4°33′
C	B	2.72	−4°32′	D	3.14	−3°50′
D	C	3.15	3°52′	E	3.28	−0°48′
E	D	3.30	0°50′	A	1.35	−3°20′

(C)

Trans-it at	Backsight Readings			Foresight Readings		
	on Point	Rod Int.	Vert. Angle	on Point	Rod Int.	Vert. Angle
C	B	2.71	−2°20′	D	3.17	−3°50′
D	C	3.15	3°47′	E	1.70	4°30′
E	D	1.68	−4°30′	A	2.05	2°13′
A	E	2.08	−2°15′	B	2.21	−3°00′
B	A	2.18	3°00′	C	2.68	2°22′

17-3. Assume that in Problem 17-2 the elevation of point A is 675.3 ft, and that in all set-ups of the transit the rod readings were taken on H.T.   (a) Determine the elevation of points using average B.S. and F.S. differences in elevation.   (b) Find closing error on point A.

(A) See stadia data of Problem 17-2(A).

> *Ans.* (a) $A = 675.3$, $B = 665.3$, $C = 676.2$, $D = 664.1$, $E = 644.8$,
> (b) -0.4

(B) See stadia data of Problem 17-2(B).

(C) See stadia data of Problem 17-2(C).

17-4. A stadia rod was held D ft from the transit and the vertical angle α was read to a point on the rod equal to H.T.   The stadia constants of the transit are: $K = 100$ and $f + c = 0$.   (a) Determine correct rod intercept between the upper stadia hair and the intersection of cross hairs.   (b) Determine correct rod intercept between the intersection of cross hairs and the lower stadia hair.   (c) Using stadia intercept found in parts (a) and (b), compute horizontal distance by stadia tables, to the nearest tenth of a foot, and find per cent of error in measured distance by stadia.   (d) Compute by trigonometry and by stadia method difference in elevation, to the nearest tenth of a foot, and find per cent of error in D.E. as computed by stadia method.

(A) $D = 250.0$ ft, $\alpha = 25°14'$.

> *Ans.* (a) 1.531, (b) 1.524, (c) 250.0, 0%, (d) 117.8, 117.8, 0%

(B) $D = 300.0$ ft, $\alpha = 22°30'$.

(C) $D = 200.0$ ft, $\alpha = 27°10'$.

17-5. Below are shown stadia notes for a trigonometric leveling circuit by stadia. The transit used had stadia constants $K = 100$ and $f + c = 0$.   The backsight and foresight for each instrument set-up were taken on the same rod.   (a) Compute the elevation of point B in the circuit if the elevation of B.M.$_1$ is 357.92.   (b) Determine the error of closure and find whether it is less or more accurate than $\sqrt{D}$, where D is the length of circuit in miles.   (c) Adjust the elevation of point B.

(A)

Station	Backsight		Foresight	
	Rod Interc.	Vert. Angle	Rod Interc.	Vert. Angle
B.M.$_1$	1.37	5°32'		
T.P.$_1$	2.15	2°46'	1.90	−3°12'
T.P.$_2$	1.79	−4°54'	1.75	4°05'
B	1.54	−7°10'	1.27	6°30'
T.P.$_3$	1.82	−3°40'	2.08	1°22'
T.P.$_4$	1.63	4°28'	1.66	−3°52'
B.M.$_1$			1.87	−6°12'

> *Ans.* (a) 365.7, (b) $-0.4 < \sqrt{D}$, (c) 365.9

(B)

Station	Backsight		Foresight	
	Rod Interc.	Vert. Angle	Rod Interc.	Vert. Angle
B.M.$_1$	1.72	−3°16′		
T.P.$_1$	1.35	4°42′	1.93	−2°34′
T.P.$_2$	2.04	2°56′	1.80	−4°28′
B	1.84	−7°20′	1.72	−1°40′
T.P.$_3$	1.67	−3°36′	1.32	6°18′
T.P.$_4$	1.72	2°10′	2.12	4°51′
B.M.$_1$			1.76	−6°32′

(C)

Station	Backsight		Foresight	
	Rod Interc.	Vert. Angle	Rod Interc.	Vert. Angle
B.M.$_1$	2.28	−2°25′		
T.P.$_1$	1.30	−4°52′	1.88	3°47′
T.P.$_2$	1.79	6°19′	1.92	−6°20′
B	1.55	−7°34′	1.96	−4°15′
T.P.$_3$	2.10	−4°11′	1.68	7°42′
T.P.$_4$	1.83	2°30′	1.73	3°35′
B.M.$_1$			1.95	−11°48′

17-6. In a plane table survey with a telescopic alidade, certain recordings of the stadia intercept S and of V-scale readings were made, as is shown below. If stadia constants for the alidade are $K = 100$ and $f + c = 0$, compute horizontal distances and the elevation of points shown in the notes using Table 17-1 given in the text (p. 335). The elevation of the point on which the plane table was set up is 625.3 ft above a datum. All sights were taken on rod R = H.T.

(A)

Point	V	S	Answers			
			H_c	H.D.	D.E.	Elev.
1	15	1.53	4	149	22.9	648.2
2	4	1.71	1	170	6.8	632.1
3	−7	2.85	1	284	−20.0	605.3
4	10	2.64	3	261	26.4	651.7
5	−18	1.31	5	126	−23.6	601.7
6	15	0.76	2	74	10.6	635.9
7	22	3.27	17	310	71.9	697.2
8	5	3.74	1	373	18.7	644.0
9	−9	2.91	2	289	−26.2	599.1
10	−11	1.44	2	142	−15.8	609.5

(B)

Point	V	S
1	12	2.31
2	−8	1.79
3	21	1.63
4	19	2.57
5	−14	3.19
6	−17	2.80
7	28	1.65
8	0	2.10
9	−13	1.62
10	11	2.44

(C)

Point	V	S
1	−10	1.57
2	−12	2.41
3	17	2.66
4	22	1.92
5	31	1.85
6	12	2.10
7	−2	2.27
8	−5	3.32
9	−18	2.81
10	15	2.68

17-7. It is required to estimate the number of vertical photographs necessary to cover a rectangular area X miles by Y miles, given the following data: average elevation of the terrain is h, flying height above the mean sea level is H, focal length of the camera lens is f, the size of photographs is as given below; the required end lap is $E\%$ and the required side lap is $S\%$. Use numerical values given below:

(A) $X = 28$ mi., $Y = 17$ mi., $h = 850$ ft, $H = 9000$ ft, $f = 8.25$ in., photographs 9 in. by 9 in., $E = 55\%$, $S = 25\%$.   *Ans.* 574 photos

(B) $X = 35$ miles, $Y = 22$ miles, $h = 950$ ft, $H = 8000$ ft, $f = 6$ in., photographs 9 in. by 9 in., $E = 52\%$, $S = 20\%$.

(C) $X = 30$ km, $Y = 20$ km, $h = 1200$ ft, $H = 12{,}000$ ft, $f = 209$ mm, photographs 17 cm by 17 cm, $E = 60\%$, $S = 25\%$.

17-8. Assume that the photographs considered in Problem 17-7 are used in making topographic maps by a stereoscopic plotting instrument. If the maximum allowable C-factor to be used with the instrument is C, and the maximum allowable ratio of stereomodel scale to the average photograph scale is R, find (a) the smallest contour interval that can be used on the compiled map and (b) the largest allowable scale in map compilation.

(A) $C = 800$, $R = 5$.   *Ans.* (a) 10 ft, (b) 1 in. = 200 ft

(B) $C = 1000$, $R = 6$.

(C) $C = 1200$, $R = 7$.

CHAPTER 18

Map Drafting

18-1. Map-drafting instruments and equipment. The basic equipment used in map drafting includes two or more triangles, engineer's scales, a protractor, a lettering triangle, a french curve, and a set of drawing instruments. The use of other equipment in map drafting is dictated more or less by the size and the kind of map being made. Such equipment may include a drafting board or a drafting table, a T-square, a straight edge, or a drafting machine. For plotting circular curves of larger radii than those that can be drawn with a compass, draftsmen use either a beam compass or "railroad" curves. All of the above mentioned drafting equipment is briefly described below.

Triangles, used for drawing straight lines at various angles, are right-angled triangles constructed with 45-degree or with 30- and 60-degree angles. They are now made of transparent plastic material in a variety of sizes. With changes of temperature, such triangles may develop slight deformations, so that in accurate map drafting it is advisable to check them from time to time.

The *scales* to which various maps are drawn vary considerably, depending on the map's intended use. However, they normally vary in increments of 10 ft to the inch from 1 in. = 10 ft to 1 in. = 100 ft and in increments of 100 ft to the inch from 1 in. = 100 ft to 1 in. = 1000 ft. Accordingly, the *engineer's scales,* which are used in plotting distances, are graduated into 10, 20, 30, and so on up to 100 divisions per inch. The size and the shape of engineer's scales vary. Flat wooden scales are made in sets ranging from 6 to 24 in. in length. Their edges are beveled, and

Fig. 18-1. Engineer's scale. (Courtesy Keuffel & Esser Co.)

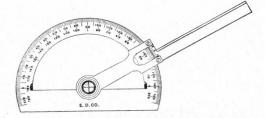

Fig. 18-2. Protractor. (Courtesy Eugene Dietzgen Co.)

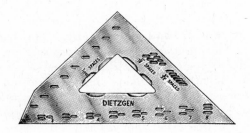

Fig. 18-3. Lettering triangle. (Courtesy Eugene Dietzgen Co.)

Fig. 18-4. Railroad pen. (Courtesy Eugene Dietzgen Co.)

Fig. 18-5. Contour pen. (Courtesy Keuffel & Esser Co.)

the graduations are shown along the beveled edge. Another type of scale extensively used in map drafting is triangular in cross section. Such a scale is shown in Fig. 18-1. The six edges of a triangular scale can accommodate six different scales. Quite commonly the six scales have, respectively, 10, 20, 30, 40, 50, and 60 divisions per inch.

A *protractor* is a device used for plotting and measuring angles on drawings. It is normally either circular or semicircular in shape, with graduations marked along the circular edge. To be employed with the sexagesimal system, used in the United States, protractors are divided into degrees and, usually, quarters or halves of a degree. They are made of wood, paper, metal, or plastic, in varying sizes. A large protractor gives more accurate results in plotting than a small one. A semicircular protractor is shown in Fig. 18-2. For more accurate work, steel protractors are made with a movable arm to which a vernier is attached for reading the angles, usually to 5'.

Lettering triangles are made as right-angled triangles with 45-degree or with 30- and 60-degree angles. The triangles have either circular or oblong holes into which one may insert a pencil point when drafting guide lines for lettering. The pencil moves the triangle along a straight edge. The holes are placed so that one may draw lines spaced from about $\frac{3}{32}$ to $\frac{7}{32}$ in. apart for the lower-case letters. The spacing of holes for the capitals makes the height of the lower-case letters equal to two-thirds of the height of the capitals.

French curves come in a variety of sizes and shapes. However, only one or two such curves are normally needed for drawing various irregular curves on maps.

A *set of drawing instruments* normally contains a pair of compasses, for drawing circles and circular arcs; dividers, for fine scaling and transferring of distances; and ruling pens, for drawing lines with ink. Two special drawing instruments useful in map drafting, but usually not included in a set of drawing instruments, are the *railroad pen* (Fig. 18-4) for drawing simultaneously two parallel lines, and the *contour pen* (Fig. 18-5) for drawing contours. The latter is made free to turn in the handle, in order to permit it to follow irregular lines, such as contours. One needs a little experience with this pen to be able to draw smooth, uniform lines.

A *T-square* is of little use in map drafting since there are normally few parallel lines to be drawn on maps. A drafting machine (Fig. 18-6), on which angles may be set usually within 5', is more useful than the T-square in plotting traverses. The machine has interchangeable scales set at a fixed 90° angle with respect to each other. In plotting long profiles, such as are drawn for the design of a route, long steel straight edges and large triangles are normally employed.

A *beam compass* has a needle-point center, such as an ordinary compass has, and a pen, both of which can be attached anywhere along a rod, which comes in lengths varying from about 6 in. to 12 in. On some sets two bars may be coupled together to form a longer beam and thus provide a longer radius for the compass.

Railroad curves are flat, curved templates about $1\frac{1}{2}$ in. wide. Each template has both edges shaped as circular arcs of a certain radius. The

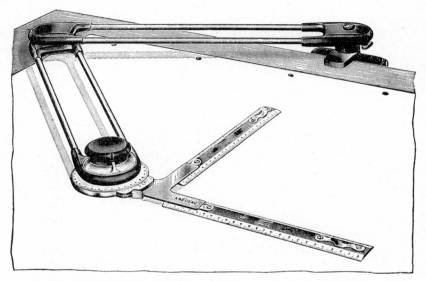

Fig. 18-6. Drafting machine. (Courtesy Keuffel & Esser Co.)

curves normally come in sets containing from about 17 to 55 curves. They are available in a wide range of radii varying from about $1\frac{1}{2}$ in. to 200 in. These curves are very useful in drawing highways and railroads on maps and plans.

18-2. Drawing paper. Among the papers and other map-drafting materials it is necessary to recognize the following classifications: (a) papers and other materials used in plotting maps and plans, (b) those used in making tracings of finished maps for the purpose of reproduction, and (c) graph papers used for special purposes, such as plotting profiles and cross sections.

(a) The paper that is most commonly used in plotting maps and plans is a heavy manila drawing paper. It is buff in color, is fairly stable when dry, and takes erasures well without leaving rough, fibrous spots. Some draftsmen prefer to use white drawing paper. The only objection that can be raised against the use of white drawing paper is that it shows soiled spots more readily.

There are waterproof, nonshrinkable papers which are used mostly in outdoor map plotting such as in plane table work. In photogrammetry, where map compilation must be done with utmost precision, nonshrinkable plastic materials are sometimes employed. Since the better materials are more expensive, economic considerations may be a factor in the selection of a drawing sheet.

(b) Tracing paper and tracing cloth are used to trace finished maps so that they can be reproduced, in a number of copies, by certain processes described in Art. 18-3 below. A tracing may be drawn either in pencil or in ink. Pencil tracings are often made on vellum-type paper. The vellum is quite durable and is easy to work on. However, tracings that are kept as a permanent record are usually made in ink on tracing cloth. Tracing cloth is made of linen fabric, impregnated with a substance that makes the cloth transparent. Tracing cloths are finished with a glossy surface on one side and with a dull surface on the other. Either side will take ink, but only the dull side can be used for pencil tracing. There are also tracing cloths that are especially made for pencil tracing.

When reproduced by various commercial processes, pencil tracings do not reproduce as well as ink tracings, although prints made from pencil tracings are quite legible if the lines are made with a soft pencil.

Special drawing inks are used in making ink tracings. Drawing inks are waterproof. Although they come in a variety of colors, black India ink is normally used in making tracings. Lines made with other colors are not as opaque as those made with black ink and consequently do not reproduce as well on prints. However, when different shadings of lines are desired on prints, several colors may be used on the same tracing. For instance, tracings of topographic maps may be made with black ink with the exception of the contours and water lines. Ground contours may be traced with brown ink and water lines with blue. On a print, all these lines will show in the same color, usually blue or brown, depending on the process used in reproduction, but the lines made in black ink will reproduce best, next, brown ink lines, and then blue ink lines.

(c) Special graph papers are often used in plotting profiles and cross sections (Arts. 10-13 and 10-16). Profile paper has more divisions per inch along vertical lines than along horizontal lines because the elevations are usually plotted to a larger scale and need be quite accurate. In road design, profiles are used for the design of grades, drainage, and foundations of various structures.

Cross-section paper is normally divided into square inches by heavy lines, and into $\frac{1}{4}$ in. or smaller divisions by lighter lines. Profile and cross-section papers are made with the lines printed in green, blue, orange, and other colors. Either profile or cross-section paper may be bought in separate sheets or in rolls of various sizes. Profile graphs may be obtained on heavy paper, on tracing paper, or on tracing cloth.

18-3. Reproduction of drawings.   Several reproduction processes are commercially available nowadays for reproduction of maps and other drawings.   Only the most commonly used processes are mentioned here.

Blueprints are reproductions made from transparent tracings by the blueprint process.   In this process the tracing and a sheet of sensitized paper beneath it are exposed to light.   After washing, the sensitized paper shows the drawing reproduced in white lines on blue background.   Blueprints can also be made on cloth.   Paper blueprints are subject to considerable shrinkage.   Reproductions of cloth tracings can be made on cloth, also by the blueprint process, but brown negatives are made first.   Reproduced cloth tracings look very much like the original tracings.

Vandyke prints are negatives that are obtained by the blueprint process using Vandyke paper.   The print shows white lines on brown background.   The advantage of Vandyke prints is that they are usually made on tracing paper so that positive prints can be made by the blueprint process from the Vandyke prints.   The positive prints are made with either blue or brown lines on white background.

Ozalid prints show drawings in black lines on white background.   Ozalid prints are made on sensitized paper directly from tracings.   The prints are developed, after exposure to light, by the action of ammonia fumes.   Ozalid prints fade rather rapidly if they are exposed to sunlight.

Photographic reproductions are made by various commercial methods.   The photostat method is widely used in reproduction of documents, maps, and other drawings.   Photostats are made by a special camera in which the negatives are made on film by the photographic process.   Reproductions can be reduced or enlarged to a desired scale.   Positive prints are made on paper, or on paper with cloth background.   The latter prints can be subjected to considerable wear and tear and are often used for maps that are to be placed in books for public use.

The *offset* printing process, known commercially by various names, such as the photo-offset process, utilizes photographically made plates for printing.   The offset method is more economical than lithograph printing, and is widely used when a considerable number of copies are needed.

Map Plotting

18-4. Various kinds of maps.   Various kinds of maps and plans that are used on engineering projects have been mentioned on many occasions in previous chapters.   In order to plan, design, and construct various structures, engineers use, on various occasions, planimetric and topographic maps, also profiles and cross sections.

Planimetric maps are made in those cases when only the planimetric features need be shown. Thus planimetric maps and plans are made to show property lines, roads, limits of rights-of-way, subdivision boundaries, and so on. Such maps may be known respectively as property survey plans, road maps, right-of-way maps, subdivision plans, and so on, depending on the type of feature they were especially drawn to portray.

Topographic maps show, besides the planimetric details, the topographic features of the terrain. Although several methods exist for showing ground topography, such as by hatchure or shading, the method of showing ground configurations by contour lines is the one that is used on engineering surveys. Other methods do not show ground elevations accurately enough for planning and design purposes. Various methods of obtaining data for drawing topographic maps have been discussed in Chapter 17.

Although special drawings such as ground profiles and cross sections are not maps, in a strict sense of the word, they must be included in a discussion of various types of maps, since profiles and cross sections are used in conjunction with maps and plans on many engineering projects. The methods of obtaining field data for drawing ground profiles and cross sections were discussed in Arts. 10-13 and 10-16, respectively.

On such projects as road construction, engineers also make soil maps. These maps show the areas of various types of soil occurring on the ground surface, and also ground cross sections, at various locations, showing the types of rocks that occur at certain depths under the surface. Knowledge of soil conditions plays a very important part in the planning and design of roads and of foundations for various types of structures. Underground soil conditions are usually investigated by means of test holes, drilled in the ground at various places in the area of proposed construction.

18-5. Property maps. Property maps, kept by municipal governments, are typical examples of planimetric maps. Such maps are drawn to a scale of about 1 in. = 50 ft and usually cover an area that bears a convenient relation to the topographic maps of the same area. Property maps show location of all streets, the lengths and bearings of property lines, the locations and the coordinates of survey monuments, and the locations of important structures.

Property survey maps, showing properties of individual owners, are normally made by land surveyors at the time when property passes from one owner to another, or when various subdivisions of a property are willed to various heirs, and on many other occasions. It is commonly required that a map showing the property being conveyed, through a purchase, be filed at the county registry at the time of registering a deed. In many cases the state or municipal laws specify the information to be shown on a map; but whatever the requirements may be, it is important from the standpoint of keeping proper surveying records that a registration of surveyed property include the following information:

(a) The bearings and the horizontal distances of property lines. It must be stated whether the bearings are true, magnetic, or state grid bearings.

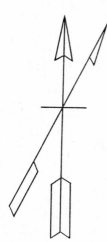

(b) The arrow showing north direction. A full arrow is used to indicate true north. If the direction of magnetic north is also shown, such direction must be shown by a half arrow (Fig. 18-7).

(c) The error of closure as computed from latitudes and departures of lines.

(d) The area of the surveyed property.

(e) The name of the owner and the names of owners of the adjoining properties.

(f) The reference monuments to which the survey is tied and the type of monuments by which the property corners are marked on the ground.

(g) The scale of the drawing and the bar graph (graphical scale, Fig. 18-8). The latter is important, because the maps are often reduced, or enlarged, thus rendering the mere statement of the scale useless.

Fig. 18-7. Arrows showing true and magnetic north.

(h) The date when survey is made.

(i) The name of the surveyor.

The location of irregular curved boundaries must be shown by offsets measured from an indicated base line. A circular boundary may be shown by a traverse along chords, or by a long chord. In either case the radius of the curve and the central angle must also be shown.

If it is legal to describe property lines by state coordinates, and if it is desirable to do so, all lines should show grid lengths and bearings, and the coordinates of each corner should be indicated.

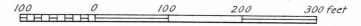

Fig. 18-8. Graphical scales.

Right-of-way maps are prepared by those public utilities which acquire rights-of-way for the construction of highways, railroads, and other facilities operated for public use. The right-of-way lines on such a map must be shown in the same manner as property lines are normally shown. The corners must be monumented and the survey must be tied to the existing net of horizontal control. The lengths and bearings of right-of-way lines must be indicated relative to the boundaries of the properties which the lines are crossing. This should be done in such a way as to leave no doubt as to the size and location of the acquired areas.

18-6. Plotting of traverses. The procedure of plotting a traverse consists of scaling the traverse distances and of plotting the angles between various courses of the traverse. First of all a traverse must be

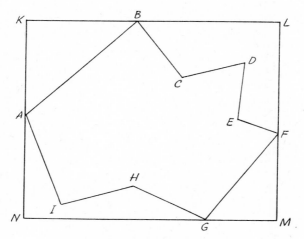

Fig. 18-9. Plotting a closed traverse.

oriented with respect to the working sheet so that it is properly centered with more-or-less equal margins on all sides. In a closed traverse the north-south and west-east extents of a traverse may be accurately determined from the latitudes and departures of various courses. First, the traverse is sketched roughly on a piece of paper. This should give enough information as to which latitudes and also which departures should be added in order to find the dimensions of a rectangle in which the traverse must be inscribed.

Let it be assumed, for instance, that it is required to plot the traverse *ABCDEFGHI* shown in Fig. 18-9. After making a rough sketch of this traverse, using the latitudes and departures of the courses, one finds that in order to obtain the greatest north-south extent of the traverse, equal to the side *KN* of the rectangle *KLMN*, the latitudes of the following courses should be added, algebraically, if one starts with the most southerly point *G* of the traverse: *GH*, *HI*, *IA*, and *AB*. Starting with the most westerly point *A* of the traverse, it is apparent from the figure that the departures of *AB*, *BC*, *CD*, *DE*, and *EF* must be added algebraically in order to obtain the side *KL* of the rectangle, showing the greatest west-east extent of the traverse.

After the dimensions of the rectangle *KLMN* have been found, it is plotted on paper and serves as a check in plotting the inscribed traverse. A practical and quite accurate method of plotting a right angle without the use of triangles (which may be distorted) is shown in Fig. 18-10. If

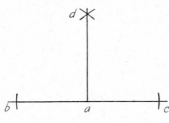

Fig. 18-10. Plotting a right angle.

one needs to plot a right angle at point *a*, using line *bc* as a base, the arcs of an arbitrary radius *ab* = *ac* are drawn at *b* and *c* and then the intersecting arcs at *d*, of a larger radius, are struck from points *b* and *c* as centers. The line connecting points *d* and *a* gives the right angle at *a*.

The method of plotting a traverse by latitudes and departures of courses, as described above, is a good practical method, since it does not involve direct plotting of angles by protractors. Unless the angles are laid out very accurately, using a large steel protractor, the protractor method of plotting angles is least reliable. With a 6 in. protractor, for instance, an angle can be laid out only to about 15′, and the error in laying out one direction is carried to the plotted directions of all subsequent lines. The best way to avoid accumulation of errors in plotted directions of lines is to draw first all traverse directions from a single point, located somewhere inside the plotted traverse. Then the directions so drawn are transferred, by the use of a parallel rule or two triangles, to their proper places in the traverse.

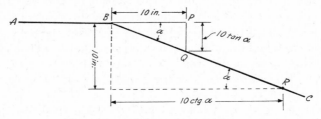

Fig. 18-11. Tangent method of plotting traverses.

One of the popular methods in plotting open traverses is the ***tangent method***. This method is especially adapted to deflection-angle traverses, such as are used in running route surveys. Let it be required, for instance, to plot the line *BC* shown in Fig. 18-11 by plotting the deflection angle α at point *B*. It is assumed that the line *AB* is already plotted on the drawing. The line *AB* is produced beyond point *B*, and a length

equal, say, to 10 in. is scaled along the produced line.   This gives point P.
Next, a perpendicular line is drawn through point P and a distance
$PQ = 10 \tan \alpha$ is scaled along this perpendicular line in the proper direction.   By connecting points B and Q by a straight line, one obtains the
required direction for the line BC.   The distance BC is then scaled along
the obtained direction.

If angle α is greater than 45°, it is better to draw a line perpendicular
to direction AB at point B, and to scale 10 in. along this perpendicular.
Another perpendicular is then drawn at the end of a scaled 10 in. length,
and a length equal to $10 \cot \alpha$ is scaled along the last-drawn perpendicular
to obtain point R on desired direction BC.   This construction is shown
by dashed lines in Fig. 18-11.   The main disadvantage of the tangent
method of plotting angles is that errors in plotted directions are carried
through subsequent plottings.

18-7. Plotting of details.   All planimetric features that must be
shown on a map, such as buildings, fences, trees, ponds, are described
by a general term—*details*.   Relatively important details such as buildings must be plotted on maps with the same accuracy as that used in
plotting traverses.   Field methods of locating or "referencing" details
to the transit line, particularly as practiced in route surveys, were discussed in Art. 6-2.   Figure 6-3 shows the location of buildings by ties,
right-angle offsets, and range lines, in reference to a transit line.   Usually
such details are plotted on a map by making the same measurements
with a scale and protractor on the drawing as those that were made in
the field with the tape and transit.   If a corner of a building was located
in the field by two ties, measured from two stations on the transit line,
the same corner is located on the drawing by two intersecting arcs drawn
with a compass from the same stations plotted on the map.

Less important details, such as trees and fences, are often located in
the field by stadia measurements from various points along a traverse.
Such details are plotted with a protractor, properly oriented at corresponding traverse points on the map, and with a scale.

Since a map is a symbolic representation of the terrain drawn on the
map, all details must be shown in proper conventional symbols.   It is
best to use the standard symbols that are published by the U.S. Geological
Survey, Washington 25, D.C.   Some symbols, those which are most
commonly used on maps, are shown in Fig. 18-12.

18-8. Plotting of ground elevations on topographic maps.
Figure 17-4 and Example 17-1 (p. 333) show samples of field notes
obtained for ground points, respectively, in the transit-stadia and in the
plane table methods.   (The transit-stadia method was discussed in
Arts. 17-2 through 17-10, and the plane table method in Arts. 17-11
through 17-20.)   Each ground point shown in the field notebook must

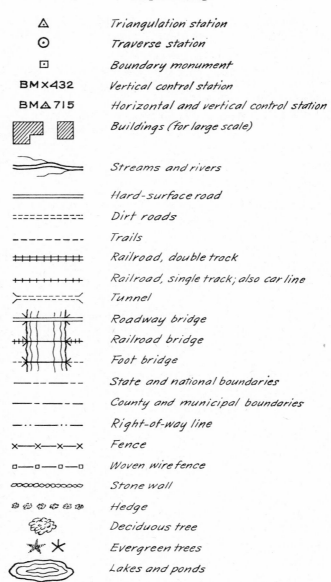

Fig. 18-12. Conventional symbols for plotting details.

be plotted on the working drawing that is used for constructing a topographic map, and the computed elevation of a point must be recorded alongside the plotted point.

In the transit-stadia method the following data are obtained: the azimuth directions to various points, the horizontal distances from the points of transit set-up to these points, and the elevations of these points. If a surveyed area is not confined within the border lines of a traverse, it is necessary first of all to estimate the north-south and the west-east extents of the surveyed area in order to assure plotting of the whole area on the working sheet. If a surveyed area does have a closed traverse for the outside boundary lines, these boundaries must be plotted on the map first.

After a surveyed area is properly oriented on the working sheet, the ground points are plotted on the drawing, and each point is labeled by its number, as it appears in the field notebook. Proper elevations of points are then marked on the drawing at each plotted point. In the plotting of the points, referred to a given transit set-up, a protractor is oriented at the plotted transit set-up point to read azimuths of points from the same reference direction from which they were measured in the field. For instance, if the reference direction is South, the zero graduation of the protractor, for the clockwise scale, is oriented south, with the protractor's central point placed at the point of transit's set-up on the map. Then computed horizontal distances are plotted on the map in the direction of the azimuths of various points, using the protractor graduations corresponding to those azimuths.

If a point that is to be plotted is covered by the protractor, a short line is drawn along its azimuth direction and this line is labeled by a number corresponding to the point in question. Later, when the protractor has been removed, proper distances to such points are scaled along the indicated directions. Full-circle protractors, constructed on heavy paper, are convenient in this kind of radial plotting. Such protractors are available on the market. When the plotting is completed, the marked elevations are used for plotting contours.

Before one plots contours it is extremely helpful to indicate on the map ridge lines and valley and stream lines. Information for such lines may be obtained from the last column of field stadia notes, showing description of points (Fig. 17-4). Ridge and valley lines are drawn as dashed lines. A sample of plotted stadia points and ridge and valley lines is shown in Fig. 18-13.

Plotting of points by the plane table method is done in the field. When a sight on the rod held at a point has been taken with the alidade, the point is plotted on the drawing along the alidade's straight edge, before the alidade is moved to take a sight on another point. The plotted

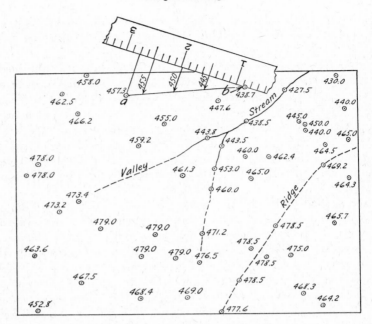

Fig. 18-13. Plotted ground elevations.

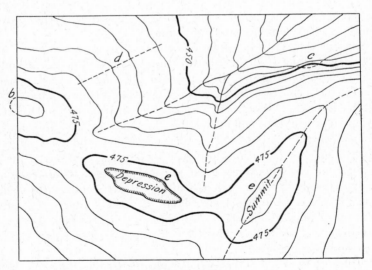

Fig. 18-14. Contours.

point is numbered, and the elevation of the point is marked at the point as soon as it is computed by the notekeeper. It is relatively easy to draw ridge and valley lines on the plane table drawing, since the plotter has full view of the terrain that he is plotting on the map.

18-9. Properties of contours. Ground contours are invisible lines of intersection of the ground surface with various, usually imaginary, level surfaces. A ground contour may become real and visible if, for instance, the top of a mountain is leveled off to a certain elevation. The visible outline of such a plateau is a ground contour. The outline of a shore line by the still water of a lake is also a ground contour, having the elevation equal to that of the lake's water surface.

For the purpose of drawing contours on a map, successive level surfaces are imagined to intersect the ground surface at definite elevations, varying by a regular vertical interval called the *contour interval*. Although a contour interval may be made equal to any integral number of feet, it is customary to vary the contour interval in certain increments. The most commonly used contour intervals are equal to 1, 2, 5, 10, 25, and 100 ft. Normally, the larger is the scale of a map the smaller is the contour interval; however, this is not universally true, because contour intervals shown on a map greatly depend on the steepness of ground slopes. The same map may show, for instance, 25 ft contours along steep slopes and only 5 ft contours on a relatively level terrain.

Although the elevations of contours drawn on a map may be referred to any arbitrarily chosen datum, normally, mean sea level is used as a datum.

Figure 18-14 shows a small map with 5 ft contour intervals. The contours have certain properties, or characteristics, which follow directly from the definition of a contour. These properties are stated below:

(a) All points of a given contour have the same elevation.
(b) All ground contours must close. Those shown on a map must close either within or outside map limits. (See dotted line at *b* in Fig. 18-14.)
(c) Contours do not cross each other except in rare cases of overhanging cliffs (shown at *c* in Fig. 18-14).
(d) The line of steepest slope crosses contours at right angles (shown at *d* in Fig. 18-14). Contours also cross ridge and valley lines at right angles.
(e) A closed contour, which has no other contours inside, indicates either a summit or a depression. If it is a depression, the contour is shown with hachures (shown at *e* in Fig. 18-14).
(f) Equally spaced contours indicate a uniform slope.
(g) Straight, equally spaced contours indicate a plane.

18-10. Contour plotting. After the ground points and their elevations are plotted on a map, it is necessary to make interpolations between
the points in order to find ground elevations corresponding to the contours that it is desired to draw. For instance, if the elevation of one
point is 457.3 and of another, 438.7, as is indicated in Fig. 18-13, and if
no intermediate elevations were taken in the field, it must be assumed
that the slope between those points is uniform, so that 455, 450, 445,
and 440 contours, which must be indicated between those points, can be
obtained by straight-line interpolation of the difference in elevation
between the two points. This is done graphically as follows:

Various scales are tried between the two plotted points to give scale
divisions that can be taken to represent the necessary contours (455,

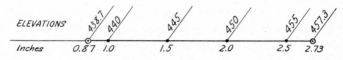

Fig. 18-15.

450, ...) between the points. For instance, if one uses 10-scale (1 in.
divided into 10 parts), the 1.0 in. mark can be taken to represent the
440 contour, the 1.5 in. mark the 445 contour, and so on, so that 0.87 in.
and 2.73 in. divisions must correspond to the respective elevations 438.7
and 457.3 of plotted points. These correlations are shown in Fig. 18-15.

In this example, as in all such graphical interpolations, the selected
distance on 10-scale, from the 0.87 in. division to 2.73, only roughly
approximates the distance between the two plotted points. Thus the
scale is placed on the drawing not along the line connecting the two points
but at some arbitrary angle to it, keeping however the 0.87 in. division
at the point having 438.7 elevation. This gives triangle *abc* shown in
Fig. 18-13. Points *a* and *c* are connected by a straight line, drawn
freehand, and the lines parallel to *ac* and passing through the 2.5, 2.0,
1.5, and 1.0 in. marks are also drawn freehand. Intersections of these
lines with the line connecting the two points give properly proportioned
distances along that line for the location of the contours sought.

The same procedure is repeated between adjacent pairs of points in
all directions. Then the points through which a given contour must pass
are connected by a smooth line. Figure 18-14 shows contours drawn from
the points plotted in Fig. 18-13. Not all surveyed points are shown in
Fig. 18-13. With a little practice, one finds that graphical interpolation
of contours proceeds quite rapidly.

Contour elevations are marked in gaps in the contour lines. Only
elevations of relatively few contours need be so marked, as is shown in

Fig. 18-14.   It is customary to draw certain contours by relatively heavy lines.   For instance, when contour interval is equal to 1 ft, every fifth contour having its elevation divisible by 5, such as 440, 445, and so on, is normally shown by heavy lines.   If contour interval is equal to 25 ft, every contour the elevation of which is a multiple of 100 is shown by heavy lines, and so on for other intervals.

18-11. Construction contours.   Construction contours are the contours drawn for cuts and fills in construction work.   When a plan shows the contours of the original ground surface, construction contours are superimposed on the original ground contours.   The purpose of construction contours is to measure on plans the areas outlined by these contours and to compute from these areas and the contour interval between them the quantities of earthwork.   This method is especially well adapted to earthwork computations on highway interchanges and on other construction sites where changes in grades occur in many different directions.   One can best understand the plotting of construction contours by drawing the traces of level planes through profiles and cross sections drawn for a given construction work.   The example below shows plotting of construction contours for a given section of a highway.

Let it be required to draw construction contours for a section of highway shown in Fig. 18-16.   The figure shows the plan view, with originally drawn ground contours, and with the profile showing the original ground surface and the proposed grade of the road.   Figure 18-17 shows a typical cross section for the same road.   The points at the end of road shoulders called the **berms** are shown on the plan view along the lines aa' and bb'.   The center-line elevations of the finished grade are shown on the plan view at the center line of each full station and +50 ft stations.   For the purpose of drawing construction contours it is normally assumed that on unsuperelevated highway the berms have the same elevation as the center line of the road.   Thus the difference in elevation between the berm point and the elevation of any contour plane may be readily obtained from the data given in Fig. 18-16.

Let it be assumed that construction contours are required to be drawn for the same elevations as those shown on the profile, considering only the "cut" shown on the profile.   Starting with Sta. 0+50 and working on the 340 ft contour, one finds that the difference in elevation between this contour and the berm point is $340.00 - 333.33 = 6.67$ ft. This is the vertical distance equal to h shown on Fig. 18-17.   If the slope is 1:1 as it is in the cut in this example (see the same figure), then the horizontal distance x from the berm to the 340 contour line must be equal to h.   Also assuming that the same cut is at both berms across the Sta. 0+50, $x = 6.67$ ft must be plotted along a line at a right angle to

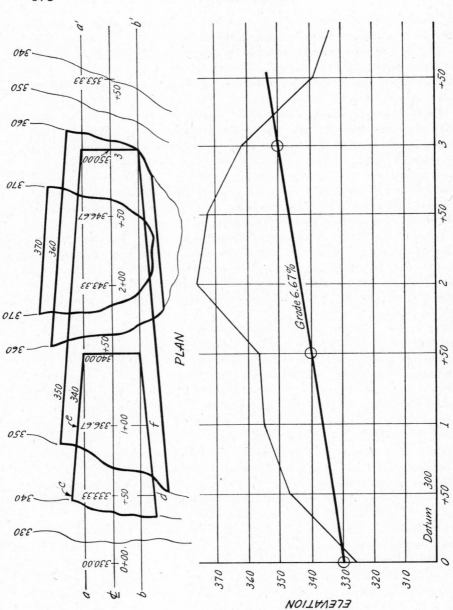

Fig. 18-16. Construction contours.

the center line of roadway, from each berm out. This gives points c and d for the 340 ft contour on each side of Sta. 0+50.

In a similar manner, the points e and f are plotted on each side of the berms at Sta. 1+00. In this case

$$x = h = 340.00 - 336.67 = 3.33 \text{ ft}$$

It may be seen on the profile that the 340 ft contour meets the road grade at Sta. 1+50. Thus this contour will cross the road at this station. However, between Sta. 0+00 and 0+50 the 340 ft construction contour coincides with the natural surface of the ground, so that it must

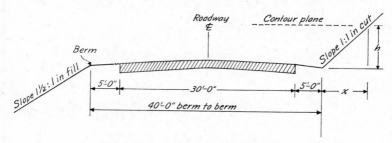

Fig. 18-17. Typical roadway cross section.

cross the road along the 340 ft ground contour. This completes the outline of the 340 ft construction contour on all sides. In a similar manner 350, 360, and 370 ft construction contours are drawn on the plan view of Fig. 18-16. These contours are shown by heavy lines.

Having construction contours drawn on the plan, and knowing the vertical distances between them, one may compute the volume of the earthwork very closely by measuring with a planimeter the areas enclosed by the contours, and by multiplying the average of each two adjacent areas by the contour interval between them. The volumes above the elevation of 370 ft and below 340 ft, in this example, may be computed as a pyramid and as a wedge, respectively.

18-12. Finished drawings. Drafting is an art, and like any art it requires practice. It is natural to expect that some people may exhibit better natural ability for drafting than others, but every person can improve his drafting skills by practice. It is important that people preparing themselves for an engineering career develop reasonably good skills for graphical presentation of the works that they expect to design and build.

Drafting of maps and plans differs from mechanical drawing mainly in that dimensions of various features, and distances between them, are not shown on maps. They simply are *drawn to scale*. This often requires better and more accurate workmanship than is needed on dimensioned drawings.

The work of drawing plans and maps must conform to certain standards. The plans must have a border; this differs on various plans from about $\frac{1}{2}$ in. to $\frac{3}{4}$ in. If a plan is one of a set, the left border should be 2 in. wide for binding. The title, the name of the organization, the names of the engineer and the draftsman, and the date are normally boxed on engineering plans. The box, with properly centered and lettered inscriptions, is placed in the lower right-hand corner of the map. On maps

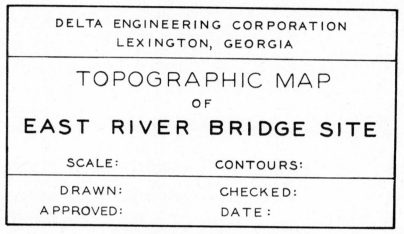

Fig. 18-18. Boxed title for drawings.

intended for public use the title may not be boxed and is often drawn where it best harmonizes with the general appearance of the map. A boxed title is shown in Fig. 18-18.

The appearance of an otherwise good drawing may be spoiled by poor lettering. The lettering must be done in certain style, although it is not necessary to follow the same style in all drawing inscriptions. The same style of lettering must be adhered to, however, in the same kind of inscriptions. For instance, the names of towns must be drawn in one style, but the names of rivers may be drawn in a different style.

On most engineering plans, which are not intended for use by the general public, single-stroke, simple lettering is used. The letters may be either vertical or inclined. Single-stroke means that the thickness of lines in the letters is the same as the width of the single pen-line with which the letters are drawn. Every engineer must know the sequence of strokes in drawing letters and figures. For instance, each circular part of figure *8* must be drawn with two symmetrical strokes, if one wants to draw a symmetrical figure *8*.   Many books and booklets have been written about lettering; future engineers must consult at least one reliable publication on this subject.   When lettering is done freehand, a lettering triangle should be used to draw guide lines.

There are different styles of lettering such as Reinhardt, Gothic, Roman, and others.   If one intends to use any of these styles he must learn its characteristics.   For instance, the lower-case Reinhardt letters are made of combinations of straight lines and ellipses.

Two types of lettering guides are extensively used nowadays on drawings.   In one type a special tubular pen follows the outline of letters cut out in the guide, and in another type, grooved letters in the guide are traced with a blunt point while an attached pen draws the letters along a parallel line above the guide strip.   These lettering guides may be obtained in different sizes, producing capitals from about 0.06 in. to 2.00 in. in height.   However, various notes which are often placed on engineering plans can be lettered freehand in a much smaller space than when lettered with a lettering set.

Various types of pens are available for freehand lettering.   These must be chosen according to the type of lettering required, and to some extent to suit individual abilities of draftsmen.   Ball-point pens, which come in various sizes, are often used for heavy-line, single-stroke lettering.

FIELD EXERCISES

18-1. Topographic map by the transit-stadia method
Party: Four men.
Equipment: Transit, brass bob, reading glass, and leveling rod or stadia rod.
Object: To gain experience in transit-stadia work and, specifically, to collect field data for drawing a topographic map of a given area.
Procedure: The instructor will assign the area to be mapped, the scale of the drawing, and the contour interval.   These data may vary according to the size and the type of the assigned terrain, but the scale may be judged by the size of a 17 by 24 in. working sheet, which is about the right size for this exercise.   On a rugged terrain, contour intervals may be made equal to 5 ft, and on rolling terrain, about 2 ft.   If the assigned area contains previously surveyed traverses, these should be included on the map and may serve as a basis in starting the survey.

To orient the transit at a point, in order to read azimuth direction from south, set up the instrument on a line of known bearing and compute the azimuth of this line from 0° south.   Set this azimuth angle on the transit's clockwise scale and sight along the direction of the computed azimuth with the lower motion of the instrument.   Clamp the lower motion and use the upper motion for sighting in various directions. Read azimuths of lines from 0° south on clockwise scale.

When sights are being taken on the rod, the rod must be held on ground points where changes in slope occur, or at objects that must be located on the map. Take a sight first with the telescope in horizontal position. If the rod comes into the field of view, read the rod at the intersection of the cross hairs and then read the stadia intercept. Record this value in the field notebook and wave to the rodman to proceed to a new point; then read and record the azimuth of the sighted direction.

If the rod cannot be read with the telescope leveled, sight, if possible, on the rod division equal to H.T. (height of telescope). Record the rod reading as "H.T." and read and record the vertical angle. Next, read the stadia intercept and the azimuth as with leveled telescope.

Refer to Arts. 17-1 through 17-10 for detailed description of measurements by the transit-stadia method, and to Fig. 17-4 for the sample of field recordings.

After finishing field work, each person is to plot the field data on a 17 by 24 in. drawing paper and to draw contours as explained in Art. 18-10. Also refer to Arts. 18-4 through 18-9 for proper procedure in map drafting. After the map is finished, make an ink tracing with proper lettering. Use freehand single-stroke letters (Art. 18-12).

18-2. Topographic map by the plane table method

Party: Four men.

Equipment: Plane table, alidade, reading glass, and stadia rod.

Object: To gain experience in plane table work and, specifically, to draw a topographic map of a given area.

Procedure: The topographic survey of the assigned area may be started from any selected line as a base. It may be a distance between two trees or any other objects. Preferably, the line should be located near the edge of the area being mapped so that a traverse can be run inside the mapped area.

Set up the table at one end of the selected line and draw this line on the working sheet so that the rest of the area can be plotted on the sheet. Then place the alidade's straight edge along the drawn line and sight along the actual line on the ground, thus orienting the table with respect to the ground. Clamp the plane table in this position and start taking shots around the set-up point. Try to visualize the part of the area that can be best covered from each set-up point, and move to a new point after the area around the first point is well surveyed. Plot each point and its elevation directly on the plane table sheet as the work progresses.

Before moving to a new point, take a sight on that point and determine the distance to it and the difference in elevation between that point and the point at which the plane table is set up. Draw the direction to that point on the map but do not plot the point. Then move the plane table to that point, set it up, and orient it by the direction already drawn, between the points of the first and the second set-up. Now, determine again the distance and the difference in elevation between the two points and take the average of the two values of each quantity. Then plot the point of the new set-up and record its elevation on the working sheet.

After completing side shots at the second point, move to a new point, repeating the same procedure as was followed between the first two set-up points; in this manner run a traverse inside the area, and plot details at the same time.

When enough elevations of ground points are plotted on a map area, start drawing contours, interpolating between the points as described in Art. 18-10. When the table is being set up on the third point, check plotting of the traverse by resection through the first set-up point (see Art. 17-18). Refer also to Arts. 17-11 through 17-20 for the detailed description of plane table work.

After finishing field work, make an ink tracing of the map. Refer to Fig. 18-12 for conventional signs for details and to Arts. 18-4 through 18-12 for proper procedures in map drafting.

CHAPTER 19

Hydrographic Surveys

19-1. Definition and purpose. Hydrographic surveys involve the determination of elevations of the bottoms of lakes, harbors, rivers, and coastal waters and the plotting of these elevations on maps and charts. Hydrographic surveys also include measurements of water depth, of direction and velocity of currents, of rates of water discharge in rivers, of stream slopes, and so on. The process of making measurements in streams and rivers, incident to studies predicting the rate of discharge at various water levels, or *stages*, is generally known as *stream gaging*.

One of the main purposes of hydrographic surveys, conducted along the United States coast line, is to provide data for making hydrographic maps and charts to serve navigation, harbor improvement, dredging, and other operations. The United States Coast and Geodetic Survey prepares such maps and charts. A typical Coast Survey hydrographic map contains the following information:

(a) *Soundings*, or depth measurements, referred to a certain water level, such as mean low water level, which in turn is referred to a definite datum used on a map. The soundings are normally plotted in fathoms (6 ft).

(b) Outline of high and low waters along the coast.

(c) Lines of equal depth; that is, depth contours. These are normally shown by dotted lines, in which the number of dots, interrupted by spacings, indicate the depth in fathoms. Thus the lines showing the depth of one fathom are drawn as continuous dotted lines; the lines showing the depth of two fathoms are drawn with 2 dots and a missing space between them, and so on.

(d) Ground contours on adjacent land.

(e) Important planimetric features including navigation lights, lighthouses, buoys, underwater pipes and cables, and the like. Standard conventional symbols and colors are used in delineating these features.*

Regular stream gaging operations are conducted on many streams and rivers in the United States. The data obtained in such surveys are used in navigation, water supply, irrigation, flood control, hydroelectric power development, design of bridges, culverts and sewage disposal plants, and so on. The measurements obtained in river surveys are used in computation of the expected rate of discharge of streams and rivers on an average day of a given month or during a year.

The places where installations are made on rivers for stream gaging are known as *stream gaging stations.* Such stations are maintained by the Water Resources Branch of the U.S. Geological Survey throughout the country. Discharge information for a given station is computed for various water stages. *Water stage* is the elevation of water surface referred to a certain datum, such as zero level of a *water gage.* Various gage readings, or *gage heights*, are plotted on charts against the corresponding discharge of water. The result of such plotting is a curve known as the *station rating curve* for a given stream gaging station. Thus, the anticipated discharge of a stream at any stage may be obtained by taking gage readings and by using the station rating curve chart. An anticipated discharge at other places along the river can be estimated by using the discharge at a gaging station adjusted for changes in drainage area and in local rainfall conditions. Some stream gaging stations are maintained by private concerns to aid in the control of water works or other installations.

19-2. Stream flow. Stream gaging is a general term describing the measurements that must be made in a stream or a river to compute its rate of discharge; that is, the volume of water flowing past a given cross section per unit of time. Normally, the rate of discharge is measured in cubic feet per second (a unit sometimes called the *second-foot*) and is abbreviated as cfs. To obtain the number of cubic feet per second flowing past a certain cross section of a stream at a given stage, it is necessary to know the cross-sectional area A of the stream, expressed in square feet, and the average velocity of the stream flow V, expressed in feet per second. The rate of discharge Q in cubic feet per second is then computed by Eq. (19-1).

$$Q = VA \qquad\qquad (19\text{-}1)$$

* Much information regarding hydrographic maps and charts may be found in the "Hydrographic Manual," Special Publication 143, by K. T. Adams, published by the USC&GS. It may be purchased from the Superintendent of Documents, Washington 25, D.C.

The velocity of stream flow is not uniform throughout the cross-sectional area of a stream; it is greater at the middle than close to the banks. Along a given depth d, the velocity is practically zero at the bottom, is maximum at about $0.3d$, and approximates the average value at about $0.6d$. Experience shows that the average velocity through a vertical section can be closely approximated by taking the average value of measured velocities at $0.2d$ and $0.8d$.

Figure 19-1 shows lines of equal velocity plotted on the cross-sectional area of a stream. To obtain the average velocity throughout a given cross section, the cross-sectional area is divided into a number of vertical

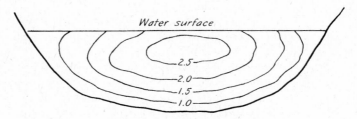

Fig. 19-1. Lines of equal velocities in a stream.

sections, as shown in Fig. 19-2; then, the velocity of flow is measured at $0.2d$ and $0.8d$ in the middle of each vertical section, and the average value of these two velocities is multiplied by the area of the section. The result is the value of discharge for each vertical section. The sum of all discharge values thus obtained gives the required discharge for the whole stream.

To compute the area of each vertical section, it is necessary to take soundings along the vertical lines separating these sections, and to measure the width of each section. The area of each section is computed then as the area of a trapezoid. The vertical subdivision lines must be close enough together so that the stream's bottom can be closely approximated by straight lines drawn between the lower ends of vertical section lines. If the bottom of a stream is fairly uniform, the vertical lines can be placed at equal intervals, as shown in Fig. 19-2. A wire may be stretched across the stream and the boundaries of each section may be marked by a tag or by paint. The soundings are then taken from a boat, under the marked places along the wire, with a *pole* or a *leadline*.

The mid-points of each section may also be marked, along the wire, for the purpose of measuring velocities at the middle of each section. Ribbons of two colors may be conveniently employed to mark the ends and the mid-points of each section. The velocities are measured by special instruments called **current meters.** (One such meter known as the *Price current meter* is shown in Fig. 19-3 and is described in Art.

19-4 below.)　Across a wide river, the soundings and the measurement of the velocities are often made from a bridge.　Care must be taken to minimize the effect of bridge piers on the velocity of flow.　The measurements must be made on the upstream side as far out from the bridge railing as possible

It is important that gage readings, registering the water level, be taken at the time of flow measurements, because the discharge of a stream computed from certain flow measurements is correct only for a definite water stage measured by the gage.　Various types of gages are discussed in Art. 19-5 below.

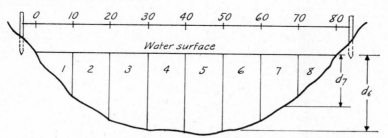

Fig. 19-2. Vertical sections for measuring velocities of flow.

19-3. Sounding equipment.　Soundings are taken either with a pole, if the depth of stream does not exceed about 12 ft, or with a leadline. Sounding poles are usually round in cross section and are about 15 ft long. A metal shoe is usually attached to one end of the pole to help keep it vertical when soundings are taken.　The poles are painted in various colors for easy identification of the various footmarks.　The poles may be marked only every half-foot, but the readings are usually taken to the nearest 0.1 ft by estimation.　If there are waves, the average of two readings, one at the wave crest and another at the trough, is normally recorded.

A length of hemp or cotton cord, or a sash chain, is used as a sounding line.　Better sounding lines are made of braided flax with a phosphor-bronze wire core.　Hemp and cotton lines must be made shrink-proof by winding them around a post, wetting them, and allowing them to dry.　After this operation is repeated several times, the cord being rewound tightly each time, the line will show little shrinkage when wet.

Footmark graduations are made on a wet line by attaching leather tags of various shapes, at proper places, so that each 5th, 10th, 15th, and so on footmark can be readily recognized when soundings are being taken.

The weight attached to a line is a cylindrically shaped lead weight, not unlike a window sash weight.　It varies from about 3 to 15 lb depending on the depth of stream and the swiftness of the current. The weight is usually tapered toward the top where it has a round hole for attaching the line. A shallow cavity at the bottom is often made for tallow, which is used when it is desired to obtain samples of the stream-bed material.

On a slowly moving boat and in a quiet stream the sounding line need not be completely withdrawn from the water between soundings. On longer courses, such as one along a range line crossing a bay, soundings may be made from a boat moving at a constant speed along a measured course. Soundings are taken at regular intervals so that their locations may be plotted on a map. On such occasions the sounding weight is swung in a vertical circle and is thrown ahead. As the boat moves forward, the reading is taken when the line assumes a vertical position.

In coastal waters, soundings taken on a ship are often automatically recorded on measuring devices called *fathometers.* Fathometers of one type, which are in common use, record the time required for a sound wave to reach the bottom and for the echo wave to come back. These automatic recording devices may be adjusted for the correct velocity of sound in the water in which the soundings are made.

There are also portable electronic sounding devices which operate on a 6 volt battery. A small, elliptically shaped transducer, about 3 in. by $4\frac{1}{2}$ in. by 1 in. thick, is connected by wires to a light portable instrument. The transducer is held at the water surface and the sounding depth is read on the instrument dial. This device may be used for sounding in shallow waters. The dial of the instrument can be read within about 6 in.

19-4. Current meters. Current meters are used for measuring the velocity of stream flow at various depths. The meters measure the velocity indirectly by the number of rotations that the meter's wheel makes per unit of time. The wheel is turned by the current as it strikes cups or vanes attached to the wheel. In some meters the wheel rotates in a vertical plane and in others in a horizontal plane.

Figure 19-3 shows a meter usually known as the *Price current meter.* The U.S. Geological Survey was instrumental in developing it. The meter has six conical cups arranged around a horizontal wheel. The axis of the wheel is held by a yoke, to which a vane is attached in order to keep the cups headed into the current. The meter is attached to a vertical rod. A weight is fastened at the bottom end of this rod and a cable at the top end.

The wheel axis is connected with a small chamber where an electrical contact is made each time the wheel makes a revolution. Electric wiring connects a battery with the contact chamber and with earphones worn by the observer. A click is produced in the system each time electrical contact is made in the contact chamber. The clicks are heard through

the earphones and are counted by the observer. By turning a switch
the observer may hear only every fifth click. This change is necessary in
swift currents when single-revolution clicks come in too rapidly. A stop
watch is used with the meter to observe time intervals.

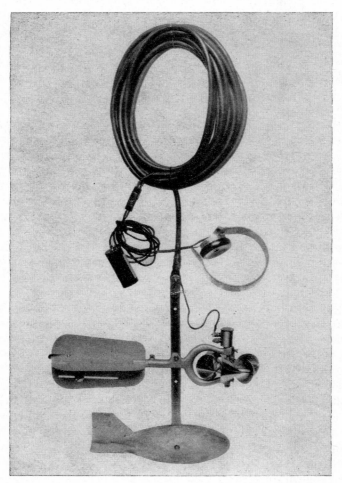

Fig. 19-3. Price current meter. (Courtesy W. & L. E. Gurley.)

The recorded number of revolutions per second is later reduced to
the corresponding velocity of flow in feet per second. This conversion
is done by means of a chart, called the *meter rating curve* chart. It shows
a curve, plotted with revolutions per second as ordinates against the
velocity of flow in feet per second as abscissas. Such a curve is plotted

for each meter when it is calibrated, in still water, by moving the meter at various uniform velocities.

Stream velocities are measured at various depths in each vertical section into which the cross-sectional area of a stream is divided. In the two-tenths and eight-tenths method the velocity is measured at depths equal to $0.2d$ and $0.8d$, where d is the average depth of the section. The average of these two velocities is taken as the average velocity of flow through a given section. In shallow waters, as for example in sections near river banks, the six-tenths method is often used; that is, the velocity is measured only at $0.6d$. This value is then taken as the average velocity through that section.

If more accurate measurements are required, the velocity may be measured at several depths in each vertical section. These velocities are then plotted as horizontal vectors at corresponding depths plotted along a vertical line. This is done for each section. The points so plotted are connected by a smooth curve and the enclosed area is measured by a planimeter. The measured area is multiplied by the width of the section to obtain the rate of discharge through the section. By adding the values of discharge in all sections, one obtains the total discharge of the stream.

19-5. Gages. All stream gaging installations include gages for measuring the height of water level. The gages generally employed are *staff gages* and *float gages*. Some float gages have a staff attached to a float.

The simplest form of a staff gage is a narrow board graduated from the bottom up. It is fixed in a vertical position in a quiet pool of water connected by pipes with the stream. Thus the height of water level in the pool is the same as the average height of water in the stream. The board, graduated in feet and tenths of a foot, is read directly. The zero graduation of the gage is placed below the low water level, so that all gage readings are positive. The elevation of the zero graduation in reference to a datum, such as the mean sea level datum, is determined by running a leveling circuit to established bench marks in the vicinity of the gaging station. Thus a gage reading may be directly related to a selected datum.

A float gage must be suspended inside a *stilling well*. If it is suspended by a graduated chain or a tape over a pulley, with a counterweight, it will maintain constant contact with the water surface. In order to read such a gage, one reads the tape at a stationary index mark.

If a float gage has a graduated staff attached to it, the staff is kept in a vertical position and is made free to move up and down, with the water level, by passing through an opening in the stilling well cover.

The staff is graduated from top to bottom and its graduations are read at the top of the cover.

Permanent stream gaging installations usually have automatic gages which record the water level continuously on a drum, operated by a clock

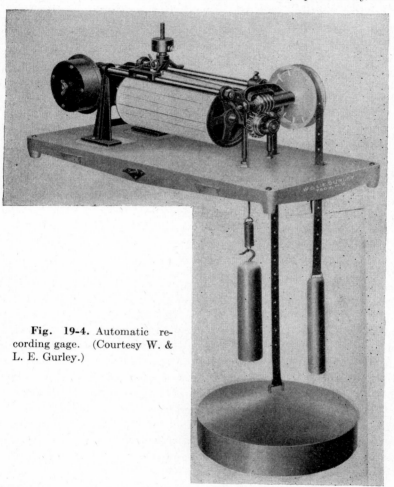

Fig. 19-4. Automatic recording gage. (Courtesy W. & L. E. Gurley.)

mechanism. Time is thus recorded simultaneously with water level. One such automatic recorder is shown in Fig. 19-4. A gage of this type is normally installed in a gage house enclosing a stilling well. The well is connected by a pipe with the *control section* of a stream. Various water stages are recorded by means of a pen which records the movement of a copper float suspended in the well.

19-6. Gaging station installations. A permanently installed gaging station, where continuous records are taken of water level, and the rate of discharge is regularly computed, has normally three distinct areas along the river. The three areas are known as the *control section,* the *gaging section,* and the *measuring section.* The sections are located along a straight stretch of a river course, with firm banks and fairly solid stream bottom.

The *measuring section* is the section, across the river, where soundings and measurements of the stream velocity are periodically taken. On relatively small streams the measuring section has a cable, across the

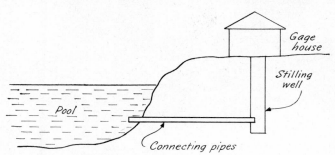

Fig. 19-5. Diagram of a gaging section.

stream, along which a suspended platform can be moved back and forth. Required measurements are taken from the platform.

Within a convenient distance from the measuring section is located a pool of water with a gage house. Usually the gage house is built on a bank of the pool; normally it has an automatic recording gage and a staff gage. The stilling well under the gage house is connected with the pool by one or two underground pipes, as is shown diagrammatically in Fig. 19-5. This section of the station is known as the *gaging section.*

Water level in the pool is controlled by a *control section* of the station. The control section is normally located next to the measuring section, upstream or downstream. The control section has a dam across the stream. The main purpose of the control section is to provide proper correlation between discharges, and gage readings at various stages.

When gage readings are plotted as ordinates and computed discharges for those readings as abscissas, the result is a *station rating curve.* Gage heights are plotted in feet and discharges in cubic feet per second. Normally, two curves are plotted, one for low water and one for high water. The zero discharge, on such charts, usually corresponds to the zero gage reading. This correlation can be easily established after repeated observations of gage readings for a zero discharge are made just at the moment when the water stops spilling over the dam.

The station rating curve permits estimation of the maximum anticipated discharge of water at various times of the year. These data are
needed for design of various engineering projects dealing with water
supply, irrigation, bridge construction, flood control, soil erosion, hydro-
electric plants, and so on.

19-7. Discharge by the stream–slope method. It is often
necessary to determine the approximate discharge of streams where no
stream gaging data are available and where measurements of the velocity
of flow by a meter are not practical. The velocity of flow may be computed by the Chezy formula

$$V = C\sqrt{RS} \tag{19-2}$$

where V is the velocity in feet per second, C is a coefficient the value of
which depends on the roughness of the stream bed, R is the hydraulic
radius in feet (which is equal to the cross-sectional area of the stream
divided by the wetted perimeter of the stream bed), and S is the slope
of the stream bed in feet per foot.

In this method of velocity computation it is necessary to know the
shape of the channel's cross section, so that one may plot it on paper and
measure its cross-sectional area by a planimeter for any given water level.
The wetted perimeter of a stream bed may be scaled on the same drawing.
The hydraulic readius R is then computed from the above measurements.
The approximate value of the coefficient C may be obtained, for the
observed roughness of the stream bed, from a hydraulics handbook.

The slope of the stream bed in the Chezy formula must be determined
by field measurements. In shallow streams a graduated rod is held at
about 50 ft intervals along the middle of the stream, and rod readings
are taken from the shore with the engineer's level. The observed elevations are plotted on paper and the mean slope is determined from the
plotted elevations.

In large streams the slope of the stream bed is approximated by
measuring the slope of the stream's surface. For accurate measurement
of a stream slope, two stilling wells may be established along a desirable
stretch of the stream, about 1000 ft apart. Staff gages are then installed
in the stilling wells, with their zero readings referred to the same elevation. The difference in simultaneously obtained gage readings divided
by the distance between the gages gives the required slope.

The value of the stream velocity, computed by Eq. (19-2), is assumed
to be the average velocity of the stream. Multiplying this value by the
cross-sectional area of the stream, one obtains an approximate value of
the stream discharge.

There are other empirical formulas and other empirical methods for
determining the velocities of flow and the rates of discharge in streams.

For instance, much discussion is devoted in books on hydraulics to dis- charge computations by various **weir** formulas. The use of weirs requires certain field measurements in streams.

In the absence of better data, engineers sometimes use empirical formulas for computing maximum anticipated discharge in streams at time of floods. This knowledge is needed in connection with the con- struction of small bridges in order to place them above flood waters. It is also necessary to know the maximum discharge of a stream for estimation of the size of culverts, of the waterway areas under bridges for proper drainage, and in many other engineering studies.

Since records of rainfall intensities are available for various locations throughout the United States, and since discharge in rivers is a function of the rainfall intensity and of the drainage area involved, the empirical formula shown by Eq. (19-3) is sometimes used to find the rate of dis- charge Q in cubic feet per second.

$$Q = CIA \qquad (19\text{-}3)$$

where C is a coefficient, depending on the nature of the run-off surface of the drainage area. It may be obtained from a handbook. I is the intensity of rainfall in inches per hour, and A is the drainage area in acres.

19-8. Hydrographic surveys in coastal waters. Hydrographic surveys are regularly conducted in coastal waters. The U.S. Coast and Geodetic Survey maintains especially equipped ships that are used in hydrographic surveys. Soundings in deep waters are made automatically by fathometers, but in shallow waters either the leadline or portable electronic sounding devices are used (Art. 19-3).

In order to cover a large area with soundings it is necessary to establish **range lines,** or courses along which the soundings are to be taken. The range lines are tied to points of known location along the shore lines and thus can be plotted on a map. The soundings are then located on the map along the range lines. Often the range lines are tied to a net of triangulation stations established for the purpose of conducting a hydro- graphic survey. Electronic distance-measuring devices are often used in establishing a net of horizontal controls. Electronic measuring devices are also used in locating offshore soundings at long distances.

Very often it is convenient to establish horizontal controls by running traverses along each shore line and tying planned range lines to these traverses. In coastal waters the points of horizontal control are often established by triangulation and by running traverses between triangula- tion points. In all such cases experience is the best guide as to how to plan and to execute a required survey.

The signals set for various range lines must be easy to distinguish one from another and must be visible over long distances. Flags of various colors, or rectangular frames covered with stretched cloth, attached to posts set in the ground, are normally visible over fairly long distances. Sometimes instead of two ground signals (Fig. 19-6) only one ground signal and one buoy are used to establish a range line.

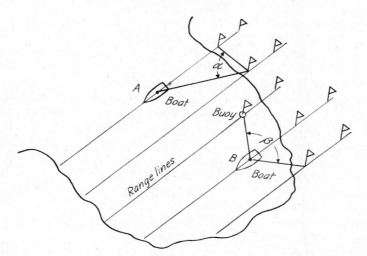

Fig. 19-6. Range lines.

The soundings taken from a boat along an established range line may be located on the map by one of the following methods:

(a) By measuring an angle with a transit, from the established line on shore to the boat, at the time when soundings are taken. (This method is shown at A in Fig. 19-6.)

(b) By measuring the angle from the boat with a sextant between two established points on shore. (This method is shown at B in Fig. 19-6.)

(c) By taking soundings at the points of intersection of range lines established along two different directions.

(d) By taking soundings at regular intervals of time from a boat moving along a range course with a constant speed. This is a less accurate method than the others mentioned above.

When the location of range lines has not been established, the soundings taken from a boat may be located by one of the following two methods:

(e) By measuring angles simultaneously by two transits located at the ends of a base line established on the shore. The angles are measured at the time of signals given from the boat.

(f) By measuring two angles from the boat, with a sextant, between three points established on shore. If the points are successively numbered as 1, 2, and 3, the angles are usually measured between the points 1 and 2 and between 2 and 3. The place of a sounding may then be located on a map by a three-arm protractor, provided that the three shore points and the sounding point do not lie on a circle. This method is less accurate than that described under (e) above.

19-9. Measurements by electronic devices. Offshore sounding operations are extended to considerable distances from the coast line. In order to tie such soundings to stations along a coast, distances of many thousands of feet must be measured. Various electronic distance-measuring devices are employed in such surveys. For example, in *radar* measurements the method consists of transmitting pulses of electro-magnetic energy from a station to distant targets and receiving reflected signals. By applying the known velocity of propagation of electro-magnetic waves in air, one can convert the time required for the wave to travel to a target and back into the corresponding distance between the station and the targets. In order to locate a sounding it is necessary to know distances from the ship to two established ground stations, or to targets of known location set out in the sea.

Transmitted pulses of electromagnetic energy may be of high or low frequencies. High-frequency waves follow the curvature of the earth better than low-frequency waves. Thus, normally, greater distances may be measured by using high-frequency electromagnetic waves. *Loran*, which is the abbreviation of "long range navigation," is an example of such a measuring device. However, the instruments using low-frequency waves also have an advantage, since the velocity of propagation of such waves may be established with greater accuracy, normally giving greater accuracy of measured distances. *Shoran* ("short range navigation") is the example of this type of measuring device.

The shoran method is widely used in offshore measurements and in establishing triangulation stations on the ground. In the operation of shoran, an *indicating station* transmits signals of a certain frequency to receiving stations, called *base stations*, and the base stations transmit return signals of different and definite frequencies, by which the various stations may be identified. The transmitted and returned signals appear on the cathode ray oscilloscope. The distances are read directly on the instrument dial. The accuracy of measurements by this method is practically independent of distance and is about ± 40 ft in a measured distance. Airborne transmitting stations, installed on airplanes, are successfully used in the shoran method to measure distances between base stations. Measurements from airborne stations increase measuring range between stations.

The *Electronic Position Indicator* (E.P.I.) method combines certain techniques that are used in the loran and shoran methods. This method was developed by the U.S. Coast and Geodetic Survey in order to increase measuring range of distances to about 500 miles, while maintaining an accuracy comparable to that in the shoran method.

PROBLEMS

19-1. In a stream gaging operation the measurements were taken as shown in the table below. It is required to compute the stream discharge from the given data.

(A)

Distance from left bank in feet	0	10	20	30	40	50	57
Total depth at above distances, in feet	0	1.8	3.2	5.6	4.8	2.3	0
Velocity at 0.2 depth		1.56	2.45	3.51	2.70	1.70	
Velocity at 0.8 depth		1.10	1.55	2.17	1.62	1.00	

Ans. 353 cfs

(B)

Distance from left bank in feet	0	12	24	36	48	60	72
Total depth at above distances, in feet	0	2.6	4.5	6.7	5.1	3.2	0
Velocity at 0.2 depth		1.42	2.31	3.62	2.50	1.43	
Velocity at 0.8 depth		1.15	1.67	2.30	1.52	1.22	

(C)

Distance from left bank in feet	0	10	20	30	40	50	62
Total depth at above distances, in feet	0	2.3	3.7	5.9	4.6	2.7	0
Velocity at 0.2 depth		1.62	2.52	4.10	2.80	1.73	
Velocity at 0.8 depth		1.30	1.92	3.50	2.00	1.41	

19-2. Stream gaging data are shown in the table below. It is required (a) to plot the cross section of the stream bed, using a horizontal scale 1 in. = 10 ft and a vertical scale 1 in. = 5 ft, (b) to plot on the cross section, obtained in part (a), the curves of equal velocity for 1.0, 2.0, 3.0, and 4.0 ft/sec, (c) to plot velocities as horizontal vectors at corresponding depths, plotted along a vertical line, for 15, 25, 35, and 45 ft sections; use velocity scale 1 in. = 1 ft/sec and the depth scale 1 in. = 2 ft; then draw smooth velocity curves and measure the areas by planimeter, thus obtaining the total velocity per foot of width of each section. (Such velocity may be closely approximated by computing each area for a section by the trapezoidal formula, see Art. 15-16.) (d) Multiply computed velocities by the corresponding widths of sections thus obtaining discharge in cubic feet per second for each section; compute total discharge of the stream by adding computed discharges. For the first 10 ft section and for the last odd section use average velocity in the section equal to the measured velocity at 0.6 depth.

(A)

			MID-POINTS OF SECTIONS					
Distances from left bank (ft)	0	5	15	25	35	45	56	62
Average depth at the middle of section		2.3	5.1	8.9	7.6	5.7	3.0	
Velocity at the surface			1.82	2.30	2.57	2.25		
Velocity at $0.2d$			2.65	3.72	4.13	3.62		
Velocity at $0.4d$			2.52	3.61	3.92	3.50		
Velocity at $0.6d$		1.05	1.30	2.77	3.00	2.68	0.96	
Velocity at $0.8d$			1.00	1.84	1.90	1.73		
Velocity at bottom			0.50	1.12	1.25	1.10		

Ans. (d) 766 cfs

(B)

			MID-POINTS OF SECTIONS					
Distance from left bank (ft)	0	5	15	25	35	45	57	64
Average depth at the middle of section		1.8	4.9	7.8	8.0	5.3	3.2	
Velocity at the surface			1.77	2.15	2.63	2.12		
Velocity at $0.2d$			2.59	3.61	4.02	3.53		
Velocity at $0.4d$			2.43	3.42	3.85	3.47		
Velocity at $0.6d$		1.12	1.32	2.67	2.97	2.59	1.05	
Velocity at $0.8d$			1.15	1.74	1.82	1.63		
Velocity at bottom			0.60	0.84	1.00	0.92		

(C)

		MID-POINTS OF SECTIONS						
Distance from left bank (ft)	0	5	15	25	35	45	55	61
Average depth at the middle of section		2.5	6.2	8.5	9.3	4.2	2.0	
Velocity at the surface			1.90	2.43	2.60	1.72		
Velocity at 0.2d			2.87	3.91	4.12	3.20		
Velocity at 0.4d			2.70	4.20	4.54	3.10		
Velocity at 0.6d		1.30	1.43	3.17	3.72	2.47	0.95	
Velocity at 0.8d			1.21	2.36	2.45	1.15		
Velocity at bottom			0.62	1.31	1.42	0.80		

19-3. Compute the cross-sectional area and scale from a drawing the wetted perimeter of the stream bed, using the data given in Problem 19-2. Determine (a) the hydraulic radius for the cross section, and (b) the coefficient C in the Chezy formula for the slope S and the discharge Q, obtained from the station rating curve. Use corresponding parts of Problem 19-2 with the data given below.

(A) $S = 0.0003$ feet per foot, $Q = 780$ cfs.   *Ans.* (a) 5.1 ft, (b) 60
(B) $S = 0.0002$ feet per foot, $Q = 710$ cfs.
(C) $S = 0.0004$ feet per foot, $Q = 850$ cfs.

APPENDIX A

Formulas

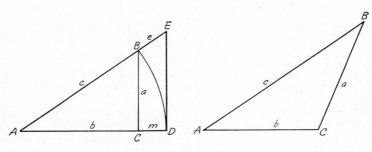

Fig. A-1.

RIGHT TRIANGLE

1. $a^2 + b^2 = c^2$
2. $a = c \sin A = b \tan A = c \cos B = \sqrt{c^2 - b^2}$
3. $b = c \sin B = a \tan B = c \cos A = \sqrt{c^2 - a^2}$
4. $c = a \sec B = b \sec A = a \csc A = b \csc B = \sqrt{a^2 + b^2}$
5. $m = c \text{ vers } A$ 6. $e = c \text{ exsec } A$
7. $\sin A = \dfrac{a}{c} = \cos B$ 8. $\cos A = \dfrac{b}{c} = \sin B$
9. $\tan A = \dfrac{a}{b} = \cot B$ 10. $\cot A = \dfrac{b}{a} = \tan B$
11. $\sec A = \dfrac{c}{b} = \csc B$ 12. $\csc A = \dfrac{c}{a} = \sec B$
13. $\text{vers } A = \dfrac{m}{c}$ 14. $\text{exsec } A = \dfrac{e}{c}$

OBLIQUE TRIANGLE

Given	Formulas
Two angles A and B and any side a, b, or c	15. $C = 180° - A - B$ 16. $a = b\dfrac{\sin A}{\sin B} = c\dfrac{\sin A}{\sin C}$
Two sides a and b and the included angle C	17. $\tan A = \dfrac{a \sin C}{b - a \cos C}$ 18. $\tan B = \dfrac{b \sin C}{a - b \cos C}$ or: 19. $\tan \frac{1}{2}(A - B) = \dfrac{a - b}{a + b} \tan \frac{1}{2}(A + B)$ 20. $\text{Area} = \dfrac{ab \sin C}{2}$
Two sides a and b and an opposite angle, either A or B	Use Eq. (16)
Three sides a, b, and c	If $s = \frac{1}{2}(a + b + c)$, 21. $\text{vers } A = \dfrac{2(s - b)(s - c)}{bc}$ 22. $\sin \dfrac{A}{2} = \sqrt{\dfrac{(s - b)(s - c)}{bc}}$ 23. $\cos \dfrac{A}{2} = \sqrt{\dfrac{s(s - a)}{bc}}$ 24. $\tan \dfrac{A}{2} = \sqrt{\dfrac{(s - b)(s - c)}{s(s - a)}}$ 25. $\text{Area} = \sqrt{s(s - a)(s - b)(s - c)}$

Appendix A

TRIGONOMETRIC FORMULAS

26. $\sin^2 A + \cos^2 A = 1$

27. $\sin^2 A = \dfrac{1 - \cos 2A}{2}$

28. $\cos^2 A = \dfrac{1 + \cos 2A}{2}$

29. $\tan A = \dfrac{\sin A}{\cos A} = \dfrac{\sin 2A}{1 + \cos 2A} = \dfrac{1 - \cos 2A}{\sin 2A} = \dfrac{\text{vers } 2A}{\sin 2A}$

30. $\cot A = \dfrac{1}{\tan A}$

31. $\sec A = \dfrac{1}{\cos A}$

32. $\csc A = \dfrac{1}{\sin A}$

33. $\sec^2 A = 1 + \tan^2 A$

34. $\csc^2 A = 1 + \cot^2 A$

35. $\text{vers } A = 1 - \cos A$

36. $\text{exsec } A = \sec A - 1$

37. $\sin 2A = 2 \sin A \cos A$

38. $\cos 2A = \cos^2 A - \sin^2 A = 2 \cos^2 A - 1 = 1 - 2 \sin^2 A$

39. $\tan 2A = \dfrac{2 \tan A}{1 - \tan^2 A}$

40. $\cot 2A = \dfrac{\cot^2 A - 1}{2 \cot A}$

41. $\text{vers } 2A = 2 \sin^2 A = 2 \sin A \cos A \tan A$

42. $\text{exsec } 2A = \dfrac{2 \tan^2 A}{1 - \tan^2 A}$

43. $\sin (A \pm B) = \sin A \cos A \cos B \pm \sin B \cos A$

44. $\cos (A \pm B) = \cos A \cos B \mp \sin A \sin B$

45. $\tan (A \pm B) = \dfrac{\tan A \pm \tan B}{1 \mp \tan A \tan B}$

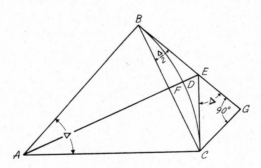

Fig. A-2.

CIRCULAR CURVE FORMULAS

If $AB = AC = R$, and $BAC = \Delta$,

46. Tangent distance $BE = EC = R \tan \dfrac{\Delta}{2}$

47. Chord $BC = 2R \sin \dfrac{\Delta}{2} = C$

48. Tangent offset $CG = C \sin \dfrac{\Delta}{2}$

49. Tangent distance $BG = C \cos \dfrac{\Delta}{2}$

50. External distance $DE = R \operatorname{exsec} \dfrac{\Delta}{2}$

51. Middle ordinate $FD = R \operatorname{vers} \dfrac{\Delta}{2}$

52. The length of curve $BC = R\Delta = \dfrac{\pi R \Delta°}{180}$

GEOMETRIC FORMULAS: AREA, SURFACE, VOLUME

53. Area of circle $= \pi R^2$, where R is the radius

54. Area of sector (ABDC, Fig. A-2) $= \dfrac{R^2 \Delta}{2}$, where Δ is in radians

55. Area of segment (BDC, Fig. A-2) $= \dfrac{R^2}{2} (\Delta - \sin \Delta)$, where Δ is in radians

56. Surface of circular cone $= \pi r s$, where r is radius of base and h is inclined height

57. Surface of cylinder $= 2\pi r h$, where r is radius of base and h is the height

58. Surface of sphere $= 4\pi r^2$, where r is the radius

59. Volume of pyramid or cone $= \dfrac{ah}{3}$ where a is the area of base and h is the height

60. Volume of cylinder or prism $= ah$, where a is the area of base and h is the height

61. Volume of sphere $= \frac{4}{3}\pi r^3$, where r is the radius

APPENDIX B

Slide Rule

Description. Slide rule operations are performed with the aid of logarithmic scales, which can slide one with respect to another and thus perform addition and subtraction of the logarithms of numbers marked along those scales.

The sliding part of the rule is called the *slide* and the rest of the rule is called the *body*. A piece of transparent rectangular plate, with a vertical hairline, attached to the face of the slide rule is called the *runner*. The runner slides over the body, so that its hairline can be set on any scale division. The line that marks the beginning of scales on the slide is called the *left index* and one which marks the end of scales is called the *right index*. Since the left index is the zero end of the scale, and log 1 = 0, the left index is marked with number 1; so is the right index. Similarly, corresponding divisions for log 2, log 3, . . ., on the logarithmic scale of numbers are marked by 2, 3, 4, . . ., respectively, as is shown on *C* and *D* scales in Fig. B-1. Although the figure shows the scales on an engineering slide rule, the log-log scales (marked by letters *LL*) are used mainly for evaluation of numbers having fractional exponents. Since the *LL* scales are not used in surveying, discussion of their use is not included in this appendix.

Multiplication and division. In order to multiply 4 by 2, log 4 is added to log 2, on the slide rule scales, and the result is log 8. Thus if the left index on the slide is set at 4 on the stationary *D*-scale and then the hairline of the runner is set at 2 on the sliding *C*-scale, the result, 8, must be on *D*-scale under the hairline.

The above operation readily suggests a reverse process, or division of 8 by 2 to obtain 4. The runner is set at 8 on *D*-scale, and 2 on *C*-scale is moved to hairline; this gives 4 on *D*-scale at left index. If the left index falls outside *D*-scale, the answer is found at the right index.

In making a logarithmic scale from 1 to 10, the scale is proportioned according to the mantissas of the logarithms of numbers, and since the mantissa for log 2 is the same as that for log 20, log 200, and so on, it is apparent that 2 on a logarithmic scale will represent 20 or 200—in fact, 2 with any number of preceding or following zeros. Thus the above

Table I

COMMON LOGARITHMS OF NUMBERS

100 — 150

N.		0	1	2	3	4	5	6	7	8	9
100	00	000	043	087	130	173	217	260	303	346	389
101		432	475	518	561	604	647	689	732	775	817
102		860	903	945	988	*030	*072	*115	*157	*199	*242
103	01	284	326	368	410	452	494	536	578	620	662
104		703	745	787	828	870	912	953	995	*036	*078
105	02	119	160	202	243	284	325	366	407	449	490
106		531	572	612	653	694	735	776	816	857	898
107		938	979	*019	*060	*100	*141	*181	*222	*262	*302
108	03	342	383	423	463	503	543	583	623	663	703
109		743	782	822	862	902	941	981	*021	*060	*100
110	04	139	179	218	258	297	336	376	415	454	493
111		532	571	610	650	689	727	766	805	844	883
112		922	961	999	*038	*077	*115	*154	*192	*231	*269
113	05	308	346	385	423	461	500	538	576	614	652
114		690	729	767	805	843	881	918	956	994	*032
115	06	070	108	145	183	221	258	296	333	371	408
116		446	483	521	558	595	633	670	707	744	781
117		819	856	893	930	967	*004	*041	*078	*115	*151
118	07	188	225	262	298	335	372	408	445	482	518
119		555	591	628	664	700	737	773	809	846	882
120		918	954	990	*027	*063	*099	*135	*171	*207	*243
121	08	279	314	350	386	422	458	493	529	565	600
122		636	672	707	743	778	814	849	884	920	955
123		991	*026	*061	*096	*132	*167	*202	*237	*272	*307
124	09	342	377	412	447	482	517	552	587	621	656
125		691	726	760	795	830	864	899	934	968	*003
126	10	037	072	106	140	175	209	243	278	312	346
127		380	415	449	483	517	551	585	619	653	687
128		721	755	789	823	857	890	924	958	992	*025
129	11	059	093	126	160	193	227	261	294	327	361
130		394	428	461	494	528	561	594	628	661	694
131		727	760	793	826	860	893	926	959	992	*024
132	12	057	090	123	156	189	222	254	287	320	352
133		385	418	450	483	516	548	581	613	646	678
134		710	743	775	808	840	872	905	937	969	*001
135	13	033	066	098	130	162	194	226	258	290	322
136		354	386	418	450	481	513	545	577	609	640
137		672	704	735	767	799	830	862	893	925	956
138		988	*019	*051	*082	*114	*145	*176	*208	*239	*270
139	14	301	333	364	395	426	457	489	520	551	582
140		613	644	675	706	737	768	799	829	860	891
141		922	953	983	*014	*045	*076	*106	*137	*168	*198
142	15	229	259	290	320	351	381	412	442	473	503
143		534	564	594	625	655	685	715	746	776	806
144		836	866	897	927	957	987	*017	*047	*077	*107
145	16	137	167	197	227	256	286	316	346	376	406
146		435	465	495	524	554	584	613	643	673	702
147		732	761	791	820	850	879	909	938	967	997
148	17	026	056	085	114	143	173	202	231	260	289
149		319	348	377	406	435	464	493	522	551	580
150	—	609	638	667	696	725	754	782	811	840	869
N.		0	1	2	3	4	5	6	7	8	9

Proportional parts

	44	43	42
1	4.4	4.3	4.2
2	8.8	8.6	8.4
3	13.2	12.9	12.6
4	17.6	17.2	16.8
5	22.0	21.5	21.0
6	26.4	25.8	25.2
7	30.8	30.1	29.4
8	35.2	34.4	33.6
9	39.6	38.7	37.8

	41	40	39
1	4.1	4.0	3.9
2	8.2	8.0	7.8
3	12.3	12.0	11.7
4	16.4	16.0	15.6
5	20.5	20.0	19.5
6	24.6	24.0	23.4
7	28.7	28.0	27.3
8	32.8	32.0	31.2
9	36.9	36.0	35.1

	38	37	36
1	3.8	3.7	3.6
2	7.6	7.4	7.2
3	11.4	11.1	10.8
4	15.2	14.8	14.4
5	19.0	18.5	18.0
6	22.8	22.2	21.6
7	26.6	25.9	25.2
8	30.4	29.6	28.8
9	34.2	33.3	32.4

	35	34	33
1	3.5	3.4	3.3
2	7.0	6.8	6.6
3	10.5	10.2	9.9
4	14.0	13.6	13.2
5	17.5	17.0	16.5
6	21.0	20.4	19.8
7	24.5	23.8	23.1
8	28.0	27.2	26.4
9	31.5	30.6	29.7

	32	31	30
1	3.2	3.1	3.0
2	6.4	6.2	6.0
3	9.6	9.3	9.0
4	12.8	12.4	12.0
5	16.0	15.5	15.0
6	19.2	18.6	18.0
7	22.4	21.7	21.0
8	25.6	24.8	24.0
9	28.8	27.9	27.0

Proportional parts

.00 000 — .17 869

Table I (Cont'd)

COMMON LOGARITHMS OF NUMBERS

150 — 200

N.	0	1	2	3	4	5	6	7	8	9
150	17 609	638	667	696	725	754	782	811	840	869
151	898	926	955	984	*013	*041	*070	*099	*127	*156
152	18 184	213	241	270	298	327	355	384	412	441
153	469	498	526	554	583	611	639	667	696	724
154	752	780	808	837	865	893	921	949	977	*005
155	19 033	061	089	117	145	173	201	229	257	285
156	312	340	368	396	424	451	479	507	535	562
157	590	618	645	673	700	728	756	783	811	838
158	866	893	921	948	976	*003	*030	*058	*085	*112
159	20 140	167	194	222	249	276	303	330	358	385
160	412	439	466	493	520	548	575	602	629	656
161	683	710	737	763	790	817	844	871	898	925
162	952	978	*005	*032	*059	*085	*112	*139	*165	*192
163	21 219	245	272	299	325	352	378	405	431	458
164	484	511	537	564	590	617	643	669	696	722
165	748	775	801	827	854	880	906	932	958	985
166	22 011	037	063	089	115	141	167	194	220	246
167	272	298	324	350	376	401	427	453	479	505
168	531	557	583	608	634	660	686	712	737	763
169	789	814	840	866	891	917	943	968	994	*019
170	23 045	070	096	121	147	172	198	223	249	274
171	300	325	350	376	401	426	452	477	502	528
172	553	578	603	629	654	679	704	729	754	779
173	805	830	855	880	905	930	955	980	*005	*030
174	24 055	080	105	130	155	180	204	229	254	279
175	304	329	353	378	403	428	452	477	502	527
176	551	576	601	625	650	674	699	724	748	773
177	797	822	846	871	895	920	944	969	993	*018
178	25 042	066	091	115	139	164	188	212	237	261
179	285	310	334	358	382	406	431	455	479	503
180	527	551	575	600	624	648	672	696	720	744
181	768	792	816	840	864	888	912	935	959	983
182	26 007	031	055	079	102	126	150	174	198	221
183	245	269	293	316	340	364	387	411	435	458
184	482	505	529	553	576	600	623	647	670	694
185	717	741	764	788	811	834	858	881	905	928
186	951	975	998	*021	*045	*068	*091	*114	*138	*161
187	27 184	207	231	254	277	300	323	346	370	393
188	416	439	462	485	508	531	554	577	600	623
189	646	669	692	715	738	761	784	807	830	852
190	875	898	921	944	967	989	*012	*035	*058	*081
191	28 103	126	149	171	194	217	240	262	285	307
192	330	353	375	398	421	443	466	488	511	533
193	556	578	601	623	646	668	691	713	735	758
194	780	803	825	847	870	892	914	937	959	981
195	29 003	026	048	070	092	115	137	159	181	203
196	226	248	270	292	314	336	358	380	403	425
197	447	469	491	513	535	557	579	601	623	645
198	667	688	710	732	754	776	798	820	842	863
199	885	907	929	951	973	994	*016	*038	*060	*081
200	30 103	125	146	168	190	211	233	255	276	298
N.	0	1	2	3	4	5	6	7	8	9

Proportional parts

	29	28
1	2.9	2.8
2	5.8	5.6
3	8.7	8.4
4	11.6	11.2
5	14.5	14.0
6	17.4	16.8
7	20.3	19.6
8	23.2	22.4
9	26.1	25.2

	27	26
1	2.7	2.6
2	5.4	5.2
3	8.1	7.8
4	10.8	10.4
5	13.5	13.0
6	16.2	15.6
7	18.9	18.2
8	21.6	20.8
9	24.3	23.4

	25
1	2.5
2	5.0
3	7.5
4	10.0
5	12.5
6	15.0
7	17.5
8	20.0
9	22.5

	24	23
1	2.4	2.3
2	4.8	4.6
3	7.2	6.9
4	9.6	9.2
5	12.0	11.5
6	14.4	13.8
7	16.8	16.1
8	19.2	18.4
9	21.6	20.7

	22	21
1	2.2	2.1
2	4.4	4.2
3	6.6	6.3
4	8.8	8.4
5	11.0	10.5
6	13.2	12.6
7	15.4	14.7
8	17.6	16.8
9	19.8	18.9

.17 609 — .30 298

Table I (Cont'd)

COMMON LOGARITHMS OF NUMBERS

200 — 250

N.		0	1	2	3	4	5	6	7	8	9	Proportional parts
200	30	103	125	146	168	190	211	233	255	276	298	
201		320	341	363	384	406	428	449	471	492	514	
202		535	557	578	600	621	643	664	685	707	728	
203		750	771	792	814	835	856	878	899	920	942	
204		963	984	*006	*027	*048	*069	*091	*112	*133	*154	
205	31	175	197	218	239	260	281	302	323	345	366	
206		387	408	429	450	471	492	513	534	555	576	
207		597	618	639	660	681	702	723	744	765	785	
208		806	827	848	869	890	911	931	952	973	994	
209	32	015	035	056	077	098	118	139	160	181	201	
210		222	243	263	284	305	325	346	366	387	408	
211		428	449	469	490	510	531	552	572	593	613	
212		634	654	675	695	715	736	756	777	797	818	
213		838	858	879	899	919	940	960	980	*001	*021	
214	33	041	062	082	102	122	143	163	183	203	224	
215		244	264	284	304	325	345	365	385	405	425	
216		445	465	486	506	526	546	566	586	606	626	
217		646	666	686	706	726	746	766	786	806	826	
218		846	866	885	905	925	945	965	985	*005	*025	
219	34	044	064	084	104	124	143	163	183	203	223	
220		242	262	282	301	321	341	361	380	400	420	
221		439	459	479	498	518	537	557	577	596	616	
222		635	655	674	694	713	733	753	772	792	811	
223		830	850	869	889	908	928	947	967	986	*005	
224	35	025	044	064	083	102	122	141	160	180	199	
225		218	238	257	276	295	315	334	353	372	392	
226		411	430	449	468	488	507	526	545	564	583	
227		603	622	641	660	679	698	717	736	755	774	
228		793	813	832	851	870	889	908	927	946	965	
229		984	*003	*021	*040	*059	*078	*097	*116	*135	*154	
230	36	173	192	211	229	248	267	286	305	324	342	
231		361	380	399	418	436	455	474	493	511	530	
232		549	568	586	605	624	642	661	680	698	717	
233		736	754	773	791	810	829	847	866	884	903	
234		922	940	959	977	996	*014	*033	*051	*070	*088	
235	37	107	125	144	162	181	199	218	236	254	273	
236		291	310	328	346	365	383	401	420	438	457	
237		475	493	511	530	548	566	585	603	621	639	
238		658	676	694	712	731	749	767	785	803	822	
239		840	858	876	894	912	931	949	967	985	*003	
240	38	021	039	057	075	093	112	130	148	166	184	
241		202	220	238	256	274	292	310	328	346	364	
242		382	399	417	435	453	471	489	507	525	543	
243		561	578	596	614	632	650	668	686	703	721	
244		739	757	775	792	810	828	846	863	881	899	
245		917	934	952	970	987	*005	*023	*041	*058	*076	
246	39	094	111	129	146	164	182	199	217	235	252	
247		270	287	305	322	340	358	375	393	410	428	
248		445	463	480	498	515	533	550	568	585	602	
249		620	637	655	672	690	707	724	742	759	777	
250		794	811	829	846	863	881	898	915	933	950	
N.		0	1	2	3	4	5	6	7	8	9	Proportional parts

Proportional parts:

	22	21
1	2.2	2.1
2	4.4	4.2
3	6.6	6.3
4	8.8	8.4
5	11.0	10.5
6	13.2	12.6
7	15.4	14.7
8	17.6	16.8
9	19.8	18.9

	20
1	2.0
2	4.0
3	6.0
4	8.0
5	10.0
6	12.0
7	14.0
8	16.0
9	18.0

	19
1	1.9
2	3.8
3	5.7
4	7.6
5	9.5
6	11.4
7	13.3
8	15.2
9	17.1

	18
1	1.8
2	3.6
3	5.4
4	7.2
5	9.0
6	10.8
7	12.6
8	14.4
9	16.2

	17
1	1.7
2	3.4
3	5.1
4	6.8
5	8.5
6	10.2
7	11.9
8	13.6
9	15.3

.30 103 — .39 950

Table I (Cont'd)

COMMON LOGARITHMS OF NUMBERS

250 — 300

N.		0	1	2	3	4	5	6	7	8	9	Proportional parts	
250	39	794	811	829	846	863	881	898	915	933	950		**18**
251		967	985	*002	*019	*037	*054	*071	*088	*106	*123	1	1.8
252	40	140	157	175	192	209	226	243	261	278	295	2	3.6
253		312	329	346	364	381	398	415	432	449	466	3	5.4
254		483	500	518	535	552	569	586	603	620	637	4	7.2
												5	9.0
255		654	671	688	705	722	739	756	773	790	807	6	10.8
256		824	841	858	875	892	909	926	943	960	976	7	12.6
257		993	*010	*027	*044	*061	*078	*095	*111	*128	*145	8	14.4
258	41	162	179	196	212	229	246	263	280	296	313	9	16.2
259		330	347	363	380	397	414	430	447	464	481		
260		497	514	531	547	564	581	597	614	631	647		**17**
261		664	681	697	714	731	747	764	780	797	814	1	1.7
262		830	847	863	880	896	913	929	946	963	979	2	3.4
263		996	*012	*029	*045	*062	*078	*095	*111	*127	*144	3	5.1
264	42	160	177	193	210	226	243	259	275	292	308	4	6.8
												5	8.5
265		325	341	357	374	390	406	423	439	455	472	6	10.2
266		488	504	521	537	553	570	586	602	619	635	7	11.9
267		651	667	684	700	716	732	749	765	781	797	8	13.6
268		813	830	846	862	878	894	911	927	943	959	9	15.3
269		975	991	*008	*024	*040	*056	*072	*088	*104	*120		
270	43	136	152	169	185	201	217	233	249	265	281		**16**
271		297	313	329	345	361	377	393	409	425	441	1	1.6
272		457	473	489	505	521	537	553	569	584	600	2	3.2
273		616	632	648	664	680	696	712	727	743	759	3	4.8
274		775	791	807	823	838	854	870	886	902	917	4	6.4
												5	8.0
275		933	949	965	981	996	*012	*028	*044	*059	*075	6	9.6
276	44	091	107	122	138	154	170	185	201	217	232	7	11.2
277		248	264	279	295	311	326	342	358	373	389	8	12.8
278		404	420	436	451	467	483	498	514	529	545	9	14.4
279		560	576	592	607	623	638	654	669	685	700		
280		716	731	747	762	778	793	809	824	840	855		**15**
281		871	886	902	917	932	948	963	979	994	*010	1	1.5
282	45	025	040	056	071	086	102	117	133	148	163	2	3.0
283		179	194	209	225	240	255	271	286	301	317	3	4.5
284		332	347	362	378	393	408	423	439	454	469	4	6.0
												5	7.5
285		484	500	515	530	545	561	576	591	606	621	6	9.0
286		637	652	667	682	697	712	728	743	758	773	7	10.5
287		788	803	818	834	849	864	879	894	909	924	8	12.0
288		939	954	969	984	*000	*015	*030	*045	*060	*075	9	13.5
289	46	090	105	120	135	150	165	180	195	210	225		
290		240	255	270	285	300	315	330	345	359	374		**14**
291		389	404	419	434	449	464	479	494	509	523	1	1.4
292		538	553	568	583	598	613	627	642	657	672	2	2.8
293		687	702	716	731	746	761	776	790	805	820	3	4.2
294		835	850	864	879	894	909	923	938	953	967	4	5.6
												5	7.0
295		982	997	*012	*026	*041	*056	*070	*085	*100	*114	6	8.4
296	47	129	144	159	173	188	202	217	232	246	261	7	9.8
297		276	290	305	319	334	349	363	378	392	407	8	11.2
298		422	436	451	465	480	494	509	524	538	553	9	12.6
299		567	582	596	611	625	640	654	669	683	698		
300		712	727	741	756	770	784	799	813	828	842	log e = 0.43429	
N.		0	1	2	3	4	5	6	7	8	9	Proportional parts	

.39 794 — .47 842

Table I (Cont'd)

COMMON LOGARITHMS OF NUMBERS

300 — 350

N.	0	1	2	3	4	5	6	7	8	9
300	47 712	727	741	756	770	784	799	813	828	842
301	857	871	885	900	914	929	943	958	972	986
302	48 001	015	029	044	058	073	087	101	116	130
303	144	159	173	187	202	216	230	244	259	273
304	287	302	316	330	344	359	373	387	401	416
305	430	444	458	473	487	501	515	530	544	558
306	572	586	601	615	629	643	657	671	686	700
307	714	728	742	756	770	785	799	813	827	841
308	855	869	883	897	911	926	940	954	968	982
309	996	*010	*024	*038	*052	*066	*080	*094	*108	*122
310	49 136	150	164	178	192	206	220	234	248	262
311	276	290	304	318	332	346	360	374	388	402
312	415	429	443	457	471	485	499	513	527	541
313	554	568	582	596	610	624	638	651	665	679
314	693	707	721	734	748	762	776	790	803	817
315	831	845	859	872	886	900	914	927	941	955
316	969	982	996	*010	*024	*037	*051	*065	*079	*092
317	50 106	120	133	147	161	174	188	202	215	229
318	243	256	270	284	297	311	325	338	352	365
319	379	393	406	420	433	447	461	474	488	501
320	515	529	542	556	569	583	596	610	623	637
321	651	664	678	691	705	718	732	745	759	772
322	786	799	813	826	840	853	866	880	893	907
323	920	934	947	961	974	987	*001	*014	*028	*041
324	51 055	068	081	095	108	121	135	148	162	175
325	188	202	215	228	242	255	268	282	295	308
326	322	335	348	362	375	388	402	415	428	441
327	455	468	481	495	508	521	534	548	561	574
328	587	601	614	627	640	654	667	680	693	706
329	720	733	746	759	772	786	799	812	825	838
330	851	865	878	891	904	917	930	943	957	970
331	983	996	*009	*022	*035	*048	*061	*075	*088	*101
332	52 114	127	140	153	166	179	192	205	218	231
333	244	257	270	284	297	310	323	336	349	362
334	375	388	401	414	427	440	453	466	479	492
335	504	517	530	543	556	569	582	595	608	621
336	634	647	660	673	686	699	711	724	737	750
337	763	776	789	802	815	827	840	853	866	879
338	892	905	917	930	943	956	969	982	994	*007
339	53 020	033	046	058	071	084	097	110	122	135
340	148	161	173	186	199	212	224	237	250	263
341	275	288	301	314	326	339	352	364	377	390
342	403	415	428	441	453	466	479	491	504	517
343	529	542	555	567	580	593	605	618	631	643
344	656	668	681	694	706	719	732	744	757	769
345	782	794	807	820	832	845	857	870	882	895
346	908	920	933	945	958	970	983	995	*008	*020
347	54 033	045	058	070	083	095	108	120	133	145
348	158	170	183	195	208	220	233	245	258	270
349	283	295	307	320	332	345	357	370	382	394
350	407	419	432	444	456	469	481	494	506	518
N.	0	1	2	3	4	5	6	7	8	9

Proportional parts

	15	14	13	12
1	1.5	1.4	1.3	1.2
2	3.0	2.8	2.6	2.4
3	4.5	4.2	3.9	3.6
4	6.0	5.6	5.2	4.8
5	7.5	7.0	6.5	6.0
6	9.0	8.4	7.8	7.2
7	10.5	9.8	9.1	8.4
8	12.0	11.2	10.4	9.6
9	13.5	12.6	11.7	10.8

$\log \pi = 0.49715$

.47 712 — .54 518

Table I (Cont'd)

COMMON LOGARITHMS OF NUMBERS

350 — 400

N.		0	1	2	3	4	5	6	7	8	9
350	54	407	419	432	444	456	469	481	494	506	518
351		531	543	555	568	580	593	605	617	630	642
352		654	667	679	691	704	716	728	741	753	765
353		777	790	802	814	827	839	851	864	876	888
354		900	913	925	937	949	962	974	986	998	*011
355	55	023	035	047	060	072	084	096	108	121	133
356		145	157	169	182	194	206	218	230	242	255
357		267	279	291	303	315	328	340	352	364	376
358		388	400	413	425	437	449	461	473	485	497
359		509	522	534	546	558	570	582	594	606	618
360		630	642	654	666	678	691	703	715	727	739
361		751	763	775	787	799	811	823	835	847	859
362		871	883	895	907	919	931	943	955	967	979
363		991	*003	*015	*027	*038	*050	*062	*074	*086	*098
364	56	110	122	134	146	158	170	182	194	205	217
365		229	241	253	265	277	289	301	312	324	336
366		348	360	372	384	396	407	419	431	443	455
367		467	478	490	502	514	526	538	549	561	573
368		585	597	608	620	632	644	656	667	679	691
369		703	714	726	738	750	761	773	785	797	808
370		820	832	844	855	867	879	891	902	914	926
371		937	949	961	972	984	996	*008	*019	*031	*043
372	57	054	066	078	089	101	113	124	136	148	159
373		171	183	194	206	217	229	241	252	264	276
374		287	299	310	322	334	345	357	368	380	392
375		403	415	426	438	449	461	473	484	496	507
376		519	530	542	553	565	576	588	600	611	623
377		634	646	657	669	680	692	703	715	726	738
378		749	761	772	784	795	807	818	830	841	852
379		864	875	887	898	910	921	933	944	955	967
380		978	990	*001	*013	*024	*035	*047	*058	*070	*081
381	58	092	104	115	127	138	149	161	172	184	195
382		206	218	229	240	252	263	274	286	297	309
383		320	331	343	354	365	377	388	399	410	422
384		433	444	456	467	478	490	501	512	524	535
385		546	557	569	580	591	602	614	625	636	647
386		659	670	681	692	704	715	726	737	749	760
387		771	782	794	805	816	827	838	850	861	872
388		883	894	906	917	928	939	950	961	973	984
389		995	*006	*017	*028	*040	*051	*062	*073	*084	*095
390	59	106	118	129	140	151	162	173	184	195	207
391		218	229	240	251	262	273	284	295	306	318
392		329	340	351	362	373	384	395	406	417	428
393		439	450	461	472	483	494	506	517	528	539
394		550	561	572	583	594	605	616	627	638	649
395		660	671	682	693	704	715	726	737	748	759
396		770	780	791	802	813	824	835	846	857	868
397		879	890	901	912	923	934	945	956	966	977
398		988	999	*010	*021	*032	*043	*054	*065	*076	*086
399	60	097	108	119	130	141	152	163	173	184	195
400		206	217	228	239	249	260	271	282	293	304
N.		0	1	2	3	4	5	6	7	8	9

Proportional parts

13
1 1.3
2 2.6
3 3.9
4 5.2
5 6.5
6 7.8
7 9.1
8 10.4
9 11.7

12
1 1.2
2 2.4
3 3.6
4 4.8
5 6.0
6 7.2
7 8.4
8 9.6
9 10.8

11
1 1.1
2 2.2
3 3.3
4 4.4
5 5.5
6 6.6
7 7.7
8 8.8
9 9.9

10
1 1.0
2 2.0
3 3.0
4 4.0
5 5.0
6 6.0
7 7.0
8 8.0
9 9.0

.54 407 — .60 304

Table I (Cont'd)

COMMON LOGARITHMS OF NUMBERS

400 — 450

N.		0	1	2	3	4	5	6	7	8	9	Proportional parts
400	60	206	217	228	239	249	260	271	282	293	304	
401		314	325	336	347	358	369	379	390	401	412	
402		423	433	444	455	466	477	487	498	509	520	
403		531	541	552	563	574	584	595	606	617	627	
404		638	649	660	670	681	692	703	713	724	735	
405		746	756	767	778	788	799	810	821	831	842	
406		853	863	874	885	895	906	917	927	938	949	
407		959	970	981	991	*002	*013	*023	*034	*045	*055	
408	61	066	077	087	098	109	119	130	140	151	162	
409		172	183	194	204	215	225	236	247	257	268	
410		278	289	300	310	321	331	342	352	363	374	
411		384	395	405	416	426	437	448	458	469	479	
412		490	500	511	521	532	542	553	563	574	584	
413		595	606	616	627	637	648	658	669	679	690	
414		700	711	721	731	742	752	763	773	784	794	
415		805	815	826	836	847	857	868	878	888	899	
416		909	920	930	941	951	962	972	982	993	*003	
417	62	014	024	034	045	055	066	076	086	097	107	
418		118	128	138	149	159	170	180	190	201	211	
419		221	232	242	252	263	273	284	294	304	315	
420		325	335	346	356	366	377	387	397	408	418	
421		428	439	449	459	469	480	490	500	511	521	
422		531	542	552	562	572	583	593	603	613	624	
423		634	644	655	665	675	685	696	706	716	726	
424		737	747	757	767	778	788	798	808	818	829	
425		839	849	859	870	880	890	900	910	921	931	
426		941	951	961	972	982	992	*002	*012	*022	*033	
427	63	043	053	063	073	083	094	104	114	124	134	
428		144	155	165	175	185	195	205	215	225	236	
429		246	256	266	276	286	296	306	317	327	337	
430		347	357	367	377	387	397	407	417	428	438	
431		448	458	468	478	488	498	508	518	528	538	
432		548	558	568	579	589	599	609	619	629	639	
433		649	659	669	679	689	699	709	719	729	739	
434		749	759	769	779	789	799	809	819	829	839	
435		849	859	869	879	889	899	909	919	929	939	
436		949	959	969	979	988	998	*008	*018	*028	*038	
437	64	048	058	068	078	088	098	108	118	128	137	
438		147	157	167	177	187	197	207	217	227	237	
439		246	256	266	276	286	296	306	316	326	335	
440		345	355	365	375	385	395	404	414	424	434	
441		444	454	464	473	483	493	503	513	523	532	
442		542	552	562	572	582	591	601	611	621	631	
443		640	650	660	670	680	689	699	709	719	729	
444		738	748	758	768	777	787	797	807	816	826	
445		836	846	856	865	875	885	895	904	914	924	
446		933	943	953	963	972	982	992	*002	*011	*021	
447	65	031	040	050	060	070	079	089	099	108	118	
448		128	137	147	157	167	176	186	196	205	215	
449		225	234	244	254	263	273	283	292	302	312	
450		321	331	341	350	360	369	379	389	398	408	
N.		0	1	2	3	4	5	6	7	8	9	Proportional parts

Proportional parts:

	11
1	1.1
2	2.2
3	3.3
4	4.4
5	5.5
6	6.6
7	7.7
8	8.8
9	9.9

	10
1	1.0
2	2.0
3	3.0
4	4.0
5	5.0
6	6.0
7	7.0
8	8.0
9	9.0

	9
1	0.9
2	1.8
3	2.7
4	3.6
5	4.5
6	5.4
7	6.3
8	7.2
9	8.1

.60 206 — .65 408

Table I (Cont'd)

COMMON LOGARITHMS OF NUMBERS
450 — 500

N.		0	1	2	3	4	5	6	7	8	9
450	65	321	331	341	350	360	369	379	389	398	408
451		418	427	437	447	456	466	475	485	495	504
452		514	523	533	543	552	562	571	581	591	600
453		610	619	629	639	648	658	667	677	686	696
454		706	715	725	734	744	753	763	772	782	792
455		801	811	820	830	839	849	858	868	877	887
456		896	906	916	925	935	944	954	963	973	982
457		992	*001	*011	*020	*030	*039	*049	*058	*068	*077
458	66	087	096	106	115	124	134	143	153	162	172
459		181	191	200	210	219	229	238	247	257	266
460		276	285	295	304	314	323	332	342	351	361
461		370	380	389	398	408	417	427	436	445	455
462		464	474	483	492	502	511	521	530	539	549
463		558	567	577	586	596	605	614	624	633	642
464		652	661	671	680	689	699	708	717	727	736
465		745	755	764	773	783	792	801	811	820	829
466		839	848	857	867	876	885	894	904	913	922
467		932	941	950	960	969	978	987	997	*006	*015
468	67	025	034	043	052	062	071	080	089	099	108
469		117	127	136	145	154	164	173	182	191	201
470		210	219	228	237	247	256	265	274	284	293
471		302	311	321	330	339	348	357	367	376	385
472		394	403	413	422	431	440	449	459	468	477
473		486	495	504	514	523	532	541	550	560	569
474		578	587	596	605	614	624	633	642	651	660
475		669	679	688	697	706	715	724	733	742	752
476		761	770	779	788	797	806	815	825	834	843
477		852	861	870	879	888	897	906	916	925	934
478		943	952	961	970	979	988	997	*006	*015	*024
479	68	034	043	052	061	070	079	088	097	106	115
480		124	133	142	151	160	169	178	187	196	205
481		215	224	233	242	251	260	269	278	287	296
482		305	314	323	332	341	350	359	368	377	386
483		395	404	413	422	431	440	449	458	467	476
484		485	494	502	511	520	529	538	547	556	565
485		574	583	592	601	610	619	728	637	646	655
486		664	673	681	690	699	708	717	726	735	744
487		753	762	771	780	789	797	806	815	824	833
488		842	851	860	869	878	886	895	904	913	922
489		931	940	949	958	966	975	984	993	*002	*011
490	69	020	028	037	046	055	064	073	082	090	099
491		108	117	126	135	144	152	161	170	179	188
492		197	205	214	223	232	241	249	258	267	276
493		285	294	302	311	320	329	338	346	355	364
494		373	381	390	399	408	417	425	434	443	452
495		461	469	478	487	496	504	513	522	531	539
496		548	557	566	574	583	592	601	609	618	627
497		636	644	653	662	671	679	688	697	705	714
498		723	732	740	749	758	767	775	784	793	801
499		810	819	827	836	845	854	862	871	880	888
500		897	906	914	923	932	940	949	958	966	975
N.		0	1	2	3	4	5	6	7	8	9

Proportional parts

	10
1	1.0
2	2.0
3	3.0
4	4.0
5	5.0
6	6.0
7	7.0
8	8.0
9	9.0

	9
1	0.9
2	1.8
3	2.7
4	3.6
5	4.5
6	5.4
7	6.3
8	7.2
9	8.1

	8
1	0.8
2	1.6
3	2.4
4	3.2
5	4.0
6	4.8
7	5.6
8	6.4
9	7.2

.65 321 — .69 975

Table I (Cont'd)

COMMON LOGARITHMS OF NUMBERS

500 — 550

N.		0	1	2	3	4	5	6	7	8	9	Proportional parts
500	69	897	906	914	923	932	940	949	958	966	975	
501		984	992	*001	*010	*018	*027	*036	*044	*053	*062	
502	70	070	079	088	096	105	114	122	131	140	148	
503		157	165	174	183	191	200	209	217	226	234	
504		243	252	260	269	278	286	295	303	312	321	
505		329	338	346	355	364	372	381	389	398	406	
506		415	424	432	441	449	458	467	475	484	492	
507		501	509	518	526	535	544	552	561	569	578	
508		586	595	603	612	621	629	638	646	655	663	
509		672	680	689	697	706	714	723	731	740	749	
510		757	766	774	783	791	800	808	817	825	834	
511		842	851	859	868	876	885	893	902	910	919	
512		927	935	944	952	961	969	978	986	995	*003	
513	71	012	020	029	037	046	054	063	071	079	088	
514		096	105	113	122	130	139	147	155	164	172	
515		181	189	198	206	214	223	231	240	248	257	
516		265	273	282	290	299	307	315	324	332	341	
517		349	357	366	374	383	391	399	408	416	425	
518		433	441	450	458	466	475	483	492	500	508	
519		517	525	533	542	550	559	567	575	584	592	
520		600	609	.617	625	634	642	650	659	667	675	
521		684	692	700	709	717	725	734	742	750	759	
522		767	775	784	792	800	809	817	825	834	842	
523		850	858	867	875	883	892	900	908	917	925	
524		933	941	950	958	966	975	983	991	999	*008	
525	72	016	024	032	041	049	057	066	074	082	090	
526		099	107	115	123	132	140	148	156	165	173	
527		181	189	198	206	214	222	230	239	247	255	
528		263	272	280	288	296	304	313	321	329	337	
529		346	354	362	370	378	387	395	403	411	419	
530		428	436	444	452	460	469	477	485	493	501	
531		509	518	526	534	542	550	558	567	575	583	
532		591	599	607	616	624	632	640	648	656	665	
533		673	681	689	697	705	713	722	730	738	746	
534		754	762	770	779	787	795	803	811	819	827	
535		835	843	852	860	868	876	884	892	900	908	
536		916	925	933	941	949	957	965	973	981	989	
537		997	*006	*014	*022	*030	*038	*046	*054	*062	*070	
538	73	078	086	094	102	111	119	127	135	143	151	
539		159	167	175	183	191	199	207	215	223	231	
540		239	247	255	263	272	280	288	296	304	312	
541		320	328	336	344	352	360	368	376	384	392	
542		400	408	416	424	432	440	448	456	464	472	
543		480	488	496	504	512	520	528	536	544	552	
544		560	568	576	584	592	600	608	616	624	632	
545		640	648	656	664	672	679	687	695	703	711	
546		719	727	735	743	751	759	767	775	783	791	
547		799	807	815	823	830	838	846	854	862	870	
548		878	886	894	902	910	918	926	933	941	949	
549		957	965	973	981	989	997	*005	*013	*020	*028	
550	74	036	044	052	060	068	076	084	092	099	107	
N.		0	1	2	3	4	5	6	7	8	9	Proportional parts

Proportional parts:

	9
1	0.9
2	1.8
3	2.7
4	3.6
5	4.5
6	5.4
7	6.3
8	7.2
9	8.1

	8
1	0.8
2	1.6
3	2.4
4	3.2
5	4.0
6	4.8
7	5.6
8	6.4
9	7.2

	7
1	0.7
2	1.4
3	2.1
4	2.8
5	3.5
6	4.2
7	4.9
8	5.6
9	6.3

.69 897 — .74 107

Table I (Cont'd)

COMMON LOGARITHMS OF NUMBERS

550 — 600

N.	0	1	2	3	4	5	6	7	8	9
550	74 036	044	052	060	068	076	084	092	099	107
551	115	123	131	139	147	155	162	170	178	186
552	194	202	210	218	225	233	241	249	257	265
553	273	280	288	296	304	312	320	327	335	343
554	351	359	367	374	382	390	398	406	414	421
555	429	437	445	453	461	468	476	484	492	500
556	507	515	523	531	539	547	554	562	570	578
557	586	593	601	609	617	624	632	640	648	656
558	663	671	679	687	695	702	710	718	726	733
559	741	749	757	764	772	780	788	796	803	811
560	819	827	834	842	850	858	865	873	881	889
561	896	904	912	920	927	935	943	950	958	966
562	974	981	989	997	*005	*012	*020	*028	*035	*043
563	75 051	059	066	074	082	089	097	105	113	120
564	128	136	143	151	159	166	174	182	189	197
565	205	213	220	228	236	243	251	259	266	274
566	282	289	297	305	312	320	328	335	343	351
567	358	366	374	381	389	397	404	412	420	427
568	435	442	450	458	465	473	481	488	496	504
569	511	519	526	534	542	549	557	565	572	580
570	587	595	603	610	618	626	633	641	648	656
571	664	671	679	686	694	702	709	717	724	732
572	740	747	755	762	770	778	785	793	800	808
573	815	823	831	838	846	853	861	868	876	884
574	891	899	906	914	921	929	937	944	952	959
575	967	974	982	989	997	*005	*012	*020	*027	*035
576	76 042	050	057	065	072	080	087	095	103	110
577	118	125	133	140	148	155	163	170	178	185
578	193	200	208	215	223	230	238	245	253	260
579	268	275	283	290	298	305	313	320	328	335
580	343	350	358	365	373	380	388	395	403	410
581	418	425	433	440	448	455	462	470	477	485
582	492	500	507	515	522	530	537	545	552	559
583	567	574	582	589	597	604	612	619	626	634
584	641	649	656	664	671	678	686	693	701	708
585	716	723	730	738	745	753	760	768	775	782
586	790	797	805	812	819	827	834	842	849	856
587	864	871	879	886	893	901	908	916	923	930
588	938	945	953	960	967	975	982	989	997	*004
589	77 012	019	026	034	041	048	056	063	070	078
590	085	093	100	107	115	122	129	137	144	151
591	159	166	173	181	188	195	203	210	217	225
592	232	240	247	254	262	269	276	283	291	298
593	305	313	320	327	335	342	349	357	364	371
594	379	386	393	401	408	415	422	430	437	444
595	452	459	466	474	481	488	495	503	510	517
596	525	532	539	546	554	561	568	576	583	590
597	597	605	612	619	627	634	641	648	656	663
598	670	677	685	692	699	706	714	721	728	735
599	743	750	757	764	772	779	786	793	801	808
600	815	822	830	837	844	851	859	866	873	880
N.	0	1	2	3	4	5	6	7	8	9

Proportional parts

	8
1	0.8
2	1.6
3	2.4
4	3.2
5	4.0
6	4.8
7	5.6
8	6.4
9	7.2

	7
1	0.7
2	1.4
3	2.1
4	2.8
5	3.5
6	4.2
7	4.9
8	5.6
9	6.3

.74 036 — .77 880

Table I (Cont'd)

COMMON LOGARITHMS OF NUMBERS

600 — 650

N.	0	1	2	3	4	5	6	7	8	9
600	77 815	822	830	837	844	851	859	866	873	880
601	887	895	902	909	916	924	931	938	945	952
602	960	967	974	981	988	996	*003	*010	*017	*025
603	78 032	039	046	053	061	068	075	082	089	097
604	104	111	118	125	132	140	147	154	161	168
605	176	183	190	197	204	211	219	226	233	240
606	247	254	262	269	276	283	290	297	305	312
607	319	326	333	340	347	355	362	369	376	383
608	390	398	405	412	419	426	433	440	447	455
609	462	469	476	483	490	497	504	512	519	526
610	533	540	547	554	561	569	576	583	590	597
611	604	611	618	625	633	640	647	654	661	668
612	675	682	689	696	704	711	718	725	732	739
613	746	753	760	767	774	781	789	796	803	810
614	817	824	831	838	845	852	859	866	873	880
615	888	895	902	909	916	923	930	937	944	951
616	958	965	972	979	986	993	*000	*007	*014	*021
617	79 029	036	043	050	057	064	071	078	085	092
618	099	106	113	120	127	134	141	148	155	162
619	169	176	183	190	197	204	211	218	225	232
620	239	246	253	260	267	274	281	288	295	302
621	309	316	323	330	337	344	351	358	365	372
622	379	386	393	400	407	414	421	428	435	442
623	449	456	463	470	477	484	491	498	505	511
624	518	525	532	539	546	553	560	567	574	581
625	588	595	602	609	616	623	630	637	644	650
626	657	664	671	678	685	692	699	706	713	720
627	727	734	741	748	754	761	768	775	782	789
628	796	803	810	817	824	831	837	844	851	858
629	865	872	879	886	893	900	906	913	920	927
630	934	941	948	955	962	969	975	982	989	996
631	80 003	010	017	024	030	037	044	051	058	065
632	072	079	085	092	099	106	113	120	127	134
633	140	147	154	161	168	175	182	188	195	202
634	209	216	223	229	236	243	250	257	264	271
635	277	284	291	298	305	312	318	325	332	339
636	346	353	359	366	373	380	387	393	400	407
637	414	421	428	434	441	448	455	462	468	475
638	482	489	496	502	509	516	523	530	536	543
639	550	557	564	570	577	584	591	598	604	611
640	618	625	632	638	645	652	659	665	672	679
641	686	693	699	706	713	720	726	733	740	747
642	754	760	767	774	781	787	794	801	808	814
643	821	828	835	841	848	855	862	868	875	882
644	889	895	902	909	916	922	929	936	943	949
645	956	963	969	976	983	990	996	*003	*010	*017
646	81 023	030	037	043	050	057	064	070	077	084
647	090	097	104	111	117	124	131	137	144	151
648	158	164	171	178	184	191	198	204	211	218
649	224	231	238	245	251	258	265	271	278	285
650	291	298	305	311	318	325	331	338	345	351
N.	0	1	2	3	4	5	6	7	8	9

Proportional parts

	8		7		6
1	0.8	1	0.7	1	0.6
2	1.6	2	1.4	2	1.2
3	2.4	3	2.1	3	1.8
4	3.2	4	2.8	4	2.4
5	4.0	5	3.5	5	3.0
6	4.8	6	4.2	6	3.6
7	5.6	7	4.9	7	4.2
8	6.4	8	5.6	8	4.8
9	7.2	9	6.3	9	5.4

.77 815 — .81 351

Table I (Cont'd)

COMMON LOGARITHMS OF NUMBERS

650 — 700

N.		0	1	2	3	4	5	6	7	8	9	Proportional parts
650	81	291	298	305	311	318	325	331	338	345	351	
651		358	365	371	378	385	391	398	405	411	418	
652		425	431	438	445	451	458	465	471	478	485	
653		491	498	505	511	518	525	531	538	544	551	
654		558	564	571	578	584	591	598	604	611	617	
655		624	631	637	644	651	657	664	671	677	684	
656		690	697	704	710	717	723	730	737	743	750	
657		757	763	770	776	783	790	796	803	809	816	
658		823	829	836	842	849	856	862	869	875	882	
659		889	895	902	908	915	921	928	935	941	948	
660		954	961	968	974	981	987	994	*000	*007	*014	7
661	82	020	027	033	040	046	053	060	066	073	079	1 0.7
662		086	092	099	105	112	119	125	132	138	145	2 1.4
663		151	158	164	171	178	184	191	197	204	210	3 2.1
664		217	223	230	236	243	249	256	263	269	276	4 2.8
												5 3.5
665		282	289	295	302	308	315	321	328	334	341	6 4.2
666		347	354	360	367	373	380	387	393	400	406	7 4.9
667		413	419	426	432	439	445	452	458	465	471	8 5.6
668		478	484	491	497	504	510	517	523	530	536	9 6.3
669		543	549	556	562	569	575	582	588	595	601	
670		607	614	620	627	633	640	646	653	659	666	
671		672	679	685	692	698	705	711	718	724	730	
672		737	743	750	756	763	769	776	782	789	795	
673		802	808	814	821	827	834	840	847	853	860	
674		866	872	879	885	892	898	905	911	918	924	
675		930	937	943	950	956	963	969	975	982	988	
676		995	*001	*008	*014	*020	*027	*033	*040	*046	*052	
677	83	059	065	072	078	085	091	097	104	110	117	
678		123	129	136	142	149	155	161	168	174	181	
679		187	193	200	206	213	219	225	232	238	245	
680		251	257	264	270	276	283	289	296	302	308	6
681		315	321	327	334	340	347	353	359	366	372	1 0.6
682		378	385	391	398	404	410	417	423	429	436	2 1.2
683		442	448	455	461	467	474	480	487	493	499	3 1.8
684		506	512	518	525	531	537	544	550	556	563	4 2.4
												5 3.0
685		569	575	582	588	594	601	607	613	620	626	6 3.6
686		632	639	645	651	658	664	670	677	683	689	7 4.2
687		696	702	708	715	721	727	734	740	746	753	8 4.8
688		759	765	771	778	784	790	797	803	809	816	9 5.4
689		822	828	835	841	847	853	860	866	872	879	
690		885	891	897	904	910	916	923	929	935	942	
691		948	954	960	967	973	979	985	992	998	*004	
692	84	011	017	023	029	036	042	048	055	061	067	
693		073	080	086	092	098	105	111	117	123	130	
694		136	142	148	155	161	167	173	180	186	192	
695		198	205	211	217	223	230	236	242	248	255	
696		261	267	273	280	286	292	298	305	311	317	
697		323	330	336	342	348	354	361	367	373	379	
698		386	392	398	404	410	417	423	429	435	442	
699		448	454	460	466	473	479	485	491	497	504	
700		510	516	522	528	535	541	547	553	559	566	
N.		0	1	2	3	4	5	6	7	8	9	Proportional parts

.81 291 — .84 566

Table I (Cont'd)

COMMON LOGARITHMS OF NUMBERS

700 — 750

N.		0	1	2	3	4	5	6	7	8	9	Proportional parts
700	84	510	516	522	528	535	541	547	553	559	566	
701		572	578	584	590	597	603	609	615	621	628	
702		634	640	646	652	658	665	671	677	683	689	
703		696	702	708	714	720	726	733	739	745	751	
704		757	763	770	776	782	788	794	800	807	813	
705		819	825	831	837	844	850	856	862	868	874	
706		880	887	893	899	905	911	917	924	930	936	
707		942	948	954	960	967	973	979	985	991	997	7
708	85	003	009	016	022	028	034	040	046	052	058	
709		065	071	077	083	089	095	101	107	114	120	1 0.7
710		126	132	138	144	150	156	163	169	175	181	2 1.4
711		187	193	199	205	211	217	224	230	236	242	3 2.1
712		248	254	260	266	272	278	285	291	297	303	4 2.8
713		309	315	321	327	333	339	345	352	358	364	5 3.5
714		370	376	382	388	394	400	406	412	418	425	6 4.2
715		431	437	443	449	455	461	467	473	479	485	7 4.9
716		491	497	503	509	516	522	528	534	540	546	8 5.6
717		552	558	564	570	576	582	588	594	600	606	9 6.3
718		612	618	625	631	637	643	649	655	661	667	
719		673	679	685	691	697	703	709	715	721	727	
720		733	739	745	751	757	763	769	775	781	788	
721		794	800	806	812	818	824	830	836	842	848	
722		854	860	866	872	878	884	890	896	902	908	6
723		914	920	926	932	938	944	950	956	962	968	
724		974	980	986	992	998	*004	*010	*016	*022	*028	1 0.6
725	86	034	040	046	052	058	064	070	076	082	088	2 1.2
726		094	100	106	112	118	124	130	136	141	147	3 1.8
727		153	159	165	171	177	183	189	195	201	207	4 2.4
728		213	219	225	231	237	243	249	255	261	267	5 3.0
729		273	279	285	291	297	303	308	314	320	326	6 3.6
730		332	338	344	350	356	362	368	374	380	386	7 4.2
731		392	398	404	410	415	421	427	433	439	445	8 4.8
732		451	457	463	469	475	481	487	493	499	504	9 5.4
733		510	516	522	528	534	540	546	552	558	564	
734		570	576	581	587	593	599	605	611	617	623	
735		629	635	641	646	652	658	664	670	676	682	
736		688	694	700	705	711	717	723	729	735	741	
737		747	753	759	764	770	776	782	788	794	800	5
738		806	812	817	823	829	835	841	847	853	859	
739		864	870	876	882	888	894	900	906	911	917	1 0.5
740		923	929	935	941	947	953	958	964	970	976	2 1.0
741		982	988	994	999	*005	*011	*017	*023	*029	*035	3 1.5
742	87	040	046	052	058	064	070	075	081	087	093	4 2.0
743		099	105	111	116	122	128	134	140	146	151	5 2.5
744		157	163	169	175	181	186	192	198	204	210	6 3.0
745		216	221	227	233	239	245	251	256	262	268	7 3.5
746		274	280	286	291	297	303	309	315	320	326	8 4.0
747		332	338	344	349	355	361	367	373	379	384	9 4.5
748		390	396	402	408	413	419	425	431	437	442	
749		448	454	460	466	471	477	483	489	495	500	
750		506	512	518	523	529	535	541	547	552	558	
N.		0	1	2	3	4	5	6	7	8	9	Proportional parts

.84 510 — .87 558

Table I (Cont'd)

COMMON LOGARITHMS OF NUMBERS

750 — 800

N.		0	1	2	3	4	5	6	7	8	9	Proportional parts
750	87	506	512	518	523	529	535	541	547	552	558	
751		564	570	576	581	587	593	599	604	610	616	
752		622	628	633	639	645	651	656	662	668	674	
753		679	685	691	697	703	708	714	720	726	731	
754		737	743	749	754	760	766	772	777	783	789	
755		795	800	806	812	818	823	829	835	841	846	
756		852	858	864	869	875	881	887	892	898	904	
757		910	915	921	927	933	938	944	950	955	961	
758		967	973	978	984	990	996	*001	*007	*013	*018	
759	88	024	030	036	041	047	053	058	064	070	076	
760		081	087	093	098	104	110	116	121	127	133	**6**
761		138	144	150	156	161	167	173	178	184	190	1 0.6
762		195	201	207	213	218	224	230	235	241	247	2 1.2
763		252	258	264	270	275	281	287	292	298	304	3 1.8
764		309	315	321	326	332	338	343	349	355	360	4 2.4
765		366	372	377	383	389	395	400	406	412	417	5 3.0 / 6 3.6
766		423	429	434	440	446	451	457	463	468	474	7 4.2
767		480	485	491	497	502	508	513	519	525	530	8 4.8
768		536	542	547	553	559	564	570	576	581	587	9 5.4
769		593	598	604	610	615	621	627	632	638	643	
770		649	655	660	666	672	677	683	689	694	700	
771		705	711	717	722	728	734	739	745	750	756	
772		762	767	773	779	784	790	795	801	807	812	
773		818	824	829	835	840	846	852	857	863	868	
774		874	880	885	891	897	902	908	913	919	925	
775		930	936	941	947	953	958	964	969	975	981	
776		986	992	997	*003	*009	*014	*020	*025	*031	*037	
777	89	042	048	053	059	064	070	076	081	087	092	
778		098	104	109	115	120	126	131	137	143	148	
779		154	159	165	170	176	182	187	193	198	204	
780		209	215	221	226	232	237	243	248	254	260	
781		265	271	276	282	287	293	298	304	310	315	**5**
782		321	326	332	337	343	348	354	360	365	371	1 0.5
783		376	382	387	393	398	404	409	415	421	426	2 1.0
784		432	437	443	448	454	459	465	470	476	481	3 1.5 / 4 2.0
785		487	492	498	504	509	515	520	526	531	537	5 2.5 / 6 3.0
786		542	548	553	559	564	570	575	581	586	592	7 3.5
787		597	603	609	614	620	625	631	636	642	647	8 4.0
788		653	658	664	669	675	680	686	691	697	702	9 4.5
789		708	713	719	724	730	735	741	746	752	757	
790		763	768	774	779	785	790	796	801	807	812	
791		818	823	829	834	840	845	851	856	862	867	
792		873	878	883	889	894	900	905	911	916	922	
793		927	933	938	944	949	955	960	966	971	977	
794		982	988	993	998	*004	*009	*015	*020	*026	*031	
795	90	037	042	048	053	059	064	069	075	080	086	
796		091	097	102	108	113	119	124	129	135	140	
797		146	151	157	162	168	173	179	184	189	195	
798		200	206	211	217	222	227	233	238	244	249	
799		255	260	266	271	276	282	287	293	298	304	
800		309	314	320	325	331	336	342	347	352	358	
N.		0	1	2	3	4	5	6	7	8	9	Proportional parts

.87 506 — .90 358

Table I (Cont'd)

COMMON LOGARITHMS OF NUMBERS

800 — 850

N.		0	1	2	3	4	5	6	7	8	9
800	90	309	314	320	325	331	336	342	347	352	358
801		363	369	374	380	385	390	396	401	407	412
802		417	423	428	434	439	445	450	455	461	466
803		472	477	482	488	493	499	504	509	515	520
804		526	531	536	542	547	553	558	563	569	574
805		580	585	590	596	601	607	612	617	623	628
806		634	639	644	650	655	660	666	671	677	682
807		687	693	698	703	709	714	720	725	730	736
808		741	747	752	757	763	768	773	779	784	789
809		795	800	806	811	816	822	827	832	838	843
810		849	854	859	865	870	875	881	886	891	897
811		902	907	913	918	924	929	934	940	945	950
812		956	961	966	972	977	982	988	993	998	*004
813	91	009	014	020	025	030	036	041	046	052	057
814		062	068	073	078	084	089	094	100	105	110
815		116	121	126	132	137	142	148	153	158	164
816		169	174	180	185	190	196	201	206	212	217
817		222	228	233	238	243	249	254	259	265	270
818		275	281	286	291	297	302	307	312	318	323
819		328	334	339	344	350	355	360	365	371	376
820		381	387	392	397	403	408	413	418	424	429
821		434	440	445	450	455	461	466	471	477	482
822		487	492	498	503	508	514	519	524	529	535
823		540	545	551	556	561	566	572	577	582	587
824		593	598	603	609	614	619	624	630	635	640
825		645	651	656	661	666	672	677	682	687	693
826		698	703	709	714	719	724	730	735	740	745
827		751	756	761	766	772	777	782	787	793	798
828		803	808	814	819	824	829	834	840	845	850
829		855	861	866	871	876	882	887	892	897	903
830		908	913	918	924	929	934	939	944	950	955
831		960	965	971	976	981	986	991	997	*002	*007
832	92	012	018	023	028	033	038	044	049	054	059
833		065	070	075	080	085	091	096	101	106	111
834		117	122	127	132	137	143	148	153	158	163
835		169	174	179	184	189	195	200	205	210	215
836		221	226	231	236	241	247	252	257	262	267
837		273	278	283	288	293	298	304	309	314	319
838		324	330	335	340	345	350	355	361	366	371
839		376	381	387	392	397	402	407	412	418	423
840		428	433	438	443	449	454	459	464	469	474
841		480	485	490	495	500	505	511	516	521	526
842		531	536	542	547	552	557	562	567	572	578
843		583	588	593	598	603	609	614	619	624	629
844		634	639	645	650	655	660	665	670	675	681
845		686	691	696	701	706	711	716	722	727	732
846		737	742	747	752	758	763	768	773	778	783
847		788	793	799	804	809	814	819	824	829	834
848		840	845	850	855	860	865	870	875	881	886
849		891	896	901	906	911	916	921	927	932	937
850		942	947	952	957	962	967	973	978	983	988
N.		0	1	2	3	4	5	6	7	8	9

Proportional parts

	6
1	0.6
2	1.2
3	1.8
4	2.4
5	3.0
6	3.6
7	4.2
8	4.8
9	5.4

	5
1	0.5
2	1.0
3	1.5
4	2.0
5	2.5
6	3.0
7	3.5
8	4.0
9	4.5

.90 309 — .92 988

Table I (Cont'd)

COMMON LOGARITHMS OF NUMBERS

850 — 900

N.		0	1	2	3	4	5	6	7	8	9	Proportional parts
850	92	942	947	952	957	962	967	973	978	983	988	
851		993	998	*003	*008	*013	*018	*024	*029	*034	*039	
852	93	044	049	054	059	064	069	075	080	085	090	
853		095	100	105	110	115	120	125	131	136	141	
854		146	151	156	161	166	171	176	181	186	192	
855		197	202	207	212	217	222	227	232	237	242	
856		247	252	258	263	268	273	278	283	288	293	
857		298	303	308	313	318	323	328	334	339	344	**6**
858		349	354	359	364	369	374	379	384	389	394	1 0.6
859		399	404	409	414	420	425	430	435	440	445	2 1.2
860		450	455	460	465	470	475	480	485	490	495	3 1.8
861		500	505	510	515	520	526	531	536	541	546	4 2.4
862		551	556	561	566	571	576	581	586	591	596	5 3.0
863		601	606	611	616	621	626	631	636	641	646	6 3.6
864		651	656	661	666	671	676	682	687	692	697	7 4.2
865		702	707	712	717	722	727	732	737	742	747	8 4.8
866		752	757	762	767	772	777	782	787	792	797	9 5.4
867		802	807	812	817	822	827	832	837	842	847	
868		852	857	862	867	872	877	882	887	892	897	
869		902	907	912	917	922	927	932	937	942	947	
870		952	957	962	967	972	977	982	987	992	997	
871	94	002	007	012	017	022	027	032	037	042	047	**5**
872		052	057	062	067	072	077	082	086	091	096	1 0.5
873		101	106	111	116	121	126	131	136	141	146	2 1.0
874		151	156	161	166	171	176	181	186	191	196	3 1.5
875		201	206	211	216	221	226	231	236	240	245	4 2.0
876		250	255	260	265	270	275	280	285	290	295	5 2.5
877		300	305	310	315	320	325	330	335	340	345	6 3.0
878		349	354	359	364	369	374	379	384	389	394	7 3.5
879		399	404	409	414	419	424	429	433	438	443	8 4.0
880		448	453	458	463	468	473	478	483	488	493	9 4.5
881		498	503	507	512	517	522	527	532	537	542	
882		547	552	557	562	567	571	576	581	586	591	
883		596	601	606	611	616	621	626	630	635	640	
884		645	650	655	660	665	670	675	680	685	689	
885		694	699	704	709	714	719	724	729	734	738	
886		743	748	753	758	763	768	773	778	783	787	**4**
887		792	797	802	807	812	817	822	827	832	836	1 0.4
888		841	846	851	856	861	866	871	876	880	885	2 0.8
889		890	895	900	905	910	915	919	924	929	934	3 1.2
890		939	944	949	954	959	963	968	973	978	983	4 1.6
891		988	993	998	*002	*007	*012	*017	*022	*027	*032	5 2.0
892	95	036	041	046	051	056	061	066	071	075	080	6 2.4
893		085	090	095	100	105	109	114	119	124	129	7 2.8
894		134	139	143	148	153	158	163	168	173	177	8 3.2
895		182	187	192	197	202	207	211	216	221	226	9 3.6
896		231	236	240	245	250	255	260	265	270	274	
897		279	284	289	294	299	303	308	313	318	323	
898		328	332	337	342	347	352	357	361	366	371	
899		376	381	386	390	395	400	405	410	415	419	
900		424	429	434	439	444	448	453	458	463	468	
N.		0	1	2	3	4	5	6	7	8	9	Proportional parts

.92 942 — .95 468

Table I (Cont'd)

COMMON LOGARITHMS OF NUMBERS

900 — 950

N.		0	1	2	3	4	5	6	7	8	9
900	95	424	429	434	439	444	448	453	458	463	468
901		472	477	482	487	492	497	501	506	511	516
902		521	525	530	535	540	545	550	554	559	564
903		569	574	578	583	588	593	598	602	607	612
904		617	622	626	631	636	641	646	650	655	660
905		665	670	674	679	684	689	694	698	703	708
906		713	718	722	727	732	737	742	746	751	756
907		761	766	770	775	780	785	789	794	799	804
908		809	813	818	823	828	832	837	842	847	852
909		856	861	866	871	875	880	885	890	895	899
910		904	909	914	918	923	928	933	938	942	947
911		952	957	961	966	971	976	980	985	990	995
912		999	*004	*009	*014	*019	*023	*028	*033	*038	*042
913	96	047	052	057	061	066	071	076	080	085	090
914		095	099	104	109	114	118	123	128	133	137
915		142	147	152	156	161	166	171	175	180	185
916		190	194	199	204	209	213	218	223	227	232
917		237	242	246	251	256	261	265	270	275	280
918		284	289	294	298	303	308	313	317	322	327
919		332	336	341	346	350	355	360	365	369	374
920		379	384	388	393	398	402	407	412	417	421
921		426	431	435	440	445	450	454	459	464	468
922		473	478	483	487	492	497	501	506	511	515
923		520	525	530	534	539	544	548	553	558	562
924		567	572	577	581	586	591	595	600	605	609
925		614	619	624	628	633	638	642	647	652	656
926		661	666	670	675	680	685	689	694	699	703
927		708	713	717	722	727	731	736	741	745	750
928		755	759	764	769	774	778	783	788	792	797
929		802	806	811	816	820	825	830	834	839	844
930		848	853	858	862	867	872	876	881	886	890
931		895	900	904	909	914	918	923	928	932	937
932		942	946	951	956	960	965	970	974	979	984
933		988	993	997	*002	*007	*011	*016	*021	*025	*030
934	97	035	039	044	049	053	058	063	067	072	077
935		081	086	090	095	100	104	109	114	118	123
936		128	132	137	142	146	151	155	160	165	169
937		174	179	183	188	192	197	202	206	211	216
938		220	225	230	234	239	243	248	253	257	262
939		267	271	276	280	285	290	294	299	304	308
940		313	317	322	327	331	336	340	345	350	354
941		359	364	368	373	377	382	387	391	396	400
942		405	410	414	419	424	428	433	437	442	447
943		451	456	460	465	470	474	479	483	488	493
944		497	502	506	511	516	520	525	529	534	539
945		543	548	552	557	562	566	571	575	580	585
946		589	594	598	603	607	612	617	621	626	630
947		635	640	644	649	653	658	663	667	672	676
948		681	685	690	695	699	704	708	713	717	722
949		727	731	736	740	745	749	754	759	763	768
950		772	777	782	786	791	795	800	804	809	813
N.		0	1	2	3	4	5	6	7	8	9

Proportional parts

	5
1	0.5
2	1.0
3	1.5
4	2.0
5	2.5
6	3.0
7	3.5
8	4.0
9	4.5

	4
1	0.4
2	0.8
3	1.2
4	1.6
5	2.0
6	2.4
7	2.8
8	3.2
9	3.6

.95 424 — .97 813

Table I (Cont'd)

COMMON LOGARITHMS OF NUMBERS

950 — 1000

N.		0	1	2	3	4	5	6	7	8	9	Proportional parts
950	97	772	777	782	786	791	795	800	804	809	813	
951		818	823	827	832	836	841	845	850	855	859	
952		864	868	873	877	882	886	891	896	900	905	
953		909	914	918	923	928	932	937	941	946	950	
954		955	959	964	968	973	978	982	987	991	996	
955	98	000	005	009	014	019	023	028	032	037	041	
956		046	050	055	059	064	068	073	078	082	087	
957		091	096	100	105	109	114	118	123	127	132	
958		137	141	146	150	155	159	164	168	173	177	
959		182	186	191	195	200	204	209	214	218	223	
960		227	232	236	241	245	250	254	259	263	268	
961		272	277	281	286	290	295	299	304	308	313	
962		318	322	327	331	336	340	345	349	354	358	
963		363	367	372	376	381	385	390	394	399	403	
964		408	412	417	421	426	430	435	439	444	448	
965		453	457	462	466	471	475	480	484	489	493	
966		498	502	507	511	516	520	525	529	534	538	
967		543	547	552	556	561	565	570	574	579	583	
968		588	592	597	601	605	610	614	619	623	628	
969		632	637	641	646	650	655	659	664	668	673	
970		677	682	686	691	695	700	704	709	713	717	
971		722	726	731	735	740	744	749	753	758	762	
972		767	771	776	780	784	789	793	798	802	807	
973		811	816	820	825	829	834	838	843	847	851	
974		856	860	865	869	874	878	883	887	892	896	
975		900	905	909	914	918	923	927	932	936	941	
976		945	949	954	958	963	967	972	976	981	985	
977		989	994	998	*003	*007	*012	*016	*021	*025	*029	
978	99	034	038	043	047	052	056	061	065	069	074	
979		078	083	087	092	096	100	105	109	114	118	
980		123	127	131	136	140	145	149	154	158	162	
981		167	171	176	180	185	189	193	198	202	207	
982		211	216	220	224	229	233	238	242	247	251	
983		255	260	264	269	273	277	282	286	291	295	
984		300	304	308	313	317	322	326	330	335	339	
985		344	348	352	357	361	366	370	374	379	383	
986		388	392	396	401	405	410	414	419	423	427	
987		432	436	441	445	449	454	458	463	467	471	
988		476	480	484	489	493	498	502	506	511	515	
989		520	524	528	533	537	542	546	550	555	559	
990		564	568	572	577	581	585	590	594	599	603	
991		607	612	616	621	625	629	634	638	642	647	
992		651	656	660	664	669	673	677	682	686	691	
993		695	699	704	708	712	717	721	726	730	734	
994		739	743	747	752	756	760	765	769	774	778	
995		782	787	791	795	800	804	808	813	817	822	
996		826	830	835	839	843	848	852	856	861	865	
997		870	874	878	883	887	891	896	900	904	909	
998		913	917	922	926	930	935	939	944	948	952	
999		957	961	965	970	974	978	983	987	991	996	
1000	00	000	004	009	013	017	022	026	030	035	039	
N.		0	1	2	3	4	5	6	7	8	9	Proportional parts

Proportional parts:

	5
1	0.5
2	1.0
3	1.5
4	2.0
5	2.5
6	3.0
7	3.5
8	4.0
9	4.5

	4
1	0.4
2	0.8
3	1.2
4	1.6
5	2.0
6	2.4
7	2.8
8	3.2
9	3.6

.97 772 — .99 996

Table I (Cont'd)

COMMON LOGARITHMS OF NUMBERS

1000 — 1050

N.		0	1	2	3	4	5	6	7	8	9	d.
1000	000	0000	0434	0869	1303	1737	2171	2605	3039	3473	3907	434
1001		4341	4775	5208	5642	6076	6510	6943	7377	7810	8244	434
1002		8677	9111	9544	9977	*0411	*0844	*1277	*1710	*2143	*2576	433
1003	001	3009	3442	3875	4308	4741	5174	5607	6039	6472	6905	433
1004		7337	7770	8202	8635	9067	9499	9932	*0364	*0796	*1228	432
1005	002	1661	2093	2525	2957	3389	3821	4253	4685	5116	5548	432
1006		5980	6411	6843	7275	7706	8138	8569	9001	9432	9863	431
1007	003	0295	0726	1157	1588	2019	2451	2882	3313	3744	4174	431
1008		4605	5036	5467	5898	6328	6759	7190	7620	8051	8481	431
1009		8912	9342	9772	*0203	*0633	*1063	*1493	*1924	*2354	*2784	430
1010	004	3214	3644	4074	4504	4933	5363	5793	6223	6652	7082	430
1011		7512	7941	8371	8800	9229	9659	*0088	*0517	*0947	*1376	429
1012	005	1805	2234	2663	3092	3521	3950	4379	4808	5237	5666	429
1013		6094	6523	6952	7380	7809	8238	8666	9094	9523	9951	429
1014	006	0380	0808	1236	1664	2092	2521	2949	3377	3805	4233	428
1015		4660	5088	5516	5944	6372	6799	7227	7655	8082	8510	428
1016		8937	9365	9792	*0219	*0647	*1074	*1501	*1928	*2355	*2782	427
1017	007	3210	3637	4064	4490	4917	5344	5771	6198	6624	7051	427
1018		7478	7904	8331	8757	9184	9610	*0037	*0463	*0889	*1316	426
1019	008	1742	2168	2594	3020	3446	3872	4298	4724	5150	5576	426
1020		6002	6427	6853	7279	7704	8130	8556	8981	9407	9832	426
1021	009	0257	0683	1108	1533	1959	2384	2809	3234	3659	4084	425
1022		4509	4934	5359	5784	6208	6633	7058	7483	7907	8332	425
1023		8756	9181	9605	*0030	*0454	*0878	*1303	*1727	*2151	*2575	424
1024	010	3000	3424	3848	4272	4696	5120	5544	5967	6391	6815	424
1025		7239	7662	8086	8510	8933	9357	9780	*0204	*0627	*1050	424
1026	011	1474	1897	2320	2743	3166	3590	4013	4436	4859	5282	423
1027		5704	6127	6550	6973	7396	7818	8241	8664	9086	9509	423
1028		9931	*0354	*0776	*1198	*1621	*2043	*2465	*2887	*3310	*3732	422
1029	012	4154	4576	4998	5420	5842	6264	6685	7107	7529	7951	422
1030		8372	8794	9215	9637	*0059	*0480	*0901	*1323	*1744	*2165	422
1031	013	2587	3008	3429	3850	4271	4692	5113	5534	5955	6376	421
1032		6797	7218	7639	8059	8480	8901	9321	9742	*0162	*0583	421
1033	014	1003	1424	1844	2264	2685	3105	3525	3945	4365	4785	420
1034		5205	5625	6045	6465	6885	7305	7725	8144	8564	8984	420
1035		9403	9823	*0243	*0662	*1082	*1501	*1920	*2340	*2759	*3178	420
1036	015	3598	4017	4436	4855	5274	5693	6112	6531	6950	7369	419
1037		7788	8206	8625	9044	9462	9881	*0300	*0718	*1137	*1555	419
1038	016	1974	2392	2810	3229	3647	4065	4483	4901	5319	5737	418
1039		6155	6573	6991	7409	7827	8245	8663	9080	9498	9916	418
1040	017	0333	0751	1168	1586	2003	2421	2838	3256	3673	4090	417
1041		4507	4924	5342	5759	6176	6593	7010	7427	7844	8260	417
1042		8677	9094	9511	9927	*0344	*0761	*1177	*1594	*2010	*2427	417
1043	018	2843	3259	3676	4092	4508	4925	5341	5757	6173	6589	416
1044		7005	7421	7837	8253	8669	9084	9500	9916	*0332	*0747	416
1045	019	1163	1578	1994	2410	2825	3240	3656	4071	4486	4902	415
1046		5317	5732	6147	6562	6977	7392	7807	8222	8637	9052	415
1047		9467	9882	*0296	*0711	*1126	*1540	*1955	*2369	*2784	*3198	415
1048	020	3613	4027	4442	4856	5270	5684	6099	6513	6927	7341	414
1049		7755	8169	8583	8997	9411	9824	*0238	*0652	*1066	*1479	414
1050	021	1893	2307	2720	3134	3547	3961	4374	4787	5201	5614	413
N.		0	1	2	3	4	5	6	7	8	9	d.

.000 0000 — .021 5614

Table I (Cont'd)

COMMON LOGARITHMS OF NUMBERS

1050 — 1100

N.		0	1	2	3	4	5	6	7	8	9	d.
1050	021	1893	2307	2720	3134	3547	3961	4374	4787	5201	5614	413
1051		6027	6440	6854	7267	7680	8093	8506	8919	9332	9745	413
1052	022	0157	0570	0983	1396	1808	2221	2634	3046	3459	3871	413
1053		4284	4696	5109	5521	5933	6345	6758	7170	7582	7994	412
1054		8406	8818	9230	9642	*0054	*0466	*0878	*1289	*1701	*2113	412
1055	023	2525	2936	3348	3759	4171	4582	4994	5405	5817	6228	411
1056		6639	7050	7462	7873	8284	8695	9106	9517	9928	*0339	411
1057	024	0750	1161	1572	1982	2393	2804	3214	3625	4036	4446	411
1058		4857	5267	5678	6088	6498	6909	7319	7729	8139	8549	410
1059		8960	9370	9780	*0190	*0600	*1010	*1419	*1829	*2239	*2649	410
1060	025	3059	3468	3878	4288	4697	5107	5516	5926	6335	6744	410
1061		7154	7563	7972	8382	8791	9200	9609	*0018	*0427	*0836	409
1062	026	1245	1654	2063	2472	2881	3289	3698	4107	4515	4924	409
1063		5333	5741	6150	6558	6967	7375	7783	8192	8600	9008	408
1064		9416	9824	*0233	*0641	*1049	*1457	*1865	*2273	*2680	*3088	408
1065	027	3496	3904	4312	4719	5127	5535	5942	6350	6757	7165	408
1066		7572	7979	8387	8794	9201	9609	*0016	*0423	*0830	*1237	407
1067	028	1644	2051	2458	2865	3272	3679	4086	4492	4899	5306	407
1068		5713	6119	6526	6932	7339	7745	8152	8558	8964	9371	406
1069		9777	*0183	*0590	*0996	*1402	*1808	*2214	*2620	*3026	*3432	406
1070	029	3838	4244	4649	5055	5461	5867	6272	6678	7084	7489	406
1071		7895	8300	8706	9111	9516	9922	*0327	*0732	*1138	*1543	405
1072	030	1948	2353	2758	3163	3568	3973	4378	4783	5188	5592	405
1073		5997	6402	6807	7211	7616	8020	8425	8830	9234	9638	405
1074	031	0043	0447	0851	1256	1660	2064	2468	2872	3277	3681	404
1075		4085	4489	4893	5296	5700	6104	6508	6912	7315	7719	404
1076		8123	8526	8930	9333	9737	*0140	*0544	*0947	*1350	*1754	403
1077	032	2157	2560	2963	3367	3770	4173	4576	4979	5382	5785	403
1078		6188	6590	6993	7396	7799	8201	8604	9007	9409	9812	403
1079	033	0214	0617	1019	1422	1824	2226	2629	3031	3433	3835	402
1080		4238	4640	5042	5444	5846	6248	6650	7052	7453	7855	402
1081		8257	8659	9060	9462	9864	*0265	*0667	*1068	*1470	*1871	402
1082	034	2273	2674	3075	3477	3878	4279	4680	5081	5482	5884	401
1083		6285	6686	7087	7487	7888	8289	8690	9091	9491	9892	401
1084	035	0293	0693	1094	1495	1895	2296	2696	3096	3497	3897	400
1085		4297	4698	5098	5498	5898	6298	6698	7098	7498	7898	400
1086		8298	8698	9098	9498	9898	*0297	*0697	*1097	*1496	*1896	400
1087	036	2295	2695	3094	3494	3893	4293	4692	5091	5491	5890	399
1088		6289	6688	7087	7486	7885	8284	8683	9082	9481	9880	399
1089	037	0279	0678	1076	1475	1874	2272	2671	3070	3468	3867	399
1090		4265	4663	5062	5460	5858	6257	6655	7053	7451	7849	398
1091		8248	8646	9044	9442	9839	*0237	*0635	*1033	*1431	*1829	398
1092	038	2226	2624	3022	3419	3817	4214	4612	5009	5407	5804	398
1093		6202	6599	6996	7393	7791	8188	8585	8982	9379	9776	397
1094	039	0173	0570	0967	1364	1761	2158	2554	2951	3348	3745	397
1095		4141	4538	4934	5331	5727	6124	6520	6917	7313	7709	397
1096		8106	8502	8898	9294	9690	*0086	*0482	*0878	*1274	*1670	396
1097	040	2066	2462	2858	3254	3650	4045	4441	4837	5232	5628	396
1098		6023	6419	6814	7210	7605	8001	8396	8791	9187	9582	395
1099		9977	*0372	*0767	*1162	*1557	*1952	*2347	*2742	*3137	*3532	395
1100	041	3927	4322	4716	5111	5506	5900	6295	6690	7084	7479	395
N.		0	1	2	3	4	5	6	7	8	9	d.

.021 1893 — .041 7479

Table I (Cont'd)

COMMON LOGARITHMS OF NUMBERS

1100 — 1150

N.		0	1	2	3	4	5	6	7	8	9	d.
1100	041	3927	4322	4716	5111	5506	5900	6295	6690	7084	7479	395
1101		7873	8268	8662	9056	9451	9845	*0239	*0633	*1028	*1422	394
1102	042	1816	2210	2604	2998	3392	3786	4180	4574	4968	5361	394
1103		5755	6149	6543	6936	7330	7723	8117	8510	8904	9297	394
1104		9691	*0084	*0477	*0871	*1264	*1657	*2050	*2444	*2837	*3230	393
1105	043	3623	4016	4409	4802	5195	5587	5980	6373	6766	7159	393
1106		7551	7944	8337	8729	9122	9514	9907	*0299	*0692	*1084	393
1107	044	1476	1869	2261	2653	3045	3437	3829	4222	4614	5006	392
1108		5398	5790	6181	6573	6965	7357	7749	8140	8532	8924	392
1109		9315	9707	*0099	*0490	*0882	*1273	*1664	*2056	*2447	*2839	392
1110	045	3230	3621	4012	4403	4795	5186	5577	5968	6359	6750	391
1111		7141	7531	7922	8313	8704	9095	9485	9876	*0267	*0657	391
1112	046	1048	1438	1829	2219	2610	3000	3391	3781	4171	4561	390
1113		4952	5342	5732	6122	6512	6902	7292	7682	8072	8462	390
1114		8852	9242	9632	*0021	*0411	*0801	*1190	*1580	*1970	*2359	390
1115	047	2749	3138	3528	3917	4306	4696	5085	5474	5864	6253	389
1116		6642	7031	7420	7809	8198	8587	8976	9365	9754	*0143	389
1117	048	0532	0921	1309	1698	2087	2475	2864	3253	3641	4030	389
1118		4418	4806	5195	5583	5972	6360	6748	7136	7525	7913	388
1119		8301	8689	9077	9465	9853	*0241	*0629	*1017	*1405	*1792	388
1120	049	2180	2568	2956	3343	3731	4119	4506	4894	5281	5669	388
1121		6056	6444	6831	7218	7606	7993	8380	8767	9154	9541	387
1122		9929	*0316	*0703	*1090	*1477	*1863	*2250	*2637	*3024	*3411	387
1123	050	3798	4184	4571	4958	5344	5731	6117	6504	6890	7277	387
1124		7663	8049	8436	8822	9208	9595	9981	*0367	*0753	*1139	386
1125	051	1525	1911	2297	2683	3069	3455	3841	4227	4612	4998	386
1126		5384	5770	6155	6541	6926	7312	7697	8083	8468	8854	386
1127		9239	9624	*0010	*0395	*0780	*1166	*1551	*1936	*2321	*2706	385
1128	052	3091	3476	3861	4246	4631	5016	5400	5785	6170	6555	385
1129		6939	7324	7709	8093	8478	8862	9247	9631	*0016	*0400	385
1130	053	0784	1169	1553	1937	2321	2706	3090	3474	3858	4242	384
1131		4626	5010	5394	5778	6162	6546	6929	7313	7697	8081	384
1132		8464	8848	9232	9615	9999	*0382	*0766	*1149	*1532	*1916	384
1133	054	2299	2682	3066	3449	3832	4215	4598	4981	5365	5748	383
1134		6131	6514	6896	7279	7662	8045	8428	8811	9193	9576	383
1135		9959	*0341	*0724	*1106	*1489	*1871	*2254	*2636	*3019	*3401	382
1136	055	3783	4166	4548	4930	5312	5694	6077	6459	6841	7223	382
1137		7605	7987	8369	8750	9132	9514	9896	*0278	*0659	*1041	382
1138	056	1423	1804	2186	2567	2949	3330	3712	4093	4475	4856	381
1139		5237	5619	6000	6381	6762	7143	7524	7905	8287	8668	381
1140		9049	9429	9810	*0191	*0572	*0953	*1334	*1714	*2095	*2476	381
1141	057	2856	3237	3618	3998	4379	4759	5140	5520	5900	6281	381
1142		6661	7041	7422	7802	8182	8562	8942	9322	9702	*0082	380
1143	058	0462	0842	1222	1602	1982	2362	2741	3121	3501	3881	380
1144		4260	4640	5019	5399	5778	6158	6537	6917	7296	7676	380
1145		8055	8434	8813	9193	9572	9951	*0330	*0709	*1088	*1467	379
1146	059	1846	2225	2604	2983	3362	3741	4119	4498	4877	5256	379
1147		5634	6013	6391	6770	7148	7527	7905	8284	8662	9041	379
1148		9419	9797	*0175	*0554	*0932	*1310	*1688	*2066	*2444	*2822	378
1149	060	3200	3578	3956	4334	4712	5090	5468	5845	6223	6601	378
1150		6978	7356	7734	8111	8489	8866	9244	9621	9999	*0376	378
N.		0	1	2	3	4	5	6	7	8	9	d.

.041 3927 — .061 0376

Table I (Cont'd)

COMMON LOGARITHMS OF NUMBERS

1150 — 1200

N.		0	1	2	3	4	5	6	7	8	9	d.
1150	060	6978	7356	7734	8111	8489	8866	9244	9621	9999	*0376	378
1151	061	0753	1131	1508	1885	2262	2639	3017	3394	3771	4148	377
1152		4525	4902	5279	5656	6032	6409	6786	7163	7540	7916	377
1153		8293	8670	9046	9423	9799	*0176	*0552	*0929	*1305	*1682	377
1154	062	2058	2434	2811	3187	3563	3939	4316	4692	5068	5444	376
1155		5820	6196	6572	6948	7324	7699	8075	8451	8827	9203	376
1156		9578	9954	*0330	*0705	*1081	*1456	*1832	*2207	*2583	*2958	376
1157	063	3334	3709	4084	4460	4835	5210	5585	5960	6335	6711	375
1158		7086	7461	7836	8211	8585	8960	9335	9710	*0085	*0460	375
1159	064	0834	1209	1584	1958	2333	2708	3082	3457	3831	4205	375
1160		4580	4954	5329	5703	6077	6451	6826	7200	7574	7948	374
1161		8322	8696	9070	9444	9818	*0192	*0566	*0940	*1314	*1688	374
1162	065	2061	2435	2809	3182	3556	3930	4303	4677	5050	5424	374
1163		5797	6171	6544	6917	7291	7664	8037	8410	8784	9157	373
1164		9530	9903	*0276	*0649	*1022	*1395	*1768	*2141	*2514	*2886	373
1165	066	3259	3632	4005	4377	4750	5123	5495	5868	6241	6613	373
1166		6986	7358	7730	8103	8475	8847	9220	9592	9964	*0336	372
1167	067	0709	1081	1453	1825	2197	2569	2941	3313	3685	4057	372
1168		4428	4800	5172	5544	5915	6287	6659	7030	7402	7774	372
1169		8145	8517	8888	9259	9631	*0002	*0374	*0745	*1116	*1487	371
1170	068	1859	2230	2601	2972	3343	3714	4085	4456	4827	5198	371
1171		5569	5940	6311	6681	7052	7423	7794	8164	8535	8906	371
1172		9276	9647	*0017	*0388	*0758	*1129	*1499	*1869	*2240	*2610	370
1173	069	2980	3350	3721	4091	4461	4831	5201	5571	5941	6311	370
1174		6681	7051	7421	7791	8160	8530	8900	9270	9639	*0009	370
1175	070	0379	0748	1118	1487	1857	2226	2596	2965	3335	3704	369
1176		4073	4442	4812	5181	5550	5919	6288	6658	7027	7396	369
1177		7765	8134	8503	8871	9240	9609	9978	*0347	*0715	*1084	369
1178	071	1453	1822	2190	2559	2927	3296	3664	4033	4401	4770	369
1179		5138	5506	5875	6243	6611	6979	7348	7716	8084	8452	368
1180		8820	9188	9556	9924	*0292	*0660	*1028	*1396	*1763	*2131	368
1181	072	2499	2867	3234	3602	3970	4337	4705	5072	5440	5807	368
1182		6175	6542	6910	7277	7644	8011	8379	8746	9113	9480	367
1183		9847	*0215	*0582	*0949	*1316	*1683	*2050	*2416	*2783	*3150	367
1184	073	3517	3884	4251	4617	4984	5351	5717	6084	6450	6817	367
1185		7184	7550	7916	8283	8649	9016	9382	9748	*0114	*0481	366
1186	074	0847	1213	1579	1945	2311	2677	3043	3409	3775	4141	366
1187		4507	4873	5239	5605	5970	6336	6702	7068	7433	7799	366
1188		8164	8530	8895	9261	9626	9992	*0357	*0723	*1088	*1453	365
1189	075	1819	2184	2549	2914	3279	3644	4010	4375	4740	5105	365
1190		5470	5835	6199	6564	6929	7294	7659	8024	8388	8753	365
1191		9118	9482	9847	*0211	*0576	*0940	*1305	*1669	*2034	*2398	364
1192	076	2763	3127	3491	3855	4220	4584	4948	5312	5676	6040	364
1193		6404	6768	7132	7496	7860	8224	8588	8952	9316	9680	364
1194	077	0043	0407	0771	1134	1498	1862	2225	2589	2952	3316	364
1195		3679	4042	4406	4769	5133	5496	5859	6222	6585	6949	363
1196		7312	7675	8038	8401	8764	9127	9490	9853	*0216	*0579	363
1197	078	0942	1304	1667	2030	2393	2755	3118	3480	3843	4206	363
1198		4568	4931	5293	5656	6018	6380	6743	7105	7467	7830	362
1199		8192	8554	8916	9278	9640	*0003	*0365	*0727	*1089	*1451	362
1200	079	1812	2174	2536	2898	3260	3622	3983	4345	4707	5068	362
N.		0	1	2	3	4	5	6	7	8	9	d.

.060 6978 — .079 5068

Table II

AUXILIARY VALUES OF S AND T FOR SMALL ANGLES

ANGLE IN MINUTES	S	ANGLE IN MINUTES	T	ANGLE IN MINUTES	T
0-40	4.68557−10	0-3	4.68557−10	128-130	4.68578−10
41-57	4.68556−10	4-28	4.68558−10	131-133	4.68579−10
58-70	4.68555−10	29-40	4.68559−10	134-136	4.68580−10
71-81	4.68554−10	41-49	4.68560−10	137-139	4.68581−10
82-90	4.68553−10	50-56	4.68561−10	140-142	4.68582−10
91-99	4.68552−10	57-63	4.68562−10	143-145	4.68583−10
100-107	4.68551−10	64-69	4.68563−10	146-148	4.68584−10
108-114	4.68550−10	70-75	4.68564−10	149-151	4.68585−10
115-121	4.68549−10	76-80	4.68565−10	152-153	4.68586−10
122-128	4.68548−10	81-85	4.68566−10	154-156	4.68587−10
129-134	4.68547−10	86-90	4.68567−10	157-158	4.68588−10
135-140	4.68546−10	91-94	4.68568−10	159-161	4.68589−10
141-145	4.68545−10	95-98	4.68569−10	162-163	4.68590−10
146-151	4.68544−10	99-102	4.68570−10	164-166	4.68591−10
152-156	4.68543−10	103-106	4.68571−10	167-168	4.68592−10
157-161	4.68542−10	107-110	4.68572−10	169-171	4.68593−10
162-166	4.68541−10	111-114	4.68573−10	172-173	4.68594−10
167-171	4.68540−10	115-117	4.68574−10	174-175	4.68595−10
172-176	4.68539−10	118-121	4.68575−10	176-178	4.68596−10
177-180	4.68538−10	122-124	4.68576−10	179-180	4.68597−10
		125-127	4.68577−10		

The values of the logarithms S and T are used for accurate interpolation for values of the logarithms of the sine and tangent of angles between $0°$ and $3°$ and of the cosine and cotangent of angles between $87°$ and $90°$, using the following relationships:

To find functions of an angle A,

$$\log \sin A = \log A'' + S \qquad \log \cos A = \log (90° - A)'' + S$$

$$\log \tan A = \log A'' + T \qquad \log \operatorname{ctn} A = \log (90° - A)'' + T$$

To find an angle A,

$$\log A'' = \log \sin A - S \qquad \log (90° - A)'' = \log \cos A - S$$

$$\log A'' = \log \tan A - T \qquad \log (90° - A)'' = \log \operatorname{ctn} A - T$$

In the above equations, A'' and $(90° - A)''$ are the values of the angles expressed in seconds.

Examples: To find $\log \sin 1° 02' 40''$ $(3760'')$:

$$\log \sin 1° 02' 40'' = \log 3760 + S$$

$$= 3.57519 + 4.68555 - 10 = 8.26074 - 10$$

To find A when $\log \tan A = 8.31217 - 10$ (A is between $1° 10'$ and $1° 11'$):

$$\log A'' = 8.31217 - 10 - 4.68564 - 10 = 3.62653$$

$$A = 4232'' = 1° 10' 32''$$

Table III

COMMON LOGARITHMS OF TRIGONOMETRIC FUNCTIONS

To obtain interpolated values of L sin and L tan for angles less than 3°
(or L cos or L ctn of angles greater than 87°) use Table II.

0° (180°)   (359°) **179°**

''	'	L Sin	d	L Tan	c d	L Ctn	L Cos	'
0	0						10.00 000	60
60	1	6.46 373	30103	6.46 373	30103	13.53 627	10.00 000	59
120	2	6.76 476	17609	6.76 476	17609	13.23 524	10.00 000	58
180	3	6.94 085	12494	6.94 085	12494	13.05 915	10.00 000	57
240	4	7.06 579	9691	7.06 579	9691	12.93 421	10.00 000	56
300	5	7.16 270	7918	7.16 270	7918	12.83 730	10.00 000	55
360	6	7.24 188	6694	7.24 188	6694	12.75 812	10.00 000	54
420	7	7.30 882	5800	7.30 882	5800	12.69 118	10.00 000	53
480	8	7.36 682	5115	7.36 682	5115	12.63 318	10.00 000	52
540	9	7.41 797	4576	7.41 797	4576	12.58 203	10.00 000	51
600	10	7.46 373	4139	7.46 373	4139	12.53 627	10.00 000	50
660	11	7.50 512	3779	7.50 512	3779	12.49 488	10.00 000	49
720	12	7.54 291	3476	7.54 291	3476	12.45 709	10.00 000	48
780	13	7.57 767	3218	7.57 767	3219	12.42 233	10.00 000	47
840	14	7.60 985	2997	7.60 986	2996	12.39 014	10.00 000	46
900	15	7.63 982	2802	7.63 982	2803	12.36 018	10.00 000	45
960	16	7.66 784	2633	7.66 785	2633	12.33 215	10.00 000	44
1020	17	7.69 417	2483	7.69 418	2482	12.30 582	9.99 999	43
1080	18	7.71 900	2348	7.71 900	2348	12.28 100	9.99 999	42
1140	19	7.74 248	2227	7.74 248	2228	12.25 752	9.99 999	41
1200	20	7.76 475	2119	7.76 476	2119	12.23 524	9.99 999	40
1260	21	7.78 594	2021	7.78 595	2020	12.21 405	9.99 999	39
1320	22	7.80 615	1930	7.80 615	1931	12.19 385	9.99 999	38
1380	23	7.82 545	1848	7.82 546	1848	12.17 454	9.99 999	37
1440	24	7.84 393	1773	7.84 394	1773	12.15 606	9.99 999	36
1500	25	7.86 166	1704	7.86 167	1704	12.13 833	9.99 999	35
1560	26	7.87 870	1639	7.87 871	1639	12.12 129	9.99 999	34
1620	27	7.89 509	1579	7.89 510	1579	12.10 490	9.99 999	33
1680	28	7.91 088	1524	7.91 089	1524	12.08 911	9.99 999	32
1740	29	7.92 612	1472	7.92 613	1473	12.07 387	9.99 998	31
1800	30	7.94 084	1424	7.94 086	1424	12.05 914	9.99 998	30
1860	31	7.95 508	1379	7.95 510	1379	12.04 490	9.99 998	29
1920	32	7.96 887	1336	7.96 889	1336	12.03 111	9.99 998	28
1980	33	7.98 223	1297	7.98 225	1297	12.01 775	9.99 998	27
2040	34	7.99 520	1259	7.99 522	1259	12.00 478	9.99 998	26
2100	35	8.00 779	1223	8.00 781	1223	11.99 219	9.99 998	25
2160	36	8.02 002	1190	8.02 004	1190	11.97 996	9.99 998	24
2220	37	8.03 192	1158	8.03 194	1159	11.96 806	9.99 997	23
2280	38	8.04 350	1128	8.04 353	1128	11.95 647	9.99 997	22
2340	39	8.05 478	1100	8.05 481	1100	11.94 519	9.99 997	21
2400	40	8.06 578	1072	8.06 581	1072	11.93 419	9.99 997	20
2460	41	8.07 650	1046	8.07 653	1047	11.92 347	9.99 997	19
2520	42	8.08 696	1022	8.08 700	1022	11.91 300	9.99 997	18
2580	43	8.09 718	999	8.09 722	998	11.90 278	9.99 997	17
2640	44	8.10 717	976	8.10 720	976	11.89 280	9.99 996	16
2700	45	8.11 693	954	8.11 696	955	11.88 304	9.99 996	15
2760	46	8.12 647	934	8.12 651	934	11.87 349	9.99 996	14
2820	47	8.13 581	914	8.13 585	915	11.86 415	9.99 996	13
2880	48	8.14 495	896	8.14 500	895	11.85 500	9.99 996	12
2940	49	8.15 391	877	8.15 395	878	11.84 605	9.99 996	11
3000	50	8.16 268	860	8.16 273	860	11.83 727	9.99 995	10
3060	51	8.17 128	843	8.17 133	843	11.82 867	9.99 995	9
3120	52	8.17 971	827	8.17 976	828	11.82 024	9.99 995	8
3180	53	8.18 798	812	8.18 804	812	11.81 196	9.99 995	7
3240	54	8.19 610	797	8.19 616	797	11.80 384	9.99 995	6
3300	55	8.20 407	782	8.20 413	782	11.79 587	9.99 994	5
3360	56	8.21 189	769	8.21 195	769	11.78 805	9.99 994	4
3420	57	8.21 958	755	8.21 964	756	11.78 036	9.99 994	3
3480	58	8.22 713	743	8.22 720	742	11.77 280	9.99 994	2
3540	59	8.23 456	730	8.23 462	730	11.76 538	9.99 994	1
3600	60	8.24 186		8.24 192		11.75 808	9.99 993	0
''	'	L Cos	d	L Ctn	c d	L Tan	L Sin	'

90° (270°)   (269°) **89°**

444

Table III (Cont'd)

COMMON LOGARITHMS OF TRIGONOMETRIC FUNCTIONS

To obtain interpolated values of L sin and L tan for angles less than 3°
(or L cos or L ctn of angles greater than 87°) use Table II.

1° (181°)   **(358°) 178°**

″	′	L Sin		d	L Tan		c d	L Ctn		L Cos		′
3600	0	8.24	186	717	8.24	192	718	11.75	808	9.99	993	60
3660	1	8.24	903	706	8.24	910	706	11.75	090	9.99	993	59
3720	2	8.25	609	695	8.25	616	696	11.74	384	9.99	993	58
3780	3	8.26	304	684	8.26	312	684	11.73	688	9.99	993	57
3840	4	8.26	988	673	8.26	996	673	11.73	004	9.99	992	56
3900	5	8.27	661	663	8.27	669	663	11.72	331	9.99	992	55
3960	6	8.28	324	653	8.28	332	654	11.71	668	9.99	992	54
4020	7	8.28	997	644	8.28	986	643	11.71	014	9.99	992	53
4080	8	8.29	621	634	8.29	629	634	11.70	371	9.99	992	52
4140	9	8.30	255	624	8.30	263	625	11.69	737	9.99	991	51
4200	10	8.30	879	616	8.30	888	617	11.69	112	9.99	991	50
4260	11	8.31	495	608	8.31	505	607	11.68	495	9.99	991	49
4320	12	8.32	103	599	8.32	112	599	11.67	888	9.99	990	48
4380	13	8.32	702	590	8.32	711	591	11.67	289	9.99	990	47
4440	14	8.33	292	583	8.33	302	584	11.66	698	9.99	990	46
4500	15	8.33	875	575	8.33	886	575	11.66	114	9.99	990	45
4560	16	8.34	450	568	8.34	461	568	11.65	539	9.99	989	44
4620	17	8.35	018	560	8.35	029	561	11.64	971	9.99	989	43
4680	18	8.35	578	553	8.35	590	553	11.64	410	9.99	989	42
4740	19	8.36	131	547	8.36	143	546	11.63	857	9.99	989	41
4800	20	8.36	678	539	8.36	689	540	11.63	311	9.99	988	40
4860	21	8.37	217	533	8.37	229	533	11.62	771	9.99	988	39
4920	22	8.37	750	526	8.37	762	527	11.62	238	9.99	988	38
4980	23	8.38	276	520	8.38	289	520	11.61	711	9.99	987	37
5040	24	8.38	796	514	8.38	809	514	11.61	191	9.99	987	36
5100	25	8.39	310	508	8.39	323	509	11.60	677	9.99	987	35
5160	26	8.39	818	502	8.39	832	502	11.60	168	9.99	986	34
5220	27	8.40	320	496	8.40	334	496	11.59	666	9.99	986	33
5280	28	8.40	816	491	8.40	830	491	11.59	170	9.99	986	32
5340	29	8.41	307	485	8.41	321	486	11.58	679	9.99	985	31
5400	30	8.41	792	480	8.41	807	480	11.58	193	9.99	985	30
5460	31	8.42	272	474	8.42	287	475	11.57	713	9.99	985	29
5520	32	8.42	746	470	8.42	762	470	11.57	238	9.99	984	28
5580	33	8.43	216	464	8.43	232	464	11.56	768	9.99	984	27
5640	34	8.43	680	459	8.43	696	460	11.56	304	9.99	984	26
5700	35	8.44	139	455	8.44	156	455	11.55	844	9.99	983	25
5760	36	8.44	594	450	8.44	611	450	11.55	389	9.99	983	24
5820	37	8.45	044	445	8.45	061	446	11.54	939	9.99	983	23
5880	38	8.45	489	441	8.45	507	441	11.54	493	9.99	982	22
5940	39	8.45	930	436	8.45	948	437	11.54	052	9.99	982	21
6000	40	8.46	366	433	8.46	385	432	11.53	615	9.99	982	20
6060	41	8.46	799	427	8.46	817	428	11.53	183	9.99	981	19
6120	42	8.47	226	424	8.47	245	424	11.52	755	9.99	981	18
6180	43	8.47	650	419	8.47	669	420	11.52	331	9.99	981	17
6240	44	8.48	069	416	8.48	089	416	11.51	911	9.99	980	16
6300	45	8.48	485	411	8.48	505	412	11.51	495	9.99	980	15
6360	46	8.48	896	408	8.48	917	408	11.51	083	9.99	979	14
6420	47	8.49	304	404	8.49	325	404	11.50	675	9.99	979	13
6480	48	8.49	708	400	8.49	729	401	11.50	271	9.99	979	12
6540	49	8.50	108	396	8.50	130	397	11.49	870	9.99	978	11
6600	50	8.50	504	393	8.50	527	393	11.49	473	9.99	978	10
6660	51	8.50	897	390	8.50	920	390	11.49	080	9.99	977	9
6720	52	8.51	287	386	8.51	310	386	11.48	690	9.99	977	8
6780	53	8.51	673	382	8.51	696	383	11.48	304	9.99	977	7
6840	54	8.52	055	379	8.52	079	380	11.47	921	9.99	976	6
6900	55	8.52	434	376	8.52	459	376	11.47	541	9.99	976	5
6960	56	8.52	810	373	8.52	835	373	11.47	165	9.99	975	4
7020	57	8.53	183	369	8.53	208	370	11.46	792	9.99	975	3
7080	58	8.53	552	367	8.53	578	367	11.46	422	9.99	974	2
7140	59	8.53	919	363	8.53	945	363	11.46	055	9.99	974	1
7200	60	8.54	282		8.54	308		11.45	692	9.99	974	0
″	′	L Cos		d	L Ctn		c d	L Tan		L Sin		′

91° (271°)   **(268°) 88°**

Table III (Cont'd)
COMMON LOGARITHMS OF TRIGONOMETRIC FUNCTIONS

To obtain interpolated values of L sin and L tan for angles less than 3°
(or L cos or L ctn of angles greater than 87°) use Table II.

2° (182°)   **(357°) 177°**

''	'	L Sin	d	L Tan	c d	L Ctn	L Cos	'
7200	0	8.54 282	360	8.54 308	361	11.45 692	9.99 974	60
7260	1	8.54 642	357	8.54 669	358	11.45 331	9.99 973	59
7320	2	8.54 999	355	8.55 027	355	11.44 973	9.99 973	58
7380	3	8.55 354	351	8.55 382	352	11.44 618	9.99 972	57
7440	4	8.55 705	349	8.55 734	349	11.44 266	9.99 972	56
7500	5	8.56 054	346	8.56 083	346	11.43 917	9.99 971	55
7560	6	8.56 400	343	8.56 429	344	11.43 571	9.99 971	54
7620	7	8.56 743	341	8.56 773	341	11.43 227	9.99 970	53
7680	8	8.57 084	337	8.57 114	338	11.42 886	9.99 970	52
7740	9	8.57 421	336	8.57 452	336	11.42 548	9.99 969	51
7800	10	8.57 757	332	8.57 788	333	11.42 212	9.99 969	50
7860	11	8.58 089	330	8.58 121	330	11.41 879	9.99 968	49
7920	12	8.58 419	328	8.58 451	328	11.41 549	9.99 968	48
7980	13	8.58 747	325	8.58 779	326	11.41 221	9.99 967	47
8040	14	8.59 072	323	8.59 105	323	11.40 895	9.99 967	46
8100	15	8.59 395	320	8.59 428	321	11.40 572	9.99 967	45
8160	16	8.59 715	318	8.59 749	319	11.40 251	9.99 966	44
8220	17	8.60 033	316	8.60 068	316	11.39 932	9.99 966	43
8280	18	8.60 349	313	8.60 384	314	11.39 616	9.99 965	42
8340	19	8.60 662	311	8.60 698	311	11.39 302	9.99 964	41
8400	20	8.60 973	309	8.61 009	310	11.38 991	9.99 964	40
8460	21	8.61 282	307	8.61 319	307	11.38 681	9.99 963	39
8520	22	8.61 589	305	8.61 626	305	11.38 374	9.99 963	38
8580	23	8.61 894	302	8.61 931	303	11.38 069	9.99 962	37
8640	24	8.62 196	301	8.62 234	301	11.37 766	9.99 962	36
8700	25	8.62 497	298	8.62 535	299	11.37 465	9.99 961	35
8760	26	8.62 795	296	8.62 834	297	11.37 166	9.99 961	34
8820	27	8.63 091	294	8.63 131	295	11.36 869	9.99 960	33
8880	28	8.63 385	293	8.63 426	292	11.36 574	9.99 960	32
8940	29	8.63 678	290	8.63 718	291	11.36 282	9.99 959	31
9000	30	8.63 968	288	8.64 009	289	11.35 991	9.99 959	30
9060	31	8.64 256	287	8.64 298	287	11.35 702	9.99 958	29
9120	32	8.64 543	284	8.64 585	285	11.35 415	9.99 958	28
9180	33	8.64 827	283	8.64 870	284	11.35 130	9.99 957	27
9240	34	8.65 110	281	8.65 154	281	11.34 846	9.99 956	26
9300	35	8.65 391	279	8.65 435	280	11.34 565	9.99 956	25
9360	36	8.65 670	277	8.65 715	278	11.34 285	9.99 955	24
9420	37	8.65 947	276	8.65 993	276	11.34 007	9.99 955	23
9480	38	8.66 223	274	8.66 269	274	11.33 731	9.99 954	22
9540	39	8.66 497	272	8.66 543	273	11.33 457	9.99 954	21
9600	40	8.66 769	270	8.66 816	271	11.33 184	9.99 953	20
9660	41	8.67 039	269	8.67 087	269	11.32 913	9.99 952	19
9720	42	8.67 308	267	8.67 356	268	11.32 644	9.99 952	18
9780	43	8.67 575	266	8.67 624	266	11.32 376	9.99 951	17
9840	44	8.67 841	263	8.67 890	264	11.32 110	9.99 951	16
9900	45	8.68 104	263	8.68 154	263	11.31 846	9.99 950	15
9960	46	8.68 367	260	8.68 417	261	11.31 583	9.99 949	14
10020	47	8.68 627	259	8.68 678	260	11.31 322	9.99 949	13
10080	48	8.68 886	258	8.68 938	258	11.31 062	9.99 948	12
10140	49	8.69 144	256	8.69 196	257	11.30 804	9.99 948	11
10200	50	8.69 400	254	8.69 453	255	11.30 547	9.99 947	10
10260	51	8.69 654	253	8.69 708	254	11.30 292	9.99 946	9
10320	52	8.69 907	252	8.69 962	252	11.30 038	9.99 946	8
10380	53	8.70 159	250	8.70 214	251	11.29 786	9.99 945	7
10440	54	8.70 409	249	8.70 465	249	11.29 535	9.99 944	6
10500	55	8.70 658	247	8.70 714	248	11.29 286	9.99 944	5
10560	56	8.70 905	246	8.70 962	246	11.29 038	9.99 943	4
10620	57	8.71 151	244	8.71 208	245	11.28 792	9.99 942	3
10680	58	8.71 395	243	8.71 453	244	11.28 547	9.99 942	2
10740	59	8.71 638	242	8.71 697	243	11.28 303	9.99 941	1
10800	60	8.71 880		8.71 940		11.28 060	9.99 940	0
''	'	L Cos	d	L Ctn	c d	L Tan	L Sin	'

92° (272°)   **(267°) 87°**

Table III (Cont'd)

COMMON LOGARITHMS OF TRIGONOMETRIC FUNCTIONS

         (356°) **176°**

′	L Sin	d	L Tan	c d	L Ctn	L Cos	′	Proportional parts
0	8.71 880	240	8.71 940	241	11.28 060	9.99 940	60	
1	8.72 120	239	8.72 181	239	11.27 819	9.99 940	59	**241 239 237 235 234**
2	8.72 359	238	8.72 420	239	11.27 580	9.99 939	58	1 4.0 4.0 4.0 3.9 3.9
3	8.72 597	237	8.72 659	237	11.27 341	9.99 938	57	2 8.0 8.0 7.9 7.8 7.8
4	8.72 834	235	8.72 896	236	11.27 104	9.99 938	56	3 12.0 12.0 11.8 11.8 11.7
								4 16.1 15.9 15.8 15.7 15.6
5	8.73 069	234	8.73 132	234	11.26 868	9.99 937	55	5 20.1 19.9 19.8 19.6 19.5
6	8.73 303	232	8.73 366	234	11.26 634	9.99 936	54	6 24.1 23.9 23.7 23.5 23.4
7	8.73 535	232	8.73 600	232	11.26 400	9.99 936	53	7 28.1 27.9 27.6 27.4 27.3
8	8.73 767	230	8.73 832	231	11.26 168	9.99 935	52	8 32.1 31.9 31.6 31.3 31.2
9	8.73 997	229	8.74 063	229	11.25 937	9.99 934	51	9 36.2 35.8 35.6 35.2 35.1
10	8.74 226	228	8.74 292	229	11.25 708	9.99 934	50	
11	8.74 454	226	8.74 521	227	11.25 479	9.99 933	49	**232 229 227 225 223**
12	8.74 680	226	8.74 748	226	11.25 252	9.99 932	48	1 3.9 3.8 3.8 3.8 3.7
13	8.74 906	224	8.74 974	225	11.25 026	9.99 932	47	2 7.7 7.6 7.6 7.5 7.4
14	8.75 130	223	8.75 199	224	11.24 801	9.99 931	46	3 11.6 11.4 11.4 11.2 11.2
								4 15.5 15.3 15.1 15.0 14.9
15	8.75 353	222	8.75 423	222	11.24 577	9.99 930	45	5 19.3 19.1 18.9 18.8 18.6
16	8.75 575	220	8.75 645	222	11.24 355	9.99 929	44	6 23.2 22.9 22.7 22.5 22.3
17	8.75 795	220	8.75 867	220	11.24 133	9.99 929	43	7 27.1 26.7 26.5 26.2 26.0
18	8.76 015	219	8.76 087	219	11.23 913	9.99 928	42	8 30.9 30.5 30.3 30.0 29.7
19	8.76 234	217	8.76 306	219	11.23 694	9.99 927	41	9 34.8 34.4 34.0 33.8 33.4
20	8.76 451	216	8.76 525	217	11.23 475	9.99 926	40	
21	8.76 667	216	8.76 742	216	11.23 258	9.99 926	39	**222 220 217 215 213**
22	8.76 883	214	8.76 958	215	11.23 042	9.99 925	38	1 3.7 3.7 3.6 3.6 3.6
23	8.77 097	213	8.77 173	214	11.22 827	9.99 924	37	2 7.4 7.3 7.2 7.2 7.1
24	8.77 310	212	8.77 387	213	11.22 613	9.99 923	36	3 11.1 11.0 10.8 10.8 10.6
								4 14.8 14.7 14.5 14.3 14.2
25	8.77 522	211	8.77 600	211	11.22 400	9.99 923	35	5 18.5 18.3 18.1 17.9 17.8
26	8.77 733	210	8.77 811	211	11.22 189	9.99 922	34	6 22.2 22.0 21.7 21.5 21.3
27	8.77 943	209	8.78 022	210	11.21 978	9.99 921	33	7 25.9 25.7 25.3 25.1 24.8
28	8.78 152	208	8.78 232	209	11.21 768	9.99 920	32	8 29.6 29.3 28.9 28.7 28.4
29	8.78 360	208	8.78 441	208	11.21 559	9.99 920	31	9 33.3 33.0 32.6 32.2 32.0
30	8.78 568	206	8.78 649	206	11.21 351	9.99 919	30	
31	8.78 774	205	8.78 855	206	11.21 145	9.99 918	29	**211 208 206 203 201**
32	8.78 979	204	8.79 061	205	11.20 939	9.99 917	28	1 3.5 3.5 3.4 3.4 3.4
33	8.79 183	203	8.79 266	204	11.20 734	9.99 917	27	2 7.0 6.9 6.9 6.8 6.7
34	8.79 386	202	8.79 470	203	11.20 530	9.99 916	26	3 10.6 10.4 10.3 10.2 10.0
								4 14.1 13.9 13.7 13.5 13.4
35	8.79 588	201	8.79 673	202	11.20 327	9.99 915	25	5 17.6 17.3 17.2 16.9 16.8
36	8.79 789	201	8.79 875	201	11.20 125	9.99 914	24	6 21.1 20.8 20.6 20.3 20.1
37	8.79 990	199	8.80 076	201	11.19 924	9.99 913	23	7 24.6 24.3 24.0 23.7 23.4
38	8.80 189	199	8.80 277	199	11.19 723	9.99 913	22	8 28.1 27.7 27.5 27.1 26.8
39	8.80 388	197	8.80 476	198	11.19 524	9.99 912	21	9 31.6 31.2 30.9 30.4 30.2
40	8.80 585	197	8.80 674	198	11.19 326	9.99 911	20	
41	8.80 782	196	8.80 872	196	11.19 128	9.99 910	19	**199 197 195 193 192**
42	8.80 978	195	8.81 068	196	11.18 932	9.99 909	18	1 3.3 3.3 3.2 3.2 3.2
43	8.81 173	194	8.81 264	195	11.18 736	9.99 909	17	2 6.6 6.6 6.5 6.4 6.4
44	8.81 367	193	8.81 459	194	11.18 541	9.99 908	16	3 10.0 9.8 9.8 9.6 9.6
								4 13.3 13.1 13.0 12.9 12.8
45	8.81 560	192	8.81 653	193	11.18 347	9.99 907	15	5 16.6 16.4 16.2 16.1 16.0
46	8.81 752	192	8.81 846	192	11.18 154	9.99 906	14	6 19.9 19.7 19.5 19.3 19.2
47	8.81 944	190	8.82 038	192	11.17 962	9.99 905	13	7 23.2 23.0 22.8 22.5 22.4
48	8.82 134	190	8.82 230	190	11.17 770	9.99 904	12	8 26.5 26.3 26.0 25.7 25.6
49	8.82 324	189	8.82 420	190	11.17 580	9.99 904	11	9 29.3 29.6 29.2 29.0 28.8
50	8.82 513	188	8.82 610	189	11.17 390	9.99 903	10	
51	8.82 701	187	8.82 799	188	11.17 201	9.99 902	9	**183 187 185 183 181**
52	8.82 888	187	8.82 987	188	11.17 013	9.99 901	8	1 3.2 3.1 3.1 3.0 3.0
53	8.83 075	186	8.83 175	186	11.16 825	9.99 900	7	2 6.3 6.2 6.2 6.1 6.0
54	8.83 261	185	8.83 361	186	11.16 639	9.99 899	6	3 9.4 9.4 9.2 9.2 9.0
								4 12.6 12.5 12.3 12.2 12.1
55	8.83 446	184	8.83 547	185	11.16 453	9.99 898	5	5 15.8 15.6 15.4 15.2 15.1
56	8.83 630	183	8.83 732	184	11.16 268	9.99 898	4	6 18.9 18.7 18.5 18.3 18.1
57	8.83 813	183	8.83 916	184	11.16 084	9.99 897	3	7 22.0 21.8 21.6 21.4 21.1
58	8.83 996	181	8.84 100	182	11.15 900	9.99 896	2	8 25.2 24.9 24.7 24.4 24.1
59	8.84 177	181	8.84 282	182	11.15 718	9.99 895	1	9 28.4 28.0 27.8 27.4 27.2
60	8.84 358		8.84 464		11.15 536	9.99 894	0	
′	L Cos	d	L Ctn	c d	L Tan	L Sin	′	Proportional parts

Table III (Cont'd)
COMMON LOGARITHMS OF TRIGONOMETRIC FUNCTIONS

4° (184°) (355°) **175°**

′	L Sin	d	L Tan	c d	L Ctn	L Cos	′	Proportional parts
0	8.84 358	181	8.84 464	182	11.15 536	9.99 894	60	
1	8.84 539	179	8.84 646	180	11.15 354	9.99 893	59	
2	8.84 718	179	8.84 826	180	11.15 174	9.99 892	58	
3	8.84 897	178	8.85 006	179	11.14 994	9.99 891	57	
4	8.85 075	177	8.85 185	178	11.14 815	9.99 891	56	
5	8.85 252	177	8.85 363	177	11.14 637	9.99 890	55	
6	8.85 429	176	8.85 540	177	11.14 460	9.99 889	54	
7	8.85 605	175	8.85 717	176	11.14 283	9.99 888	53	
8	8.85 780	175	8.85 893	176	11.14 107	9.99 887	52	
9	8.85 955	173	8.86 069	174	11.13 931	9.99 886	51	
10	8.86 128	173	8.86 243	174	11.13 757	9.99 885	50	
11	8.86 301	173	8.86 417	174	11.13 583	9.99 884	49	
12	8.86 474	171	8.86 591	172	11.13 409	9.99 883	48	
13	8.86 645	171	8.86 763	172	11.13 237	9.99 882	47	
14	8.86 816	171	8.86 935	171	11.13 065	9.99 881	46	
15	8.86 987	169	8.87 106	171	11.12 894	9.99 880	45	
16	8.87 156	169	8.87 277	170	11.12 723	9.99 879	44	
17	8.87 325	169	8.87 447	169	11.12 553	9.99 879	43	
18	8.87 494	167	8.87 616	169	11.12 384	9.99 878	42	
19	8.87 661	168	8.87 785	168	11.12 215	9.99 877	41	
20	8.87 829	166	8.87 953	167	11.12 047	9.99 876	40	
21	8.87 995	166	8.88 120	167	11.11 880	9.99 875	39	
22	8.88 161	165	8.88 287	166	11.11 713	9.99 874	38	
23	8.88 326	164	8.88 453	165	11.11 547	9.99 873	37	
24	8.88 490	164	8.88 618	165	11.11 382	9.99 872	36	
25	8.88 654	163	8.88 783	165	11.11 217	9.99 871	35	
26	8.88 817	163	8.88 948	163	11.11 052	9.99 870	34	
27	8.88 980	162	8.89 111	163	11.10 889	9.99 869	33	
28	8.89 142	162	8.89 274	163	11.10 726	9.99 868	32	
29	8.89 304	160	8.89 437	161	11.10 563	9.99 867	31	
30	8.89 464	161	8.89 598	162	11.10 402	9.99 866	30	
31	8.89 625	159	8.89 760	160	11.10 240	9.99 865	29	
32	8.89 784	159	8.89 920	160	11.10 080	9.99 864	28	
33	8.89 943	159	8.90 080	160	11.09 920	9.99 863	27	
34	8.90 102	158	8.90 240	159	11.09 760	9.99 862	26	
35	8.90 260	157	8.90 399	158	11.09 601	9.99 861	25	
36	8.90 417	157	8.90 557	158	11.09 443	9.99 860	24	
37	8.90 574	156	8.90 715	157	11.09 285	9.99 859	23	
38	8.90 730	155	8.90 872	157	11.09 128	9.99 858	22	
39	8.90 885	155	8.91 029	156	11.08 971	9.99 857	21	
40	8.91 040	155	8.91 185	155	11.08 815	9.99 856	20	
41	8.91 195	154	8.91 340	155	11.08 660	9.99 855	19	
42	8.91 349	153	8.91 495	155	11.08 505	9.99 854	18	
43	8.91 502	153	8.91 650	153	11.08 350	9.99 853	17	
44	8.91 655	152	8.91 803	154	11.08 197	9.99 852	16	
45	8.91 807	152	8.91 957	153	11.08 043	9.99 851	15	
46	8.91 959	151	8.92 110	152	11.07 890	9.99 850	14	
47	8.92 110	151	8.92 262	152	11.07 738	9.99 848	13	
48	8.92 261	150	8.92 414	151	11.07 586	9.99 847	12	
49	8.92 411	150	8.92 565	151	11.07 435	9.99 846	11	
50	8.92 561	149	8.92 716	150	11.07 284	9.99 845	10	
51	8.92 710	149	8.92 866	150	11.07 134	9.99 844	9	
52	8.92 859	148	8.93 016	149	11.06 984	9.99 843	8	
53	8.93 007	147	8.93 165	148	11.06 835	9.99 842	7	
54	8.93 154	147	8.93 313	149	11.06 687	9.99 841	6	
55	8.93 301	147	8.93 462	147	11.06 538	9.99 840	5	
56	8.93 448	146	8.93 609	147	11.06 391	9.99 839	4	
57	8.93 594	146	8.93 756	147	11.06 244	9.99 838	3	
58	8.93 740	145	8.93 903	146	11.06 097	9.99 837	2	
59	8.93 885	145	8.94 049	146	11.05 951	9.99 836	1	
60	8.94 030		8.94 195		11.05 805	9.99 834	0	
′	L Cos	d	L Ctn	c d	L Tan	L Sin	′	Proportional parts

Proportional parts

″	182	181	179	178	177
1	3.0	3.0	3.0	3.0	3.0
2	6.1	6.0	6.0	5.9	5.9
3	9.1	9.0	9.0	8.9	8.8
4	12.1	12.1	11.9	11.9	11.8
5	15.2	15.1	14.9	14.8	14.8
6	18.2	18.1	17.9	17.8	17.7
7	21.2	21.1	20.9	20.8	20.6
8	24.3	24.1	23.9	23.7	23.6
9	27.3	27.2	26.8	26.7	26.6

″	176	175	174	173	172
1	2.9	2.9	2.9	2.9	2.9
2	5.9	5.8	5.8	5.8	5.7
3	8.8	8.8	8.7	8.6	8.6
4	11.7	11.7	11.6	11.5	11.5
5	14.7	14.6	14.5	14.4	14.3
6	17.6	17.5	17.4	17.3	17.2
7	20.5	20.4	20.3	20.2	20.1
8	23.5	23.3	23.2	23.1	22.9
9	26.4	26.2	26.1	26.0	25.8

″	171	170	169	168	167
1	2.8	2.8	2.8	2.8	2.8
2	5.7	5.7	5.6	5.6	5.6
3	8.6	8.5	8.4	8.4	8.4
4	11.4	11.3	11.3	11.2	11.1
5	14.2	14.2	14.1	14.0	13.9
6	17.1	17.0	16.9	16.8	16.7
7	20.0	19.8	19.7	19.6	19.5
8	22.8	22.7	22.5	22.4	22.3
9	25.6	25.5	25.4	25.2	25.0

″	166	165	164	163	162
1	2.8	2.8	2.7	2.7	2.7
2	5.5	5.5	5.5	5.4	5.4
3	8.3	8.2	8.2	8.2	8.1
4	11.1	11.0	10.9	10.9	10.8
5	13.8	13.8	13.7	13.6	13.5
6	16.6	16.5	16.4	16.3	16.2
7	19.4	19.2	19.1	19.0	18.9
8	22.1	22.0	21.9	21.7	21.6
9	24.9	24.8	24.6	24.4	24.3

″	161	160	159	158	157
1	2.7	2.7	2.6	2.6	2.6
2	5.4	5.3	5.3	5.3	5.2
3	8.0	8.0	8.0	7.9	7.8
4	10.7	10.7	10.6	10.5	10.5
5	13.4	13.3	13.2	13.2	13.1
6	16.1	16.0	15.9	15.8	15.7
7	18.8	18.7	18.6	18.4	18.3
8	21.5	21.3	21.2	21.1	20.9
9	24.2	24.0	23.8	23.7	23.6

″	156	155	154	153	152
1	2.6	2.6	2.6	2.6	2.5
2	6.2	5.2	5.1	5.1	5.1
3	7.8	7.8	7.7	7.6	7.6
4	10.4	10.3	10.3	10.2	10.1
5	13.0	12.9	12.8	12.8	12.7
6	15.6	15.5	15.4	15.3	15.2
7	18.2	18.1	18.0	17.8	17.7
8	20.8	20.7	20.5	20.4	20.3
9	23.4	23.2	23.1	23.0	22.8

94° (274°) (265°) **85°**

Table III (Cont'd)

COMMON LOGARITHMS OF TRIGONOMETRIC FUNCTIONS

5° (185°) (354°) **174°**

′	L Sin	d	L Tan	c d	L Ctn	L Cos	′	Proportional parts				
0	8.94 030	144	8.94 195	145	11.05 805	9.99 834	60	′′	151	149	148	147	146
1	8.94 174	143	8.94 340	145	11.05 660	9.99 833	59	1	2.5	2.5	2.5	2.4	2.4
2	8.94 317	144	8.94 485	145	11.05 515	9.99 832	58	2	5.0	5.0	4.9	4.9	4.9
3	8.94 461	142	8.94 630	143	11.05 370	9.99 831	57	3	7.6	7.4	7.4	7.4	7.3
4	8.94 603	143	8.94 773	144	11.05 227	9.99 830	56	4	10.1	9.9	9.9	9.8	9.7
5	8.94 746	141	8.94 917	143	11.05 083	9.99 829	55	5	12.6	12.4	12.3	12.2	12.2
6	8.94 887	142	8.95 060	142	11.04 940	9.99 828	54	6	15.1	14.9	14.8	14.7	14.6
7	8.95 029	141	8.95 202	142	11.04 798	9.99 827	53	7	17.6	17.4	17.3	17.2	17.0
8	8.95 170	140	8.95 344	142	11.04 656	9.99 825	52	8	20.1	19.9	19.7	19.6	19.5
9	8.95 310	140	8.95 486	141	11.04 514	9.99 824	51	9	22.6	22.4	22.2	22.0	21.9
10	8.95 450	139	8.95 627	140	11.04 373	9.99 823	50	′′	145	144	143	142	141
11	8.95 589	139	8.95 767	141	11.04 233	9.99 822	49	1	2.4	2.4	2.4	2.4	2.4
12	8.95 728	139	8.95 908	139	11.04 092	9.99 821	48	2	4.8	4.8	4.8	4.7	4.7
13	8.95 867	138	8.96 047	140	11.03 953	9.99 820	47	3	7.2	7.2	7.2	7.1	7.0
14	8.96 005	138	8.96 187	138	11.03 813	9.99 819	46	4	9.7	9.6	9.5	9.5	9.4
15	8.96 143	137	8.96 325	139	11.03 675	9.99 817	45	5	12.1	12.0	11.9	11.8	11.8
16	8.96 280	137	8.96 464	138	11.03 536	9.99 816	44	6	14.5	14.4	14.3	14.2	14.1
17	8.96 417	136	8.96 602	137	11.03 398	9.99 815	43	7	16.9	16.8	16.7	16.6	16.4
18	8.96 553	136	8.96 739	138	11.03 261	9.99 814	42	8	19.3	19.2	19.1	18.9	18.8
19	8.96 689	136	8.96 877	136	11.03 123	9.99 813	41	9	21.8	21.6	21.4	21.3	21.2
20	8.96 825	135	8.97 013	137	11.02 987	9.99 812	40	′′	140	139	138	137	136
21	8.96 960	135	8.97 150	135	11.02 850	9.99 810	39	1	2.3	2.3	2.3	2.3	2.3
22	8.97 095	134	8.97 285	136	11.02 715	9.99 809	38	2	4.7	4.6	4.6	4.6	4.5
23	8.97 229	134	8.97 421	135	11.02 579	9.99 808	37	3	7.0	7.0	6.9	6.8	6.8
24	8.97 363	133	8.97 556	135	11.02 444	9.99 807	36	4	9.3	9.3	9.2	9.1	9.1
25	8.97 496	133	8.97 691	134	11.02 309	9.99 806	35	5	11.7	11.6	11.5	11.4	11.3
26	8.97 629	133	8.97 825	134	11.02 175	9.99 804	34	6	14.0	13.9	13.8	13.7	13.6
27	8.97 762	132	8.97 959	133	11.02 041	9.99 803	33	7	16.3	16.2	16.1	16.0	15.9
28	8.97 894	132	8.98 092	133	11.01 908	9.99 802	32	8	18.7	18.5	18.4	18.3	18.1
29	8.98 026	131	8.98 225	133	11.01 775	9.99 801	31	9	21.0	20.8	20.7	20.6	20.4
30	8.98 157	131	8.98 358	132	11.01 642	9.99 800	30	′′	135	134	133	132	131
31	8.98 288	131	8.98 490	132	11.01 510	9.99 798	29	1	2.2	2.2	2.2	2.2	2.2
32	8.98 419	130	8.98 622	131	11.01 378	9.99 797	28	2	4.5	4.5	4.4	4.4	4.4
33	8.98 549	130	8.98 753	131	11.01 247	9.99 796	27	3	6.8	6.7	6.6	6.6	6.6
34	8.98 679	129	8.98 884	131	11.01 116	9.99 795	26	4	9.0	8.9	8.9	8.8	8.7
35	8.98 808	129	8.99 015	130	11.00 985	9.99 793	25	5	11.2	11.2	11.1	11.0	10.9
36	8.98 937	129	8.99 145	130	11.00 855	9.99 792	24	6	13.5	13.4	13.3	13.2	13.1
37	8.99 066	128	8.99 275	130	11.00 725	9.99 791	23	7	15.8	15.6	15.5	15.4	15.3
38	8.99 194	128	8.99 405	129	11.00 595	9.99 790	22	8	18.0	17.9	17.7	17.6	17.5
39	8.99 322	128	8.99 534	128	11.00 466	9.99 788	21	9	20.2	20.1	20.0	19.8	19.6
40	8.99 450	127	8.99 662	129	11.00 338	9.99 787	20	′′	130	129	128	127	126
41	8.99 577	127	8.99 791	128	11.00 209	9.99 786	19	1	2.2	2.2	2.1	2.1	2.1
42	8.99 704	126	8.99 919	127	11.00 081	9.99 785	18	2	4.3	4.3	4.3	4.2	4.2
43	8.99 830	126	9.00 046	128	10.99 954	9.99 783	17	3	6.5	6.4	6.4	6.4	6.3
44	8.99 956	126	9.00 174	127	10.99 826	9.99 782	16	4	8.7	8.6	8.5	8.5	8.4
45	9.00 082	125	9.00 301	126	10.99 699	9.99 781	15	5	10.8	10.8	10.7	10.6	10.5
46	9.00 207	125	9.00 427	126	10.99 573	9.99 780	14	6	13.0	12.9	12.8	12.7	12.6
47	9.00 332	124	9.00 553	126	10.99 447	9.99 778	13	7	15.2	15.0	14.9	14.8	14.7
48	9.00 456	125	9.00 679	126	10.99 321	9.99 777	12	8	17.3	17.2	17.1	16.9	16.8
49	9.00 581	123	9.00 805	125	10.99 195	9.99 776	11	9	19.5	19.4	19.2	19.0	18.9
50	9.00 704	124	9.00 930	125	10.99 070	9.99 775	10	′′	125	124	123	122	121
51	9.00 828	123	9.01 055	124	10.98 945	9.99 773	9	1	2.1	2.1	2.0	2.0	2.0
52	9.00 951	123	9.01 179	124	10.98 821	9.99 772	8	2	4.2	4.1	4.1	4.1	4.0
53	9.01 074	122	9.01 303	124	10.98 697	9.99 771	7	3	6.2	6.2	6.2	6.1	6.0
54	9.01 196	122	9.01 427	123	10.98 573	9.99 769	6	4	8.3	8.3	8.2	8.1	8.1
55	9.01 318	122	9.01 550	123	10.98 450	9.99 768	5	5	10.4	10.3	10.2	10.2	10.1
56	9.01 440	121	9.01 673	123	10.98 327	9.99 767	4	6	12.5	12.4	12.3	12.2	12.1
57	9.01 561	121	9.01 796	122	10.98 204	9.99 765	3	7	14.6	14.5	14.4	14.2	14.1
58	9.01 682	121	9.01 918	122	10.98 082	9.99 764	2	8	16.7	16.5	16.4	16.3	16.1
59	9.01 803	120	9.02 040	122	10.97 960	9.99 763	1	9	18.8	18.6	18.4	18.3	18.2
60	9.01 923		9.02 162		10.97 838	9.99 761	0						
′	L Cos	d	L Ctn	c d	L Tan	L Sin	′	Proportional parts				

95° (275°) (264°) **84°**

Table III (Cont'd)

COMMON LOGARITHMS OF TRIGONOMETRIC FUNCTIONS

6° (186°) (353°) **173°**

′	L Sin	d	L Tan	c d	L Ctn	L Cos	′	Proportional parts			
0	9.01 923	120	9.02 162	121	10.97 838	9.99 761	60	′′	121	120	119	118
1	9.02 043	120	9.02 283	121	10.97 717	9.99 760	59	1	2.0	2.0	2.0	2.0
2	9.02 163	120	9.02 404	121	10.97 596	9.99 759	58	2	4.0	4.0	4.0	3.9
3	9.02 283	119	9.02 525	120	10.97 475	9.99 757	57	3	6.0	6.0	6.0	5.9
4	9.02 402	118	9.02 645	121	10.97 355	9.99 756	56	4	8.1	8.0	7.9	7.9
5	9.02 520	119	9.02 766	119	10.97 234	9.99 755	55	5	10.1	10.0	9.9	9.8
6	9.02 639	118	9.02 885	120	10.97 115	9.99 753	54	6	12.1	12.0	11.9	11.8
7	9.02 757	117	9.03 005	119	10.96 995	9.99 752	53	7	14.1	14.0	13.9	13.8
8	9.02 874	118	9.03 124	118	10.96 876	9.99 751	52	8	16.1	16.0	15.9	15.7
9	9.02 992	117	9.03 242	119	10.96 758	9.99 749	51	9	18.2	18.0	17.8	17.7
10	9.03 109	117	9.03 361	118	10.96 639	9.99 748	50					
11	9.03 226	116	9.03 479	118	10.96 521	9.99 747	49	10	20.2	20.0	19.8	19.7
12	9.03 342	116	9.03 597	117	10.96 403	9.99 745	48	20	40.3	40.0	39.7	39.3
13	9.03 458	116	9.03 714	118	10.96 286	9.99 744	47	30	60.5	60.0	59.5	59.0
14	9.03 574	116	9.03 832	116	10.96 168	9.99 742	46	40	80.7	80.0	79.3	78.7
								50	100.8	100.0	99.2	98.3
15	9.03 690	115	9.03 948	117	10.96 052	9.99 741	45	′′	117	116	115	114
16	9.03 805	115	9.04 065	116	10.95 935	9.99 740	44	1	2.0	1.9	1.9	1.9
17	9.03 920	114	9.04 181	116	10.95 819	9.99 738	43	2	3.9	3.9	3.8	3.8
18	9.04 034	115	9.04 297	116	10.95 703	9.99 737	42	3	5.8	5.8	5.8	5.7
19	9.04 149	113	9.04 413	115	10.95 587	9.99 736	41	4	7.8	7.7	7.7	7.6
20	9.04 262	114	9.04 528	115	10.95 472	9.99 734	40	5	9.8	9.7	9.6	9.5
21	9.04 376	114	9.04 643	115	10.95 357	9.99 733	39	6	11.7	11.6	11.5	11.4
22	9.04 490	113	9.04 758	115	10.95 242	9.99 731	38	7	13.6	13.5	13.4	13.3
23	9.04 603	112	9.04 873	114	10.95 127	9.99 730	37	8	15.6	15.5	15.3	15.2
24	9.04 715	113	9.04 987	114	10.95 013	9.99 728	36	9	17.6	17.4	17.2	17.1
25	9.04 828	112	9.05 101	113	10.94 899	9.99 727	35					
26	9.04 940	112	9.05 214	114	10.94 786	9.99 726	34	10	19.5	19.3	19.2	19.0
27	9.05 052	112	9.05 328	113	10.94 672	9.99 724	33	20	39.0	38.7	38.3	38.0
28	9.05 164	111	9.05 441	112	10.94 559	9.99 723	32	30	58.5	58.0	57.5	57.0
29	9.05 275	111	9.05 553	113	10.94 447	9.99 721	31	40	78.0	77.3	76.7	76.0
								50	97.5	96.7	95.8	95.0
30	9.05 386	111	9.05 666	112	10.94 334	9.99 720	30					
31	9.05 497	110	9.05 778	112	10.94 222	9.99 718	29	′′	113	112	111	110
32	9.05 607	110	9.05 890	112	10.94 110	9.99 717	28	1	1.9	1.9	1.8	1.8
33	9.05 717	110	9.06 002	111	10.93 998	9.99 716	27	2	3.8	3.7	3.7	3.7
34	9.05 827	110	9.06 113	111	10.93 887	9.99 714	26	3	5.6	5.6	5.6	5.5
								4	7.5	7.5	7.4	7.3
35	9.05 937	109	9.06 224	111	10.93 776	9.99 713	25	5	9.4	9.3	9.2	9.2
36	9.06 046	109	9.06 335	110	10.93 665	9.99 711	24	6	11.3	11.2	11.1	11.0
37	9.06 155	109	9.06 445	111	10.93 555	9.99 710	23	7	13.2	13.1	13.0	12.8
38	9.06 264	108	9.06 556	110	10.93 444	9.99 708	22	8	15.1	14.9	14.8	14.7
39	9.06 372	109	9.06 666	109	10.93 334	9.99 707	21	9	17.0	16.8	16.6	16.5
40	9.06 481	108	9.06 775	110	10.93 225	9.99 705	20					
41	9.06 589	107	9.06 885	109	10.93 115	9.99 704	19	10	18.8	18.7	18.5	18.3
42	9.06 696	108	9.06 994	109	10.93 006	9.99 702	18	20	37.7	37.3	37.0	36.7
43	9.06 804	107	9.07 103	108	10.92 897	9.99 701	17	30	56.5	56.0	55.5	55.0
44	9.06 911	107	9.07 211	109	10.92 789	9.99 699	16	40	75.3	74.7	74.0	73.3
								50	94.2	93.3	92.5	91.7
45	9.07 018	106	9.07 320	108	10.92 680	9.99 698	15					
46	9.07 124	107	9.07 428	108	10.92 572	9.99 696	14	′′	109	108	107	106
47	9.07 231	106	9.07 536	107	10.92 464	9.99 695	13	1	1.8	1.8	1.8	1.8
48	9.07 337	105	9.07 643	108	10.92 357	9.99 693	12	2	3.6	3.6	3.6	3.5
49	9.07 442	106	9.07 751	107	10.92 249	9.99 692	11	3	5.4	5.4	5.4	5.3
								4	7.3	7.2	7.1	7.1
50	9.07 548	105	9.07 858	106	10.92 142	9.99 690	10	5	9.1	9.0	8.9	8.8
51	9.07 653	105	9.07 964	107	10.92 036	9.99 689	9	6	10.9	10.8	10.7	10.6
52	9.07 758	105	9.08 071	106	10.91 929	9.99 687	8	7	12.7	12.6	12.5	12.4
53	9.07 863	105	9.08 177	106	10.91 823	9.99 686	7	8	14.5	14.4	14.3	14.1
54	9.07 968	104	9.08 283	106	10.91 717	9.99 684	6	9	16.4	16.2	16.0	15.9
55	9.08 072	104	9.08 389	106	10.91 611	9.99 683	5					
56	9.08 176	104	9.08 495	105	10.91 505	9.99 681	4	10	18.2	18.0	17.8	17.7
57	9.08 280	103	9.08 600	105	10.91 400	9.99 680	3	20	36.3	36.0	35.7	35.3
58	9.08 383	103	9.08 705	105	10.91 295	9.99 678	2	30	54.5	54.0	53.5	53.0
59	9.08 486	103	9.08 810	104	10.91 190	9.99 677	1	40	72.7	72.0	71.3	70.7
								50	90.8	90.0	89.2	88.3
60	9.08 589		9.08 914		10.91 086	9.99 675	0					
′	L Cos	d	L Ctn	c d	L Tan	L Sin	′	Proportional parts			

96° (276°) (263°) **83°**

Table III (Cont'd)

COMMON LOGARITHMS OF TRIGONOMETRIC FUNCTIONS

7° (187°)   (352°) 172°

′	L Sin	d	L Tan	c d	L Ctn	L Cos	′	Proportional parts			
0	9.08 589	103	9.08 914	105	10.91 086	9.99 675	60	′′	105	104	103	102
1	9.08 692	103	9.09 019	104	10.90 981	9.99 674	59					
2	9.08 795	102	9.09 123	104	10.90 877	9.99 672	58	1	1.8	1.7	1.7	1.7
3	9.08 897	102	9.09 227	103	10.90 773	9.99 670	57	2	3.5	3.5	3.4	3.4
4	9.08 999	102	9.09 330	104	10.90 670	9.99 669	56	3	5.2	5.2	5.2	5.1
								4	7.0	6.9	6.9	6.8
5	9.09 101	101	9.09 434	103	10.90 566	9.99 667	55					
6	9.09 202	102	9.09 537	103	10.90 463	9.99 666	54	5	8.8	8.7	8.6	8.5
7	9.09 304	101	9.09 640	102	10.90 360	9.99 664	53	6	10.5	10.4	10.3	10.2
8	9.09 405	101	9.09 742	103	10.90 258	9.99 663	52	7	12.2	12.1	12.0	11.9
9	9.09 506	100	9.09 845	102	10.90 155	9.99 661	51	8	14.0	13.9	13.7	13.6
								9	15.8	15.6	15.4	15.3
10	9.09 606	101	9.09 947	102	10.90 053	9.99 659	50					
11	9.09 707	100	9.10 049	101	10.89 951	9.99 658	49	10	17.5	17.3	17.2	17.0
12	9.09 807	100	9.10 150	102	10.89 850	9.99 656	48	20	35.0	34.7	34.3	34.0
13	9.09 907	99	9.10 252	101	10.89 748	9.99 655	47	30	52.5	52.0	51.5	51.0
14	9.10 006	100	9.10 353	101	10.89 647	9.99 653	46	40	70.0	69.3	68.7	68.0
								50	87.5	86.7	85.8	85.0
15	9.10 106	99	9.10 454	101	10.89 546	9.99 651	45					
16	9.10 205	99	9.10 555	101	10.89 445	9.99 650	44	′′	101	100	99	98
17	9.10 304	98	9.10 656	100	10.89 344	9.99 648	43					
18	9.10 402	99	9.10 756	100	10.89 244	9.99 647	42	1	1.7	1.7	1.6	1.6
19	9.10 501	98	9.10 856	100	10.89 144	9.99 645	41	2	3.4	3.3	3.3	3.3
								3	5.0	5.0	5.0	4.9
20	9.10 599	98	9.10 956	100	10.89 044	9.99 643	40	4	6.7	6.7	6.6	6.5
21	9.10 697	98	9.11 056	99	10.88 944	9.99 642	39					
22	9.10 795	98	9.11 155	99	10.88 845	9.99 640	38	5	8.4	8.3	8.2	8.2
23	9.10 893	97	9.11 254	99	10.88 746	9.99 638	37	6	10.1	10.0	9.9	9.8
24	9.10 990	97	9.11 353	99	10.88 647	9.99 637	36	7	11.8	11.7	11.6	11.4
								8	13.5	13.3	13.2	13.1
25	9.11 087	97	9.11 452	99	10.88 548	9.99 635	35	9	15.2	15.0	14.8	14.7
26	9.11 184	97	9.11 551	98	10.88 449	9.99 633	34					
27	9.11 281	96	9.11 649	98	10.88 351	9.99 632	33	10	16.8	16.7	16.5	16.3
28	9.11 377	97	9.11 747	98	10.88 253	9.99 630	32	20	33.7	33.3	33.0	32.7
29	9.11 474	96	9.11 845	98	10.88 155	9.99 629	31	30	50.5	50.0	49.5	49.0
								40	67.3	66.7	66.0	65.3
30	9.11 570	96	9.11 943	97	10.88 057	9.99 627	30	50	84.2	83.3	82.5	81.7
31	9.11 666	95	9.12 040	98	10.87 960	9.99 625	29					
32	9.11 761	96	9.12 138	97	10.87 862	9.99 624	28	′′	97	96	95	94
33	9.11 857	95	9.12 235	97	10.87 765	9.99 622	27					
34	9.11 952	95	9.12 332	96	10.87 668	9.99 620	26	1	1.6	1.6	1.6	1.6
								2	3.2	3.2	3.2	3.1
35	9.12 047	95	9.12 428	97	10.87 572	9.99 618	25	3	4.8	4.8	4.8	4.7
36	9.12 142	94	9.12 525	96	10.87 475	9.99 617	24	4	6.5	6.4	6.3	6.3
37	9.12 236	95	9.12 621	96	10.87 379	9.99 615	23					
38	9.12 331	94	9.12 717	96	10.87 283	9.99 613	22	5	8.1	8.0	7.9	7.8
39	9.12 425	94	9.12 813	96	10.87 187	9.99 612	21	6	9.7	9.6	9.5	9.4
								7	11.3	11.2	11.1	11.0
40	9.12 519	93	9.12 909	95	10.87 091	9.99 610	20	8	12.9	12.8	12.7	12.5
41	9.12 612	94	9.13 004	95	10.86 996	9.99 608	19	9	14.6	14.4	14.2	14.1
42	9.12 706	93	9.13 099	95	10.86 901	9.99 607	18					
43	9.12 799	93	9.13 194	95	10.86 806	9.99 605	17	10	16.2	16.0	15.8	15.7
44	9.12 892	93	9.13 289	95	10.86 711	9.99 603	16	20	32.3	32.0	31.7	31.3
								30	48.5	48.0	47.5	47.0
45	9.12 985	93	9.13 384	94	10.86 616	9.99 601	15	40	64.7	64.0	63.3	62.7
46	9.13 078	93	9.13 478	95	10.86 522	9.99 600	14	50	80.8	80.0	79.2	78.3
47	9.13 171	92	9.13 573	94	10.86 427	9.99 598	13					
48	9.13 263	92	9.13 667	94	10.86 333	9.99 596	12	′′	93	92	91	90
49	9.13 355	92	9.13 761	93	10.86 239	9.99 595	11					
								1	1.6	1.5	1.5	1.5
50	9.13 447	92	9.13 854	94	10.86 146	9.99 593	10	2	3.1	3.1	3.0	3.0
51	9.13 539	91	9.13 948	93	10.86 052	9.99 591	9	3	4.6	4.6	4.6	4.5
52	9.13 630	92	9.14 041	93	10.85 959	9.99 589	8	4	6.2	6.1	6.1	6.0
53	9.13 722	91	9.14 134	93	10.85 866	9.99 588	7					
54	9.13 813	91	9.14 227	93	10.85 773	9.99 586	6	5	7.8	7.7	7.6	7.5
								6	9.3	9.2	9.1	9.0
55	9.13 904	90	9.14 320	92	10.85 680	9.99 584	5	7	10.8	10.7	10.6	10.5
56	9.13 994	91	9.14 412	92	10.85 588	9.99 582	4	8	12.4	12.3	12.1	12.0
57	9.14 085	90	9.14 504	93	10.85 496	9.99 581	3	9	14.0	13.8	13.6	13.5
58	9.14 175	91	9.14 597	91	10.85 403	9.99 579	2					
59	9.14 266	90	9.14 688	92	10.85 312	9.99 577	1	10	15.5	15.3	15.2	15.0
								20	31.0	30.7	30.3	30.0
60	9.14 356		9.14 780		10.85 220	9.99 575	0	30	46.5	36.0	45.5	45.0
								40	62.0	61.3	60.7	60.0
								50	77.5	76.7	75.8	75.0
′	L Cos	d	L Ctn	c d	L Tan	L Sin	′	Proportional parts			

Table III (Cont'd)

COMMON LOGARITHMS OF TRIGONOMETRIC FUNCTIONS

8° (188°) (351°) **171°**

′	L Sin	d	L Tan	c d	L Ctn	L Cos	′	Proportional parts			
								′′	92	91	90
0	9.14 356	89	9.14 780	92	10.85 220	9.99 575	60				
1	9.14 455	90	9.14 872	91	10.85 128	9.99 574	59	1	1.5	1.5	1.5
2	9.14 535	89	9.14 963	91	10.85 037	9.99 572	58	2	3.1	3.0	3.0
3	9.14 624	90	9.15 054	91	10.84 946	9.99 570	57	3	4.6	4.6	4.5
4	9.14 714	89	9.15 145	91	10.84 855	9.99 568	56	4	6.1	6.1	6.0
5	9.14 803	88	9.15 236	91	10.84 764	9.99 566	55				
6	9.14 891	89	9.15 327	90	10.84 673	9.99 565	54	5	7.7	7.6	7.5
7	9.14 980	89	9.15 417	91	10.84 583	9.99 563	53	6	9.2	9.1	9.0
8	9.15 069	88	9.15 508	90	10.84 492	9.99 561	52	7	10.7	10.6	10.5
9	9.15 157	88	9.15 598	90	10.84 402	9.99 559	51	8	12.3	12.1	12.0
								9	13.8	13.6	13.5
10	9.15 245	88	9.15 688	89	10.84 312	9.99 557	50				
11	9.15 333	88	9.15 777	90	10.84 223	9.99 556	49	10	15.3	15.2	15.0
12	9.15 421	87	9.15 867	89	10.84 133	9.99 554	48	20	30.7	30.3	30.0
13	9.15 508	88	9.15 956	90	10.84 044	9.99 552	47	30	46.0	45.5	45.0
14	9.15 596	87	9.16 046	89	10.83 954	9.99 550	46	40	61.3	60.7	60.0
								50	76.7	75.8	75.0
15	9.15 683	87	9.16 135	89	10.83 865	9.99 548	45				
16	9.15 770	87	9.16 224	88	10.83 776	9.99 546	44	′′	89	88	87
17	9.15 857	87	9.16 312	89	10.83 688	9.99 545	43	1	1.5	1.5	1.4
18	9.15 944	86	9.16 401	88	10.83 599	9.99 543	42	2	3.0	2.9	2.9
19	9.16 030	86	9.16 489	88	10.83 511	9.99 541	41	3	4.4	4.4	4.4
								4	5.9	5.9	5.8
20	9.16 116	87	9.16 577	88	10.83 423	9.99 539	40				
21	9.16 203	86	9.16 665	88	10.83 335	9.99 537	39	5	7.4	7.3	7.2
22	9.16 289	85	9.16 753	88	10.83 247	9.99 535	38	6	8.9	8.8	8.7
23	9.16 374	86	9.16 841	87	10.83 159	9.99 533	37	7	10.4	10.3	10.2
24	9.16 460	85	9.16 928	88	10.83 072	9.99 532	36	8	11.9	11.7	11.6
								9	13.4	13.2	13.0
25	9.16 545	86	9.17 016	87	10.82 984	9.99 530	35				
26	9.16 631	85	9.17 103	87	10.82 897	9.99 528	34	10	14.8	14.7	14.5
27	9.16 716	85	9.17 190	87	10.82 810	9.99 526	33	20	29.7	29.3	29.0
28	9.16 801	85	9.17 277	86	10.82 723	9.99 524	32	30	44.5	44.0	43.5
29	9.16 886	84	9.17 363	87	10.82 637	9.99 522	31	40	59.3	58.7	58.0
								50	74.2	73.3	72.5
30	9.16 970	85	9.17 450	86	10.82 550	9.99 520	30				
31	9.17 055	84	9.17 536	86	10.82 464	9.99 518	29	′′	86	85	84
32	9.17 139	84	9.17 622	86	10.82 378	9.99 517	28	1	1.4	1.4	1.4
33	9.17 223	84	9.17 708	86	10.82 292	9.99 515	27	2	2.9	2.8	2.8
34	9.17 307	84	9.17 794	86	10.82 206	9.99 513	26	3	4.3	4.2	4.2
								4	5.7	5.7	5.6
35	9.17 391	83	9.17 880	85	10.82 120	9.99 511	25				
36	9.17 474	84	9.17 965	86	10.82 035	9.99 509	24	5	7.2	7.1	7.0
37	9.17 558	83	9.18 051	85	10.81 949	9.99 507	23	6	8.6	8.5	8.4
38	9.17 641	83	9.18 136	85	10.81 864	9.99 505	22	7	10.0	9.9	9.8
39	9.17 724	83	9.18 221	85	10.81 779	9.99 503	21	8	11.5	11.3	11.2
								9	12.9	12.8	12.6
40	9.17 807	83	9.18 306	85	10.81 694	9.99 501	20				
41	9.17 890	83	9.18 391	84	10.81 609	9.99 499	19	10	14.3	14.2	14.0
42	9.17 973	82	9.18 475	85	10.81 525	9.99 497	18	20	28.7	28.3	28.0
43	9.18 055	82	9.18 560	84	10.81 440	9.99 495	17	30	43.0	42.5	42.0
44	9.18 137	83	9.18 644	84	10.81 356	9.99 494	16	40	57.3	56.7	56.0
								50	71.7	70.8	70.0
45	9.18 220	82	9.18 728	84	10.81 272	9.99 492	15				
46	9.18 302	81	9.18 812	84	10.81 188	9.99 490	14	′′	83	82	81
47	9.18 383	82	9.18 896	83	10.81 104	9.99 488	13	1	1.4	1.4	1.4
48	9.18 465	82	9.18 979	84	10.81 021	9.99 486	12	2	2.8	2.7	2.7
49	9.18 547	81	9.19 063	83	10.80 937	9.99 484	11	3	4.2	4.1	4.0
								4	5.5	5.5	5.4
50	9.18 628	81	9.19 146	83	10.80 854	9.99 482	10				
51	9.18 709	81	9.19 229	83	10.80 771	9.99 480	9	5	6.9	6.8	6.8
52	9.18 790	81	9.19 312	83	10.80 688	9.99 478	8	6	8.3	8.2	8.1
53	9.18 871	81	9.19 395	83	10.80 605	9.99 476	7	7	9.7	9.6	9.4
54	9.18 952	81	9.19 478	83	10.80 522	9.99 474	6	8	11.1	10.9	10.8
								9	12.4	12.3	12.2
55	9.19 033	80	9.19 561	82	10.80 439	9.99 472	5				
56	9.19 113	80	9.19 643	82	10.80 357	9.99 470	4	10	13.8	13.7	13.5
57	9.19 193	80	9.19 725	82	10.80 275	9.99 468	3	20	27.7	27.3	27.0
58	9.19 273	80	9.19 807	82	10.80 193	9.99 466	2	30	41.5	41.0	40.5
59	9.19 353	80	9.19 889	82	10.80 111	9.99 464	1	40	55.3	54.7	54.0
								50	69.2	68.3	67.5
60	9.19 433		9.19 971		10.80 029	9.99 462	0				
′	L Cos	d	L Ctn	c d	L Tan	L Sin	′	Proportional parts			

98° (278°) (261°) **81°**

Table III (Cont'd)
COMMON LOGARITHMS OF TRIGONOMETRIC FUNCTIONS

9° (189°)   (350°) 170°

′	L Sin	d	L Tan	c d	L Ctn	L Cos	′
0	9.19 433	80	9.19 971	82	10.80 029	9.99 462	60
1	9.19 513	79	9.20 053	81	10.79 947	9.99 460	59
2	9.19 592	80	9.20 134	82	10.79 866	9.99 458	58
3	9.19 672	79	9.20 216	81	10.79 784	9.99 456	57
4	9.19 751	79	9.20 297	81	10.79 703	9.99 454	56
5	9.19 830	79	9.20 378	81	10.79 622	9.99 452	55
6	9.19 909	79	9.20 459	81	10.79 541	9.99 450	54
7	9.19 988	79	9.20 540	81	10.79 460	9.99 448	53
8	9.20 067	78	9.20 621	80	10.79 379	9.99 446	52
9	9.20 145	78	9.20 701	81	10.79 299	9.99 444	51
10	9.20 223	79	9.20 782	80	10.79 218	9.99 442	50
11	9.20 302	78	9.20 862	80	10.79 138	9.99 440	49
12	9.20 380	78	9.20 942	80	10.79 058	9.99 438	48
13	9.20 458	77	9.21 022	80	10.78 978	9.99 436	47
14	9.20 535	78	9.21 102	80	10.78 898	9.99 434	46
15	9.20 613	78	9.21 182	79	10.78 818	9.99 432	45
16	9.20 691	77	9.21 261	80	10.78 739	9.99 429	44
17	9.20 768	77	9.21 341	79	10.78 659	9.99 427	43
18	9.20 845	77	9.21 420	79	10.78 580	9.99 425	42
19	9.20 922	77	9.21 499	79	10.78 501	9.99 423	41
20	9.20 999	77	9.21 578	79	10.78 422	9.99 421	40
21	9.21 076	77	9.21 657	79	10.78 343	9.99 419	39
22	9.21 153	76	9.21 736	78	10.78 264	9.99 417	38
23	9.21 229	77	9.21 814	79	10.78 186	9.99 415	37
24	9.21 306	76	9.21 893	78	10.78 107	9.99 413	36
25	9.21 382	76	9.21 971	78	10.78 029	9.99 411	35
26	9.21 458	76	9.22 049	78	10.77 951	9.99 409	34
27	9.21 534	76	9.22 127	78	10.77 873	9.99 407	33
28	9.21 610	75	9.22 205	78	10.77 795	9.99 404	32
29	9.21 685	76	9.22 283	78	10.77 717	9.99 402	31
30	9.21 761	75	9.22 361	77	10.77 639	9.99 400	30
31	9.21 836	76	9.22 438	78	10.77 562	9.99 398	29
32	9.21 912	75	9.22 516	77	10.77 484	9.99 396	28
33	9.21 987	75	9.22 593	77	10.77 407	9.99 394	27
34	9.22 062	75	9.22 670	77	10.77 330	9.99 392	26
35	9.22 137	74	9.22 747	77	10.77 253	9.99 390	25
36	9.22 211	75	9.22 824	77	10.77 176	9.99 388	24
37	9.22 286	75	9.22 901	76	10.77 099	9.99 385	23
38	9.22 361	74	9.22 977	77	10.77 023	9.99 383	22
39	9.22 435	74	9.23 054	76	10.76 946	9.99 381	21
40	9.22 509	74	9.23 130	76	10.76 870	9.99 379	20
41	9.22 583	74	9.23 206	77	10.76 794	9.99 377	19
42	9.22 657	74	9.23 283	76	10.76 717	9.99 375	18
43	9.22 731	74	9.23 359	76	10.76 641	9.99 372	17
44	9.22 805	73	9.23 435	75	10.76 565	9.99 370	16
45	9.22 878	74	9.23 510	76	10.76 490	9.99 368	15
46	9.22 952	73	9.23 586	75	10.76 414	9.99 366	14
47	9.23 025	73	9.23 661	76	10.76 339	9.99 364	13
48	9.23 098	73	9.23 737	75	10.76 263	9.99 362	12
49	9.23 171	73	9.23 812	75	10.76 188	9.99 359	11
50	9.23 244	73	9.23 887	75	10.76 113	9.99 357	10
51	9.23 317	73	9.23 962	75	10.76 038	9.99 355	9
52	9.23 390	72	9.24 037	75	10.75 963	9.99 353	8
53	9.23 462	73	9.24 112	74	10.75 888	9.99 351	7
54	9.23 535	72	9.24 186	75	10.75 814	9.99 348	6
55	9.23 607	72	9.24 261	74	10.75 739	9.99 346	5
56	9.23 679	73	9.24 335	75	10.75 665	9.99 344	4
57	9.23 752	71	9.24 410	74	10.75 590	9.99 342	3
58	9.23 823	72	9.24 484	74	10.75 516	9.99 340	2
59	9.23 895	72	9.24 558	74	10.75 442	9.99 337	1
60	9.23 967		9.24 632		10.75 368	9.99 335	0
′	L Cos	d	L Ctn	c d	L Tan	L Sin	′

Proportional parts

″	80	79	78	77
1	1.3	1.3	1.3	1.3
2	2.7	2.6	2.6	2.6
3	4.0	4.0	3.9	3.8
4	5.3	5.3	5.2	5.1
5	6.7	6.6	6.5	6.4
6	8.0	7.9	7.8	7.7
7	9.3	9.2	9.1	9.0
8	10.7	10.5	10.4	10.3
9	12.0	11.8	11.7	11.6
10	13.3	13.2	13.0	12.8
20	26.7	26.3	26.0	25.7
30	40.0	39.5	39.0	38.5
40	53.3	52.7	52.0	51.3
50	66.7	65.8	65.0	64.2

″	76	75	74	73
1	1.3	1.2	1.2	1.2
2	2.5	2.5	2.5	2.4
3	3.8	3.8	3.7	3.6
4	5.1	5.0	4.9	4.9
5	6.3	6.2	6.2	6.1
6	7.6	7.5	7.4	7.3
7	8.9	8.8	8.6	8.5
8	10.1	10.0	9.9	9.7
9	11.4	11.2	11.1	11.0
10	12.7	12.5	12.3	12.2
20	25.3	25.0	24.7	24.3
30	38.0	37.5	37.0	36.5
40	50.7	50.0	49.3	48.7
50	63.3	62.5	61.7	60.8

″	72	71	3	2
1	1.2	1.2	0.0	0.0
2	2.4	2.4	0.1	0.1
3	3.6	3.6	0.2	0.1
4	4.8	4.7	0.2	0.1
5	6.0	5.9	0.2	0.2
6	7.2	7.1	0.3	0.2
7	8.4	8.3	0.4	0.2
8	9.6	9.5	0.4	0.3
9	10.8	10.6	0.4	0.3
10	12.0	11.8	0.5	0.3
20	24.0	23.7	1.0	0.7
30	36.0	35.5	1.5	1.0
40	48.0	47.3	2.0	1.3
50	60.0	59.2	2.5	1.7

Proportional parts

99° (279°)   (260°) 80°

Table III (Cont'd)

COMMON LOGARITHMS OF TRIGONOMETRIC FUNCTIONS

10° (190°)   (349°) **169°**

′	L Sin	d	L Tan	c d	L Ctn	L Cos	d	′	Proportional parts		
0	9.23 967	72	9.24 632	74	10.75 368	9.99 335	2	60			
1	9.24 039	71	9.24 706	73	10.75 294	9.99 333	2	59			
2	9.24 110	71	9.24 779	74	10.75 221	9.99 331	3	58			
3	9.24 181	72	9.24 853	73	10.75 147	9.99 328	2	57			
4	9.24 253	71	9.24 926	74	10.75 074	9.99 326	2	56			
5	9.24 324	71	9.25 000	73	10.75 000	9.99 324	2	55	′′	74	73	72
6	9.24 395	71	9.25 073	73	10.74 927	9.99 322	3	54	1	1.2	1.2	1.2
7	9.24 466	70	9.25 146	73	10.74 854	9.99 319	2	53	2	2.5	2.4	2.4
8	9.24 536	71	9.25 219	73	10.74 781	9.99 317	2	52	3	3.7	3.6	3.6
9	9.24 607	70	9.25 292	73	10.74 708	9.99 315	2	51	4	4.9	4.9	4.8
10	9.24 677	71	9.25 365	72	10.74 635	9.99 313	3	50	5	6.2	6.1	6.0
11	9.24 748	70	9.25 437	73	10.74 563	9.99 310	2	49	6	7.4	7.3	7.2
12	9.24 818	70	9.25 510	72	10.74 490	9.99 308	2	48	7	8.6	8.5	8.4
13	9.24 888	70	9.25 582	73	10.74 418	9.99 306	2	47	8	9.9	9.7	9.6
14	9.24 958	70	9.25 655	72	10.74 345	9.99 304	3	46	9	11.1	11.0	10.8
15	9.25 028	70	9.25 727	72	10.74 273	9.99 301	2	45				
16	9.25 098	70	9.25 799	72	10.74 201	9.99 299	2	44	10	12.3	12.2	12.0
17	9.25 168	69	9.25 871	72	10.74 129	9.99 297	3	43	20	24.7	24.3	24.0
18	9.25 237	70	9.25 943	72	10.74 057	9.99 294	2	42	30	37.0	36.5	36.0
19	9.25 307	69	9.26 015	71	10.73 985	9.99 292	2	41	40	49.3	48.7	48.0
20	9.25 376	69	9.26 086	72	10.73 914	9.99 290	2	40	50	61.7	60.8	60.0
21	9.25 445	69	9.26 158	71	10.73 842	9.99 288	3	39				
22	9.25 514	69	9.26 229	72	10.73 771	9.99 285	2	38				
23	9.25 583	69	9.26 301	71	10.73 699	9.99 283	2	37	′′	71	70	69
24	9.25 652	69	9.26 372	71	10.73 628	9.99 281	3	36	1	1.2	1.2	1.2
25	9.25 721	69	9.26 443	71	10.73 557	9.99 278	2	35	2	2.4	2.3	2.3
26	9.25 790	68	9.26 514	71	10.73 486	9.99 276	2	34	3	3.6	3.5	3.4
27	9.25 858	69	9.26 585	70	10.73 415	9.99 274	3	33	4	4.7	4.7	4.6
28	9.25 927	68	9.26 655	71	10.73 345	9.99 271	2	32				
29	9.25 995	68	9.26 726	71	10.73 274	9.99 269	2	31	5	5.9	5.8	5.8
30	9.26 063	68	9.26 797	70	10.73 203	9.99 267	3	30	6	7.1	7.0	6.9
31	9.26 131	68	9.26 867	70	10.73 133	9.99 264	2	29	7	8.3	8.2	8.0
32	9.26 199	68	9.26 937	71	10.73 063	9.99 262	2	28	8	9.5	9.3	9.2
33	9.26 267	68	9.27 008	70	10.72 992	9.99 260	3	27	9	10.6	10.5	10.4
34	9.26 335	68	9.27 078	70	10.72 922	9.99 257	2	26				
35	9.26 403	67	9.27 148	70	10.72 852	9.99 255	2	25	10	11.8	11.7	11.5
36	9.26 470	68	9.27 218	70	10.72 782	9.99 252	2	24	20	23.7	23.3	23.0
37	9.26 538	67	9.27 288	69	10.72 712	9.99 250	2	23	30	35.5	35.0	34.5
38	9.26 605	67	9.27 357	70	10.72 643	9.99 248	3	22	40	47.3	46.7	46.0
39	9.26 672	67	9.27 427	69	10.72 573	9.99 245	2	21	50	59.2	58.3	57.5
40	9.26 739	67	9.27 496	70	10.72 504	9.99 243	2	20	′′	68	67	66
41	9.26 806	67	9.27 566	69	10.72 434	9.99 241	3	19	1	1.1	1.1	1.1
42	9.26 873	67	9.27 635	69	10.72 365	9.99 238	2	18	2	2.3	2.2	2.2
43	9.26 940	67	9.27 704	69	10.72 296	9.99 236	3	17	3	3.4	3.4	3.3
44	9.27 007	66	9.27 773	69	10.72 227	9.99 233	2	16	4	4.5	4.5	4.4
45	9.27 073	67	9.27 842	69	10.72 158	9.99 231	2	15	5	5.7	5.6	5.5
46	9.27 140	66	9.27 911	69	10.72 089	9.99 229	3	14	6	6.8	6.7	6.6
47	9.27 206	67	9.27 980	69	10.72 020	9.99 226	2	13	7	7.9	7.8	7.7
48	9.27 273	66	9.28 049	68	10.71 951	9.99 224	3	12	8	9.1	8.9	8.8
49	9.27 339	66	9.28 117	69	10.71 883	9.99 221	2	11	9	10.2	10.0	9.9
50	9.27 405	66	9.28 186	68	10.71 814	9.99 219	2	10	10	11.3	11.2	11.0
51	9.27 471	66	9.28 254	69	10.71 746	9.99 217	3	9	20	22.7	22.3	22.0
52	9.27 537	65	9.28 323	68	10.71 677	9.99 214	2	8	30	34.0	33.5	33.0
53	9.27 602	66	9.28 391	68	10.71 609	9.99 212	3	7	40	45.3	44.7	44.0
54	9.27 668	66	9.28 459	68	10.71 541	9.99 209	2	6	50	56.7	55.8	55.0
55	9.27 734	65	9.28 527	68	10.71 473	9.99 207	3	5				
56	9.27 799	65	9.28 595	67	10.71 405	9.99 204	2	4				
57	9.27 864	66	9.28 662	68	10.71 338	9.99 202	2	3				
58	9.27 930	65	9.28 730	68	10.71 270	9.99 200	3	2				
59	9.27 995	65	9.28 798	67	10.71 202	9.99 197	2	1				
60	9.28 060	—	9.28 865		10.71 135	9.99 195		0				
′	L Cos	d	L Ctn	c d	L Tan	L Sin	d	′	Proportional parts		

100° (280°)   (259°) **79°**

Table III (Cont'd)

COMMON LOGARITHMS OF TRIGONOMETRIC FUNCTIONS

11° (191°)   (348°) **168°**

′	L Sin	d	L Tan	c d	L Ctn	L Cos	d	′	Proportional parts		
0	9.28 060	65	9.28 865	68	10.71 135	9.99 195	3	60			
1	9.28 125	65	9.28 933	67	10.71 067	9.99 192	2	59			
2	9.28 190	64	9.29 000	67	10.71 000	9.99 190	3	58			
3	9.28 254	65	9.29 067	67	10.70 933	9.99 187	2	57			
4	9.28 319	65	9.29 134	67	10.70 866	9.99 185	3	56			
5	9.28 384	64	9.29 201	67	10.70 799	9.99 182	2	55			
6	9.28 448	64	9.29 268	67	10.70 732	9.99 180	3	54	′′	65	64	63
7	9.28 512	65	9.29 335	67	10.70 665	9.99 177	2	53				
8	9.28 577	64	9.29 402	66	10.70 598	9.99 175	3	52	1	1.1	1.1	1.0
9	9.28 641	64	9.29 468	67	10.70 532	9.99 172	2	51	2	2.2	2.1	2.1
									3	3.2	3.2	3.2
10	9.28 705	64	9.29 535	66	10.70 465	9.99 170	3	50	4	4.3	4.3	4.2
11	9.28 769	64	9.29 601	67	10.70 399	9.99 167	2	49				
12	9.28 833	63	9.29 668	66	10.70 332	9.99 165	3	48	5	5.4	5.3	5.2
13	9.28 896	64	9.29 734	66	10.70 266	9.99 162	2	47	6	6.5	6.4	6.3
14	9.28 960	64	9.29 800	66	10.70 200	9.99 160	3	46	7	7.6	7.5	7.4
									8	8.7	8.5	8.4
15	9.29 024	63	9.29 866	66	10.70 134	9.99 157	2	45	9	9.8	9.6	9.4
16	9.29 087	63	9.29 932	66	10.70 068	9.99 155	3	44				
17	9.29 150	64	9.29 998	66	10.70 002	9.99 152	2	43	10	10.8	10.7	10.5
18	9.29 214	63	9.30 064	66	10.69 936	9.99 150	3	42	20	21.7	21.3	21.0
19	9.29 277	63	9.30 130	65	10.69 870	9.99 147	2	41	30	32.5	32.0	31.5
									40	43.3	42.7	42.0
20	9.29 340	63	9.30 195	66	10.69 805	9.99 145	3	40	50	54.2	53.3	52.5
21	9.29 403	63	9.30 261	65	10.69 739	9.99 142	2	39				
22	9.29 466	63	9.30 326	65	10.69 674	9.99 140	3	38				
23	9.29 529	62	9.30 391	66	10.69 609	9.99 137	2	37	′′	62	61	60
24	9.29 591	63	9.30 457	65	10.69 543	9.99 135	3	36				
									1	1.0	1.0	1.0
25	9.29 654	62	9.30 522	65	10.69 478	9.99 132	2	35	2	2.1	2.0	2.0
26	9.29 716	63	9.30 587	65	10.69 413	9.99 130	3	34	3	3.1	3.0	3.0
27	9.29 779	62	9.30 652	65	10.69 348	9.99 127	3	33	4	4.1	4.1	4.0
28	9.29 841	62	9.30 717	65	10.69 283	9.99 124	2	32				
29	9.29 903	63	9.30 782	64	10.69 218	9.99 122	3	31	5	5.2	5.1	5.0
									6	6.2	6.1	6.0
30	9.29 966	62	9.30 846	65	10.69 154	9.99 119	2	30	7	7.2	7.1	7.0
31	9.30 028	62	9.30 911	64	10.69 089	9.99 117	3	29	8	8.3	8.1	8.0
32	9.30 090	61	9.30 975	65	10.69 025	9.99 114	2	28	9	9.3	9.2	9.0
33	9.30 151	62	9.31 040	64	10.68 960	9.99 112	3	27				
34	9.30 213	62	9.31 104	64	10.68 896	9.99 109	3	26	10	10.3	10.2	10.0
									20	20.7	20.3	20.0
35	9.30 275	61	9.31 168	65	10.68 832	9.99 106	2	25	30	31.0	30.5	30.0
36	9.30 336	62	9.31 233	64	10.68 767	9.99 104	3	24	40	41.3	40.7	40.0
37	9.30 398	61	9.31 297	64	10.68 703	9.99 101	2	23	50	51.7	50.8	50.0
38	9.30 459	62	9.31 361	64	10.68 639	9.99 099	3	22				
39	9.30 521	61	9.31 425	64	10.68 575	9.99 096	3	21				
40	9.30 582	61	9.31 489	63	10.68 511	9.99 093	2	20	′′	59	3	2
41	9.30 643	61	9.31 552	64	10.68 448	9.99 091	3	19	1	1.0	0.0	0.0
42	9.30 704	61	9.31 616	63	10.68 384	9.99 088	2	18	2	2.0	0.1	0.1
43	9.30 765	61	9.31 679	64	10.68 321	9.99 086	3	17	3	3.0	0.2	0.1
44	9.30 826	61	9.31 743	63	10.68 257	9.99 083	3	16	4	3.9	0.2	0.1
45	9.30 887	60	9.31 806	64	10.68 194	9.99 080	2	15	5	4.9	0.2	0.2
46	9.30 947	61	9.31 870	63	10.68 130	9.99 078	3	14	6	5.9	0.3	0.2
47	9.31 008	60	9.31 933	63	10.68 067	9.99 075	3	13	7	6.9	0.4	0.2
48	9.31 068	61	9.31 996	63	10.68 004	9.99 072	2	12	8	7.9	0.4	0.3
49	9.31 129	60	9.32 059	63	10.67 941	9.99 070	3	11	9	8.8	0.4	0.3
50	9.31 189	61	9.32 122	63	10.67 878	9.99 067	3	10	10	9.8	0.5	0.3
51	9.31 250	60	9.32 185	63	10.67 815	9.99 064	2	9	20	19.7	1.0	0.7
52	9.31 310	60	9.32 248	63	10.67 752	9.99 062	3	8	30	29.5	1.5	1.0
53	9.31 370	60	9.32 311	62	10.67 689	9.99 059	3	7	40	39.3	2.0	1.3
54	9.31 430	60	9.32 373	63	10.67 627	9.99 056	2	6	50	49.2	2.5	1.7
55	9.31 490	59	9.32 436	62	10.67 564	9.99 054	3	5				
56	9.31 549	60	9.32 498	63	10.67 502	9.99 051	3	4				
57	9.31 609	60	9.32 561	62	10.67 439	9.99 048	2	3				
58	9.31 669	59	9.32 623	62	10.67 377	9.99 046	3	2				
59	9.31 728	60	9.32 685	62	10.67 315	9.99 043	3	1				
60	9.31 788	—	9.32 747		10.67 253	9.99 040		0				
′	L Cos	d	L Ctn	c d	L Tan	L Sin	d	′	Proportional parts		

101° (281°)   (258°) **78°**

Table III (Cont'd)
COMMON LOGARITHMS OF TRIGONOMETRIC FUNCTIONS

′	L Sin	d	L Tan	c d	L Ctn	L Cos	d	′	Proportional parts		
0	9.31 788	59	9.32 747	63	10.67 253	9.99 040	2	60			
1	9.31 847	60	9.32 810	62	10.67 190	9.99 038	3	59			
2	9.31 907	59	9.32 872	61	10.67 128	9.99 035	3	58			
3	9.31 966	59	9.32 933	62	10.67 067	9.99 032	2	57			
4	9.32 025	59	9.32 995	62	10.67 005	9.99 030	3	56			
5	9.32 084	59	9.33 057	62	10.66 943	9.99 027	3	55	″	63	62	61
6	9.32 143	59	9.33 119	61	10.66 881	9.99 024	2	54				
7	9.32 202	59	9.33 180	62	10.66 820	9.99 022	3	53	1	1.0	1.0	1.0
8	9.32 261	58	9.33 242	61	10.66 758	9.99 019	3	52	2	2.1	2.1	2.0
9	9.32 319	59	9.33 303	62	10.66 697	9.99 016	3	51	3	3.2	3.1	3.0
									4	4.2	4.1	4.1
10	9.32 378	59	9.33 365	61	10.66 635	9.99 013	2	50				
11	9.32 437	58	9.33 426	61	10.66 574	9.99 011	3	49	5	5.2	5.2	5.1
12	9.32 495	58	9.33 487	61	10.66 513	9.99 008	3	48	6	6.3	6.2	6.1
13	9.32 553	59	9.33 548	61	10.66 452	9.99 005	3	47	7	7.4	7.2	7.1
14	9.32 612	58	9.33 609	61	10.66 391	9.99 002	2	46	8	8.4	8.3	8.1
									9	9.4	9.3	9.2
15	9.32 670	58	9.33 670	61	10.66 330	9.99 000	3	45				
16	9.32 728	58	9.33 731	61	10.66 269	9.98 997	3	44	10	10.5	10.3	10.2
17	9.32 786	58	9.33 792	61	10.66 208	9.98 994	3	43	20	21.0	20.7	20.3
18	9.32 844	58	9.33 853	60	10.66 147	9.98 991	2	42	30	31.5	31.0	30.5
19	9.32 902	58	9.33 913	61	10.66 087	9.98 989	3	41	40	42.0	41.3	40.7
									50	52.5	51.7	50.8
20	9.32 960	58	9.33 974	60	10.66 026	9.98 986	3	40				
21	9.33 018	57	9.34 034	61	10.65 966	9.98 983	3	39				
22	9.33 075	58	9.34 095	60	10.65 905	9.98 980	2	38				
23	9.33 133	57	9.34 155	60	10.65 845	9.98 978	3	37	″	60	59	58
24	9.33 190	58	9.34 215	61	10.65 785	9.98 975	3	36	1	1.0	1.0	1.0
									2	2.0	2.0	1.9
25	9.33 248	57	9.34 276	60	10.65 724	9.98 972	3	35	3	3.0	3.0	2.9
26	9.33 305	57	9.34 336	60	10.65 664	9.98 969	2	34	4	4.0	3.9	3.9
27	9.33 362	58	9.34 396	60	10.65 604	9.98 967	3	33				
28	9.33 420	57	9.34 456	60	10.65 544	9.98 964	3	32	5	5.0	4.9	4.8
29	9.33 477	57	9.34 516	60	10.65 484	9.98 961	3	31	6	6.0	5.9	5.8
									7	7.0	6.9	6.8
30	9.33 534	57	9.34 576	59	10.65 424	9.98 958	3	30	8	8.0	7.9	7.7
31	9.33 591	56	9.34 635	60	10.65 365	9.98 955	2	29	9	9.0	8.8	8.7
32	9.33 647	57	9.34 695	60	10.65 305	9.98 953	3	28				
33	9.33 704	57	9.34 755	59	10.65 245	9.98 950	3	27	10	10.0	9.8	9.7
34	9.33 761	57	9.34 814	60	10.65 186	9.98 947	3	26	20	20.0	19.7	19.3
									30	30.0	29.5	29.0
35	9.33 818	56	9.34 874	59	10.65 126	9.98 944	3	25	40	40.0	39.3	38.7
36	9.33 874	57	9.34 933	59	10.65 067	9.98 941	3	24	50	50.0	49.2	48.3
37	9.33 931	56	9.34 992	59	10.65 008	9.98 938	2	23				
38	9.33 987	56	9.35 051	60	10.64 949	9.98 936	3	22				
39	9.34 043	57	9.35 111	59	10.64 889	9.98 933	3	21				
40	9.34 100	56	9.35 170	59	10.64 830	9.98 930	3	20	″	57	56	55
41	9.34 156	56	9.35 229	59	10.64 771	9.98 927	3	19	1	1.0	0.9	0.9
42	9.34 212	56	9.35 288	59	10.64 712	9.98 924	3	18	2	1.9	1.9	1.8
43	9.34 268	56	9.35 347	58	10.64 653	9.98 921	2	17	3	2.8	2.8	2.8
44	9.34 324	56	9.35 405	59	10.64 595	9.98 919	3	16	4	3.8	3.7	3.7
45	9.34 380	56	9.35 464	59	10.64 536	9.98 916	3	15	5	4.8	4.7	4.6
46	9.34 436	55	9.35 523	58	10.64 477	9.98 913	3	14	6	5.7	5.6	5.5
47	9.34 491	56	9.35 581	59	10.64 419	9.98 910	3	13	7	6.6	6.5	6.4
48	9.34 547	55	9.35 640	58	10.64 360	9.98 907	3	12	8	7.6	7.5	7.3
49	9.34 602	56	9.35 698	59	10.64 302	9.93 904	3	11	9	8.6	8.4	8.2
50	9.34 658	56	9.35 757	58	10.64 243	9.98 901	3	10	10	9.5	9.3	9.2
51	9.34 713	56	9.35 815	58	10.64 185	9.98 898	2	9	20	19.0	18.7	18.3
52	9.34 769	55	9.35 873	58	10.64 127	9.98 896	3	8	30	28.5	28.0	27.5
53	9.34 824	55	9.35 931	58	10.64 069	9.98 893	3	7	40	38.0	37.3	36.7
54	9.34 879	55	9.35 989	58	10.64 011	9.98 890	3	6	50	47.5	46.7	45.8
55	9.34 934	55	9.36 047	58	10.63 953	9.98 887	3	5				
56	9.34 989	55	9.36 105	58	10.63 895	9.98 884	3	4				
57	9.35 044	55	9.36 163	58	10.63 837	9.98 881	3	3				
58	9.35 099	55	9.36 221	58	10.63 779	9.98 878	3	2				
59	9.35 154	55	9.36 279	57	10.63 721	9.98 875	3	1				
60	9.35 209		9.36 336		10.63 664	9.98 872		0				
′	L Cos	d	L Ctn	c d	L Tan	L Sin	d	′	Proportional parts		

Table III (Cont'd)

COMMON LOGARITHMS OF TRIGONOMETRIC FUNCTIONS

13° (193°)   **(346°) 166°**

′	L Sin	d	L Tan	c d	L Ctn	L Cos	d	′	Proportional parts		
0	9.35 209	54	9.36 336	58	10.63 664 ⊛	9.98 872	3	60			
1	9.35 263	55	9.36 394	58	10.63 606	9.98 869	2	59			
2	9.35 318	55	9.36 452	57	10.63 548	9.98 867	3	58			
3	9.35 373	54	9.36 509	57	10.63 491	9.98 864	3	57			
4	9.35 427	54	9.36 566	58	10.63 434	9.98 861	3	56			
5	9.35 481	55	9.36 624	57	10.63 376	9.98 858	3	55			
6	9.35 536	54	9.36 681	57	10.63 319	9.98 855	3	54			
7	9.35 590	54	9.36 738	57	10.63 262	9.98 852	3	53	′′	57	56	55
8	9.35 644	54	9.36 795	57	10.63 205	9.98 849	3	52	1	1.0	0.9	0.9
9	9.35 698	54	9.36 852	57	10.63 148	9.98 846	3	51	2	1.9	1.9	1.8
10	9.35 752	54	9.36 909	57	10.63 091	9.98 843	3	50	3	2.8	2.8	2.8
11	9.35 806	54	9.36 966	57	10.63 034	9.98 840	3	49	4	3.8	3.7	3.7
12	9.35 860	54	9.37 023	57	10.62 977	9.98 837	3	48				
13	9.35 914	54	9.37 080	57	10.62 920	9.98 834	3	47	5	4.8	4.7	4.6
14	9.35 968	54	9.37 137	56	10.62 863	9.98 831	3	46	6	5.7	5.6	5.5
									7	6.6	6.5	6.4
15	9.36 022	53	9.37 193	57	10.62 807	9.98 828	3	45	8	7.6	7.5	7.3
16	9.36 075	54	9.37 250	56	10.62 750	9.98 825	3	44	9	8.6	8.4	8.2
17	9.36 129	53	9.37 306	57	10.62 694	9.98 822	3	43				
18	9.36 182	54	9.37 363	56	10.62 637	9.98 819	3	42	10	9.5	9.3	9.2
19	9.36 236	53	9.37 419	57	10.62 581	9.98 816	3	41	20	19.0	18.7	18.3
									30	28.5	28.0	27.5
20	9.36 289	53	9.37 476	56	10.62 524	9.98 813	3	40	40	38.0	37.3	36.7
21	9.36 342	53	9.37 532	56	10.62 468	9.98 810	3	39	50	47.5	46.7	45.8
22	9.36 395	54	9.37 588	56	10.62 412	9.98 807	3	38				
23	9.36 449	53	9.37 644	56	10.62 356	9.98 804	3	37	′′	54	53	52
24	9.36 502	53	9.37 700	56	10.62 300	9.98 801	3	36	1	0.9	0.9	0.9
25	9.36 555	53	9.37 756	56	10.62 244	9.98 798	3	35	2	1.8	1.8	1.7
26	9.36 608	52	9.37 812	56	10.62 188	9.98 795	3	34	3	2.7	2.6	2.6
27	9.36 660	53	9.37 868	56	10.62 132	9.98 792	3	33	4	3.6	3.5	3.5
28	9.36 713	53	9.37 924	56	10.62 076	9.98 789	3	32				
29	9.36 766	53	9.37 980	55	10.62 020	9.98 786	3	31	5	4.5	4.4	4.3
									6	5.4	5.3	5.2
30	9.36 819	52	9.38 035	56	10.61 965	9.98 783	3	30	7	6.3	6.2	6.1
31	9.36 871	53	9.38 091	56	10.61 909	9.98 780	3	29	8	7.2	7.1	6.9
32	9.36 924	52	9.38 147	55	10.61 853	9.98 777	3	28	9	8.1	8.0	7.8
33	9.36 976	52	9.38 202	55	10.61 798	9.98 774	3	27				
34	9.37 028	53	9.38 257	56	10.61 743	9.98 771	3	26	10	9.0	8.8	8.7
									20	18.0	17.7	17.3
35	9.37 081	52	9.38 313	55	10.61 687	9.98 768	3	25	30	27.0	26.5	26.0
36	9.37 133	52	9.38 368	55	10.61 632	9.98 765	3	24	40	36.0	35.3	34.7
37	9.37 185	52	9.38 423	56	10.61 577	9.98 762	3	23	50	45.0	44.2	43.3
38	9.37 237	52	9.38 479	55	10.61 521	9.98 759	3	22				
39	9.37 289	52	9.38 534	55	10.61 466	9.98 756	3	21	′′	5I	4	3	2
40	9.37 341	52	9.38 589	55	10.61 411	9.98 753	3	20	1	0.8	0.1	0.0	0.0
41	9.37 393	52	9.38 644	55	10.61 356	9.98 750	4	19	2	1.7	0.1	0.1	0.1
42	9.37 445	52	9.38 699	55	10.61 301	9.98 746	3	18	3	2.6	0.2	0.2	0.1
43	9.37 497	52	9.38 754	55	10.61 246	9.98 743	3	17	4	3.4	0.3	0.2	0.1
44	9.37 549	51	9.38 808	55	10.61 192	9.98 740	3	16					
									5	4.2	0.3	0.2	0.2
45	9.37 600	52	9.38 863	55	10.61 137	9.98 737	3	15	6	5.1	0.4	0.3	0.2
46	9.37 652	51	9.38 918	54	10.61 082	9.98 734	3	14	7	6.0	0.5	0.4	0.2
47	9.37 703	52	9.38 972	55	10.61 028	9.98 731	3	13	8	6.8	0.5	0.4	0.3
48	9.37 755	51	9.39 027	55	10.60 973	9.98 728	3	12	9	7.6	0.6	0.4	0.3
49	9.37 806	52	9.39 082	54	10.60 918	9.98 725	3	11					
									10	8.5	0.7	0.5	0.3
50	9.37 858	51	9.39 136	54	10.60 864	9.98 722	3	10	20	17.0	1.3	1.0	0.7
51	9.37 909	51	9.39 190	55	10.60 810	9.98 719	4	9	30	25.5	2.0	1.5	1.0
52	9.37 960	51	9.39 245	54	10.60 755	9.98 715	3	8	40	34.0	2.7	2.0	1.3
53	9.38 011	51	9.39 299	54	10.60 701	9.98 712	3	7	50	42.5	3.3	2.5	1.7
54	9.38 062	51	9.39 353	54	10.60 647	9.98 709	3	6					
55	9.38 113	51	9.39 407	54	10.60 593	9.98 706	3	5			
56	9.38 164	51	9.39 461	54	10.60 539	9.98 703	3	4			
57	9.38 215	51	9.39 515	54	10.60 485	9.98 700	3	3			
58	9.38 266	51	9.39 569	54	10.60 431	9.98 697	3	2			
59	9.38 317	51	9.39 623	54	10.60 377	9.98 694	4	1			
60	9.38 368		9.39 677		10.60 323	9.98 690		0			
′	L Cos	d	L Ctn	c d	L Tan	L Sin	d	′	Proportional parts		

103° (283°)   **(256°) 76°**

Table III (Cont'd)

COMMON LOGARITHMS OF TRIGONOMETRIC FUNCTIONS

14° (194°)   **(345°) 165°**

′	L Sin	d	L Tan	c d	L Ctn	L Cos	d	′	Proportional parts		
0	9.38 368	50	9.39 677	54	10.60 323	9.98 690	3	60			
1	9.38 418	51	9.39 731	54	10.60 269	9.98 687	3	59			
2	9.38 469	50	9.39 785	53	10.60 215	9.98 684	3	58			
3	9.38 519	51	9.39 838	54	10.60 162	9.98 681	3	57			
4	9.38 570	50	9.39 892	53	10.60 108	9.98 678	3	56			
5	9.38 620	50	9.39 945	54	10.60 055	9.98 675	4	55			
6	9.38 670	50	9.39 999	53	10.60 001	9.98 671	3	54			
7	9.38 721	50	9.40 052	54	10.59 948	9.98 668	3	53			
8	9.38 771	50	9.40 106	53	10.59 894	9.98 665	3	52	′′	54	53	52
9	9.38 821	50	9.40 159	53	10.59 841	9.98 662	3	51	1	0.9	0.9	0.9
10	9.38 871	50	9.40 212	54	10.59 788	9.98 659	3	50	2	1.8	1.8	1.7
11	9.38 921	50	9.40 266	53	10.59 734	9.98 656	4	49	3	2.7	2.6	2.6
12	9.38 971	50	9.40 319	53	10.59 681	9.98 652	3	48	4	3.6	3.5	3.5
13	9.39 021	50	9.40 372	53	10.59 628	9.98 649	3	47				
14	9.39 071	50	9.40 425	53	10.59 575	9.98 646	3	46	5	4.5	4.4	4.3
15	9.39 121	49	9.40 478	53	10.59 522	9.98 643	3	45	6	5.4	5.3	5.2
16	9.39 170	50	9.40 531	53	10.59 469	9.98 640	4	44	7	6.3	6.2	6.1
17	9.39 220	50	9.40 584	52	10.59 416	9.98 636	3	43	8	7.2	7.1	6.9
18	9.39 270	49	9.40 636	53	10.59 364	9.98 633	3	42	9	8.1	8.0	7.8
19	9.39 319	50	9.40 689	53	10.59 311	9.98 630	3	41				
20	9.39 369	49	9.40 742	53	10.59 258	9.98 627	4	40	10	9.0	8.8	8.7
21	9.39 418	49	9.40 795	52	10.59 205	9.98 623	3	39	20	18.0	17.7	17.3
22	9.39 467	50	9.40 847	53	10.59 153	9.98 620	3	38	30	27.0	26.5	26.0
23	9.39 517	49	9.40 900	52	10.59 100	9.98 617	3	37	40	36.0	35.3	34.7
24	9.39 566	49	9.40 952	53	10.59 048	9.98 614	4	36	50	45.0	44.2	43.3
25	9.39 615	49	9.41 005	52	10.58 995	9.98 610	3	35				
26	9.39 664	49	9.41 057	52	10.58 943	9.98 607	3	34	′′	51	50	49
27	9.39 713	49	9.41 109	52	10.58 891	9.98 604	3	33	1	0.8	0.8	0.8
28	9.39 762	49	9.41 161	53	10.58 839	9.98 601	4	32	2	1.7	1.7	1.6
29	9.39 811	49	9.41 214	52	10.58 786	9.98 597	3	31	3	2.6	2.5	2.4
30	9.39 860	49	9.41 266	52	10.58 734	9.98 594	3	30	4	3.4	3.3	3.3
31	9.39 909	49	9.41 318	52	10.58 682	9.98 591	3	29				
32	9.39 958	48	9.41 370	52	10.58 630	9.98 588	4	28	5	4.2	4.2	4.1
33	9.40 006	49	9.41 422	52	10.58 578	9.98 584	3	27	6	5.1	5.0	4.9
34	9.40 055	48	9.41 474	52	10.58 526	9.98 581	3	26	7	6.0	5.8	5.7
35	9.40 103	49	9.41 526	52	10.58 474	9.98 578	4	25	8	6.8	6.7	6.5
36	9.40 152	48	9.41 578	51	10.58 422	9.98 574	3	24	9	7.6	7.5	7.4
37	9.40 200	49	9.41 629	52	10.58 371	9.98 571	3	23				
38	9.40 249	48	9.41 681	52	10.58 319	9.98 568	3	22	10	8.5	8.3	8.2
39	9.40 297	49	9.41 733	51	10.58 267	9.98 565	4	21	20	17.0	16.7	16.3
40	9.40 346	48	9.41 784	52	10.58 216	9.98 561	3	20	30	25.5	25.0	24.5
41	9.40 394	48	9.41 836	51	10.58 164	9.98 558	3	19	40	34.0	33.3	32.7
42	9.40 442	48	9.41 887	52	10.58 113	9.98 555	4	18	50	42.5	41.7	40.8
43	9.40 490	48	9.41 939	51	10.58 061	9.98 551	3	17				
44	9.40 538	48	9.41 990	51	10.58 010	9.98 548	3	16	′′	48	47	4	3
45	9.40 586	48	9.42 041	52	10.57 959	9.98 545	4	15	1	0.8	0.8	0.1	0.0
46	9.40 634	48	9.42 093	51	10.57 907	9.98 541	3	14	2	1.6	1.6	0.1	0.1
47	9.40 682	48	9.42 144	51	10.57 856	9.98 538	4	13	3	2.4	2.4	0.2	0.2
48	9.40 730	48	9.42 195	51	10.57 805	9.98 535	4	12	4	3.2	3.1	0.3	0.2
49	9.40 778	47	9.42 246	51	10.57 754	9.98 531	3	11				
50	9.40 825	48	9.42 297	51	10.57 703	9.98 528	3	10	5	4.0	3.9	0.3	0.2
51	9.40 873	48	9.42 348	51	10.57 652	9.98 525	4	9	6	4.8	4.7	0.4	0.3
52	9.40 921	47	9.42 399	51	10.57 601	9.98 521	3	8	7	5.6	5.5	0.5	0.4
53	9.40 968	48	9.42 450	51	10.57 550	9.98 518	3	7	8	6.4	6.3	0.5	0.4
54	9.41 016	47	9.42 501	51	10.57 499	9.98 515	4	6	9	7.2	7.0	0.6	0.4
55	9.41 063	48	9.42 552	51	10.57 448	9.98 511	3	5				
56	9.41 111	47	9.42 603	50	10.57 397	9.98 508	3	4	10	8.0	7.8	0.7	0.5
57	9.41 158	47	9.42 653	51	10.57 347	9.98 505	4	3	20	16.0	15.7	1.3	1.0
58	9.41 205	47	9.42 704	51	10.57 296	9.98 501	3	2	30	24.0	23.5	2.0	1.5
59	9.41 252	48	9.42 755	50	10.57 245	9.98 498	4	1	40	32.0	31.3	2.7	2.0
60	9.41 300		9.42 805		10.57 195	9.98 494		0	50	40.0	39.2	3.3	2.5
′	L Cos	d	L Ctn	c d	L Tan	L Sin	d	′	Proportional parts		

104° (284°)   **(255°) 75°**

Table III (Cont'd)
COMMON LOGARITHMS OF TRIGONOMETRIC FUNCTIONS

15° (195°)   (344°) **164°**

′	L Sin	d	L Tan	c d	L Ctn	L Cos	d	′	Proportional parts
0	9.41 300	47	9.42 805	51	10.57 195	9.98 494	3	60	
1	9.41 347	47	9.42 856	50	10.57 144	9.98 491	3	59	
2	9.41 394	47	9.42 906	51	10.57 094	9.98 488	4	58	
3	9.41 441	47	9.42 957	50	10.57 043	9.98 484	3	57	
4	9.41 488	47	9.43 007	50	10.56 993	9.98 481	4	56	
5	9.41 535	47	9.43 057	51	10.56 943	9.98 477	3	55	
6	9.41 582	46	9.43 108	50	10.56 892	9.98 474	3	54	
7	9.41 628	47	9.43 158	50	10.56 842	9.98 471	4	53	″ 51 50 49
8	9.41 675	47	9.43 208	50	10.56 792	9.98 467	3	52	1 0.8 0.8 0.8
9	9.41 722	46	9.43 258	50	10.56 742	9.98 464	4	51	2 1.7 1.7 1.6
10	9.41 768	47	9.43 308	50	10.56 692	9.98 460	3	50	3 2.6 2.5 2.4
11	9.41 815	46	9.43 358	50	10.56 642	9.98 457	4	49	4 3.4 3.3 3.3
12	9.41 861	47	9.43 408	50	10.56 592	9.98 453	3	48	
13	9.41 908	46	9.43 458	50	10.56 542	9.98 450	3	47	5 4.2 4.2 4.1
14	9.41 954	47	9.43 508	50	10.56 492	9.98 447	4	46	6 5.1 5.0 4.9
									7 6.0 5.8 5.7
15	9.42 001	46	9.43 558	49	10.56 442	9.98 443	3	45	8 6.8 6.7 6.5
16	9.42 047	46	9.43 607	50	10.56 393	9.98 440	4	44	9 7.6 7.5 7.4
17	9.42 093	47	9.43 657	50	10.56 343	9.98 436	3	43	
18	9.42 140	46	9.43 707	49	10.56 293	9.98 433	4	42	10 8.5 8.3 8.2
19	9.42 186	46	9.43 756	50	10.56 244	9.98 429	3	41	20 17.0 16.7 16.3
									30 25.5 25.0 24.5
20	9.42 232	46	9.43 806	49	10.56 194	9.98 426	4	40	40 34.0 33.3 32.7
21	9.42 278	46	9.43 855	50	10.56 145	9.98 422	3	39	50 42.5 41.7 40.8
22	9.42 324	46	9.43 905	49	10.56 095	9.98 419	4	38	
23	9.42 370	46	9.43 954	50	10.56 046	9.98 415	3	37	″ 48 47 46
24	9.42 416	45	9.44 004	49	10.55 996	9.98 412	3	36	1 0.8 0.8 0.8
25	9.42 461	46	9.44 053	49	10.55 947	9.98 409	4	35	2 1.6 1.6 1.5
26	9.42 507	46	9.44 102	49	10.55 898	9.98 405	4	34	3 2.4 2.4 2.3
27	9.42 553	46	9.44 151	50	10.55 849	9.98 402	4	33	4 3.2 3.1 3.1
28	9.42 599	45	9.44 201	49	10.55 799	9.98 398	3	32	
29	9.42 644	46	9.44 250	49	10.55 750	9.98 395	4	31	5 4.0 3.9 3.8
									6 4.8 4.7 4.6
30	9.42 690	45	9.44 299	49	10.55 701	9.98 391	3	30	7 5.6 5.5 5.4
31	9.42 735	46	9.44 348	49	10.55 652	9.98 388	3	29	8 6.4 6.3 6.1
32	9.42 781	45	9.44 397	49	10.55 603	9.98 384	4	28	9 7.2 7.0 6.9
33	9.42 826	46	9.44 446	49	10.55 554	9.98 381	4	27	
34	9.42 872	45	9.44 495	49	10.55 505	9.98 377	4	26	10 8.0 7.8 7.7
									20 16.0 15.7 15.3
35	9.42 917	45	9.44 544	48	10.55 456	9.98 373	3	25	30 24.0 23.5 23.0
36	9.42 962	46	9.44 592	49	10.55 408	9.98 370	4	24	40 32.0 31.3 30.7
37	9.43 008	45	9.44 641	49	10.55 359	9.98 366	3	23	50 40.0 39.2 38.3
38	9.43 053	45	9.44 690	48	10.55 310	9.98 363	4	22	
39	9.43 098	45	9.44 738	49	10.55 262	9.98 359	3	21	″ 45 44 4 3
40	9.43 143	45	9.44 787	49	10.55 213	9.98 356	4	20	1 0.8 0.7 0.1 0.0
41	9.43 188	45	9.44 836	48	10.55 164	9.98 352	3	19	2 1.5 1.5 0.1 0.1
42	9.43 233	45	9.44 884	49	10.55 116	9.98 349	4	18	3 2.2 2.2 0.2 0.2
43	9.43 278	45	9.44 933	48	10.55 067	9.99 345	4	17	4 3.0 2.9 0.3 0.2
44	9.43 323	44	9.44 981	48	10.55 019	9.98 342	4	16	
									5 3.8 3.7 0.3 0.2
45	9.43 367	45	9.45 029	49	10.54 971	9.98 338	4	15	6 4.5 4.4 0.4 0.3
46	9.43 412	45	9.45 078	48	10.54 922	9.98 334	3	14	7 5.2 5.1 0.5 0.4
47	9.43 457	45	9.45 126	48	10.54 874	9.98 331	4	13	8 6.0 5.9 0.5 0.4
48	9.43 502	44	9.45 174	48	10.54 826	9.98 327	3	12	9 6.8 6.6 0.6 0.4
49	9.43 546	45	9.45 222	49	10.54 778	9.98 324	4	11	
									10 7.5 7.3 0.7 0.5
50	9.43 591	44	9.45 271	48	10.54 729	9.98 320	3	10	20 15.0 14.7 1.3 1.0
51	9.43 635	45	9.45 319	48	10.54 681	9.98 317	4	9	30 22.5 22.0 2.0 1.5
52	9.43 680	44	9.45 367	48	10.54 633	9.98 313	4	8	40 30.0 29.3 2.7 2.0
53	9.43 724	45	9.45 415	48	10.54 585	9.98 309	3	7	50 37.5 36.7 3.3 2.5
54	9.43 769	44	9.45 463	48	10.54 537	9.98 306	4	6	
55	9.43 813	44	9.45 511	48	10.54 489	9.98 302	3	5	
56	9.43 857	44	9.45 559	47	10.54 441	9.98 299	4	4	
57	9.43 901	45	9.45 606	48	10.54 394	9.98 295	4	3	
58	9.43 946	44	9.45 654	48	10.54 346	9.98 291	3	2	
59	9.43 990	44	9.45 702	48	10.54 298	9.98 288	4	1	
60	9.44 034		9.45 750		10.54 250	9.98 284		0	
′	L Cos	d	L Ctn	c d	L Tan	L Sin	d	′	Proportional parts

105° (285°)   (254°) **74°**

Table III (Cont'd)
COMMON LOGARITHMS OF TRIGONOMETRIC FUNCTIONS

16° (196°)   **(343°) 163°**

′	L Sin	d	L Tan	c d	L Ctn	L Cos	d	′	Proportional parts		
0	9.44 034	44	9.45 750	47	10.54 250	9.98 284	3	60			
1	9.44 078	44	9.45 797	48	10.54 203	9.98 281	4	59			
2	9.44 122	44	9.45 845	47	10.54 155	9.98 277	4	58			
3	9.44 166	44	9.45 892	48	10.54 108	9.98 273	3	57			
4	9.44 210	43	9.45 940	47	10.54 060	9.98 270	4	56			
5	9.44 253	44	9.45 987	48	10.54 013	9.98 266	4	55			
6	9.44 297	44	9.46 035	47	10.53 965	9.98 262	3	54			
7	9.44 341	44	9.46 082	48	10.53 918	9.98 259	4	53	′′	48	47	46
8	9.44 385	43	9.46 130	47	10.53 870	9.98 255	4	52	1	0.8	0.8	0.8
9	9.44 428	44	9.46 177	47	10.53 823	9.98 251	3	51	2	1.6	1.6	1.5
									3	2.4	2.4	2.3
10	9.44 472	44	9.46 224	47	10.53 776	9.98 248	4	50	4	3.2	3.1	3.1
11	9.44 516	43	9.46 271	48	10.53 729	9.98 244	4	49				
12	9.44 559	43	9.46 319	47	10.53 681	9.98 240	3	48	5	4.0	3.9	3.8
13	9.44 602	44	9.46 366	47	10.53 634	9.98 237	4	47	6	4.8	4.7	4.6
14	9.44 646	43	9.46 413	47	10.53 587	9.98 233	4	46	7	5.6	5.5	5.4
									8	6.4	6.3	6.1
15	9.44 689	44	9.46 460	47	10.53 540	9.98 229	3	45	9	7.2	7.0	6.9
16	9.44 733	43	9.46 507	47	10.53 493	9.98 226	4	44				
17	9.44 776	43	9.46 554	47	10.53 446	9.98 222	4	43	10	8.0	7.8	7.7
18	9.44 819	43	9.46 601	47	10.53 399	9.98 218	3	42	20	16.0	15.7	15.3
19	9.44 862	43	9.46 648	46	10.53 352	9.98 215	4	41	30	24.0	23.5	23.0
									40	32.0	31.3	30.7
20	9.44 905	43	9.46 694	47	10.53 306	9.98 211	4	40	50	40.0	39.2	38.3
21	9.44 948	44	9.46 741	47	10.53 259	9.98 207	3	39				
22	9.44 992	43	9.46 788	47	10.53 212	9.98 204	4	38				
23	9.45 035	42	9.46 835	46	10.53 165	9.98 200	4	37	′′	45	44	43
24	9.45 077	43	9.46 881	47	10.53 119	9.98 196	4	36	1	0.8	0.7	0.7
									2	1.5	1.5	1.4
25	9.45 120	43	9.46 928	47	10.53 072	9.98 192	4	35	3	2.2	2.2	2.2
26	9.45 163	43	9.46 975	46	10.53 025	9.98 189	4	34	4	3.0	2.9	2.9
27	9.45 206	43	9.47 021	47	10.52 979	9.98 185	4	33				
28	9.45 249	43	9.47 068	46	10.52 932	9.98 181	4	32	5	3.8	3.7	3.6
29	9.45 292	42	9.47 114	46	10.52 886	9.98 177	3	31	6	4.5	4.4	4.3
									7	5.2	5.1	5.0
30	9.45 334	43	9.47 160	47	10.52 840	9.98 174	4	30	8	6.0	5.9	5.7
31	9.45 377	42	9.47 207	46	10.52 793	9.98 170	4	29	9	6.8	6.6	6.4
32	9.45 419	43	9.47 253	46	10.52 747	9.98 166	4	28				
33	9.45 462	42	9.47 299	47	10.52 701	9.98 162	3	27	10	7.5	7.3	7.2
34	9.45 504	43	9.47 346	46	10.52 654	9.98 159	4	26	20	15.0	14.7	14.3
									30	22.5	22.0	21.5
35	9.45 547	42	9.47 392	46	10.52 608	9.98 155	4	25	40	30.0	29.3	28.7
36	9.45 589	43	9.47 438	46	10.52 562	9.98 151	4	24	50	37.5	36.7	35.8
37	9.45 632	42	9.47 484	46	10.52 516	9.98 147	3	23				
38	9.45 674	42	9.47 530	46	10.52 470	9.98 144	4	22				
39	9.45 716	42	9.47 576	46	10.52 424	9.98 140	4	21	′′	42	41	4	3
40	9.45 758	43	9.47 622	46	10.52 378	9.98 136	4	20	1	0.7	0.7	0.1	0.0
41	9.45 801	42	9.47 668	46	10.52 332	9.98 132	3	19	2	1.4	1.4	0.1	0.1
42	9.45 843	42	9.47 714	46	10.52 286	9.98 129	4	18	3	2.1	2.0	0.2	0.2
43	9.45 885	42	9.47 760	46	10.52 240	9.98 125	4	17	4	2.8	2.7	0.3	0.2
44	9.45 927	42	9.47 806	46	10.52 194	9.98 121	4	16				
									5	3.5	3.4	0.3	0.2
45	9.45 969	42	9.47 852	45	10.52 148	9.98 117	4	15	6	4.2	4.1	0.4	0.3
46	9.46 011	42	9.47 897	46	10.52 103	9.98 113	3	14	7	4.9	4.8	0.5	0.4
47	9.46 053	42	9.47 943	46	10.52 057	9.98 110	4	13	8	5.6	5.5	0.5	0.4
48	9.46 095	41	9.47 989	46	10.52 011	9.98 106	4	12	9	6.3	6.2	0.6	0.4
49	9.46 136	42	9.48 035	45	10.51 965	9.98 102	4	11				
									10	7.0	6.8	0.7	0.5
50	9.46 178	42	9.48 080	46	10.51 920	9.98 098	4	10	20	14.0	13.7	1.3	1.0
51	9.46 220	42	9.48 126	45	10.51 874	9.98 094	4	9	30	21.0	20.5	2.0	1.5
52	9.46 262	41	9.48 171	46	10.51 829	9.98 090	3	8	40	28.0	27.3	2.7	2.0
53	9.46 303	42	9.48 217	45	10.51 783	9.98 087	4	7	50	35.0	34.2	3.3	2.5
54	9.46 345	41	9.48 262	45	10.51 738	9.98 083	4	6				
55	9.46 386	42	9.48 307	46	10.51 693	9.98 079	4	5				
56	9.46 428	41	9.48 353	45	10.51 647	9.98 075	4	4				
57	9.46 469	42	9.48 398	45	10.51 602	9.98 071	4	3				
58	9.46 511	41	9.48 443	46	10.51 557	9.98 067	4	2				
59	9.46 552	42	9.48 489	45	10.51 511	9.98 063	3	1				
60	9 46 594		9.48 534		10.51 466	9.98 060		0				
′	L Cos	d	L Ctn	c d	L Tan	L Sin	d	′	Proportional parts		

106° (286°)   **(253°) 73°**

Table III (Cont'd)

COMMON LOGARITHMS OF TRIGONOMETRIC FUNCTIONS

17° (197°)   (342°) **162°**

ʹ	L Sin	d	L Tan	c d	L Ctn	L Cos	d	ʹ	Proportional parts		
0	9.46 594	41	9.48 534	45	10.51 466	9.98 060	4	60			
1	9.46 635	41	9.48 579	45	10.51 421	9.98 056	4	59			
2	9.46 676	41	9.48 624	45	10.51 376	9.98 052	4	58			
3	9.46 717	41	9.48 669	45	10.51 331	9.98 048	4	57			
4	9.46 758	42	9.48 714	45	10.51 286	9.98 044	4	56			
5	9.46 800	41	9.48 759	45	10.51 241	9.98 040	4	55			
6	9.46 841	41	9.48 804	45	10.51 196	9.98 036	4	54			
7	9.46 882	41	9.48 849	45	10.51 151	9.98 032	3	53	ʹʹ	45	44	43
8	9.46 923	41	9.48 894	45	10.51 106	9.98 029	4	52	1	0.8	0.7	0.7
9	9.46 964	41	9.48 939	45	10.51 061	9.98 025	4	51	2	1.5	1.5	1.4
10	9.47 005	40	9.48 984	45	10.51 016	9.98 021	4	50	3	2.2	2.2	2.2
11	9.47 045	41	9.49 029	44	10.50 971	9.98 017	4	49	4	3.0	2.9	2.9
12	9.47 086	41	9.49 073	45	10.50 927	9.98 013	4	48				
13	9.47 127	41	9.49 118	45	10.50 882	9.98 009	4	47	5	3.8	3.7	3.6
14	9.47 168	41	9.49 163	44	10.50 837	9.98 005	4	46	6	4.5	4.4	4.3
15	9.47 209	40	9.49 207	45	10.50 793	9.98 001	4	45	7	5.2	5.1	5.0
16	9.47 249	41	9.49 252	44	10.50 748	9.97 997	4	44	8	6.0	5.9	5.7
17	9.47 290	40	9.49 296	45	10.50 704	9.97 993	4	43	9	6.8	6.6	6.4
18	9.47 330	41	9.49 341	44	10.50 659	9.97 989	3	42				
19	9.47 371	40	9.49 385	45	10.50 615	9.97 986	4	41	10	7.5	7.3	7.2
20	9.47 411	41	9.49 430	44	10.50 570	9.97 982	4	40	20	15.0	14.7	14.3
21	9.47 452	40	9.49 474	45	10.50 526	9.97 978	4	39	30	22.5	22.0	21.5
22	9.47 492	41	9.49 519	44	10.50 481	9.97 974	4	38	40	30.0	29.2	28.7
23	9.47 533	40	9.49 563	44	10.50 437	9.97 970	4	37	50	37.5	36.7	35.8
24	9.47 573	40	9.49 607	45	10.50 393	9.97 966	4	36				
25	9.47 613	41	9.49 652	44	10.50 348	9.97 962	4	35	ʹʹ	42	41	40
26	9.47 654	40	9.49 696	44	10.50 304	9.97 958	4	34	1	0.7	0.7	0.7
27	9.47 694	40	9.49 740	44	10.50 260	9.97 954	4	33	2	1.4	1.4	1.3
28	9.47 734	40	9.49 784	44	10.50 216	9.97 950	4	32	3	2.1	2.0	2.0
29	9.47 774	40	9.49 828	44	10.50 172	9.97 946	4	31	4	2.8	2.7	2.7
30	9.47 814	40	9.49 872	44	10.50 128	9.97 942	4	30				
31	9.47 854	40	9.49 916	44	10.50 084	9.97 938	4	29	5	3.5	3.4	3.3
32	9.47 894	40	9.49 960	44	10.50 040	9.97 934	4	28	6	4.2	4.1	4.0
33	9.47 934	40	9.50 004	44	10.49 996	9.97 930	4	27	7	4.9	4.8	4.7
34	9.47 974	40	9.50 048	44	10.49 952	9.97 926	4	26	8	5.6	5.5	5.3
35	9.48 014	40	9.50 092	44	10.49 908	9.97 922	4	25	9	6.3	6.2	6.0
36	9.48 054	40	9.50 136	44	10.49 864	9.97 918	4	24				
37	9.48 094	39	9.50 180	43	10.49 820	9.97 914	4	23	10	7.0	6.8	6.7
38	9.48 133	40	9.50 223	44	10.49 777	9.97 910	4	22	20	14.0	13.7	13.3
39	9.48 173	40	9.50 267	44	10.49 733	9.97 906	4	21	30	21.0	20.5	20.0
40	9.48 213	39	9.50 311	44	10.49 689	9.97 902	4	20	40	28.0	27.3	26.7
41	9.48 252	40	9.50 355	43	10.49 645	9.97 898	4	19	50	35.0	34.2	33.3
42	9.48 292	40	9.50 398	44	10.49 602	9.97 894	4	18				
43	9.48 332	39	9.50 442	43	10.49 558	9.97 890	4	17	ʹʹ	39	5	4	3
44	9.48 371	40	9.50 485	44	10.49 515	9.97 886	4	16	1	0.6	0.1	0.1	0.0
45	9.48 411	39	9.50 529	43	10.49 471	9.97 882	4	15	2	1.3	0.2	0.1	0.1
46	9.48 450	40	9.50 572	44	10.49 428	9.97 878	4	14	3	2.0	0.2	0.2	0.2
47	9.48 490	39	9.50 616	43	10.49 384	9.97 874	4	13	4	2.6	0.3	0.3	0.2
48	9.48 529	39	9.50 659	44	10.49 341	9.97 870	4	12				
49	9.48 568	39	9.50 703	43	10.49 297	9.97 866	5	11	5	3.2	0.4	0.3	0.2
50	9.48 607	40	9.50 746	43	10.49 254	9.97 861	4	10	6	3.9	0.5	0.4	0.3
51	9.48 647	39	9.50 789	44	10.49 211	9.97 857	4	9	7	4.6	0.6	0.5	0.4
52	9.48 686	39	9.50 833	43	10.49 167	9.97 853	4	8	8	5.2	0.7	0.5	0.5
53	9.48 725	39	9.50 876	43	10.49 124	9.97 849	4	7	9	5.8	0.8	0.6	0.4
54	9.48 764	39	9.50 919	43	10.49 081	9.97 845	4	6				
55	9.48 803	39	9.50 962	43	10.49 038	9.97 841	4	5	10	6.5	0.8	0.7	0.5
56	9.48 842	39	9.51 005	43	10.48 995	9.97 837	4	4	20	13.0	1.7	1.3	1.0
57	9.48 881	39	9.51 048	44	10.48 952	9.97 833	4	3	30	19.5	2.5	2.0	1.5
58	9.48 920	39	9.51 092	43	10.48 908	9.97 829	4	2	40	26.0	3.3	2.7	2.0
59	9.48 959	39	9.51 135	43	10.48 865	9.97 825	4	1	20	32.5	4.2	3.3	2.5
60	9.48 998		9.51 178		10.48 822	9.97 821		0				
ʹ	L Cos	d	L Ctn	c d	L Tan	L Sin	d	ʹ	Proportional parts		

107° (287°)   (252°) **72°**

461

Table III (Cont'd)

COMMON LOGARITHMS OF TRIGONOMETRIC FUNCTIONS

18° (198°)   (341°) **161°**

′	L Sin	d	L Tan	c d	L Ctn	L Cos	d	′	Proportional parts		
0	9.48 998	39	9.51 178	43	10.48 822	9.97 821	4	60			
1	9.49 037	39	9.51 221	43	10.48 779	9.97 817	5	59			
2	9.49 076	39	9.51 264	42	10.48 736	9.97 812	4	58			
3	9.49 115	38	9.51 306	43	10.48 694	9.97 808	4	57			
4	9.49 153	39	9.51 349	43	10.48 651	9.97 804	4	56			
5	9.49 192	39	9.51 392	43	10.48 608	9.97 800	4	55			
6	9.49 231	38	9.51 435	43	10.48 565	9.97 796	4	54			
7	9.49 269	39	9.51 478	42	10.48 522	9.97 792	4	53	″	43	42	41
8	9.49 308	39	9.51 520	43	10.48 480	9.97 788	4	52	1	0.7	0.7	0.7
9	9.49 347	38	9.51 563	43	10.48 437	9.97 784	5	51	2	1.4	1.4	1.4
10	9.49 385	39	9.51 606	42	10.48 394	9.97 779	4	50	3	2.2	2.1	2.0
11	9.49 424	38	9.51 648	43	10.48 352	9.97 775	4	49	4	2.9	2.8	2.7
12	9.49 462	38	9.51 691	43	10.48 309	9.97 771	4	48				
13	9.49 500	39	9.51 734	42	10.48 266	9.97 767	4	47	5	3.6	3.5	3.4
14	9.49 539	38	9.51 776	43	10.48 224	9.97 763	4	46	6	4.3	4.2	4.1
15	9.49 577	38	9.51 819	42	10.48 181	9.97 759	5	45	7	5.0	4.9	4.8
16	9.49 615	39	9.51 861	42	10.48 139	9.97 754	4	44	8	5.7	5.6	5.5
17	9.49 654	38	9.51 903	43	10.48 097	9.97 750	4	43	9	6.4	6.3	6.2
18	9.49 692	38	9.51 946	42	10.48 054	9.97 746	4	42				
19	9.49 730	38	9.51 988	43	10.48 012	9.97 742	4	41	10	7.2	7.0	6.8
20	9.49 768	38	9.52 031	42	10.47 969	9.97 738	4	40	20	14.3	14.0	13.7
21	9.49 806	38	9.52 073	42	10.47 927	9.97 734	5	39	30	21.5	21.0	20.5
22	9.49 844	38	9.52 115	42	10.47 885	9.97 729	4	38	40	28.7	28.0	27.3
23	9.49 882	38	9.52 157	43	10.47 843	9.97 725	4	37	50	35.8	35.0	34.2
24	9.49 920	38	9.52 200	42	10.47 800	9.97 721	4	36				
25	9.49 958	38	9.52 242	42	10.47 758	9.97 717	4	35	″	39	38	37
26	9.49 996	38	9.52 284	42	10.47 716	9.97 713	5	34	1	0.6	0.6	0.6
27	9.50 034	38	9.52 326	42	10.47 674	9.97 708	4	33	2	1.3	1.3	1.2
28	9.50 072	38	9.52 368	42	10.47 632	9.97 704	4	32	3	2.0	1.9	1.8
29	9.50 110	38	9.52 410	42	10.47 590	9.97 700	4	31	4	2.6	2.5	2.5
30	9.50 148	37	9.52 452	42	10.47 548	9.97 696	5	30				
31	9.50 185	38	9.52 494	42	10.47 506	9.97 691	4	29	5	3.2	3.2	3.1
32	9.50 223	38	9.52 536	42	10.47 464	9.97 687	4	28	6	3.9	3.8	3.7
33	9.50 261	37	9.52 578	42	10.47 422	9.97 683	4	27	7	4.6	4.4	4.3
34	9.50 298	38	9.52 620	41	10.47 380	9.97 679	5	26	8	5.2	5.1	4.9
35	9.50 336	38	9.52 661	42	10.47 339	9.97 674	4	25	9	5.8	5.7	5.6
36	9.50 374	37	9.52 703	42	10.47 297	9.97 670	4	24				
37	9.50 411	38	9.52 745	42	10.47 255	9.97 666	4	23	10	6.5	6.3	6.2
38	9.50 449	37	9.52 787	42	10.47 213	9.97 662	5	22	20	13.0	12.7	12.3
39	9.50 486	37	9.52 829	41	10.47 171	9.97 657	4	21	30	19.5	19.0	18.5
40	9.50 523	38	9.52 870	42	10.47 130	9.97 653	4	20	40	26.0	25.3	24.7
41	9.50 561	37	9.52 912	41	10.47 088	9.97 649	4	19	50	32.5	31.7	30.8
42	9.50 598	37	9.52 953	42	10.47 047	9.97 645	5	18				
43	9.50 635	38	9.52 995	42	10.47 005	9.97 640	4	17	″	36	5	4
44	9.50 673	37	9.53 037	41	10.46 963	9.97 636	4	16	1	0.6	0.1	0.1
45	9.50 710	37	9.53 078	42	10.46 922	9.97 632	4	15	2	1.2	0.2	0.1
46	9.50 747	37	9.53 120	41	10.46 880	9.97 628	5	14	3	1.8	0.2	0.2
47	9.50 784	37	9.53 161	41	10.46 839	9.97 623	4	13	4	2.4	0.3	0.3
48	9.50 821	37	9.53 202	42	10.46 798	9.97 619	4	12				
49	9.50 858	38	9.53 244	41	10.46 756	9.97 615	5	11	5	3.0	0.4	0.3
50	9.50 896	37	9.53 285	42	10.46 715	9.97 610	4	10	6	3.6	0.5	0.4
51	9.50 933	37	9.53 327	41	10.46 673	9.97 606	4	9	7	4.2	0.6	0.5
52	9.50 970	37	9.53 368	41	10.46 632	9.97 602	5	8	8	4.8	0.7	0.5
53	9.51 007	37	9.53 409	41	10.46 591	9.97 597	4	7	9	5.4	0.8	0.6
54	9.51 043	37	9.53 450	42	10.46 550	9.97 593	4	6				
55	9.51 080	37	9.53 492	41	10.46 508	9.97 589	5	5	10	6.0	0.8	0.7
56	9.51 117	37	9.53 533	41	10.46 467	9.97 584	4	4	20	12.0	1.7	1.3
57	9.51 154	37	9.53 574	41	10.46 426	9.97 580	4	3	30	18.0	2.5	2.0
58	9.51 191	36	9.53 615	41	10.46 385	9.97 576	5	2	40	24.0	3.3	2.7
59	9.51 227	37	9.53 656	41	10.46 344	9.97 571	4	1	50	30.0	4.2	3.3
60	9.51 264		9.53 697		10.46 303	9.97 567		0				
′	L Cos	d	L Ctn	c d	L Tan	L Sin	d	′	Proportional parts		

108° (288°)   (251°) **71°**

Table III (Cont'd)

COMMON LOGARITHMS OF TRIGONOMETRIC FUNCTIONS

19° (199°) (340°) **160°**

′	L Sin	d	L Tan	c d	L Ctn	L Cos	d	′	Proportional parts
0	9.51 264	37	9.53 697	41	10.46 303	9.97 567	4	60	
1	9.51 301	37	9.53 738	41	10.46 262	9.97 563	5	59	
2	9.51 338	36	9.53 779	41	10.46 221	9.97 558	4	58	
3	9.51 374	37	9.53 820	41	10.46 180	9.97 554	4	57	
4	9.51 411	36	9.53 861	41	10.46 139	9.97 550	5	56	

′	L Sin	d	L Tan	c d	L Ctn	L Cos	d	′			
5	9.51 447	37	9.53 902	41	10.46 098	9.97 545	4	55			
6	9.51 484	36	9.53 943	41	10.46 057	9.97 541	5	54			
7	9.51 520	37	9.53 984	41	10.46 016	9.97 536	4	53	′′	41	40	39
8	9.51 557	36	9.54 025	40	10.45 975	9.97 532	4	52	1	0.7	0.7	0.6
9	9.51 593	36	9.54 065	41	10.45 935	9.97 528	5	51	2	1.4	1.3	1.3
10	9.51 629	37	9.54 106	41	10.45 894	9.97 523	4	50	3	2.0	2.0	2.0
11	9.51 666	36	9.54 147	40	10.45 853	9.97 519	4	49	4	2.7	2.7	2.6
12	9.51 702	36	9.54 187	41	10.45 813	9.97 515	5	48				
13	9.51 738	36	9.54 228	41	10.45 772	9.97 510	4	47	5	3.4	3.3	3.2
14	9.51 774	37	9.54 269	40	10.45 731	9.97 506	5	46	6	4.1	4.0	3.9
									7	4.8	4.7	4.6
15	9.51 811	36	9.54 309	41	10.45 691	9.97 501	4	45	8	5.5	5.3	5.2
16	9.51 847	36	9.54 350	40	10.45 650	9.97 497	5	44	9	6.2	6.0	5.8
17	9.51 883	36	9.54 390	41	10.45 610	9.97 492	4	43				
18	9.51 919	36	9.54 431	40	10.45 569	9.97 488	4	42	10	6.8	6.7	6.5
19	9.51 955	36	9.54 471	41	10.45 529	9.97 484	5	41	20	13.7	13.3	13.0
									30	20.5	20.0	19.5
20	9.51 991	36	9.54 512	40	10.45 488	9.97 479	4	40	40	27.3	26.7	26.0
21	9.52 027	36	9.54 552	41	10.45 448	9.97 475	5	39	50	34.2	33.3	32.5
22	9.52 063	36	9.54 593	40	10.45 407	9.97 470	4	38				
23	9.52 099	36	9.54 633	40	10.45 367	9.97 466	5	37	′′	37	36	35
24	9.52 135	36	9.54 673	41	10.45 327	9.97 461	4	36	1	0.6	0.6	0.6
25	9.52 171	36	9.54 714	40	10.45 286	9.97 457	4	35	2	1.2	1.2	1.2
26	9.52 207	35	9.54 754	40	10.45 246	9.97 453	5	34	3	1.8	1.8	1.8
27	9.52 242	36	9.54 794	41	10.45 206	9.97 448	4	33	4	2.5	2.4	2.3
28	9.52 278	36	9.54 835	40	10.45 165	9.97 444	5	32				
29	9.52 314	36	9.54 875	40	10.45 125	9.97 439	4	31	5	3.1	3.0	2.9
									6	3.7	3.6	3.5
30	9.52 350	35	9.54 915	40	10.45 085	9.97 435	5	30	7	4.3	4.2	4.1
31	9.52 385	36	9.54 955	40	10.45 045	9.97 430	4	29	8	4.9	4.8	4.7
32	9.52 421	35	9.54 995	40	10.45 005	9.97 426	5	28	9	5.6	5.4	5.2
33	9.52 456	36	9.55 035	40	10.44 965	9.97 421	4	27				
34	9.52 492	35	9.55 075	40	10.44 925	9.97 417	5	26	10	6.2	6.0	5.8
									20	12.3	12.0	11.7
35	9.52 527	36	9.55 115	40	10.44 885	9.97 412	4	25	30	18.5	18.0	17.5
36	9.52 563	35	9.55 155	40	10.44 845	9.97 408	5	24	40	24.7	24.0	23.3
37	9.52 598	36	9.55 195	40	10.44 805	9.97 403	4	23	50	30.8	30.0	29.2
38	9.52 634	35	9.55 235	40	10.44 765	9.97 399	5	22				
39	9.52 669	36	9.55 275	40	10.44 725	9.97 394	4	21	′′	34	5	4
40	9.52 705	35	9.55 315	40	10.44 685	9.97 390	5	20	1	0.6	0.1	0.1
41	9.52 740	35	9.55 355	40	10.44 645	9.97 385	4	19	2	1.1	0.2	0.1
42	9.52 775	36	9.55 395	39	10.44 605	9.97 381	5	18	3	1.7	0.2	0.2
43	9.52 811	35	9.55 434	40	10.44 566	9.97 376	4	17	4	2.3	0.3	0.3
44	9.52 846	35	9.55 474	40	10.44 526	9.97 372	5	16				
									5	2.8	0.4	0.3
45	9.52 881	35	9.55 514	40	10.44 486	9.97 367	4	15	6	3.4	0.5	0.4
46	9.52 916	35	9.55 554	39	10.44 446	9.97 363	5	14	7	4.0	0.6	0.5
47	9.52 951	35	9.55 593	40	10.44 407	9.97 358	5	13	8	4.5	0.7	0.5
48	9.52 986	35	9.55 633	40	10.44 367	9.97 353	4	12	9	5.1	0.8	0.6
49	9.53 021	35	9.55 673	39	10.44 327	9.97 349	5	11				
									10	5.7	0.8	0.7
50	9.53 056	36	9.55 712	40	10.44 288	9.97 344	4	10	20	11.3	1.7	1.3
51	9.53 092	34	9.55 752	39	10.44 248	9.97 340	5	9	30	17.0	2.5	2.0
52	9.53 126	35	9.55 791	40	10.44 209	9.97 335	4	8	40	22.7	3.3	2.7
53	9.53 161	35	9.55 831	39	10.44 169	9.97 331	5	7	50	28.3	4.2	3.3
54	9.53 196	35	9.55 870	40	10.44 130	9.97 326	4	6				
55	9.53 231	35	9.55 910	39	10.44 090	9.97 322	5	5				
56	9.53 266	35	9.55 949	40	10.44 051	9.97 317	5	4				
57	9.53 301	35	9.55 989	39	10.44 011	9.97 312	4	3				
58	9.53 336	34	9.56 028	39	10.43 972	9.97 308	5	2				
59	9.53 370	35	9.56 067	40	10.43 933	9.97 303	4	1				
60	9.53 405		9.56 107		10.43 893	9.97 299		0				
′	L Cos	d	L Ctn	c d	L Tan	L Sin	d	′	Proportional parts

109° (289°) (250°) **70°**

Table III (Cont'd)

COMMON LOGARITHMS OF TRIGONOMETRIC FUNCTIONS

20° (200°)   **(339°) 159°**

′	L Sin	d	L Tan	c d	L Ctn	L Cos	d	′	Proportional parts		
0	9.53 405	35	9.56 107	39	10.43 893	9.97 299	5	60			
1	9.53 440	35	9.56 146	39	10.43 854	9.97 294	5	59			
2	9.53 475	34	9.56 185	39	10.43 815	9.97 289	4	58			
3	9.53 509	35	9.56 224	40	10.43 776	9.97 285	5	57			
4	9.53 544	34	9.56 264	39	10.43 736	9.97 280	4	56			
5	9.53 578	35	9.56 303	39	10.43 697	9.97 276	5	55			
6	9.53 613	35	9.56 342	39	10.43 658	9.97 271	5	54			
7	9.53 647	35	9.56 381	39	10.43 619	9.97 266	4	53	′′	40	39	38
8	9.53 682	34	9.56 420	39	10.43 580	9.97 262	5	52	1	0.7	0.6	0.6
9	9.53 716	35	9.56 459	39	10.43 541	9.97 257	5	51	2	1.3	1.3	1.3
10	9.53 751	34	9.56 498	39	10.43 502	9.97 252	4	50	3	2.0	2.0	1.9
11	9.53 785	34	9.56 537	39	10.43 463	9.97 248	5	49	4	2.7	2.6	2.5
12	9.53 819	35	9.56 576	39	10.43 424	9.97 243	5	48				
13	9.53 854	34	9.56 615	39	10.43 385	9.97 238	4	47	5	3.3	3.2	3.2
14	9.53 888	34	9.56 654	39	10.43 346	9.97 234	5	46	6	4.0	3.9	3.8
15	9.53 922	35	9.56 693	39	10.43 307	9.97 229	5	45	7	4.7	4.6	4.4
16	9.53 957	34	9.56 732	39	10.43 268	9.97 224	4	44	8	5.3	5.2	5.1
17	9.53 991	34	9.56 771	39	10.43 229	9.97 220	5	43	9	6.0	5.8	5.7
18	9.54 025	34	9.56 810	39	10.43 190	9.97 215	5	42				
19	9.54 059	34	9.56 849	38	10.43 151	9.97 210	4	41	10	6.7	6.5	6.3
20	9.54 093	34	9.56 887	39	10.43 113	9.97 206	5	40	20	13.3	13.0	12.7
21	9.54 127	34	9.56 926	39	10.43 074	9.97 201	5	39	30	20.0	19.5	19.0
22	9.54 161	34	9.56 965	39	10.43 035	9.97 196	4	38	40	26.7	26.0	25.3
23	9.54 195	34	9.57 004	38	10.42 996	9.97 192	5	37	50	33.3	32.5	31.7
24	9.54 229	34	9.57 042	39	10.42 958	9.97 187	5	36				
25	9.54 263	34	9.57 081	39	10.42 919	9.97 182	4	35	′′	37	35	34
26	9.54 297	34	9.57 120	38	10.42 880	9.97 178	5	34	1	0.6	0.6	0.6
27	9.54 331	34	9.57 158	39	10.42 842	9.97 173	5	33	2	1.2	1.2	1.1
28	9.54 365	34	9.57 197	38	10.42 803	9.97 168	5	32	3	1.8	1.8	1.7
29	9.54 399	34	9.57 235	39	10.42 765	9.97 163	4	31	4	2.5	2.3	2.3
30	9.54 433	33	9.57 274	38	10.42 726	9.97 159	5	30				
31	9.54 466	34	9.57 312	39	10.42 688	9.97 154	5	29	5	3.1	2.9	2.8
32	9.54 500	34	9.57 351	38	10.42 649	9.97 149	4	28	6	3.7	3.5	3.4
33	9.54 534	33	9.57 389	39	10.42 611	9.97 145	5	27	7	4.3	4.1	4.0
34	9.54 567	34	9.57 428	38	10.42 572	9.97 140	5	26	8	4.9	4.7	4.5
35	9.54 601	34	9.57 466	38	10.42 534	9.97 135	5	25	9	5.6	5.2	5.1
36	9.54 635	33	9.57 504	39	10.42 496	9.97 130	4	24				
37	9.54 668	34	9.57 543	38	10.42 457	9.97 126	5	23	10	6.2	5.8	5.7
38	9.54 702	33	9.57 581	38	10.42 419	9.97 121	5	22	20	12.3	11.7	11.3
39	9.54 735	34	9.57 619	39	10.42 381	9.97 116	5	21	30	18.5	17.5	17.0
40	9.54 769	33	9.57 658	38	10.42 342	9.97 111	4	20	40	24.7	23.3	22.7
41	9.54 802	34	9.57 696	38	10.42 304	9.97 107	5	19	50	30.8	29.2	28.3
42	9.54 836	33	9.57 734	38	10.42 266	9.97 102	5	18				
43	9.54 869	34	9.57 772	38	10.42 228	9.97 097	5	17	′′	33	5	4
44	9.54 903	33	9.57 810	39	10.42 190	9.97 092	5	16	1	0.6	0.1	0.1
45	9.54 936	33	9.57 849	38	10.42 151	9.97 087	4	15	2	1.1	0.2	0.1
46	9.54 969	34	9.57 887	38	10.42 113	9.97 083	5	14	3	1.6	0.2	0.2
47	9.55 003	33	9.57 925	38	10.42 075	9.97 078	5	13	4	2.2	0.3	0.3
48	9.55 036	33	9.57 963	38	10.42 037	9.97 073	5	12				
49	9.55 069	33	9.58 001	38	10.41 999	9.97 068	5	11	5	2.8	0.4	0.3
50	9.55 102	34	9.58 039	38	10.41 961	9.97 063	4	10	6	3.3	0.5	0.4
51	9.55 136	33	9.58 077	38	10.41 923	9.97 059	5	9	7	3.8	0.6	0.5
52	9.55 169	33	9.58 115	38	10.41 885	9.97 054	5	8	8	4.4	0.7	0.5
53	9.55 202	33	9.58 153	38	10.41 847	9.97 049	5	7	9	5.0	0.8	0.6
54	9.55 235	33	9.58 191	38	10.41 809	9.97 044	5	6				
55	9.55 268	33	9.58 229	38	10.41 771	9.97 039	4	5	10	5.5	0.8	0.7
56	9.55 301	33	9.58 267	37	10.41 733	9.97 035	5	4	20	11.0	1.7	1.3
57	9.55 334	33	9.58 304	38	10.41 696	9.97 030	5	3	30	16.5	2.5	2.0
58	9.55 367	33	9.58 342	38	10.41 658	9.97 025	5	2	40	22.0	3.3	2.7
59	9.55 400	33	9.58 380	38	10.41 620	9.97 020	5	1	50	27.5	4.2	3.3
60	9.55 433	—	9.58 418	—	10.41 582	9.97 015	—	0			
′	L Cos	d	L Ctn	c d	L Tan	L Sin	d	′	Proportional parts		

110° (290°)   **(249°) 69°**

Table III (Cont'd)

COMMON LOGARITHMS OF TRIGONOMETRIC FUNCTIONS

21° (201°)   (338°) **158°**

′	L Sin	d	L Tan	c d	L Ctn	L Cos	d	′	Proportional parts
0	9.55 433	33	9.58 418	37	10.41 582	9.97 015	5	60	
1	9.55 466	33	9.58 455	38	10.41 545	9.97 010	5	59	
2	9.55 499	33	9.58 493	38	10.41 507	9.97 005	4	58	
3	9.55 532	32	9.58 531	38	10.41 469	9.97 001	5	57	
4	9.55 564	33	9.58 569	37	10.41 431	9.96 996	5	56	

′	L Sin	d	L Tan	c d	L Ctn	L Cos	d	′	″	38	37	36
5	9.55 597	33	9.58 606	38	10.41 394	9.96 991	5	55				
6	9.55 630	33	9.58 644	37	10.41 356	9.96 986	5	54				
7	9.55 663	32	9.58 681	38	10.41 319	9.96 981	5	53	1	0.6	0.6	0.6
8	9.55 695	33	9.58 719	38	10.41 281	9.96 976	5	52	2	1.3	1.2	1.2
9	9.55 728	33	9.58 757	37	10.41 243	9.96 971	5	51	3	1.9	1.8	1.8
10	9.55 761	32	9.58 794	38	10.41 206	9.96 966	4	50	4	2.5	2.5	2.4
11	9.55 793	33	9.58 832	37	10.41 168	9.96 962	5	49				
12	9.55 826	32	9.58 869	38	10.41 131	9.96 957	5	48	5	3.2	3.1	3.0
13	9.55 858	33	9.58 907	37	10.41 093	9.96 952	5	47	6	3.8	3.7	3.6
14	9.55 891	32	9.58 944	37	10.41 056	9.96 947	5	46	7	4.4	4.3	4.2
									8	5.1	4.9	4.8
15	9.55 923	33	9.58 981	38	10.41 019	9.96 942	5	45	9	5.7	5.6	5.4
16	9.55 956	32	9.59 019	37	10.40 981	9.96 937	5	44				
17	9.55 988	33	9.59 056	38	10.40 944	9.96 932	5	43	10	6.3	6.2	6.0
18	9.56 021	32	9.59 094	37	10.40 906	9.96 927	5	42	20	12.7	12.3	12.0
19	9.56 053	32	9.59 131	37	10.40 869	9.96 922	5	41	30	19.0	18.5	18.0
20	9.56 085	33	9.59 168	37	10.40 832	9.96 917	5	40	40	25.3	24.7	24.0
21	9.56 118	32	9.59 205	38	10.40 795	9.96 912	5	39	50	31.7	30.8	30.0
22	9.56 150	32	9.59 243	37	10.40 757	9.96 907	4	38				
23	9.56 182	33	9.59 280	37	10.40 720	9.96 903	5	37	″	33	32	31
24	9.56 215	32	9.59 317	37	10.40 683	9.96 898	5	36	1	0.6	0.5	0.5
25	9.56 247	32	9.59 354	37	10.40 646	9.96 893	5	35	2	1.1	1.1	1.0
26	9.56 279	32	9.59 391	38	10.40 609	9.96 888	5	34	3	1.6	1.6	1.6
27	9.56 311	32	9.59 429	37	10.40 571	9.96 883	5	33	4	2.2	2.1	2.1
28	9.56 343	32	9.59 466	37	10.40 534	9.96 878	5	32				
29	9.56 375	33	9.59 503	37	10.40 497	9.96 873	5	31	5	2.8	2.7	2.6
									6	3.3	3.2	3.1
30	9.56 408	32	9.59 540	37	10.40 460	9.96 868	5	30	7	3.8	3.7	3.6
31	9.56 440	32	9.59 577	37	10.40 423	9.96 863	5	29	8	4.4	4.3	4.1
32	9.56 472	32	9.59 614	37	10.40 386	9.96 858	5	28	9	5.0	4.8	4.6
33	9.56 504	32	9.59 651	37	10.40 349	9.96 853	5	27				
34	9.56 536	32	9.59 688	37	10.40 312	9.96 848	5	26	10	5.5	5.3	5.2
									20	11.0	10.7	10.3
35	9.56 568	31	9.59 725	37	10.40 275	9.96 843	5	25	30	16.5	16.0	15.5
36	9.56 599	32	9.59 762	37	10.40 238	9.96 838	5	24	40	22.0	21.3	20.7
37	9.56 631	32	9.59 799	36	10.40 201	9.96 833	5	23	50	27.5	26.7	25.8
38	9.56 663	32	9.59 835	37	10.40 165	9.96 828	5	22				
39	9.56 695	32	9.59 872	37	10.40 128	9.96 823	5	21	″	6	5	4
40	9.56 727	32	9.59 909	37	10.40 091	9.96 818	5	20	1	0.1	0.1	0.1
41	9.56 759	31	9.59 946	37	10.40 054	9.96 813	5	19	2	0.2	0.2	0.1
42	9.56 790	32	9.59 983	36	10.40 017	9.96 808	5	18	3	0.3	0.2	0.2
43	9.56 822	32	9.60 019	37	10.39 981	9.96 803	5	17	4	0.4	0.3	0.3
44	9.56 854	32	9.60 056	37	10.39 944	9.96 798	5	16				
									5	0.5	0.4	0.3
45	9.56 886	31	9.60 093	37	10.39 907	9.96 793	5	15	6	0.6	0.5	0.4
46	9.56 917	32	9.60 130	36	10.39 870	9.96 788	5	14	7	0.7	0.6	0.5
47	9.56 949	31	9.60 166	37	10.39 834	9.96 783	5	13	8	0.8	0.7	0.5
48	9.56 980	32	9.60 203	37	10.39 797	9.96 778	5	12	9	0.9	0.8	0.6
49	9.57 012	32	9.60 240	36	10.39 760	9.96 772	5	11				
									10	1.0	0.8	0.7
50	9.57 044	31	9.60 276	37	10.39 724	9.96 767	5	10	20	2.0	1.7	1.3
51	9.57 075	32	9.60 313	36	10.39 687	9.96 762	5	9	30	3.0	2.5	2.0
52	9.57 107	31	9.60 349	37	10.39 651	9.96 757	5	8	40	4.0	3.3	2.7
53	9.57 138	31	9.60 386	36	10.39 614	9.96 752	5	7	50	5.0	4.2	3.3
54	9.57 169	32	9.60 422	37	10.39 578	9.96 747	5	6				
55	9.57 201	31	9.60 459	36	10.39 541	9.96 742	5	5				
56	9.57 232	32	9.60 495	37	10.39 505	9.96 737	5	4				
57	9.57 264	31	9.60 532	36	10.39 468	9.96 732	5	3				
58	9.57 295	31	9.60 568	37	10.39 432	9.96 727	5	2				
59	9.57 326	32	9.60 605	36	10.39 395	9.96 722	5	1				
60	9.57 358		9.60 641		10.39 359	9.96 717		0				
′	L Cos	d	L Ctn	c d	L Tan	L Sin	d	′	Proportional parts

111° (291°)   (248°) **68°**

Table III (Cont'd)
COMMON LOGARITHMS OF TRIGONOMETRIC FUNCTIONS

22° (202°)   (337°) **157°**

'	L Sin	d	L Tan	c d	L Ctn	L Cos	d	'	Proportional parts		
0	9.57 358	31	9.60 641	36	10.39 359	9.96 717	6	60			
1	9.57 389	31	9.60 677	37	10.39 323	9.96 711	5	59			
2	9.57 420	31	9.60 714	36	10.39 286	9.96 706	5	58			
3	9.57 451	31	9.60 750	36	10.39 250	9.96 701	5	57			
4	9.57 482	32	9.60 786	37	10.39 214	9.96 696	5	56			
5	9.57 514	31	9.60 823	36	10.39 177	9.96 691	5	55			
6	9.57 545	31	9.60 859	36	10.39 141	9.96 686	5	54			
7	9.57 576	31	9.60 895	36	10.39 105	9.96 681	5	53	''	37	36	35
8	9.57 607	31	9.60 931	36	10.39 069	9.96 676	6	52	1	0.6	0.6	0.6
9	9.57 638	31	9.60 967	37	10.39 033	9.96 670	5	51	2	1.2	1.2	1.2
									3	1.8	1.8	1.8
10	9.57 669	31	9.61 004	36	10.38 996	9.96 665	5	50	4	2.5	2.4	2.3
11	9.57 700	31	9.61 040	36	10.38 960	9.96 660	5	49				
12	9.57 731	31	9.61 076	36	10.38 924	9.96 655	5	48	5	3.1	3.0	2.9
13	9.57 762	31	9.61 112	36	10.38 888	9.96 650	5	47	6	3.7	3.6	3.5
14	9.57 793	31	9.61 148	36	10.38 852	9.96 645	5	46	7	4.3	4.2	4.1
									8	4.9	4.8	4.7
15	9.57 824	31	9.61 184	36	10.38 816	9.96 640	6	45	9	5.6	5.4	5.2
16	9.57 855	30	9.61 220	36	10.38 780	9.96 634	5	44				
17	9.57 885	31	9.61 256	36	10.38 744	9.96 629	5	43	10	6.2	6.0	5.8
18	9.57 916	31	9.61 292	36	10.38 708	9.96 624	5	42	20	12.3	12.0	11.7
19	9.57 947	31	9.61 328	36	10.38 672	9.96 619	5	41	30	18.5	18.0	17.5
									40	24.7	24.0	23.3
20	9.57 978	30	9.61 364	36	10.38 636	9.96 614	6	40	50	30.8	30.0	29.2
21	9.58 008	31	9.61 400	36	10.38 600	9.96 608	5	39				
22	9.58 039	31	9.61 436	36	10.38 564	9.96 603	5	38				
23	9.58 070	31	9.61 472	36	10.38 528	9.96 598	5	37	''	32	31	30
24	9.58 101	30	9.61 508	36	10.38 492	9.96 593	5	36	1	0.5	0.5	0.5
									2	1.1	1.0	1.0
25	9.58 131	31	9.61 544	35	10.38 456	9.96 588	6	35	3	1.6	1.6	1.5
26	9.58 162	30	9.61 579	36	10.38 421	9.96 582	5	34	4	2.1	2.1	2.0
27	9.58 192	31	9.61 615	36	10.38 385	9.96 577	5	33				
28	9.58 223	30	9.61 651	36	10.38 349	9.96 572	5	32	5	2.7	2.6	2.5
29	9.58 253	31	9.61 687	35	10.38 313	9.96 567	5	31	6	3.2	3.1	3.0
									7	3.7	3.6	3.5
30	9.58 284	30	9.61 722	36	10.38 278	9.96 562	6	30	8	4.3	4.1	4.0
31	9.58 314	31	9.61 758	36	10.38 242	9.96 556	5	29	9	4.8	4.6	4.5
32	9.58 345	30	9.61 794	36	10.38 206	9.96 551	5	28				
33	9.58 375	31	9.61 830	35	10.38 170	9.96 546	5	27	10	5.3	5.2	5.0
34	9.58 406	30	9.61 865	36	10.38 135	9.96 541	6	26	20	10.7	10.3	10.0
									30	16.0	15.5	15.0
35	9.58 436	31	9.61 901	35	10.38 099	9.96 535	5	25	40	21.3	20.7	20.0
36	9.58 467	30	9.61 936	36	10.38 064	9.96 530	5	24	50	26.7	25.8	25.0
37	9.58 497	30	9.61 972	36	10.38 028	9.96 525	5	23				
38	9.58 527	30	9.62 008	35	10.37 992	9.96 520	6	22				
39	9.58 557	31	9.62 043	36	10.37 957	9.96 514	5	21	''	29	6	5
									1	0.5	0.1	0.1
40	9.58 588	30	9.62 079	35	10.37 921	9.96 509	5	20	2	1.0	0.2	0.2
41	9.58 618	30	9.62 114	36	10.37 886	9.96 504	6	19	3	1.4	0.3	0.2
42	9.58 648	30	9.62 150	35	10.37 850	9.96 498	5	18	4	1.9	0.4	0.3
43	9.58 678	31	9.62 185	36	10.37 815	9.96 493	5	17				
44	9.58 709	30	9.62 221	35	10.37 779	9.96 488	5	16	5	2.4	0.5	0.4
									6	2.9	0.6	0.5
45	9.58 739	30	9.62 256	36	10.37 744	9.96 483	6	15	7	3.4	0.7	0.6
46	9.58 769	30	9.62 292	35	10.37 708	9.96 477	5	14	8	3.9	0.8	0.7
47	9.58 799	30	9.62 327	35	10.37 673	9.96 472	5	13	9	4.4	0.9	0.8
48	9.58 829	30	9.62 362	36	10.37 638	9.96 467	6	12				
49	9.58 859	30	9.62 398	35	10.37 602	9.96 461	5	11	10	4.8	1.0	0.8
									20	9.7	2.0	1.7
50	9.58 889	30	9.62 433	35	10.37 567	9.96 456	5	10	30	14.5	3.0	2.5
51	9.58 919	30	9.62 468	36	10.37 532	9.96 451	6	9	40	19.3	4.0	3.3
52	9.58 949	30	9.62 504	35	10.37 496	9.96 445	5	8	50	24.2	5.0	4.2
53	9.58 979	30	9.62 539	35	10.37 461	9.96 440	5	7				
54	9.59 009	30	9.62 574	35	10.37 426	9.96 435	6	6				
55	9.59 039	30	9.62 609	36	10.37 391	9.96 429	5	5				
56	9.59 069	29	9.62 645	35	10.37 355	9.96 424	5	4				
57	9.59 098	30	9.62 680	35	10.37 320	9.96 419	6	3				
58	9.59 128	30	9.62 715	35	10.37 285	9.96 413	5	2				
59	9.59 158	30	9.62 750	35	10.37 250	9.96 408	5	1				
60	9.59 188		9.62 785		10.37 215	9.96 403		0				
'	L Cos	d	L Ctn	c d	L Tan	L Sin	d	'	Proportional parts		

112° (292°)   (247°) **67°**

Table III (Cont'd)

COMMON LOGARITHMS OF TRIGONOMETRIC FUNCTIONS

23° (203°)   (336°) 156°

′	L Sin	d	L Tan	c d	L Ctn	L Cos	d	′	Proportional parts		
0	9.59 188	30	9.62 785	35	10.37 215	9.96 403	6	60			
1	9.59 218	29	9.62 820	35	10.37 180	9.96 397	5	59			
2	9.59 247	30	9.62 855	35	10.37 145	9.96 392	5	58			
3	9.59 277	30	9.62 890	36	10.37 110	9.96 387	6	57			
4	9.59 307	29	9.62 926	35	10.37 074	9.96 381	5	56			
5	9.59 336	30	9.62 961	35	10.37 039	9.96 376	6	55			
6	9.59 366	30	9.62 996	35	10.37 004	9.96 370	5	54			
7	9.59 396	29	9.63 031	35	10.36 969	9.96 365	5	53	′′	36	35	34
8	9.59 425	30	9.63 066	35	10.36 934	9.96 360	6	52	1	0.6	0.6	0.6
9	9.59 455	29	9.63 101	34	10.36 899	9.96 354	5	51	2	1.2	1.2	1.1
10	9.59 484	30	9.63 135	35	10.36 865	9.96 349	6	50	3	1.8	1.8	1.7
11	9.59 514	29	9.63 170	35	10.36 830	9.96 343	5	49	4	2.4	2.3	2.3
12	9.59 543	30	9.63 205	35	10.36 795	9.96 338	5	48				
13	9.59 573	29	9.63 240	35	10.36 760	9.96 333	6	47	5	3.0	2.9	2.8
14	9.59 602	30	9.63 275	35	10.36 725	9.96 327	5	46	6	3.6	3.5	3.4
15	9.59 632	29	9.63 310	35	10.36 690	9.96 322	6	45	7	4.2	4.1	4.0
16	9.59 661	29	9.63 345	34	10.36 655	9.96 316	5	44	8	4.8	4.7	4.5
17	9.59 690	30	9.63 379	35	10.36 621	9.96 311	6	43	9	5.4	5.2	5.1
18	9.59 720	29	9.63 414	35	10.36 586	9.96 305	5	42				
19	9.59 749	29	9.63 449	35	10.36 551	9.96 300	6	41	10	6.0	5.8	5.7
20	9.59 778	30	9.63 484	35	10.36 516	9.96 294	5	40	20	12.0	11.7	11.3
21	9.59 808	29	9.63 519	34	10.36 481	9.96 289	5	39	30	18.0	17.5	17.0
22	9.59 837	29	9.63 553	35	10.36 447	9.96 284	6	38	40	24.0	23.3	22.7
23	9.59 866	29	9.63 588	35	10.36 412	9.96 278	5	37	50	30.0	29.2	28.3
24	9.59 895	29	9.63 623	34	10.36 377	9.96 273	6	36				
25	9.59 924	30	9.63 657	35	10.36 343	9.96 267	5	35	′′	30	29	28
26	9.59 954	29	9.63 692	34	10.36 308	9.96 262	6	34	1	0.5	0.5	0.5
27	9.59 983	29	9.63 726	35	10.36 274	9.96 256	5	33	2	1.0	1.0	0.9
28	9.60 012	29	9.63 761	35	10.36 239	9.96 251	6	32	3	1.5	1.4	1.4
29	9.60 041	29	9.63 796	34	10.36 204	9.96 245	5	31	4	2.0	1.9	1.9
30	9.60 070	29	9.63 830	35	10.36 170	9.96 240	6	30	5	2.5	2.4	2.3
31	9.60 099	29	9.63 865	34	10.36 135	9.96 234	5	29	6	3.0	2.9	2.8
32	9.60 128	29	9.63 899	35	10.36 101	9.96 229	6	28	7	3.5	3.4	3.3
33	9.60 157	29	9.63 934	34	10.36 066	9.96 223	5	27	8	4.0	3.9	3.7
34	9.60 186	29	9.63 968	35	10.36 032	9.96 218	6	26	9	4.5	4.4	4.2
35	9.60 215	29	9.64 003	34	10.35 997	9.96 212	5	25				
36	9.60 244	29	9.64 037	35	10.35 963	9.96 207	6	24	10	5.0	4.8	4.7
37	9.60 273	29	9.64 072	34	10.35 928	9.96 201	5	23	20	10.0	9.7	9.3
38	9.60 302	29	9.64 106	34	10.35 894	9.96 196	6	22	30	15.0	14.5	14.0
39	9.60 331	28	9.64 140	35	10.35 860	9.96 190	5	21	40	20.0	19.3	18.7
40	9.60 359	29	9.64 175	34	10.35 825	9.96 185	6	20	50	25.0	24.2	23.3
41	9.60 388	29	9.64 209	34	10.35 791	9.96 179	5	19				
42	9.60 417	29	9.64 243	35	10.35 757	9.96 174	6	18	′′	6	5	
43	9.60 446	28	9.64 278	34	10.35 722	9.96 168	6	17	1	0.1	0.1	
44	9.60 474	29	9.64 312	34	10.35 688	9.96 162	5	16	2	0.2	0.2	
45	9.60 503	29	9.64 346	35	10.35 654	9.96 157	6	15	3	0.3	0.2	
46	9.60 532	29	9.64 381	34	10.35 619	9.96 151	5	14	4	0.4	0.3	
47	9.60 561	28	9.64 415	34	10.35 585	9.96 146	6	13				
48	9.60 589	29	9.64 449	34	10.35 551	9.96 140	5	12	5	0.5	0.4	
49	9.60 618	28	9.64 483	34	10.35 517	9.96 135	6	11	6	0.6	0.5	
50	9.60 646	29	9.64 517	35	10.35 483	9.96 129	6	10	7	0.7	0.6	
51	9.60 675	29	9.64 552	34	10.35 448	9.96 123	5	9	8	0.8	0.7	
52	9.60 704	28	9.64 586	34	10.35 414	9.96 118	6	8	9	0.9	0.8	
53	9.60 732	29	9.64 620	34	10.35 380	9.96 112	5	7				
54	9.60 761	28	9.64 654	34	10.35 346	9.96 107	6	6	10	1.0	0.8	
55	9.60 789	29	9.64 688	34	10.35 312	9.96 101	6	5	20	2.0	1.7	
56	9.60 818	28	9.64 722	34	10.35 278	9.96 095	5	4	30	3.0	2.5	
57	9.60 846	29	9.64 756	34	10.35 244	9.96 090	6	3	40	4.0	3.3	
58	9.60 875	28	9.64 790	34	10.35 210	9.96 084	5	2	50	5.0	4.2	
59	9.60 903	28	9.64 824	34	10.35 176	9.96 079	6	1				
60	9.60 931		9.64 858		10.35 142	9.96 073		0				
′	L Cos	d	L Ctn	c d	L Tan	L Sin	d	′	Proportional parts		

113° (293°)   (246°) 66°

Table III (Cont'd)

COMMON LOGARITHMS OF TRIGONOMETRIC FUNCTIONS

24° (204°)   **(335°) 155°**

′	L Sin	d	L Tan	c d	L Ctn	L Cos	d	′
0	9.60 931	29	9.64 858	34	10.35 142	9.96 073	6	60
1	9.60 960	28	9.64 892	34	10.35 108	9.96 067	5	59
2	9.60 988	28	9.64 926	34	10.35 074	9.96 062	6	58
3	9.61 016	29	9.64 960	34	10.35 040	9.96 056	6	57
4	9.61 045	28	9.64 994	34	10.35 006	9.96 050	5	56
5	9.61 073	28	9.65 028	34	10.34 972	9.96 045	6	55
6	9.61 101	28	9.65 062	34	10.34 938	9.96 039	5	54
7	9.61 129	29	9.65 096	34	10.34 904	9.96 034	6	53
8	9.61 158	28	9.65 130	34	10.34 870	9.96 028	6	52
9	9.61 186	28	9.65 164	33	10.34 836	9.96 022	5	51
10	9.61 214	28	9.65 197	34	10.34 803	9.96 017	6	50
11	9.61 242	28	9.65 231	34	10.34 769	9.96 011	6	49
12	9.61 270	28	9.65 265	34	10.34 735	9.96 005	5	48
13	9.61 298	28	9.65 299	34	10.34 701	9.96 000	6	47
14	9.61 326	28	9.65 333	33	10.34 667	9.95 994	6	46
15	9.61 354	28	9.65 366	34	10.34 634	9.95 988	6	45
16	9.61 382	29	9.65 400	34	10.34 600	9.95 982	5	44
17	9.61 411	27	9.65 434	33	10.34 566	9.95 977	6	43
18	9.61 438	28	9.65 467	34	10.34 533	9.95 971	6	42
19	9.61 466	28	9.65 501	34	10.34 499	9.95 965	5	41
20	9.61 494	28	9.65 535	33	10.34 465	9.95 960	6	40
21	9.61 522	28	9.65 568	34	10.34 432	9.95 954	6	39
22	9.61 550	28	9.65 602	34	10.34 398	9.95 948	6	38
23	9.61 578	28	9.65 636	33	10.34 364	9.95 942	5	37
24	9.61 606	28	9.65 669	34	10.34 331	9.95 937	6	36
25	9.61 634	28	9.65 703	33	10.34 297	9.95 931	6	35
26	9.61 662	27	9.65 736	34	10.34 264	9.95 925	5	34
27	9.61 689	28	9.65 770	33	10.34 230	9.95 920	6	33
28	9.61 717	28	9.65 803	34	10.34 197	9.95 914	6	32
29	9.61 745	28	9.65 837	33	10.34 163	9.95 908	6	31
30	9.61 773	27	9.65 870	34	10.34 130	9.95 902	5	30
31	9.61 800	28	9.65 904	33	10.34 096	9.95 897	6	29
32	9.61 828	28	9.65 937	34	10.34 063	9.95 891	6	28
33	9.61 856	27	9.65 971	33	10.34 029	9.95 885	6	27
34	9.61 883	28	9.66 004	34	10.33 996	9.95 879	6	26
35	9.61 911	28	9.66 038	33	10.33 962	9.95 873	5	25
36	9.61 939	27	9.66 071	33	10.33 929	9.95 868	6	24
37	9.61 966	28	9.66 104	34	10.33 896	9.95 862	6	23
38	9.61 994	27	9.66 138	33	10.33 862	9.95 856	6	22
39	9.62 021	28	9.66 171	33	10.33 829	9.95 850	6	21
40	9.62 049	27	9.66 204	34	10.33 796	9.95 844	5	20
41	9.62 076	28	9.66 238	33	10.33 762	9.95 839	6	19
42	9.62 104	27	9.66 271	33	10.33 729	9.95 833	6	18
43	9.62 131	28	9.66 304	33	10.33 696	9.95 827	6	17
44	9.62 159	27	9.66 337	34	10.33 663	9.95 821	6	16
45	9.62 186	28	9.66 371	33	10.33 629	9.95 815	5	15
46	9.62 214	27	9.66 404	33	10.33 596	9.95 810	6	14
47	9.62 241	27	9.66 437	33	10.33 563	9.95 804	6	13
48	9.62 268	28	9.66 470	33	10.33 530	9.95 798	6	12
49	9.62 296	27	9.66 503	34	10.33 497	9.95 792	6	11
50	9.62 323	27	9.66 537	33	10.33 463	9.95 786	6	10
51	9.62 350	27	9.66 570	33	10.33 430	9.95 780	5	9
52	9.62 377	28	9.66 603	33	10.33 397	9.95 775	6	8
53	9.62 405	27	9.66 636	33	10.33 364	9.95 769	6	7
54	9.62 432	27	9.66 669	33	10.33 331	9.95 763	6	6
55	9.62 459	27	9.66 702	33	10.33 298	9.95 757	6	5
56	9.62 486	27	9.66 735	33	10.33 265	9.95 751	6	4
57	9.62 513	28	9.66 768	33	10.33 232	9.98 745	6	3
58	9.62 541	27	9.66 801	33	10.33 199	9.95 739	6	2
59	9.62 568	27	9.66 834	33	10.33 166	9.95 733	6	1
60	9.62 595		9.66 867		10.33 133	9.95 728		0

′	L Cos	d	L Ctn	c d	L Tan	L Sin	d	′

Proportional parts

″	34	33
1	0.6	0.6
2	1.1	1.1
3	1.7	1.6
4	2.3	2.2
5	2.8	2.8
6	3.4	3.3
7	4.0	3.8
8	4.5	4.4
9	5.1	5.0
10	5.7	5.5
20	11.3	11.0
30	17.0	16.5
40	22.7	22.0
50	28.3	27.5

″	29	28	27
1	0.5	0.5	0.4
2	1.0	0.9	0.9
3	1.4	1.4	1.4
4	1.9	1.9	1.8
5	2.4	2.3	2.2
6	2.9	2.8	2.7
7	3.4	3.3	3.2
8	3.9	3.7	3.6
9	4.4	4.2	4.0
10	4.8	4.7	4.5
20	9.7	9.3	9.0
30	14.5	14.0	13.5
40	19.3	18.7	18.0
50	24.2	23.3	22.5

″	6	5
1	0.1	0.1
2	0.2	0.2
3	0.3	0.2
4	0.4	0.3
5	0.5	0.4
6	0.6	0.5
7	0.7	0.6
8	0.8	0.7
9	0.9	0.8
10	1.0	0.8
20	2.0	1.7
30	3.0	2.5
40	4.0	3.3
50	5.0	4.2

114° (294°)   **(245°) 65°**

Proportional parts

Table III (Cont'd)

COMMON LOGARITHMS OF TRIGONOMETRIC FUNCTIONS

25° (205°)   (334°) **154°**

′	L Sin	d	L Tan	c d	L Ctn	L Cos	d	′	Proportional parts		
0	9.62 595	27	9.66 867	33	10.33 133	9.95 728	6	60			
1	9.62 622	27	9.66 900	33	10.33 100	9.95 722	6	59			
2	9.62 649	27	9.66 933	33	10.33 067	9.95 716	6	58			
3	9.62 676	27	9.66 966	33	10.33 034	9.95 710	6	57			
4	9.62 703	27	9.66 999	33	10.33 001	9.95 704	6	56			
5	9.62 730	27	9.67 032	33	10.32 968	9.95 698	6	55			
6	9.62 757	27	9.67 065	33	10.32 935	9.95 692	6	54			
7	9.62 784	27	9.67 098	33	10.32 902	9.95 686	6	53	′′	33	32
8	9.62 811	27	9.67 131	32	10.32 869	9.95 680	6	52	1	0.6	0.5
9	9.62 838	27	9.67 163	33	10.32 837	9.95 674	6	51	2	1.1	1.1
10	9.62 865	27	9.67 196	33	10.32 804	9.95 668	5	50	3	1.6	1.6
11	9.62 892	26	9.67 229	33	10.32 771	9.95 663	6	49	4	2.2	2.1
12	9.62 918	27	9.67 262	33	10.32 738	9.95 657	6	48			
13	9.62 945	27	9.67 295	32	10.32 705	9.95 651	6	47	5	2.8	2.7
14	9.62 972	27	9.67 327	33	10.32 673	9.95 645	6	46	6	3.3	3.2
									7	3.8	3.7
15	9.62 999	27	9.67 360	33	10.32 640	9.95 639	6	45	8	4.4	4.3
16	9.63 026	26	9.67 393	33	10.32 607	9.95 633	6	44	9	5.0	4.8
17	9.63 052	27	9.67 426	32	10.32 574	9.95 627	6	43			
18	9.63 079	27	9.67 458	33	10.32 542	9.95 621	6	42	10	5.5	5.3
19	9.63 106	27	9.67 491	33	10.32 509	9.95 615	6	41	20	11.0	10.7
									30	16.5	16.0
20	9.63 133	26	9.67 524	32	10.32 476	9.95 609	6	40	40	22.0	21.3
21	9.63 159	27	9.67 556	33	10.32 444	9.95 603	6	39	50	27.5	26.7
22	9.63 186	27	9.67 589	33	10.32 411	9.95 597	6	38			
23	9.63 213	26	9.67 622	32	10.32 378	9.95 591	6	37	′′	27	26
24	9.63 239	27	9.67 654	33	10.32 346	9.95 585	6	36	1	0.4	0.4
25	9.63 266	26	9.67 687	32	10.32 313	9.95 579	6	35	2	0.9	0.9
26	9.63 292	27	9.67 719	33	10.32 281	9.95 573	6	34	3	1.4	1.3
27	9.63 319	26	9.67 752	33	10.32 248	9.95 567	6	33	4	1.8	1.7
28	9.63 345	27	9.67 785	32	10.32 215	9.95 561	6	32			
29	9.63 372	26	9.67 817	33	10.32 183	9.95 555	6	31	5	2.2	2.2
									6	2.7	2.6
30	9.63 398	27	9.67 850	32	10.32 150	9.95 549	6	30	7	3.2	3.0
31	9.63 425	26	9.67 882	33	10.32 118	9.95 543	6	29	8	3.6	3.5
32	9.63 451	27	9.67 915	32	10.32 085	9.95 537	6	28	9	4.0	3.9
33	9.63 478	26	9.67 947	33	10.32 053	9.95 531	6	27			
34	9.63 504	27	9.67 980	32	10.32 020	9.95 525	6	26	10	4.5	4.3
									20	9.0	8.7
35	9.63 531	26	9.68 012	32	10.31 988	9.95 519	6	25	30	13.5	13.0
36	9.63 557	26	9.68 044	33	10.31 956	9.95 513	6	24	40	18.0	17.3
37	9.63 583	27	9.68 077	32	10.31 923	9.95 507	7	23	50	22.5	21.7
38	9.63 610	26	9.68 109	33	10.31 891	9.95 500	6	22			
39	9.63 636	26	9.68 142	32	10.31 858	9.95 494	6	21	′′	7 | 6 | 5	
40	9.63 662	27	9.68 174	32	10.31 826	9.95 488	6	20	1	0.1 0.1 0.1	
41	9.63 689	26	9.68 206	33	10.31 794	9.95 482	6	19	2	0.2 0.2 0.2	
42	9.63 715	26	9.68 239	32	10.31 761	9.95 476	6	18	3	0.4 0.3 0.2	
43	9.63 741	26	9.68 271	32	10.31 729	9.95 470	6	17	4	0.5 0.4 0.3	
44	9.63 767	27	9.68 303	33	10.31 697	9.95 464	6	16			
									5	0.6 0.5 0.4	
45	9.63 794	26	9.68 336	32	10.31 664	9.95 458	6	15	6	0.7 0.6 0.5	
46	9.63 820	26	9.68 368	32	10.31 632	9.95 452	6	14	7	0.8 0.7 0.6	
47	9.63 846	26	9.68 400	32	10.31 600	9.95 446	6	13	8	0.9 0.8 0.7	
48	9.63 872	26	9.68 432	33	10.31 568	9.95 440	6	12	9	1.0 0.9 0.8	
49	9.63 898	26	9.68 465	32	10.31 535	9.95 434	7	11			
									10	1.2 1.0 0.8	
50	9.63 924	26	9.68 497	32	10.31 503	9.95 427	6	10	20	2.3 2.0 1.7	
51	9.63 950	26	9.68 529	32	10.31 471	9.95 421	6	9	30	3.5 3.0 2.5	
52	9.63 976	26	9.68 561	32	10.31 439	9.95 415	6	8	40	4.7 4.0 3.3	
53	9.64 002	26	9.68 593	33	10.31 407	9.95 409	6	7	50	5.8 5.0 4.2	
54	9.64 028	26	9.68 626	32	10.31 374	9.95 403	6	6			
55	9.64 054	26	9.68 658	32	10.31 342	9.95 397	6	5			
56	9.64 080	26	9.68 690	32	10.31 310	9.95 391	7	4			
57	9.64 106	26	9.68 722	32	10.31 278	9.95 384	6	3			
58	9.64 132	26	9.68 754	32	10.31 246	9.95 378	6	2			
59	9.64 158	26	9.68 786	32	10.31 214	9.95 372	6	1			
60	9.64 184		9.68 818		10.31 182	9.95 366		0			
′	L Cos	d	L Ctn	c d	L Tan	L Sin	d	′	Proportional parts		

115° (295°)   (244°) **64°**

469

Table III (Cont'd)

COMMON LOGARITHMS OF TRIGONOMETRIC FUNCTIONS

26° (206°)   (333°) **153°**

′	L Sin	d	L Tan	c d	L Ctn	L Cos	d	′	Proportional parts
0	9.64 184	26	9.68 818	32	10.31 182	9.95 366	6	60	
1	9.64 210	26	9.68 850	32	10.31 150	9 95 360	6	59	
2	9.64 236	26	9.68 882	32	10.31 118	9.95 354	6	58	
3	9.64 262	26	9.68 914	32	10.31 086	9.95 348	7	57	
4	9.64 288	25	9.68 946	32	10.31 054	9.95 341	6	56	
5	9.64 313	26	9.68 978	32	10.31 022	9.95 335	6	55	
6	9.64 339	26	9.69 010	32	10.30 990	9.95 329	6	54	″ 32 31
7	9.64 365	26	9.69 042	32	10.30 958	9.95 323	6	53	1 0.5 0.5
8	9.64 391	26	9.69 074	32	10.30 926	9.95 317	7	52	2 1.1 1.0
9	9.64 417	25	9.69 106	32	10.30 894	9.95 310	6	51	3 1.6 1.6
10	9.64 442	26	9.69 138	32	10.30 862	9.95 304	6	50	4 2.1 2.1
11	9.64 468	26	9.69 170	32	10.30 830	9.95 298	6	49	
12	9.64 494	26	9.69 202	32	10.30 798	9.95 292	6	48	5 2.7 2.6
13	9.64 519	26	9.69 234	32	10.30 766	9.95 286	7	47	6 3.2 3.1
14	9.64 545	26	9.69 266	32	10.30 734	9.95 279	6	46	7 3.7 3.6
									8 4.3 4.1
15	9.64 571	25	9.69 298	31	10.30 702	9.95 273	6	45	9 4.8 4.6
16	9.64 596	26	9.69 329	32	10.30 671	9.95 267	6	44	
17	9.64 622	25	9.69 361	32	10.30 639	9.95 261	7	43	10 5.3 5.2
18	9.64 647	26	9.69 393	32	10.30 607	9.95 254	6	42	20 10.7 10.3
19	9.64 673	25	9.69 425	32	10.30 575	9.95 248	6	41	30 16.0 15.5
									40 21.3 20.7
20	9.64 698	26	9.69 457	31	10.30 543	9.95 242	6	40	50 26.7 25.8
21	9.64 724	25	9.69 488	32	10.30 512	9.95 236	7	39	
22	9.64 749	26	9.69 520	32	10.30 480	9.95 229	6	38	
23	9.64 775	25	9.69 552	32	10.30 448	9.95 223	6	37	″ 26 25 24
24	9.64 800	26	9.69 584	31	10.30 416	9.95 217	6	36	1 0.4 0.4 0.4
									2 0.9 0.8 0.8
25	9.64 826	25	9.69 615	32	10.30 385	9.95 211	7	35	3 1.3 1.2 1.2
26	9.64 851	26	9.69 647	32	10.30 353	9.95 204	6	34	4 1.7 1.7 1.6
27	9.64 877	25	9.69 679	31	10.30 321	9.95 198	6	33	
28	9.64 902	25	9.69 710	32	10.30 290	9.95 192	7	32	5 2.2 2.1 2.0
29	9.64 927	26	9.69 742	32	10.30 258	9.95 185	6	31	6 2.6 2.5 2.4
									7 3.0 2.9 2.8
30	9.64 953	25	9.69 774	31	10.30 226	9.95 179	6	30	8 3.5 3.3 3.2
31	9.64 978	25	9.69 805	32	10.30 195	9.95 173	6	29	9 3.9 3.8 3.6
32	9.65 003	26	9.69 837	31	10.30 163	9.95 167	7	28	
33	9.65 029	25	9.69 868	32	10.30 132	9.95 160	6	27	10 4.3 4.2 4.0
34	9.65 054	25	9.69 900	32	10.30 100	9.95 154	6	26	20 8.7 8.3 8.0
									30 13.0 12.5 12.0
35	9.65 079	25	9.69 932	31	10.30 068	9.95 148	7	25	40 17.3 16.7 16.0
36	9.65 104	26	9.69 963	32	10.30 037	9.95 141	6	24	50 21.7 20.8 20.0
37	9.65 130	25	9.69 995	31	10.30 005	9.95 135	6	23	
38	9.65 155	25	9.70 026	32	10.29 974	9.95 129	7	22	
39	9.65 180	25	9.70 058	31	10.29 942	9.95 122	6	21	″ 7 6
40	9.65 205	25	9.70 089	32	10.29 911	9.95 116	6	20	1 0.1 0.1
41	9.65 230	25	9.70 121	31	10.29 879	9.95 110	7	19	2 0.2 0.2
42	9.65 255	26	9.70 152	32	10.29 848	9.95 103	6	18	3 0.4 0.3
43	9.65 281	25	9.70 184	31	10.29 816	9.95 097	7	17	4 0.5 0.4
44	9.65 306	25	9.70 215	32	10.29 785	9.95 090	6	16	
									5 0.6 0.5
45	9.65 331	25	9.70 247	31	10.29 753	9.95 084	6	15	6 0.7 0.6
46	9.65 356	25	9.70 278	31	10.29 722	9.95 078	7	14	7 0.8 0.7
47	9.65 381	25	9.70 309	32	10.29 691	9.95 071	6	13	8 0.9 0.8
48	9.65 406	25	9.70 341	31	10.29 659	9.95 065	6	12	9 1.0 0.9
49	9.65 431	25	9.70 372	32	10.29 628	9.95 059	7	11	
									10 1.2 1.0
50	9.65 456	25	9.70 404	31	10.29 596	9.95 052	6	10	20 2.3 2.0
51	9.65 481	25	9.70 435	31	10.29 565	9.95 046	7	9	30 3.5 3.0
52	9.65 506	25	9.70 466	32	10.29 534	9.95 039	6	8	40 4.7 4.0
53	9.65 531	25	9.70 498	31	10.29 502	9.95 033	6	7	50 5.8 5.0
54	9.65 556	24	9.70 529	31	10.29 471	9.95 027	7	6	
55	9.65 580	25	9.70 560	32	10.29 440	9.95 020	6	5	
56	9.65 605	25	9.70 592	31	10.29 408	9.95 014	7	4	
57	9.65 630	25	9.70 623	31	10.29 377	9.95 007	6	3	
58	9.65 655	25	9.70 654	31	10.29 346	9.95 001	6	2	
59	0.65 680	25	9.70 685	32	10.29 315	9.94 995	7	1	
60	9.65 705		9.70 717		10.29 283	9.94 988		0	
′	L Cos	d	L Ctn	c d	L Tan	L Sin	d	′	Proportional parts

116° (296°)   (243°) **63°**

470

Table III (Cont'd)
COMMON LOGARITHMS OF TRIGONOMETRIC FUNCTIONS

27° (207°)   (332°) **152°**

′	L Sin	d	L Tan	c d	L Ctn	L Cos	d	′	Proportional parts			
0	9.65 705	24	9.70 717	31	10.29 283	9.94 988	6	60				
1	9.65 729	25	9.70 748	31	10.29 252	9.94 982	7	59				
2	9.65 754	25	9.70 779	31	10.29 221	9.94 975	6	58				
3	9.65 779	25	9.70 810	31	10.29 190	9.94 969	7	57				
4	9.65 804	24	9.70 841	32	10.29 159	9.94 962	6	56				
5	9.65 828	25	9.70 873	31	10.29 127	9.94 956	7	55				
6	9.65 853	25	9.70 904	31	10.29 096	9.94 949	6	54				
7	9.65 878	24	9.70 935	31	10.29 065	9.94 943	7	53	′′	32	31	30
8	9.65 902	25	9.70 966	31	10.29 034	9.94 936	6	52	1	0.5	0.5	0.5
9	9.65 927	25	9.70 997	31	10.29 003	9.94 930	7	51	2	1.1	1.0	1.0
									3	1.6	1.6	1.5
10	9.65 952	24	9.71 028	31	10.28 972	9.94 923	6	50	4	2.1	2.1	2.0
11	9.65 976	25	9.71 059	31	10.28 941	9.94 917	6	49				
12	9.66 001	24	9.71 090	31	10.28 910	9.94 911	7	48	5	2.7	2.6	2.5
13	9.66 025	25	9.71 121	32	10.28 879	9.94 904	6	47	6	3.2	3.1	3.0
14	9.66 050	25	9.71 153	31	10.28 847	9.94 898	7	46	7	3.7	3.6	3.5
									8	4.3	4.1	4.0
15	9.66 075	24	9.71 184	31	10.28 816	9.94 891	6	45	9	4.8	4.6	4.5
16	9.66 099	25	9.71 215	31	10.28 785	9.94 885	7	44				
17	9.66 124	24	9.71 246	31	10.28 754	9.94 878	7	43	10	5.3	5.2	5.0
18	9.66 148	25	9.71 277	31	10.28 723	9.94 871	6	42	20	10.7	10.3	10.0
19	9.66 173	24	9.71 308	31	10.28 692	9.94 865	7	41	30	16.0	15.5	15.0
									40	21.3	20.7	20.0
20	9.66 197	24	9.71 339	31	10.28 661	9.94 858	6	40	50	26.7	25.8	25.0
21	9.66 221	25	9.71 370	31	10.28 630	9.94 852	7	39				
22	9.66 246	24	9.71 401	30	10.28 599	9.94 845	6	38				
23	9.66 270	25	9.71 431	31	10.28 569	9.94 839	7	37	′′	25	24	23
24	9.66 295	24	9.71 462	31	10.28 538	9.94 832	6	36	1	0.4	0.4	0.4
									2	0.8	0.8	0.8
25	9.66 319	24	9.71 493	31	10.28 507	9.94 826	7	35	3	1.2	1.2	1.2
26	9.66 343	25	9.71 524	31	10.28 476	9.94 819	6	34	4	1.7	1.6	1.5
27	9.66 368	24	9.71 555	31	10.28 445	9.94 813	7	33				
28	9.66 392	24	9.71 586	31	10.28 414	9.94 806	7	32	5	2.1	2.0	1.9
29	9.66 416	25	9.71 617	31	10.28 383	9.94 799	6	31	6	2.5	2.4	2.3
									7	2.9	2.8	2.7
30	9.66 441	24	9.71 648	31	10.28 352	9.94 793	7	30	8	3.3	3.2	3.1
31	9.66 465	24	9.71 679	30	10.28 321	9.94 786	6	29	9	3.8	3.6	3.4
32	9.66 489	24	9.71 709	31	10.28 291	9.94 780	7	28				
33	9.66 513	24	9.71 740	31	10.28 260	9.94 773	6	27	10	4.2	4.0	3.8
34	9.66 537	25	9.71 771	31	10.28 229	9.94 767	7	26	20	8.3	8.0	7.7
									30	12.5	12.0	11.5
35	9.66 562	24	9.71 802	31	10.28 198	9.94 760	7	25	40	16.7	16.0	15.3
36	9.66 586	24	9.71 833	30	10.28 167	9.94 753	6	24	50	20.8	20.0	19.2
37	9.66 610	24	9.71 863	31	10.28 137	9.94 747	7	23				
38	9.66 634	24	9.71 894	31	10.28 106	9.94 740	6	22				
39	9.66 658	24	9.71 925	30	10.28 075	9.94 734	7	21	′′		7	6
									1		0.1	0.1
40	9.66 682	24	9.71 955	31	10.28 045	9.94 727	7	20	2		0.2	0.2
41	9.66 706	25	9.71 986	31	10.28 014	9.94 720	6	19	3		0.4	0.3
42	9.66 731	24	9.72 017	31	10.27 983	9.94 714	7	18	4		0.5	0.4
43	9.66 755	24	9.72 048	30	10.27 952	9.94 707	7	17				
44	9.66 779	24	9.72 078	31	10.27 922	9.94 700	6	16	5		0.6	0.5
									6		0.7	0.6
45	9.66 803	24	9.72 109	31	10.27 891	9.94 694	7	15	7		0.8	0.7
46	9.66 827	24	9.72 140	30	10.27 860	9.94 687	7	14	8		0.9	0.8
47	9.66 851	24	9.72 170	31	10.27 830	9.94 680	6	13	9		1.0	0.9
48	9.66 875	24	9.72 201	30	10.27 799	9.94 674	7	12				
49	9.66 899	23	9.72 231	31	10.27 769	9.94 667	7	11	10		1.2	1.0
									20		2.3	2.0
50	9.66 922	24	9.72 262	31	10.27 738	9.94 660	6	10	30		3.5	3.0
51	9.66 946	24	9.72 293	30	10.27 707	9.94 654	7	9	40		4.7	4.0
52	9.66 970	24	9.72 323	31	10.27 677	9.94 647	7	8	50		5.8	5.0
53	9.66 994	24	9.72 354	30	10.27 646	9.94 640	6	7				
54	9.67 018	24	9.72 384	31	10.27 616	9.94 634	7	6				
55	9.67 042	24	9.72 415	30	10.27 585	9.94 627	7	5				
56	9.67 066	24	9.72 445	31	10.27 555	9.94 620	6	4				
57	9.67 090	23	9.72 476	30	10.27 524	9.94 614	7	3				
58	9.67 113	24	9.72 506	31	10.27 494	9.94 607	7	2				
59	9.67 137	24	9.72 537	30	10.27 463	9.94 600	7	1				
60	9.67 161		9.72 567		10.27 433	9.94 593		0				
′	L Cos	d	L Ctn	c d	L Tan	L Sin	d	′	Proportional parts			

117° (297°)   (242°) **62°**

Table III (Cont'd)

COMMON LOGARITHMS OF TRIGONOMETRIC FUNCTIONS

28° (208°) (331°) **151°**

′	L Sin	d	L Tan	c d	L Ctn	L Cos	d	′	Proportional parts		
0	9.67 161	24	9.72 567	31	10.27 433	9.94 593	6	60			
1	9.67 185	23	9.72 598	30	10.27 402	9.94 587	7	59			
2	9.67 208	24	9.72 628	31	10.27 372	9.94 580	7	58			
3	9.67 232	24	9.72 659	30	10.27 341	9.94 573	6	57			
4	9.67 256	24	9.72 689	31	10.27 311	9.94 567	7	56			
5	9.67 280	23	9.72 720	30	10.27 280	9.94 560	7	55	″	31	30	29
6	9.67 303	24	9.72 750	30	10.27 250	9.94 553	7	54				
7	9.67 327	23	9.72 780	31	10.27 220	9.94 546	6	53	1	0.5	0.5	0.5
8	9.67 350	24	9.72 811	30	10.27 189	9.94 540	7	52	2	1.0	1.0	1.0
9	9.67 374	24	9.72 841	31	10.27 159	9.94 533	7	51	3	1.6	1.5	1.4
10	9.67 398	23	9.72 872	30	10.27 128	9.94 526	7	50	4	2.1	2.0	1.9
11	9.67 421	24	9.72 902	30	10.27 098	9.94 519	6	49				
12	9.67 445	23	9.72 932	31	10.27 068	9.94 513	7	48	5	2.6	2.5	2.4
13	9 67 468	24	9.72 963	30	10.27 037	9.94 506	7	47	6	3.1	3.0	2.9
14	9.67 492	23	9.72 993	30	10.27 007	9.94 499	7	46	7	3.6	3.5	3.4
15	9.67 515	24	9.73 023	31	10.26 977	9.94 492	7	45	8	4.1	4.0	3.9
16	9.67 539	23	9.73 054	30	10.26 946	9.94 485	6	44	9	4.6	4.5	4.4
17	9.67 562	24	9.73 084	30	10.26 916	9.94 479	7	43				
18	9.67 586	23	9.73 114	30	10.26 886	9.94 472	7	42	10	5.2	5.0	4.8
19	9.67 609	24	9.73 144	31	10.26 856	9.94 465	7	41	20	10.3	10.0	9.7
									30	15.5	15.0	14.5
20	9.67 633	23	9.73 175	30	10.26 825	9.94 458	7	40	40	20.7	20.0	19.3
21	9.67 656	24	9.73 205	30	10.26 795	9.94 451	6	39	50	25.8	25.0	24.2
22	9.67 680	23	9.73 235	30	10.26 765	9.94 445	7	38				
23	9.67 703	23	9.73 265	30	10.26 735	9.94 438	7	37	″	24	23	22
24	9.67 726	24	9.73 295	31	10.26 705	9.94 431	7	36	1	0.4	0.4	0.4
25	9.67 750	23	9.73 326	30	10.26 674	9.94 424	7	35	2	0.8	0.8	0.7
26	9.67 773	23	9.73 356	30	10.26 644	9.94 417	7	34	3	1.2	1.2	1.1
27	9.67 796	23	9.73 386	30	10.26 614	9.94 410	6	33	4	1.6	1.5	1.5
28	9.67 820	23	9.73 416	30	10.26 584	9.94 404	7	32				
29	9.67 843	23	9.73 446	30	10.26 554	9.94 397	7	31	5	2.0	1.9	1.8
									6	2.4	2.3	2.2
30	9.67 866	24	9.73 476	31	10.26 524	9.94 390	7	30	7	2.8	2.7	2.6
31	9.67 890	23	9.73 507	30	10.26 493	9.94 383	7	29	8	3.2	3.1	2.9
32	9.67 913	23	9.73 537	30	10.26 463	9.94 376	7	28	9	3.6	3.4	3.3
33	9.67 936	23	9.73 567	30	10.26 433	9.94 369	7	27				
34	9.67 959	23	9.73 597	30	10.26 403	9.94 362	7	26	10	4.0	3.8	3.7
									20	8.0	7.7	7.3
35	9.67 982	24	9.73 627	30	10.26 373	9.94 355	6	25	30	12.0	11.5	11.0
36	9.68 006	23	9.73 657	30	10.26 343	9.94 349	7	24	40	16.0	15.3	14.7
37	9.68 029	23	9.73 687	30	10.26 313	9.94 342	7	23	50	20.0	19.2	18.3
38	9.68 052	23	9.73 717	30	10.26 283	9.94 335	7	22				
39	9.68 075	23	9.73 747	30	10.26 253	9.94 328	7	21	″	7	6	
40	9.68 098	23	9.73 777	30	10.26 223	9.94 321	7	20	1	0.1	0.1	
41	9.68 121	23	9.73 807	30	10.26 193	9.94 314	7	19	2	0.2	0.2	
42	9.68 144	23	9.73 837	30	10.26 163	9.94 307	7	18	3	0.4	0.3	
43	9.68 167	23	9.73 867	30	10.26 133	9.94 300	7	17	4	0.5	0.4	
44	9.68 190	23	9.73 897	30	10.26 103	9.94 293	7	16				
45	9.68 213	24	9.73 927	30	10.26 073	9.94 286	7	15	5	0.6	0.5	
46	9.68 237	23	9.73 957	30	10.26 043	9.94 279	6	14	6	0.7	0.6	
47	9.68 260	23	9.73 987	30	10.26 013	9.94 273	7	13	7	0.8	0.7	
48	9.68 283	22	9.74 017	30	10.25 983	9.94 266	7	12	8	0.9	0.8	
49	9.68 305	23	9.74 047	30	10.25 953	9.94 259	7	11	9	1.0	0.9	
50	9.68 328	23	9.74 077	30	10.25 923	9.94 252	7	10	10	1.2	1.0	
51	9.68 351	23	9.74 107	30	10.25 893	9.94 245	7	9	20	2.3	2.0	
52	9.68 374	23	9.74 137	29	10.25 863	9.94 238	7	8	30	3.5	3.0	
53	9.68 397	23	9.74 166	30	10.25 834	9.94 231	7	7	40	4.7	4.0	
54	9.68 420	23	9.74 196	30	10.25 804	9.94 224	7	6	50	5.8	5.0	
55	9.68 443	23	9.74 226	30	10.25 774	9.94 217	7	5				
56	9.68 466	23	9.74 256	30	10.25 744	9.94 210	7	4				
57	9.68 489	23	9.74 286	30	10.25 714	9.94 203	7	3				
58	9.68 512	22	9.74 316	29	10.25 684	9.94 196	7	2				
59	9.68 534	23	9.74 345	30	10.25 655	9.94 189	7	1				
60	9.68 557		9.74 375		10.25 625	9.94 182		0				
′	L Cos	d	L Ctn	c d	L Tan	L Sin	d	′	Proportional parts		

118° (298°)   (241°) **61°**

Table III (Cont'd)

COMMON LOGARITHMS OF TRIGONOMETRIC FUNCTIONS

29° (209°)   (330°) **150°**

′	L Sin	d	L Tan	c d	L Ctn	L Cos	d	′	Proportional parts		
0	9.68 557	23	9.74 375	30	10.25 625	9.94 182	7	60			
1	9.68 580	23	9.74 405	30	10.25 595	9.94 175	7	59			
2	9.68 603	22	9.74 435	30	10.25 565	9.94 168	7	58			
3	9.68 625	23	9.74 465	29	10.25 535	9.94 161	7	57			
4	9.68 648	23	9.74 494	30	10.25 506	9.94 154	7	56			
5	9.68 671	23	9.74 524	30	10.25 476	9.94 147	7	55			
6	9.68 694	22	9.74 554	29	10.25 446	9.94 140	7	54			
7	9.68 716	23	9.74 583	30	10.25 417	9.94 133	7	53			
8	9.68 739	23	9.74 613	30	10.25 387	9.94 126	7	52			
9	9.68 762	22	9.74 643	30	10.25 357	9.94 119	7	51			
10	9.68 784	23	9.74 673	29	10.25 327	9.94 112	7	50			
11	9.68 807	22	9.74 702	30	10.25 298	9.94 105	7	49			
12	9.68 829	23	9.74 732	30	10.25 268	9.94 098	8	48			
13	9.68 852	23	9.74 762	29	10.25 238	9.94 090	7	47			
14	9.68 875	22	9.74 791	30	10.25 209	9.94 083	7	46			
15	9.68 897	23	9.74 821	30	10.25 179	9.94 076	7	45	′′	30	29	23
16	9.68 920	22	9.74 851	29	10.25 149	9.94 069	7	44	1	0.5	0.5	0.4
17	9.68 942	23	9.74 880	30	10.25 120	9.94 062	7	43	2	1.0	1.0	0.8
18	9.68 965	22	9.74 910	29	10.25 090	9.94 055	7	42	3	1.5	1.4	1.2
19	9.68 987	23	9.74 939	30	10.25 061	9.94 048	7	41	4	2.0	1.9	1.5
20	9.69 010	22	9.74 969	29	10.25 031	9.94 041	7	40	5	2.5	2.4	1.9
21	9.69 032	23	9.74 998	30	10.25 002	9.94 034	7	39	6	3.0	2.9	2.3
22	9.69 055	22	9.75 028	30	10.24 972	9.94 027	7	38	7	3.5	3.4	2.7
23	9.69 077	23	9.75 058	29	10.24 942	9.94 020	8	37	8	4.0	3.9	3.1
24	9.69 100	22	9.75 087	30	10.24 913	9.94 012	7	36	9	4.5	4.4	3.4
25	9.69 122	22	9.75 117	29	10.24 883	9.94 005	7	35	10	5.0	4.8	3.8
26	9.69 144	23	9.75 146	30	10.24 854	9.93 998	7	34	20	10.0	9.7	7.7
27	9.69 167	22	9.75 176	29	10.24 824	9.93 991	7	33	30	15.0	14.5	11.5
28	9.69 189	23	9.75 205	30	10.24 795	9.93 984	7	32	40	20.0	19.3	15.3
29	9.69 212	22	9.75 235	29	10.24 765	9.93 977	7	31	50	25.0	24.2	19.2
30	9.69 234	22	9.75 264	30	10.24 736	9.93 970	7	30			
31	9.69 256	23	9.75 294	29	10.24 706	9.93 963	8	29			
32	9.69 279	22	9.75 323	30	10.24 677	9.93 955	7	28	′′	22	8	7
33	9.69 301	22	9.75 353	29	10.24 647	9.93 948	7	27	1	0.4	0.1	0.1
34	9.69 323	22	9.75 382	29	10.24 618	9.93 941	7	26	2	0.7	0.3	0.2
35	9.69 345	23	9.75 411	30	10.24 589	9.93 934	7	25	3	1.1	0.4	0.4
36	9.69 368	22	9.75 441	29	10.24 559	9.93 927	7	24	4	1.5	0.5	0.5
37	9.69 390	22	9.75 470	30	10.24 530	9.93 920	8	23	5	1.8	0.7	0.6
38	9.69 412	22	9.75 500	29	10.24 500	9.93 912	7	22	6	2.2	0.8	0.7
39	9.69 434	22	9.75 529	29	10.24 471	9.93 905	7	21	7	2.6	0.9	0.8
40	9.69 456	23	9.75 558	30	10.24 442	9.93 898	7	20	8	2.9	1.1	0.9
41	9.69 479	22	9.75 588	29	10.24 412	9.93 891	7	19	9	3.3	1.2	1.0
42	9.69 501	22	9.75 617	30	10.24 383	9.93 884	8	18	10	3.7	1.3	1.2
43	9.69 523	22	9.75 647	29	10.24 353	9.93 876	7	17	20	7.3	2.7	2.3
44	9.69 545	22	9.75 676	29	10.24 324	9.93 869	7	16	30	11.0	4.0	3.5
45	9.69 567	22	9.75 705	30	10.24 295	9.93 862	7	15	40	14.7	5.3	4.7
46	9.69 589	22	9.75 735	29	10.24 265	9.93 855	8	14	50	18.3	6.7	5.8
47	9.69 611	22	9.75 764	29	10.24 236	9.93 847	7	13			
48	9.69 633	22	9.75 793	29	10.24 207	9.93 840	7	12			
49	9.69 655	22	9.75 822	30	10.24 178	9.93 833	7	11			
50	9.69 677	22	9.75 852	29	10.24 148	9.93 826	7	10			
51	9.69 699	22	9.75 881	29	10.24 119	9.93 819	8	9			
52	9.69 721	22	9.75 910	29	10.24 090	9.93 811	7	8			
53	9.69 743	22	9.75 939	30	10.24 061	9.93 804	7	7			
54	9.69 765	22	9.75 969	29	10.24 031	9.93 797	8	6			
55	9.69 787	22	9.75 998	29	10.24 002	9.93 789	7	5			
56	9.69 809	22	9.76 027	29	10.23 973	9.93 782	7	4			
57	9.69 831	22	9.76 056	30	10.23 944	9.93 775	7	3			
58	9.69 853	22	9.76 086	29	10.23 914	9.93 768	8	2			
59	9.69 875	22	9.76 115	29	10.23 885	9.93 760	7	1			
60	9.69 897		9.76 144		10.23 856	9.93 753		0			
′	L Cos	d	L Ctn	c d	L Tan	L Sin	d	′	Proportional parts		

119° (299)   (240°) **60°**

Table III (Cont'd)

COMMON LOGARITHMS OF TRIGONOMETRIC FUNCTIONS

30° (210)   **(329°) 149°**

′	L Sin	d	L Tan	c d	L Ctn	L Cos	d	′	Proportional parts		
0	9.69 897	22	9.76 144	29	10.23 856	9.93 753	7	60			
1	9.69 919	22	9.76 173	29	10.23 827	9.93 746	8	59			
2	9.69 941	22	9.76 202	29	10.23 798	9.93 738	7	58			
3	9.69 963	21	9.76 231	30	10.23 769	9.93 731	7	57			
4	9.69 984	22	9.76 261	29	10.23 739	9.93 724	7	56			
5	9.70 006	22	9.76 290	29	10.23 710	9.93 717	8	55			
6	9.70 028	22	9.76 319	29	10.23 681	9.93 709	7	54			
7	9.70 050	22	9.76 348	29	10.23 652	9.93 702	7	53	′′	30 29 28	
8	9.70 072	21	9.76 377	29	10.23 623	9.93 695	8	52	1	0.5 0.5 0.5	
9	9.70 093	22	9.76 406	29	10.23 594	9.93 687	7	51	2	1.0 1.0 0.9	
									3	1.5 1.4 1.4	
10	9.70 115	22	9.76 435	29	10.23 565	9.93 680	7	50	4	2.0 1.9 1.9	
11	9.70 137	22	9.76 464	29	10.23 536	9.93 673	8	49			
12	9.70 159	21	9.76 493	29	10.23 507	9.93 665	7	48	5	2.5 2.4 2.3	
13	9.70 180	22	9.76 522	29	10.23 478	9.93 758	8	47	6	3.0 2.9 2.8	
14	9.70 202	22	9.76 551	29	10.23 449	9.93 650	7	46	7	3.5 3.4 3.3	
									8	4.0 3.9 3.7	
15	9.70 224	21	9.76 580	29	10.23 420	9.93 643	7	45	9	4.5 4.4 4.2	
16	9.70 245	22	9.76 609	30	10.23 391	9.93 636	8	44			
17	9.70 267	21	9.76 639	29	10.23 361	9.93 628	7	43	10	5.0 4.8 4.7	
18	9.70 288	22	9.76 668	29	10.23 332	9.93 621	7	42	20	10.0 9.7 9.3	
19	9.70 310	22	9.76 697	28	10.23 303	9.93 614	8	41	30	15.0 14.5 14.0	
									40	20.0 19.3 18.7	
20	9.70 332	21	9.76 725	29	10.23 275	9.93 606	7	40	50	25.0 24.2 23.3	
21	9.70 353	22	9.76 754	29	10.23 246	9.93 599	8	39			
22	9.70 375	21	9.76 783	29	10.23 217	9.93 591	7	38			
23	9.70 396	22	9.76 812	29	10.23 188	9.93 584	7	37	′′	22 21	
24	9.70 418	21	9.76 841	29	10.23 159	9.93 577	8	36	1	0.4 0.4	
									2	0.7 0.7	
25	9.70 439	22	9.76 870	29	10.23 130	9.93 569	7	35	3	1.1 1.0	
26	9.70 461	21	9.76 899	29	10.23 101	9.93 562	8	34	4	1.5 1.4	
27	9.70 482	22	9.76 928	29	10.23 072	9.93 554	7	33			
28	9.70 504	21	9.76 957	29	10.23 043	9.93 547	8	32	5	1.8 1.8	
29	9.70 525	22	9.76 986	29	10.23 014	9.93 539	7	31	6	2.2 2.1	
									7	2.6 2.4	
30	9.70 547	21	9.77 015	29	10.22 985	9.93 532	7	30	8	2.9 2.8	
31	9.70 568	22	9.77 044	29	10.22 956	9.93 525	8	29	9	3.3 3.2	
32	9.70 590	21	9.77 073	28	10.22 927	9.93 517	7	28			
33	9.70 611	22	9.77 101	29	10.22 899	9.93 510	8	27	10	3.7 3.5	
34	9.70 633	21	9.77 130	29	10.22 870	9.93 502	7	26	20	7.3 7.0	
									30	11.0 10.5	
35	9.70 654	21	9.77 159	29	10.22 841	9.93 495	8	25	40	14.7 14.0	
36	9.70 675	22	9.77 188	29	10.22 812	9.93 487	7	24	50	18.3 17.5	
37	9.70 697	21	9.77 217	29	10.22 783	9.93 480	8	23			
38	9.70 718	21	9.77 246	28	10.22 754	9.93 472	7	22			
39	9.70 739	22	9.77 274	29	10.22 726	9.93 465	8	21	′′	8 7	
									1	0.1 0.1	
40	9.70 761	21	9.77 303	29	10.22 697	9.93 457	7	20	2	0.3 0.2	
41	9.70 782	21	9.77 332	29	10.22 668	9.93 450	8	19	3	0.4 0.4	
42	9.70 803	21	9.77 361	29	10.22 639	9.93 442	7	18	4	0.5 0.5	
43	9.70 824	22	9.77 390	28	10.22 610	9.93 435	8	17			
44	9.70 846	21	9.77 418	29	10.22 582	9.93 427	7	16	5	0.7 0.6	
									6	0.8 0.7	
45	9.70 867	21	9.77 447	29	10.22 553	9.93 420	8	15	7	0.9 0.8	
46	9.70 888	21	9.77 476	29	10.22 524	9.93 412	7	14	8	1.1 0.9	
47	9.70 909	22	9.77 505	28	10.22 495	9.93 405	8	13	9	1.2 1.0	
48	9.70 931	21	9.77 533	29	10.22 467	9.93 397	7	12			
49	9.70 952	21	9.77 562	29	10.22 438	9.93 390	8	11	10	1.3 1.2	
									20	2.7 2.3	
50	9.70 973	21	9.77 591	28	10.22 409	9.93 382	7	10	30	4.0 3.5	
51	9.70 994	21	9.77 619	29	10.22 381	9.93 375	8	9	40	5.3 4.7	
52	9.71 015	21	9.77 648	29	10.22 352	9.93 367	8	8	50	6.7 5.8	
53	9.71 036	22	9.77 677	29	10.22 323	9.93 360	8	7			
54	9.71 058	21	9.77 706	28	10.22 294	9.93 352	8	6			
55	9.71 079	21	9.77 734	29	10.22 266	9.93 344	7	5			
56	9.71 100	21	9.77 763	28	10.22 237	9.93 337	8	4			
57	9.71 121	21	9.77 791	29	10.22 209	9.93 329	7	3			
58	9.71 142	21	9.77 820	29	10.22 180	9.93 322	8	2			
59	9.71 163	21	9.77 849	28	10.22 151	9.93 314	7	1			
60	9.71 184		9.77 877		10.22 123	9.93 307		0			
′	L Cos	d	L Ctn	c d	L Tan	L Sin	d	′	Proportional parts		

120° (300°)   **(239°) 59°**

Table III (Cont'd)
COMMON LOGARITHMS OF TRIGONOMETRIC FUNCTIONS

31° (211°)   **(328°) 148°**

′	L Sin	d	L Tan	c d	L Ctn	L Cos	d	′
0	9.71 184	21	9.77 877	29	10.22 123	9.93 307	8	60
1	9.71 205	21	9.77 906	29	10.22 094	9.93 299	8	59
2	9.71 226	21	9.77 935	28	10.22 065	9.93 291	7	58
3	9.71 247	21	9.77 963	29	10.22 037	9.93 284	8	57
4	9.71 268	21	9.77 992	28	10.22 008	9.93 276	7	56
5	9.71 289	21	9.78 020	29	10.21 980	9.93 269	8	55
6	9.71 310	21	9.78 049	28	10.21 951	9.93 261	8	54
7	9.71 331	21	9.78 077	29	10.21 923	9.93 253	7	53
8	9.71 352	21	9.78 106	29	10.21 894	9.93 246	8	52
9	9.71 373	20	9.78 135	28	10.21 865	9.93 238	8	51
10	9.71 393	21	9.78 163	29	10.21 837	9.93 230	7	50
11	9.71 414	21	9.78 192	28	10.21 808	9.93 223	8	49
12	9.71 435	21	9.78 220	29	10.21 780	9.93 215	8	48
13	9.71 456	21	9.78 249	28	10.21 751	9.93 207	7	47
14	9.71 477	21	9.78 277	29	10.21 723	9.93 200	8	46
15	9.71 498	21	9.78 306	28	10.21 694	9.93 192	8	45
16	9.71 519	20	9.78 334	29	10.21 666	9.93 184	7	44
17	9.71 539	21	9.78 363	28	10.21 637	9.93 177	8	43
18	9.71 560	21	9.78 391	28	10.21 609	9.93 169	8	42
19	9.71 581	21	9.78 419	29	10.21 581	9.93 161	7	41
20	9.71 602	20	9.78 448	28	10.21 552	9.93 154	8	40
21	9.71 622	21	9.78 476	29	10.21 524	9.93 146	8	39
22	9.71 643	21	9.78 505	28	10.21 495	9.93 138	7	38
23	9.71 664	21	9.78 533	29	10.21 467	9.93 131	8	37
24	9.71 685	20	9.78 562	28	10.21 438	9.93 123	8	36
25	9.71 705	21	9.78 590	28	10.21 410	9.93 115	7	35
26	9.71 726	21	9.78 618	29	10.21 382	9.93 108	8	34
27	9.71 747	20	9.78 647	28	10.21 353	9.93 100	8	33
28	9.71 767	21	9.78 675	28	10.21 325	9.93 092	8	32
29	9.71 788	21	9.78 704	28	10.21 296	9.93 084	7	31
30	9.71 809	20	9.78 732	28	10.21 268	9.93 077	8	30
31	9.71 829	21	9.78 760	28	10.21 240	9.93 069	8	29
32	9.71 850	20	9.78 789	28	10.21 211	9.93 061	8	28
33	9.71 870	21	9.78 817	28	10.21 183	9.93 053	7	27
34	9.71 891	20	9.78 845	29	10.21 155	9.93 046	8	26
35	9.71 911	21	9.78 874	28	10.21 126	9.93 038	8	25
36	9.71 932	20	9.78 902	28	10.21 098	9.93 030	8	24
37	9.71 952	21	9.78 930	29	10.21 070	9.93 022	8	23
38	9.71 973	21	9.78 959	28	10.21 041	9.93 014	7	22
39	9.71 994	20	9.78 987	28	10.21 013	9.93 007	8	21
40	9.72 014	20	9.79 015	28	10.20 985	9.92 999	8	20
41	9.72 034	21	9.79 043	29	10.20 957	9.92 991	8	19
42	9.72 055	20	9.79 072	28	10.20 928	9.92 983	7	18
43	9.72 075	21	9.79 100	28	10.20 900	9.92 976	8	17
44	9.72 096	20	9.79 128	28	10.20 872	9.92 968	8	16
45	9.72 116	21	9.79 156	29	10.20 844	9.92 960	8	15
46	9.72 137	20	9.79 185	28	10.20 815	9.92 952	8	14
47	9.72 157	20	9.79 213	28	10.20 787	9.92 944	8	13
48	9.72 177	21	9.79 241	28	10.20 759	9.92 936	7	12
49	9.72 198	20	9.79 269	28	10.20 731	9.92 929	8	11
50	9.72 218	20	9.79 297	29	10.20 703	9.92 921	8	10
51	9.72 238	21	9.79 326	28	10.20 674	9.92 913	8	9
52	9.72 259	20	9.79 354	28	10.20 646	9.92 905	8	8
53	9.72 279	20	9.79 382	28	10.20 618	9.92 897	8	7
54	9.72 299	21	9.79 410	28	10.20 590	9.92 889	8	6
55	9.72 320	20	9.79 438	28	10.20 562	9.92 881	7	5
56	9.72 340	20	9.79 466	29	10.20 534	9.92 874	8	4
57	9.72 360	21	9.79 495	28	10.20 505	9.92 866	8	3
58	9.72 381	20	9.79 523	28	10.20 477	9.92 858	8	2
59	9.72 401	20	9.79 551	28	10.20 449	9.92 850	8	1
60	9.72 421	—	9.79 579		10.20 421	9.92 842		0
′	L Cos	d	L Ctn	c d	L Tan	L Sin	d	′

Proportional parts

″	29	28
1	0.5	0.5
2	1.0	1.0
3	1.4	1.4
4	1.9	1.9
5	2.4	2.3
6	2.9	2.8
7	3.4	3.3
8	3.9	3.7
9	4.4	4.2
10	4.8	4.7
20	9.7	9.3
30	14.5	14.0
40	19.3	18.7
50	24.2	23.3

″	21	20
1	0.4	0.3
2	0.7	0.7
3	1.0	1.0
4	1.4	1.3
5	1.8	1.7
6	2.1	2.0
7	2.4	2.3
8	2.8	2.7
9	3.2	3.0
10	3.5	3.3
20	7.0	6.7
30	10.5	10.0
40	14.0	13.3
50	17.5	16.7

″	8	7
1	0.1	0.1
2	0.3	0.2
3	0.4	0.4
4	0.5	0.5
5	0.7	0.6
6	0.8	0.7
7	0.9	0.8
8	1.1	0.9
9	1.2	1.0
10	1.3	1.2
20	2.7	2.3
30	4.0	3.5
40	5.3	4.7
50	6.7	5.8

121° (301°)   **(238°) 58°**

Table III (Cont'd)

COMMON LOGARITHMS OF TRIGONOMETRIC FUNCTIONS

32° (212°)   **(327°) 147°**

′	L Sin	d	L Tan	c d	L Ctn	L Cos	d	′
0	9.72 421	20	9.79 579	28	10.20 421	9.92 842	8	60
1	9.72 441	20	9.79 607	28	10.20 393	9.92 834	8	59
2	9.72 461	21	9.79 635	28	10.20 365	9.92 826	8	58
3	9.72 482	20	9.79 663	28	10.20 337	9.92 818	8	57
4	9.72 502	20	9.79 691	28	10.20 309	9.92 810	7	56
5	9.72 522	20	9.79 719	28	10.20 281	9.92 803	8	55
6	9.72 542	20	9.79 747	29	10.20 253	9.92 795	8	54
7	9.72 562	20	9.79 776	28	10.20 224	9.92 787	8	53
8	9.72 582	20	9.79 804	28	10.20 196	9.92 779	8	52
9	9.72 602	20	9.79 832	28	10.20 168	9.92 771	8	51
10	9.72 622	21	9.79 860	28	10.20 140	9.92 763	8	50
11	9.72 643	20	9.79 888	28	10.20 112	9.92 755	8	49
12	9.72 663	20	9.79 916	28	10.20 084	9.92 747	8	48
13	9.72 683	20	9.79 944	28	10.20 056	9.92 739	8	47
14	9.72 703	20	9.79 972	28	10.20 028	9.92 731	8	46
15	9.72 723	20	9.80 000	28	10.20 000	9.92 723	8	45
16	9.72 743	20	9.80 028	28	10.19 972	9.92 715	8	44
17	9.72 763	20	9.80 056	28	10.19 944	9.92 707	8	43
18	9.72 783	20	9.80 084	28	10.19 916	9.92 699	8	42
19	9.72 803	20	9.80 112	28	10.19 888	9.92 691	8	41
20	9.72 823	20	9.80 140	28	10.19 860	9.92 683	8	40
21	9.72 843	20	9.80 168	27	10.19 832	9.92 675	8	39
22	9.72 863	20	9.80 195	28	10.19 805	9.92 667	8	38
23	9.72 883	19	9.80 223	28	10.19 777	9.92 659	8	37
24	9.72 902	20	9.80 251	28	10.19 749	9.92 651	8	36
25	9.72 922	20	9.80 279	28	10.19 721	9.92 643	8	35
26	9.72 942	20	9.80 307	28	10.19 693	9.92 635	8	34
27	9.72 962	20	9.80 335	28	10.19 665	9.92 627	8	33
28	9.72 982	20	9.80 363	28	10.19 637	9.92 619	8	32
29	9.73 002	20	9.80 391	28	10.19 609	9.92 611	8	31
30	9.73 022	19	9.80 419	28	10.19 581	9.92 603	8	30
31	9.73 041	20	9.80 447	27	10.19 553	9.92 595	8	29
32	9.73 061	20	9.80 474	28	10.19 526	9.92 587	8	28
33	9.73 081	20	9.80 502	28	10.19 498	9.92 579	8	27
34	9.73 101	20	9.80 530	28	10.19 470	9.92 571	8	26
35	9.73 121	19	9.80 558	28	10.19 442	9.92 563	8	25
36	9.73 140	20	9.80 586	28	10.19 414	9.92 555	9	24
37	9.73 160	20	9.80 614	28	10.19 386	9.92 546	8	23
38	9.73 180	20	9.80 642	27	10.19 358	9.92 538	8	22
39	9.73 200	19	9.80 669	28	10.19 331	9.92 530	8	21
40	9.73 219	20	9.80 697	28	10.19 303	9.92 522	8	20
41	9.73 239	20	9.80 725	28	10.19 275	9.92 514	8	19
42	9.73 259	19	9.80 753	28	10.19 247	9.92 506	8	18
43	9.73 278	20	9.80 781	27	10.19 219	9.92 498	8	17
44	9.73 298	20	9.80 808	28	10.19 192	9.92 490	8	16
45	9.73 318	19	9.80 836	28	10.19 164	9.92 482	9	15
46	9.73 337	20	9.80 864	28	10.19 136	9.92 473	8	14
47	9.73 357	20	9.80 892	27	10.19 108	9.92 465	8	13
48	9.73 377	19	9.80 919	28	10.19 081	9.92 457	8	12
49	9.73 396	20	9.80 947	28	10.19 053	9.92 449	8	11
50	9.73 416	19	9.80 975	28	10.19 025	9.92 441	8	10
51	9.73 435	20	9.81 003	27	10.18 997	9.92 433	8	9
52	9.73 455	19	9.81 030	28	10.18 970	9.92 425	9	8
53	9.73 474	20	9.81 058	28	10.18 942	9.92 416	8	7
54	9.73 494	19	9.81 086	27	10.18 914	9.92 408	8	6
55	9.73 513	20	9.81 113	28	10.18 887	9.92 400	8	5
56	9.73 533	19	9.81 141	28	10.18 859	9.92 392	8	4
57	9.73 552	20	9.81 169	27	10.18 831	9.92 384	8	3
58	9.73 572	19	9.81 196	28	10.18 804	9.92 376	9	2
59	9.73 591	20	9.81 224	28	10.18 776	9.92 367	8	1
60	9.73 611		9.81 252		10.18 748	9.92 359		0
′	L Cos	d	L Ctn	c d	L Tan	L Sin	d	′

Proportional parts

″	29	28	27
1	0.5	0.5	0.4
2	1.0	0.9	0.9
3	1.4	1.4	1.4
4	1.9	1.9	1.8
5	2.4	2.3	2.2
6	2.9	2.8	2.7
7	3.4	3.3	3.2
8	3.9	3.7	3.6
9	4.4	4.2	4.0
10	4.8	4.7	4.5
20	9.7	9.3	9.0
30	14.5	14.0	13.5
40	19.3	18.7	18.0
50	24.2	23.3	22.5

″	21	20	19
1	0.4	0.3	0.3
2	0.7	0.7	0.6
3	1.0	1.0	1.0
4	1.4	1.3	1.3
5	1.8	1.7	1.6
6	2.1	2.0	1.9
7	2.4	2.3	2.2
8	2.8	2.7	2.5
9	3.2	3.0	2.8
10	3.5	3.3	3.2
20	7.0	6.7	6.3
30	10.5	10.0	9.5
40	14.0	13.3	12.7
50	17.5	16.7	15.8

″	9	8	7
1	0.2	0.1	0.1
2	0.3	0.3	0.2
3	0.4	0.4	0.4
4	0.6	0.5	0.5
5	0.8	0.7	0.6
6	0.9	0.8	0.7
7	1.0	0.9	0.8
8	1.2	1.1	0.9
9	1.4	1.2	1.0
10	1.5	1.3	1.2
20	3.0	2.7	2.3
30	4.5	4.0	3.5
40	6.0	5.3	4.7
50	7.5	6.7	5.8

122° (302°)   **(237°) 57°**

Table III (Cont'd)

COMMON LOGARITHMS OF TRIGONOMETRIC FUNCTIONS

33° (213°)   (326°) **146°**

′	L Sin	d	L Tan	c d	L Ctn	L Cos	d	′	Proportional parts
0	9.73 611	19	9.81 252	27	10.18 748	9.92 359	8	60	
1	9.73 630	20	9.81 279	28	10.18 721	9.92 351	8	59	
2	9.73 650	19	9.81 307	28	10.18 693	9.92 343	8	58	
3	9.73 669	20	9.81 335	27	10.18 665	9.92 335	9	57	
4	9.73 689	19	9.81 362	28	10.18 638	9.92 326	8	56	
5	9.73 708	19	9.81 390	28	10.18 610	9.92 318	8	55	
6	9.73 727	20	9.81 418	27	10.18 582	9.92 310	8	54	″ 28 27
7	9.73 747	19	9.81 445	28	10.18 555	9.92 302	9	53	1 0.5 0.4
8	9.73 766	19	9.81 473	27	10.18 527	9.92 293	8	52	2 0.9 0.9
9	9.73 785	20	9.81 500	28	10.18 500	9.92 285	8	51	3 1.4 1.4
10	9.73 805	19	9.81 528	28	10.18 472	9.92 277	8	50	4 1.9 1.8
11	9.73 824	19	9.81 556	27	10.18 444	9.92 269	9	49	
12	9.73 843	20	9.81 583	28	10.18 417	9.92 260	8	48	5 2.3 2.2
13	9.73 863	19	9.81 611	27	10.18 389	9.92 252	8	47	6 2.8 2.7
14	9.73 882	19	9.81 638	28	10.18 362	9.92 244	9	46	7 3.3 3.2
15	9.73 901	20	9.81 666	27	10.18 334	9.92 235	8	45	8 3.7 3.6
16	9.73 921	19	9.81 693	28	10.18 307	9.92 227	8	44	9 4.2 4.0
17	9.73 940	19	9.81 721	27	10.18 279	9.92 219	8	43	
18	9.73 959	19	9.81 748	28	10.18 252	9.92 211	9	42	10 4.7 4.5
19	9.73 978	19	9.81 776	27	10.18 224	9.92 202	8	41	20 9.3 9.0
20	9.73 997	20	9.81 803	28	10.18 197	9.92 194	8	40	30 14.0 13.5
21	9.74 017	19	9.81 831	27	10.18 169	9.92 186	9	39	40 18.7 18.0
22	9.74 036	19	9.81 858	28	10.18 142	9.92 177	8	38	50 23.3 22.5
23	9.74 055	19	9.81 886	28	10.18 114	9.92 169	8	37	
24	9.74 074	19	9.81 913	28	10.18 087	9.92 161	9	36	″ 20 19 18
25	9.74 093	20	9.81 941	27	10.18 059	9.92 152	8	35	1 0.3 0.3 0.3
26	9.74 113	19	9.81 968	28	10.18 032	9.92 144	8	34	2 0.7 0.6 0.6
27	9.74 132	19	9.81 996	27	10.18 004	9.92 136	9	33	3 1.0 1.0 0.9
28	9.74 151	19	9.82 023	28	10.17 977	9.92 127	8	32	4 1.3 1.3 1.2
29	9.74 170	19	9.82 051	27	10.17 949	9.92 119	8	31	
30	9.74 189	19	9.82 078	28	10.17 922	9.92 111	9	30	5 1.7 1.6 1.5
31	9.74 208	19	9.82 106	27	10.17 894	9.92 102	8	29	6 2.0 1.9 1.8
32	9.74 227	19	9.82 133	28	10.17 867	9.92 094	8	28	7 2.3 2.2 2.1
33	9.74 246	19	9.82 161	27	10.17 839	9.92 086	9	27	8 2.7 2.5 2.4
34	9.74 265	19	9.82 188	27	10.17 812	9.92 077	8	26	9 3.0 2.8 2.7
35	9.74 284	19	9.82 215	28	10.17 785	9.92 069	9	25	
36	9.74 303	19	9.82 243	27	10.17 757	9.92 060	8	24	10 3.3 3.2 3.0
37	9.74 322	19	9.82 270	28	10.17 730	9.92 052	8	23	20 6.7 6.3 6.0
38	9.74 341	19	9.82 298	27	10.17 702	9.92 044	9	22	30 10.0 9.5 9.0
39	9.74 360	19	9.82 325	27	10.17 675	9.92 035	8	21	40 13.3 12.7 12.0
40	9.74 379	19	9.82 352	28	10.17 648	9.92 027	9	20	50 16.7 15.8 15.0
41	9.74 398	19	9.82 380	27	10.17 620	9.92 018	8	19	
42	9.74 417	19	9.82 407	28	10.17 593	9.92 010	8	18	
43	9.74 436	19	9.82 435	27	10.17 565	9.92 002	9	17	″ 9 8
44	9.74 455	19	9.82 462	27	10.17 538	9.91 993	8	16	1 0.2 0.1
45	9.74 474	19	9.82 489	28	10.17 511	9.91 985	9	15	2 0.3 0.3
46	9.74 493	19	9.82 517	27	10.17 483	9.91 976	8	14	3 0.4 0.4
47	9.74 512	19	9.82 544	27	10.17 456	9.91 968	8	13	4 0.6 0.5
48	9.74 531	18	9.82 571	28	10.17 429	9.91 959	9	12	
49	9.74 549	19	9.82 599	27	10.17 401	9.91 951	9	11	5 0.8 0.7
50	9.74 568	19	9.82 626	27	10.17 374	9.91 942	8	10	6 0.9 0.8
51	9.74 587	19	9.82 653	28	10.17 347	9.91 934	9	9	7 1.0 0.9
52	9.74 606	19	9.82 681	27	10.17 319	9.91 925	8	8	8 1.2 1.1
53	9.74 625	19	9.82 708	27	10.17 292	9.91 917	9	7	9 1.4 1.2
54	9.74 644	18	9.82 735	27	10.17 265	9.91 908	8	6	
55	9.74 662	19	9.82 762	28	10.17 238	9.91 900	9	5	10 1.5 1.3
56	9.74 681	19	9.82 790	27	10.17 210	9.91 891	8	4	20 3.0 2.7
57	9.74 700	19	9.82 817	27	10.17 183	9.91 883	9	3	30 4.5 4.0
58	9.74 719	19	9.82 844	27	10.17 156	9.91 874	8	2	40 6.0 5.3
59	9.74 737	19	9.82 871	28	10.17 129	9.91 866	9	1	50 7.5 6.7
60	9.74 756		9.82 899		10.17 101	9.91 857		0	
′	L Cos	d	L Ctn	c d	L Tan	L Sin	d	′	Proportional parts

123° (303°)   (236°) **56°**

Table III (Cont'd)

COMMON LOGARITHMS OF TRIGONOMETRIC FUNCTIONS

34° (214°)   **(325°) 145°**

′	L Sin	d	L Tan	c d	L Ctn	L Cos	d	′	Proportional parts
0	9.74 756	19	9.82 899	27	10.17 101	9.91 857	8	60	
1	9.74 775	19	9.82 926	27	10.17 074	9.91 849	9	59	
2	9.74 794	18	9.82 953	27	10.17 047	9.91 840	8	58	
3	9.74 812	19	9.82 980	28	10.17 020	9.91 832	9	57	
4	9.74 831	19	9.83 008	27	10.16 992	9.91 823	8	56	
5	9.74 850	18	9.83 035	27	10.16 965	9.91 815	9	55	
6	9.74 868	19	9.83 062	27	10.16 938	9.91 806	8	54	
7	9.74 887	19	9.83 089	28	10.16 911	9.91 798	9	53	″ 28 27 26
8	9.74 906	18	9.83 117	27	10.16 883	9.91 789	8	52	1 0.5 0.4 0.4
9	9.74 924	19	9.83 144	27	10.16 856	9.91 781	9	51	2 0.9 0.9 0.9
10	9.74 943	18	9.83 171	27	10.16 829	9.91 772	9	50	3 1.4 1.4 1.3
11	9.74 961	19	9.83 198	27	10.16 802	9.91 763	8	49	4 1.9 1.8 1.7
12	9.74 980	19	9.83 225	27	10.16 775	9.91 755	9	48	
13	9.74 999	18	9.83 252	28	10.16 748	9.91 746	8	47	5 2.3 2.2 2.2
14	9.75 017	19	9.83 280	27	10.16 720	9.91 738	9	46	6 2.8 2.7 2.6
15	9.75 036	18	9.83 307	27	10.16 693	9.91 729	9	45	7 3.3 3.2 3.0
16	9.75 054	19	9.83 334	27	10.16 666	9.91 720	8	44	8 3.7 3.6 3.5
17	9.75 073	18	9.83 361	27	10.16 639	9.91 712	9	43	9 4.2 4.0 3.9
18	9.75 091	19	9.83 388	27	10.16 612	9.91 703	8	42	
19	9.75 110	18	9.83 415	27	10.16 585	9.91 695	9	41	10 4.7 4.5 4.3
20	9.75 128	19	9.83 442	28	10.16 558	9.91 686	9	40	20 9.3 9.0 8.7
21	9.75 147	18	9.83 470	27	10.16 530	9.91 677	8	39	30 14.0 13.5 13.0
22	9.75 165	19	9.83 497	27	10.16 503	9.91 669	9	38	40 18.7 18.0 17.3
23	9.75 184	18	9.83 524	27	10.16 476	9.91 660	9	37	50 23.3 22.5 21.7
24	9.75 202	19	9.83 551	27	10.16 449	9.91 651	8	36	
25	9.75 221	18	9.83 578	27	10.16 422	9.91 643	9	35	″ 19 18
26	9.75 239	19	9.83 605	27	10.16 395	9.91 634	9	34	1 0.3 0.3
27	9.75 258	18	9.83 632	27	10.16 368	9.91 625	8	33	2 0.6 0.6
28	9.75 276	18	9.83 659	27	10.16 341	9.91 617	9	32	3 1.0 0.9
29	9.75 294	19	9.83 686	27	10.16 314	9.91 608	9	31	4 1.3 1.2
30	9.75 313	18	9.83 713	27	10.16 287	9.91 599	8	30	5 1.6 1.5
31	9.75 331	19	9.83 740	28	10.16 260	9.91 591	9	29	6 1.9 1.8
32	9.75 350	18	9.83 768	27	10.16 232	9.91 582	9	28	7 2.2 2.1
33	9.75 368	18	9.83 795	27	10.16 205	9.91 573	8	27	8 2.5 2.4
34	9.75 386	19	9.83 822	27	10.16 178	9.91 565	9	26	9 2.8 2.7
35	9.75 405	18	9.83 849	27	10.16 151	9.91 556	9	25	10 3.2 3.0
36	9.75 423	18	9.83 876	27	10.16 124	9.91 547	9	24	20 6.3 6.0
37	9.75 441	18	9.83 903	27	10.16 097	9.91 538	8	23	30 9.5 9.0
38	9.75 459	19	9.83 930	27	10.16 070	9.91 530	9	22	40 12.7 12.0
39	9.75 478	18	9.83 957	27	10.16 043	9.91 521	9	21	50 15.8 15.0
40	9.75 496	18	9.83 984	27	10.16 016	9.91 512	8	20	
41	9.75 514	19	9.84 011	27	10.15 989	9.91 504	9	19	″ 9 8
42	9.75 533	18	9.84 038	27	10.15 962	9.91 495	9	18	1 0.2 0.1
43	9.75 551	18	9.84 065	27	10.15 935	9.91 486	9	17	2 0.3 0.3
44	9.75 569	18	9.84 092	27	10.15 908	9.91 477	8	16	3 0.4 0.4
45	9.75 587	18	9.84 119	27	10.15 881	9.91 469	9	15	4 0.6 0.5
46	9.75 605	19	9.84 146	27	10.15 854	9.91 460	9	14	5 0.8 0.7
47	9.75 624	18	9.84 173	27	10.15 827	9.91 451	9	13	6 0.9 0.8
48	9.75 642	18	9.84 200	27	10.15 800	9.91 442	9	12	7 1.0 0.9
49	9.75 660	18	9.84 227	27	10.15 773	9.91 433	8	11	8 1.2 1.1
50	9.75 678	18	9.84 254	26	10.15 746	9.91 425	9	10	9 1.4 1.2
51	9.75 696	18	9.84 280	27	10.15 720	9.91 416	9	9	10 1.5 1.3
52	9.75 714	19	9.84 307	27	10.15 693	9.91 407	9	8	20 3.0 2.7
53	9.75 733	18	9.84 334	27	10.15 666	9.91 398	9	7	30 4.5 4.0
54	9.75 751	18	9.84 361	27	10.15 639	9.91 389	8	6	40 6.0 5.3
55	9.75 769	18	9.84 388	27	10.15 612	9.91 381	9	5	50 7.5 6.7
56	9 75 787	18	9.84 415	27	10.15 585	9.91 372	9	4	
57	9.75 805	18	9.84 442	27	10.15 558	9.91 363	9	3	
58	9.75 823	18	9.84 469	27	10.15 531	9.91 354	9	2	
59	9.75 841	18	9.84 496	27	10.15 504	9.91 345	9	1	
60	9.75 859		9.84 523		10.15 477	9.91 336		0	
′	L Cos	d	L Ctn	c d	L Tan	L Sin	d	′	Proportional parts

124° (304°)   **(235°) 55°**

Table III (Cont'd)

COMMON LOGARITHMS OF TRIGONOMETRIC FUNCTIONS

35° (215°)   **(324°) 144°**

′	L Sin	d	L Tan	cd	L Ctn	L Cos	d	′	Proportional parts
0	9.75 859	18	9.84 523	27	10.15 477	9.91 336	8	60	
1	9.75 877	18	9.84 550	26	10.15 450	9.91 328	9	59	
2	9.75 895	18	9.84 576	27	10.15 424	9.91 319	9	58	
3	9.75 913	18	9.84 603	27	10.15 397	9.91 310	9	57	
4	9.75 931	18	9.84 630	27	10.15 370	9.91 301	9	56	
5	9.75 949	18	9.84 657	27	10.15 343	9.91 292	9	55	
6	9.75 967	18	9.84 684	27	10.15 316	9.91 283	9	54	
7	9.75 985	18	9.84 711	27	10.15 289	9.91 274	8	53	
8	9.76 003	18	9.84 738	26	10.15 262	9.91 266	9	52	
9	9.76 021	18	9.84 764	27	10.15 236	9.91 257	9	51	
10	9.76 039	18	9.84 791	27	10.15 209	9.91 248	9	50	
11	9.76 057	18	9.84 818	27	10.15 182	9.91 239	9	49	
12	9.76 075	18	9.84 845	27	10.15 155	9.91 230	9	48	
13	9.76 093	18	9.84 872	27	10.15 128	9.91 221	9	47	
14	9.76 111	18	9.84 899	26	10.15 101	9.91 212	9	46	
15	9.76 129	17	9.84 925	27	10.15 075	9.91 203	9	45	
16	9.76 146	18	9.84 952	27	10.15 048	9.91 194	9	44	
17	9.76 164	18	9.84 979	27	10.15 021	9.91 185	9	43	
18	9.76 182	18	9.85 006	27	10.14 994	9.91 176	9	42	
19	9.76 200	18	9.85 033	26	10.14 967	9.91 167	9	41	
20	9.76 218	18	9.85 059	27	10.14 941	9.91 158	9	40	
21	9.76 236	17	9.85 086	27	10.14 914	9.91 149	8	39	
22	9.76 253	18	9.85 113	27	10.14 887	9.91 141	9	38	
23	9.76 271	18	9.85 140	26	10.14 860	9.91 132	9	37	
24	9.76 289	18	9.85 166	27	10.14 834	9.91 123	9	36	
25	9.76 307	17	9.85 193	27	10.14 807	9.91 114	9	35	
26	9.76 324	18	9.85 220	27	10.14 780	9.91 105	9	34	
27	9.76 342	18	9.85 247	26	10.14 753	9.91 096	9	33	
28	9.76 360	18	9.85 273	27	10.14 727	9.91 087	9	32	
29	9.76 378	17	9.85 300	27	10.14 700	9.91 078	9	31	
30	9.76 395	18	9.85 327	27	10.14 673	9.91 069	9	30	
31	9.76 413	18	9.85 354	26	10.14 646	9.91 060	9	29	
32	9.76 431	17	9.85 380	27	10.14 620	9.91 051	9	28	
33	9.76 448	18	9.85 407	27	10.14 593	9.91 042	9	27	
34	9.76 466	18	9.85 434	26	10.14 566	9.91 033	10	26	
35	9.76 484	17	9.85 460	27	10.14 540	9.91 023	9	25	
36	9.76 501	18	9.85 487	27	10.14 513	9.91 014	9	24	
37	9.76 519	18	9.85 514	26	10.14 486	9.91 005	9	23	
38	9.76 537	17	9.85 540	27	10.14 460	9.90 996	9	22	
39	9.76 554	18	9.85 567	27	10.14 433	9.90 987	9	21	
40	9.76 572	18	9.85 594	26	10.14 406	9.90 978	9	20	
41	9.76 590	17	9.85 620	27	10.14 380	9.90 969	9	19	
42	9.76 607	18	9.85 647	27	10.14 353	9.90 960	9	18	
43	9.76 625	17	9.85 674	26	10.14 326	9.90 951	9	17	
44	9.76 642	18	9.85 700	27	10.14 300	9.90 942	9	16	
45	9.76 660	17	9.85 727	27	10.14 273	9.90 933	9	15	
46	9.76 677	18	9.85 754	26	10.14 246	9.90 924	9	14	
47	9.76 695	17	9.85 780	27	10.14 220	9.90 915	9	13	
48	9.76 712	18	9.85 807	27	10.14 193	9.90 906	10	12	
49	9.76 730	17	9.85 834	26	10.14 166	9.90 896	9	11	
50	9.76 747	18	9.85 860	27	10.14 140	9.90 887	9	10	
51	9.76 765	17	9.85 887	26	10.14 113	9.90 878	9	9	
52	9.76 782	18	9.85 913	27	10.14 087	9.90 869	9	8	
53	9.76 800	17	9.85 940	27	10.14 060	9.90 860	9	7	
54	9.76 817	18	9.85 967	26	10.14 033	9.90 851	9	6	
55	9.76 835	17	9.85 993	27	10.14 007	9.90 842	10	5	
56	9.76 852	18	9.86 020	26	10.13 980	9.90 832	9	4	
57	9.76 870	17	9.86 046	27	10.13 954	9.90 823	9	3	
58	9.76 887	17	9.86 073	27	10.13 927	9.90 814	9	2	
59	9.76 904	18	9.86 100	26	10.13 900	9.90 805	9	1	
60	9.76 922		9.86 126		10.13 874	9.90 796		0	
′	L Cos	d	L Ctn	c d	L Tan	L Sin	d	′	Proportional parts

Proportional parts:

′′	27	26	18
1	0.4	0.4	0.3
2	0.9	0.9	0.6
3	1.4	1.3	0.9
4	1.8	1.7	1.2
5	2.2	2.2	1.5
6	2.7	2.6	1.8
7	3.2	3.0	2.1
8	3.6	3.5	2.4
9	4.0	3.9	2.7
10	4.5	4.3	3.0
20	9.0	8.7	6.0
30	13.5	13.0	9.0
40	18.0	17.3	12.0
50	22.5	21.7	15.0

′′	17	10
1	0.3	0.2
2	0.6	0.3
3	0.8	0.5
4	1.1	0.7
5	1.4	0.8
6	1.7	1.0
7	2.0	1.2
8	2.3	1.3
9	2.6	1.5
10	2.8	1.7
20	5.7	3.3
30	8.5	5.0
40	11.3	6.7
50	14.2	8.3

′′	9	8
1	0.2	0.1
2	0.3	0.3
3	0.4	0.4
4	0.6	0.5
5	0.8	0.7
6	0.9	0.8
7	1.0	0.9
8	1.2	1.1
9	1.4	1.2
10	1.5	1.3
20	3.0	2.7
30	4.5	4.0
40	6.0	5.3
50	7.5	6.7

125° (305°)   **(234°) 54°**

Table III (Cont'd)

COMMON LOGARITHMS OF TRIGONOMETRIC FUNCTIONS

36° (216)   **(323°) 143°**

′	L Sin	d	L Tan	c d	L Ctn	L Cos	d	′
0	9.76 922	17	9.86 126	27	10.13 874	9.90 796	9	60
1	9.76 939	18	9.86 153	26	10.13 847	9.90 787	10	59
2	9.76 957	17	9.86 179	26	10.13 821	9.90 777	9	58
3	9.76 974	17	9.86 206	26	10.13 794	9.90 768	9	57
4	9.76 991	18	9.86 232	27	10.13 768	9.90 759	9	56
5	9.77 009	17	9.86 259	26	10.13 741	9.90 750	9	55
6	9.77 026	17	9.86 285	27	10.13 715	9.90 741	10	54
7	9.77 043	18	9.86 312	26	10.13 688	9.90 731	9	53
8	9.77 061	17	9.86 338	27	10.13 662	9.90 722	9	52
9	9.77 078	17	9.86 365	27	10.13 635	9.90 713	9	51
10	9.77 095	17	9.86 392	26	10.13 608	9.90 704	10	50
11	9.77 112	18	9.86 418	27	10.13 582	9.90 694	9	49
12	9.77 130	17	9.86 445	26	10.13 555	9.90 685	9	48
13	9.77 147	17	9.86 471	27	10.13 529	9.90 676	9	47
14	9.77 164	17	9.86 498	26	10.13 502	9.90 667	10	46
15	9.77 181	18	9.86 524	27	10.13 476	9.90 657	9	45
16	9.77 199	17	9.86 551	26	10.13 449	9.90 648	9	44
17	9.77 216	17	9.86 577	26	10.13 423	9.90 639	9	43
18	9.77 233	17	9.86 603	27	10.13 397	9.90 630	10	42
19	9.77 250	18	9.86 630	26	10.13 370	9.90 620	9	41
20	9.77 268	17	9.86 656	27	10.13 344	9.90 611	9	40
21	9.77 285	17	9.86 683	26	10.13 317	9.90 602	10	39
22	9.77 302	17	9.86 709	27	10.13 291	9.90 592	9	38
23	9.77 319	17	9.86 736	26	10.13 264	9.90 583	9	37
24	9.77 336	17	9.86 762	27	10.13 238	9.90 574	9	36
25	9.77 353	17	9.86 789	26	10.13 211	9.90 565	10	35
26	9.77 370	17	9.86 815	27	10.13 185	9.90 555	9	34
27	9.77 387	18	9.86 842	26	10.13 158	9.90 546	9	33
28	9.77 405	17	9.86 868	26	10.13 132	9.90 537	10	32
29	9.77 422	17	9.86 894	27	10.13 106	9.90 527	9	31
30	9.77 439	17	9.86 921	26	10.13 079	9.90 518	9	30
31	9.77 456	17	9.86 947	27	10.13 053	9.90 509	10	29
32	9.77 473	17	9.86 974	26	10.13 026	9.90 499	9	28
33	9.77 490	17	9.87 000	27	10.13 000	9.90 490	10	27
34	9.77 507	17	9.87 027	26	10.12 973	9.90 480	9	26
35	9.77 524	17	9.87 053	26	10.12 947	9.90 471	9	25
36	9.77 541	17	9.87 079	27	10.12 921	9.90 462	10	24
37	9.77 558	17	9.87 106	26	10.12 894	9.90 452	9	23
38	9.77 575	17	9.87 132	26	10.12 868	9.90 443	9	22
39	9.77 592	17	9.87 158	27	10.12 842	9.90 434	10	21
40	9.77 609	17	9.87 185	26	10.12 815	9.90 424	9	20
41	9.77 626	17	9.87 211	27	10.12 789	9.90 415	10	19
42	9.77 643	17	9.87 238	26	10.12 762	9.90 405	9	18
43	9.77 660	17	9.87 264	26	10.12 736	9.90 396	10	17
44	9.77 677	17	9.87 290	27	10.12 710	9.90 386	9	16
45	9.77 694	17	9.87 317	26	10.12 683	9.90 377	9	15
46	9.77 711	17	9.87 343	26	10.12 657	9.90 368	10	14
47	9.77 728	16	9.87 369	27	10 12 631	9.90 358	9	13
48	9.77 744	17	9.87 396	26	10.12 604	9.90 349	10	12
49	9.77 761	17	9.87 422	26	10.12 578	9.90 339	9	11
50	9.77 778	17	9.87 448	27	10.12 552	9.90 330	10	10
51	9.77 795	17	9.87 475	26	10.12 525	9.90 320	9	9
52	9.77 812	17	9.87 501	26	10.12 499	9.90 311	10	8
53	9.77 829	17	9.87 527	27	10.12 473	9.90 301	9	7
54	9.77 846	16	9.87 554	26	10.12 446	9.90 292	10	6
55	9.77 862	17	9.87 580	26	10.12 420	9.90 282	9	5
56	9.77 879	17	9.87 606	27	10.12 394	9.90 273	10	4
57	9.77 896	17	9.87 633	26	10.12 367	9.90 263	9	3
58	9.77 913	17	9.87 659	26	10.12 341	9.90 254	10	2
59	9.77 930	16	9.87 685	26	10.12 315	9.90 244	9	1
60	9.77 946		9.87 711		10.12 289	9.90 235		0
′	L Cos	d	L Ctn	c d	L Tan	L Sin	d	′

Proportional parts

″	27	26
1	0.4	0.4
2	0.9	0.9
3	1.4	1.3
4	1.8	1.7
5	2.2	2.2
6	2.7	2.6
7	3.2	3.0
8	3.6	3.5
9	4.0	3.9
10	4.5	4.3
20	9.0	8.7
30	13.5	13.0
40	18.0	17.3
50	22.5	21.7

″	18	17	16
1	0.3	0.3	0.3
2	0.6	0.6	0.5
3	0.9	0.8	0.8
4	1.2	1.1	1.1
5	1.5	1.4	1.3
6	1.8	1.7	1.6
7	2.1	2.0	1.9
8	2.4	2.3	2.1
9	2.7	2.6	2.4
10	3.0	2.8	2.7
20	6.0	5.7	5.3
30	9.0	8.5	8.0
40	12.0	11.3	10.7
50	15.0	14.2	13.3

″	10	9
1	0.2	0.2
2	0.3	0.3
3	0.5	0.4
4	0.7	0.6
5	0.8	0.8
6	1.0	0.9
7	1.2	1.0
8	1.3	1.2
9	1.5	1.4
10	1.7	1.5
20	3.3	3.0
30	5.0	4.5
40	6.7	6.0
50	8.3	7.5

126° (306°)   **(233°) 53°**

Table III (Cont'd)

COMMON LOGARITHMS OF TRIGONOMETRIC FUNCTIONS

37° (217°)   (322°) **142°**

′	L Sin	d	L Tan	c d	L Ctn	L Cos	d	′	Proportional parts
0	9.77 946	17	9.87 711	27	10.12 289	9.90 235	10	60	
1	9.77 963	17	9.87 738	26	10.12 262	9.90 225	9	59	
2	9.77 980	17	9.87 764	26	10.12 236	9.90 216	10	58	
3	9.77 997	16	9.87 790	27	10.12 210	9.90 206	9	57	
4	9.78 013	17	9.87 817	26	10.12 183	9.90 197	10	56	
5	9.78 030	17	9.87 843	26	10.12 157	9.90 187	9	55	
6	9.78 047	16	9.87 869	26	10.12 131	9.90 178	10	54	
7	9.78 063	17	9.87 895	27	10.12 105	9.90 168	9	53	
8	9.78 080	17	9.87 922	26	10.12 078	9.90 159	10	52	
9	9.78 097	16	9.87 948	26	10.12 052	9.90 149	10	51	
10	9.78 113	17	9.87 974	26	10.12 026	9.90 139	9	50	
11	9.78 130	17	9.88 000	27	10.12 000	9.90 130	10	49	
12	9.78 147	16	9.88 027	26	10.11 973	9.90 120	9	48	
13	9.78 163	17	9.88 053	26	10.11 947	9.90 111	10	47	
14	9.78 180	17	9.88 079	26	10.11 921	9.90 101	10	46	
15	9.78 197	16	9.88 105	26	10.11 895	9.90 091	9	45	
16	9.78 213	17	9.88 131	27	10.11 869	9.90 082	10	44	
17	9.78 230	16	9.88 158	26	10.11 842	9.90 072	9	43	
18	9.78 246	17	9.88 184	26	10.11 816	9.90 063	10	42	
19	9.78 263	17	9.88 210	26	10.11 790	9.90 053	10	41	
20	9.78 280	16	9.88 236	26	10.11 764	9.90 043	9	40	
21	9.78 296	17	9.88 262	27	10.11 738	9.90 034	10	39	
22	9.78 313	16	9.88 289	26	10.11 711	9.90 024	10	38	
23	9.78 329	17	9.88 315	26	10.11 685	9.90 014	9	37	
24	9.78 346	16	9.88 341	26	10.11 659	9.90 005	10	36	
25	9.78 362	17	9.88 367	26	10.11 633	9.89 995	10	35	
26	9.78 379	16	9.88 393	27	10.11 607	9.89 985	9	34	
27	9.78 395	17	9.88 420	26	10.11 580	9.89 976	10	33	
28	9.78 412	16	9.88 446	26	10.11 554	9.89 966	10	32	
29	9.78 428	17	9.88 472	26	10.11 528	9.89 956	9	31	
30	9.78 445	16	9.88 498	26	10.11 502	9.89 947	10	30	
31	9.78 461	17	9.88 524	26	10.11 476	9.89 937	10	29	
32	9.78 478	16	9.88 550	27	10.11 450	9.89 927	9	28	
33	9.78 494	16	9.88 577	26	10.11 423	9.89 918	10	27	
34	9.78 510	17	9.88 603	26	10.11 397	9.89 908	10	26	
35	9.78 527	16	9.88 629	26	10.11 371	9.89 898	10	25	
36	9.78 543	17	9.88 655	26	10.11 345	9.89 888	9	24	
37	9.78 560	16	9.88 681	26	10.11 319	9.89 879	10	23	
38	9.78 576	16	9.88 707	26	10.11 293	9.89 869	10	22	
39	9.78 592	17	9.88 733	26	10.11 267	9.89 859	10	21	
40	9.78 609	16	9.88 759	27	10.11 241	9.89 849	9	20	
41	9.78 625	17	9.88 786	26	10.11 214	9.89 840	10	19	
42	9.78 642	16	9.88 812	26	10.11 188	9.89 830	10	18	
43	9.78 658	16	9.88 838	26	10.11 162	9.89 820	10	17	
44	9.78 674	17	9.88 864	26	10.11 136	9.89 810	9	16	
45	9.78 691	16	9.88 890	26	10.11 110	9.89 801	10	15	
46	9.78 707	16	9.88 916	26	10.11 084	9.89 791	10	14	
47	9.78 723	16	9.88 942	26	10.11 058	9.89 781	10	13	
48	9.78 739	17	9.88 968	26	10.11 032	9.89 771	10	12	
49	9.78 756	16	9.88 994	26	10.11 006	9.89 761	9	11	
50	9.78 772	16	9.89 020	26	10.10 980	9.89 752	10	10	
51	9.78 788	17	9.89 046	27	10.10 954	9.89 742	10	9	
52	9.78 805	16	9.89 073	26	10.10 927	9.89 732	10	8	
53	9.78 821	16	9.89 099	26	10.10 901	9.89 722	10	7	
54	9.78 837	16	9.89 125	26	10.10 875	9.89 712	10	6	
55	9.78 853	16	9.89 151	26	10.10 849	9.89 702	9	5	
56	9.78 869	17	9.89 177	26	10.10 823	9.89 693	10	4	
57	9.78 886	16	9.89 203	26	10.10 797	9.89 683	10	3	
58	9.78 902	16	9.89 229	26	10.10 771	9.89 673	10	2	
59	9.78 918	16	9.89 255	26	10.10 745	9.89 663	10	1	
60	9.78 934	—	9.89 281	—	10.10 719	9.89 653	—	0	
′	L Cos	d	L Ctn	c d	L Tan	L Sin	d	′	Proportional parts

Proportional parts:

″	27	26
1	0.4	0.4
2	0.9	0.9
3	1.4	1.3
4	1.8	1.7
5	2.2	2.2
6	2.7	2.6
7	3.2	3.0
8	3.6	3.5
9	4.0	3.9
10	4.5	4.3
20	9.0	8.7
30	13.5	13.0
40	18.0	17.3
50	22.5	21.7

″	17	16
1	0.3	0.3
2	0.6	0.5
3	0.8	0.8
4	1.1	1.1
5	1.4	1.3
6	1.7	1.6
7	2.0	1.9
8	2.3	2.1
9	2.6	2.4
10	2.8	2.7
20	5.7	5.3
30	8.5	8.0
40	11.3	10.7
50	14.2	13.3

″	10	9
1	0.2	0.2
2	0.3	0.3
3	0.5	0.4
4	0.7	0.6
5	0.8	0.8
6	1.0	0.9
7	1.2	1.0
8	1.3	1.2
9	1.5	1.4
10	1.7	1.5
20	3.3	3.0
30	5.0	4.5
40	6.7	6.0
50	8.3	7.5

127° (307°)   (232°) **52°**

Table III (Cont'd)

COMMON LOGARITHMS OF TRIGONOMETRIC FUNCTIONS

38° (218°)   (321°) **141°**

′	L Sin	d	L Tan	c d	L Ctn	L Cos	d	′
0	9.78 934	16	9.89 281	26	10.10 719	9.89 653	10	60
1	9.78 950	17	9.89 307	26	10.10 693	9.89 643	10	59
2	9.78 967	16	9.89 333	26	10.10 667	9.89 633	9	58
3	9.78 983	16	9.89 359	26	10.10 641	9.89 624	10	57
4	9.78 999	16	9.89 385	26	10.10 615	9.89 614	10	56
5	9.79 015	16	9.89 411	26	10.10 589	9.89 604	10	55
6	9.79 031	16	9.89 437	26	10.10 563	9.89 594	10	54
7	9.79 047	16	9.89 463	26	10.10 537	9.89 584	10	53
8	9.79 063	16	9.89 489	26	10.10 511	9.89 574	10	52
9	9.79 079	16	9.89 515	26	10.10 485	9.89 564	10	51
10	9.79 095	16	9.89 541	26	10.10 459	9.89 554	10	50
11	9.79 111	17	9.89 567	26	10.10 433	9.89 544	10	49
12	9.79 128	16	9.89 593	26	10.10 407	9.89 534	10	48
13	9.79 144	16	9.89 619	26	10.10 381	9.89 524	10	47
14	9.79 160	16	9.89 645	26	10.10 355	9.89 514	10	46
15	9.79 176	16	9.89 671	26	10.10 329	9.89 504	9	45
16	9.79 192	16	9.89 697	26	10.10 303	9.89 495	10	44
17	9.79 208	16	9.89 723	26	10.10 277	9.89 485	10	43
18	9.79 224	16	9.89 749	26	10.10 251	9.89 475	10	42
19	9.79 240	16	9.89 775	26	10.10 225	9.89 465	10	41
20	9.79 256	16	9.89 801	26	10.10 199	9.89 455	10	40
21	9.79 272	16	9.89 827	26	10.10 173	9.89 445	10	39
22	9.79 288	16	9.89 853	26	10.10 147	9.89 435	10	38
23	9.79 304	15	9.89 879	26	10.10 121	9.89 425	10	37
24	9.79 319	16	9.89 905	26	10.10 095	9.89 415	10	36
25	9.79 335	16	9.89 931	26	10.10 069	9.89 405	10	35
26	9.79 351	16	9.89 957	26	10.10 043	9.89 395	10	34
27	9.79 367	16	9.89 983	26	10.10 017	9.89 385	10	33
28	9.79 383	16	9.90 009	26	10.09 991	9.89 375	11	32
29	9.79 399	16	9.90 035	26	10.09 965	9.89 364	10	31
30	9.79 415	16	9.90 061	25	10.09 939	9.89 354	10	30
31	9.79 431	16	9.90 086	26	10.09 914	9.89 344	10	29
32	9.79 447	16	9.90 112	26	10.09 888	9.89 334	10	28
33	9.79 463	15	9.90 138	26	10.09 862	9.89 324	10	27
34	9.79 478	16	9.90 164	26	10.09 836	9.89 314	10	26
35	9.79 494	16	9.90 190	26	10.09 810	9.89 304	10	25
36	9.79 510	16	9.90 216	26	10.09 784	9.89 294	10	24
37	9.79 526	16	9.90 242	26	10.09 758	9.89 284	10	23
38	9.79 542	16	9.90 268	26	10.09 732	9.89 274	10	22
39	9.79 558	15	9.90 294	26	10.09 706	9.89 264	10	21
40	9.79 573	16	9.90 320	26	10.09 680	9.89 254	10	20
41	9.79 589	16	9.90 346	25	10.09 654	9.89 244	11	19
42	9.79 605	16	9.90 371	26	10.09 629	9.89 233	10	18
43	9.79 621	15	9.90 397	26	10.09 603	9.89 223	10	17
44	9.79 636	16	9.90 423	26	10.09 577	9.89 213	10	16
45	9.79 652	16	9.90 449	26	10.09 551	9.89 203	10	15
46	9.79 668	16	9.90 475	26	10.09 525	9.89 193	10	14
47	9.79 684	16	9.90 501	26	10.09 499	9.89 183	10	13
48	9.79 699	16	9.90 527	26	10.09 473	9.89 173	11	12
49	9.79 715	16	9.90 553	25	10.09 447	9.89 162	10	11
50	9.79 731	15	9.90 578	26	10.09 422	9.89 152	10	10
51	9.79 746	16	9.90 604	26	10.09 396	9.89 142	10	9
52	9.79 762	16	9.90 630	26	10.09 370	9.89 132	10	8
53	9.79 778	15	9.90 656	26	10.09 344	9.89 122	10	7
54	9.79 793	16	9.90 682	26	10.09 318	9.89 112	11	6
55	9.79 809	16	9.90 708	26	10.09 292	9.89 101	10	5
56	9.79 825	16	9.90 734	25	10.09 266	9.89 091	10	4
57	9.79 840	16	9.90 759	26	10.09 241	9.89 081	10	3
58	9.79 856	16	9.90 785	26	10.09 215	9.89 071	11	2
59	9.79 872	15	9.90 811	26	10.09 189	9.89 060	10	1
60	9.79 887		9.90 837		10.09 163	9.89 050		0
′	L Cos	d	L Ctn	c d	L Tan	L Sin	d	′

Proportional parts

′′	26	25
1	0.4	0.4
2	0.9	0.8
3	1.3	1.2
4	1.7	1.7
5	2.2	2.1
6	2.6	2.5
7	3.0	2.9
8	3.5	3.3
9	3.9	3.8
10	4.3	4.2
20	8.7	8.3
30	13.0	12.5
40	17.3	16.7
50	21.7	20.8

′′	17	16	15
1	0.3	0.3	0.2
2	0.6	0.5	0.5
3	0.8	0.8	0.8
4	1.1	1.1	1.0
5	1.4	1.3	1.2
6	1.7	1.6	1.5
7	2.0	1.9	1.8
8	2.3	2.1	2.0
9	2.6	2.4	2.2
10	2.8	2.7	2.5
20	5.7	5.3	5.0
30	8.5	8.0	7.5
40	11.3	10.7	10.0
50	14.2	13.3	12.5

′′	11	10	9
1	0.2	0.2	0.2
2	0.4	0.3	0.3
3	0.6	0.5	0.4
4	0.7	0.7	0.6
5	0.9	0.8	0.8
6	1.1	1.0	0.9
7	1.3	1.2	1.0
8	1.5	1.3	1.2
9	1.6	1.5	1.4
10	1.8	1.7	1.5
20	3.7	3.3	3.0
30	5.5	5.0	4.5
40	7.3	6.7	6.0
50	9.2	8.3	7.5

Proportional parts

128° (308°)   (231°) **51°**

Table III (Cont'd)

COMMON LOGARITHMS OF TRIGONOMETRIC FUNCTIONS

39° (219°) (320°) **140°**

′	L Sin	d	L Tan	c d	L Ctn	L Cos	d	′	Proportional parts		
0	9.79 887	16	9.90 837	26	10.09 163	9.89 050	10	60			
1	9.79 903	15	9.90 863	26	10.09 137	9.89 040	10	59			
2	9.79 918	16	9.90 889	25	10.09 111	9.89 030	10	58			
3	9.79 934	16	9.90 914	26	10.09 086	9.89 020	11	57			
4	9.79 950	15	9.90 940	26	10.09 060	9.89 009	10	56			
5	9.79 965	16	9.90 966	26	10.09 034	9.88 999	10	55			
6	9.79 981	15	9.90 992	26	10.09 008	9.88 989	11	54			
7	9.79 996	16	9.91 018	25	10.08 982	9.88 978	10	53	′′	26	25
8	9.80 012	15	9.91 043	26	10.08 957	9.88 968	10	52	1	0.4	0.4
9	9.80 027	16	9.91 069	26	10.08 931	9.88 958	10	51	2	0.9	0.8
10	9.80 043	15	9.91 095	26	10.08 905	9.88 948	11	50	3	1.3	1.2
11	9.80 058	16	9.91 121	26	10.08 879	9.88 937	10	49	4	1.7	1.7
12	9.80 074	15	9.91 147	25	10.08 853	9.88 927	10	48			
13	9.80 089	16	9.91 172	26	10.08 828	9.88 917	11	47	5	2.2	2.1
14	9.80 105	15	9.91 198	26	10.08 802	9.88 906	10	46	6	2.6	2.5
									7	3.0	2.9
15	9.80 120	16	9.91 224	26	10.08 776	9.88 896	10	45	8	3.5	3.3
16	9.80 136	15	9.91 250	26	10.08 750	9.88 886	11	44	9	3.9	3.8
17	9.80 151	15	9.91 276	25	10.08 724	9.88 875	10	43			
18	9.80 166	16	9.91 301	26	10.08 699	9.88 865	10	42	10	4.3	4.2
19	9.80 182	15	9.91 327	26	10.08 673	9.88 855	11	41	20	8.7	8.3
									30	13.0	12.5
20	9.80 197	16	9.91 353	26	10.08 647	9.88 844	10	40	40	17.3	16.7
21	9.80 213	15	9.91 379	25	10.08 621	9.88 834	10	39	50	21.7	20.8
22	9.80 228	16	9.91 404	26	10.08 596	9.88 824	11	38			
23	9.80 244	15	9.91 430	26	10.08 570	9.88 813	10	37	′′	16	15
24	9.80 259	15	9.91 456	26	10.08 544	9.88 803	10	36	1	0.3	0.2
25	9.80 274	16	9.91 482	25	10.08 518	9.88 793	11	35	2	0.5	0.5
26	9.80 290	15	9.91 507	26	10.08 493	9.88 782	10	34	3	0.8	0.8
27	9.80 305	15	9.91 533	26	10.08 467	9.88 772	11	33	4	1.1	1.0
28	9.80 320	16	9.91 559	26	10.08 441	9.88 761	10	32			
29	9.80 336	15	9.91 585	25	10.08 415	9.88 751	10	31	5	1.3	1.2
									6	1.6	1.5
30	9.80 351	15	9.91 610	26	10.08 390	9.88 741	11	30	7	1.9	1.8
31	9.80 366	16	9.91 636	26	10.08 364	9.88 730	10	29	8	2.1	2.0
32	9.80 382	15	9.91 662	26	10.08 338	9.88 720	11	28	9	2.4	2.2
33	9.80 397	15	9.91 688	25	10.08 312	9.88 709	10	27			
34	9.80 412	16	9.91 713	26	10.08 287	9.88 699	11	26	10	2.7	2.5
									20	5.3	5.0
35	9.80 428	15	9.91 739	26	10.08 261	9.88 688	10	25	30	8.0	7.5
36	9.80 443	15	9.91 765	26	10.08 235	9.88 678	10	24	40	10.7	10.0
37	9.80 458	15	9.91 791	25	10.08 209	9.88 668	11	23	50	13.3	12.5
38	9.80 473	16	9.91 816	26	10.08 184	9.88 657	10	22			
39	9.80 489	15	9.91 842	26	10.08 158	9.88 647	11	21	′′	11	10
40	9.80 504	15	9.91 868	25	10.08 132	9.88 636	10	20	1	0.2	0.2
41	9.80 519	15	9.91 893	26	10.08 107	9.88 626	10	19	2	0.4	0.3
42	9.80 534	16	9.91 919	26	10.08 081	9.88 615	10	18	3	0.6	0.5
43	9.80 550	15	9.91 945	26	10.08 055	9.88 605	11	17	4	0.7	0.7
44	9.80 565	15	9.91 971	25	10.08 029	9.88 594	10	16			
									5	0.9	0.8
45	9.80 580	15	9.91 996	26	10.08 004	9.88 584	11	15	6	1.1	1.0
46	9.80 595	15	9.92 022	26	10.07 978	9.88 573	10	14	7	1.3	1.2
47	9.80 610	15	9.92 048	25	10.07 952	9.88 563	11	13	8	1.5	1.3
48	9.80 625	16	9.92 073	26	10.07 927	9.88 552	10	12	9	1.6	1.5
49	9.80 641	15	9.92 099	26	10.07 901	9.88 542	11	11			
									10	1.8	1.7
50	9.80 656	15	9.92 125	25	10.07 875	9.88 531	10	10	20	3.7	3.3
51	9.80 671	15	9.92 150	26	10.07 850	9.88 521	11	9	30	5.5	5.0
52	9.80 686	15	9.92 176	26	10.07 824	9.88 510	11	8	40	7.3	6.7
53	9.80 701	15	9.92 202	25	10.07 798	9.88 499	10	7	50	9.2	8.3
54	9.80 716	15	9.92 227	26	10.07 773	9.88 489	11	6			
55	9.80 731	15	9.92 253	26	10.07 747	9.88 478	10	5			
56	9.80 746	16	9.92 279	25	10.07 721	9.88 468	11	4			
57	9.80 762	15	9.92 304	26	10.07 696	9.88 457	10	3			
58	9.80 777	15	9.92 330	26	10.07 670	9.88 447	11	2			
59	9.80 792	15	9.92 356	25	10.07 644	9.88 436	11	1			
60	9.80 807		9.92 381		10.07 619	9.88 425		0			
′	L Cos	d	L Ctn	c d	L Tan	L Sin	d	′	Proportional parts		

129° (309°) (230°) **50°**

Table III (Cont'd)

COMMON LOGARITHMS OF TRIGONOMETRIC FUNCTIONS

40° (220°)   **(319°) 139°**

′	L Sin	d	L Tan	c d	L Ctn	L Cos	d	′	Proportional parts		
0	9.80 807	15	9.92 381	26	10.07 619	9.88 425	10	60			
1	9.80 822	15	9.92 407	26	10.07 593	9.88 415	11	59			
2	9.80 837	15	9.92 433	25	10.07 567	9.88 404	10	58			
3	9.80 852	15	9.92 458	26	10.07 542	9.88 394	11	57			
4	9.80 867	15	9.92 484	26	10.07 516	9.88 383	11	56			
5	9.80 882	15	9.92 510	25	10.07 490	9.88 372	10	55			
6	9.80 897	15	9.92 535	26	10.07 465	9.88 362	11	54			
7	9.80 912	15	9.92 561	26	10.07 439	9.88 351	11	53	′′	26	25
8	9.80 927	15	9.92 587	25	10.07 413	9.88 340	10	52	1	0.4	0.4
9	9.80 942	15	9.92 612	26	10.07 388	9.88 330	11	51	2	0.9	0.8
10	9.80 957	15	9.92 638	25	10.07 362	9.88 319	11	50	3	1.3	1.2
11	9.80 972	15	9.92 663	26	10.07 337	9.88 308	10	49	4	1.7	1.7
12	9.80 987	15	9.92 689	26	10.07 311	9.88 298	11	48			
13	9.81 002	15	9.92 715	25	10.07 285	9.88 287	11	47	5	2.2	2.1
14	9.81 017	15	9.92 740	26	10.07 260	9.88 276	10	46	6	2.6	2.5
15	9.81 032	15	9.92 766	26	10.07 234	9.88 266	11	45	7	3.0	2.9
16	9.81 047	14	9.92 792	25	10.07 208	9.88 255	11	44	8	3.5	3.3
17	9.81 061	15	9.92 817	26	10.07 183	9.88 244	10	43	9	3.9	3.8
18	9.81 076	15	9.92 843	25	10.07 157	9.88 234	11	42			
19	9.81 091	15	9.92 868	26	10.07 132	9.88 223	11	41	10	4.3	4.2
20	9.81 106	15	9.92 894	26	10.07 106	9.88 212	11	40	20	8.7	8.3
21	9.81 121	15	9.92 920	25	10.07 080	9.88 201	10	39	30	13.0	12.5
22	9.81 136	15	9.92 945	26	10.07 055	9.88 191	11	38	40	17.3	16.7
23	9.81 151	15	9.92 971	25	10.07 029	9.88 180	11	37	50	21.7	20.8
24	9.81 166	14	9.92 996	26	10.07 004	9.88 169	11	36			
25	9.81 180	15	9.93 022	26	10.06 978	9.88 158	10	35	′′	15	14
26	9.81 195	15	9.93 048	25	10.06 952	9.88 148	11	34	1	0.2	0.2
27	9.81 210	15	9.93 073	26	10.06 927	9.88 137	11	33	2	0.5	0.5
28	9.81 225	15	9.93 099	26	10.06 901	9.88 126	11	32	3	0.8	0.7
29	9.81 240	14	9.93 124	26	10.06 876	9.88 115	10	31	4	1.0	0.9
30	9.81 254	15	9.93 150	25	10.06 850	9.88 105	11	30	5	1.2	1.2
31	9.81 269	15	9.93 175	26	10.06 825	9.88 094	11	29	6	1.5	1.4
32	9.81 284	15	9.93 201	26	10.06 799	9.88 083	11	28	7	1.8	1.6
33	9.81 299	15	9.93 227	25	10.06 773	9.88 072	11	27	8	2.0	1.9
34	9.81 314	14	9.93 252	26	10.06 748	9.88 061	10	26	9	2.2	2.1
35	9.81 328	15	9.93 278	25	10.06 722	9.88 051	11	25	10	2.5	2.3
36	9.81 343	15	9.93 303	26	10.06 697	9.88 040	11	24	20	5.0	4.7
37	9.81 358	14	9.93 329	25	10.06 671	9.88 029	11	23	30	7.5	7.0
38	9.81 372	15	9.93 354	26	10.06 646	9.88 018	11	22	40	10.0	9.3
39	9.81 387	15	9.93 380	26	10.06 620	9.88 007	11	21	50	12.5	11.7
40	9.81 402	15	9.93 406	25	10.06 594	9.87 996	11	20			
41	9.81 417	14	9.93 431	26	10.06 569	9.87 985	10	19	′′	11	10
42	9.81 431	15	9.93 457	25	10.06 543	9.87 975	11	18	1	0.2	0.2
43	9.81 446	15	9.93 482	26	10.06 518	9.87 964	11	17	2	0.4	0.3
44	9.81 461	14	9.93 508	25	10.06 492	9.87 953	11	16	3	0.6	0.5
45	9.81 475	15	9.93 533	26	10.06 467	9.87 942	11	15	4	0.7	0.7
46	9.81 490	15	9.93 559	25	10.06 441	9.87 931	11	14	5	0.9	0.8
47	9.81 505	14	9.93 584	26	10.06 416	9.87 920	11	13	6	1.1	1.0
48	9.81 519	15	9.93 610	26	10.06 390	9.87 909	11	12	7	1.3	1.2
49	9.81 534	15	9.93 636	25	10.06 364	9.87 898	11	11	8	1.5	1.3
50	9.81 549	14	9.93 661	26	10.06 339	9.87 887	10	10	9	1.6	1.5
51	9.81 563	15	9.93 687	25	10.06 313	9.87 877	11	9	10	1.8	1.7
52	9.81 578	14	9.93 712	26	10.06 288	9.87 866	11	8	20	3.7	3.3
53	9.81 592	15	9.93 738	25	10.06 262	9.87 855	11	7	30	5.5	5.0
54	9.81 607	15	9.93 763	26	10.06 237	9.87 844	11	6	40	7.3	6.7
55	9.81 622	14	9.93 789	25	10.06 211	9.87 833	11	5	50	9.2	8.3
56	9.81 636	15	9.93 814	26	10.06 186	9.87 822	11	4			
57	9.81 651	15	9.93 840	25	10.06 160	9.87 811	11	3			
58	9.81 665	15	9.93 865	26	10.06 135	9.87 800	11	2			
59	9.81 680	14	9.93 891	25	10.06 109	9.87 789	11	1			
60	9.81 694		9.93 916		10.06 084	9.87 778		0			
′	L Cos	d	L Ctn	c d	L Tan	L Sin	d	′	Proportional parts		

130° (310°)   **(229°) 49°**

Table III (Cont'd)

COMMON LOGARITHMS OF TRIGONOMETRIC FUNCTIONS

41° (221°)   **(318°) 138°**

′	L Sin	d	L Tan	c d	L Ctn	L Cos	d	′	Proportional parts
0	9.81 694	15	9.93 916	26	10.06 084	9.87 778	11	60	
1	9.81 709	14	9.93 942	26	10.06 058	9.87 767	11	59	
2	9.81 723	15	9.93 967	26	10.06 033	9.87 756	11	58	
3	9.81 738	14	9.93 993	25	10.06 007	9.87 745	11	57	
4	9.81 752	15	9.94 018	26	10.05 982	9.87 734	11	56	
5	9.81 767	14	9.94 044	25	10.05 956	9.87 723	11	55	
6	9.81 781	15	9.94 069	26	10.05 931	9.87 712	11	54	
7	9.81 796	14	9.94 095	25	10.05 905	9.87 701	11	53	
8	9.81 810	15	9.94 120	26	10.05 880	9.87 690	11	52	
9	9.81 825	14	9.94 146	25	10.05 854	9.87 679	11	51	
10	9.81 839	15	9.94 171	26	10.05 829	9.87 668	11	50	
11	9.81 854	14	9.94 197	25	10.05 803	9.87 657	11	49	
12	9.81 868	14	9.94 222	26	10.05 778	9.87 646	11	48	
13	9.81 882	15	9.94 248	25	10.05 752	9.87 635	11	47	
14	9.81 897	14	9.94 273	26	10.05 727	9.87 624	11	46	
15	9.81 911	15	9.94 299	25	10.05 701	9.87 613	12	45	
16	9.81 926	14	9.94 324	26	10.05 676	9.87 601	11	44	
17	9.81 940	15	9.94 350	25	10.05 650	9.87 590	11	43	
18	9.81 955	14	9.94 375	26	10.05 625	9.87 579	11	42	
19	9.81 969	14	9.94 401	25	10.05 599	9.87 568	11	41	
20	9.81 983	15	9.94 426	26	10.05 574	9.87 557	11	40	
21	9.81 998	14	9.94 452	25	10.05 548	9.87 546	11	39	
22	9.82 012	14	9.94 477	26	10.05 523	9.87 535	11	38	
23	9.82 026	15	9.94 503	25	10.05 497	9.87 524	11	37	
24	9.82 041	14	9.94 528	26	10.05 472	9.87 513	12	36	
25	9.82 055	14	9.94 554	25	10.05 446	9.87 501	11	35	
26	9.82 069	15	9.94 579	25	10.05 421	9.87 490	11	34	
27	9.82 084	14	9.94 604	26	10.05 396	9.87 479	11	33	
28	9.82 098	14	9.94 630	25	10.05 370	9.87 468	11	32	
29	9.82 112	14	9.94 655	26	10.05 345	9.87 457	11	31	
30	9.82 126	15	9.94 681	25	10.05 319	9.87 446	12	30	
31	9.82 141	14	9.94 706	26	10.05 294	9.87 434	11	29	
32	9.82 155	14	9.94 732	25	10.05 268	9.87 423	11	28	
33	9.82 169	15	9.94 757	26	10.05 243	9.87 412	11	27	
34	9.82 184	14	9.94 783	25	10.05 217	9.87 401	11	26	
35	9.82 198	14	9.94 808	26	10.05 192	9.87 390	12	25	
36	9.82 212	14	9.94 834	25	10.05 166	9.87 378	11	24	
37	9.82 226	14	9.94 859	25	10.05 141	9.87 367	11	23	
38	9.82 240	15	9.94 884	26	10.05 116	9.87 356	11	22	
39	9.82 255	14	9.94 910	25	10.05 090	9.87 345	11	21	
40	9.82 269	14	9.94 935	26	10.05 065	9.87 334	12	20	
41	9.82 283	14	9.94 961	25	10.05 039	9.87 322	11	19	
42	9.82 297	14	9.94 986	26	10.05 014	9.87 311	11	18	
43	9.82 311	15	9.95 012	25	10.04 988	9.87 300	12	17	
44	9.82 326	14	9.95 037	25	10.04 963	9.87 288	11	16	
45	9.82 340	14	9.95 062	26	10.04 938	9.87 277	11	15	
46	9.82 354	14	9.95 088	25	10.04 912	9.87 266	11	14	
47	9.82 368	14	9.95 113	26	10.04 887	9.87 255	12	13	
48	9.82 382	14	9.95 139	25	10.04 861	9.87 243	11	12	
49	9.82 396	14	9.95 164	26	10.04 836	9.87 232	11	11	
50	9.82 410	14	9.95 190	25	10.04 810	9.87 221	12	10	
51	9.82 424	15	9.95 215	25	10.04 785	9.87 209	11	9	
52	9.82 439	14	9.95 240	26	10.04 760	9.87 198	11	8	
53	9.82 453	14	9.95 266	25	10.04 734	9.87 187	12	7	
54	9.82 467	14	9.95 291	26	10.04 709	9.87 175	11	6	
55	9.82 481	14	9.95 317	25	10.04 683	9.87 164	11	5	
56	9.82 495	14	9.95 342	26	10.04 658	9.87 153	12	4	
57	9.82 509	14	9.95 368	25	10.04 632	9.87 141	11	3	
58	9.82 523	14	9.95 393	25	10.04 607	9.87 130	11	2	
59	9.82 537	14	9.95 418	26	10.04 582	9.87 119	12	1	
60	9.82 551		9.95 444		10.04 556	9.87 107		0	
′	L Cos	d	L Ctn	c d	L Tan	L Sin	d	′	Proportional parts

Proportional parts:

″	26	25
1	0.4	0.4
2	0.9	0.8
3	1.3	1.2
4	1.7	1.7
5	2.2	2.1
6	2.6	2.5
7	3.0	2.9
8	3.5	3.3
9	3.9	3.8
10	4.3	4.2
20	8.7	8.3
30	13.0	12.5
40	17.3	16.7
50	21.7	20.8

″	15	14
1	0.2	0.2
2	0.5	0.5
3	0.8	0.7
4	1.0	0.9
5	1.2	1.2
6	1.5	1.4
7	1.8	1.6
8	2.0	1.9
9	2.2	2.1
10	2.5	2.3
20	5.0	4.7
30	7.5	7.0
40	10.0	9.3
50	12.5	11.7

″	12	11
1	0.2	0.2
2	0.4	0.4
3	0.6	0.6
4	0.8	0.7
5	1.0	0.9
6	1.2	1.1
7	1.4	1.3
8	1.6	1.5
9	1.8	1.6
10	2.0	1.8
20	4.0	3.7
30	6.0	5.5
40	8.0	7.3
50	10.0	9.2

131° (311°)   **(228°) 48°**

Table III (Cont'd)

COMMON LOGARITHMS OF TRIGONOMETRIC FUNCTIONS

42° (222°)   (317°) **137°**

′	L Sin	d	L Tan	c d	L Ctn	L Cos	d	′	Proportional parts		
0	9.82 551	14	9.95 444	25	10.04 556	9.87 107	11	60			
1	9.82 565	14	9.95 469	26	10.04 531	9.87 096	11	59			
2	9.82 579	14	9.95 495	25	10.04 505	9.87 085	12	58			
3	9.82 593	14	9.95 520	25	10.04 480	9.87 073	11	57			
4	9.82 607	14	9.95 545	26	10.04 455	9.87 062	12	56			
5	9.82 621	14	9.95 571	25	10.04 429	9.87 050	11	55			
6	9.82 635	14	9.95 596	26	10.04 404	9.87 039	11	54			
7	9.82 649	14	9.95 622	25	10.04 378	9.87 028	12	53	″	26	25
8	9.82 663	14	9.95 647	25	10.04 353	9.87 016	11	52	1	0.4	0.4
9	9.82 677	14	9.95 672	26	10.04 328	9.87 005	12	51	2	0.9	0.8
									3	1.3	1.2
10	9.82 691	14	9.95 698	25	10.04 302	9.86 993	11	50	4	1.7	1.7
11	9.82 705	14	9.95 723	25	10.04 277	9.86 982	12	49			
12	9.82 719	14	9.95 748	26	10.04 252	9.86 970	11	48	5	2.2	2.1
13	9.82 733	14	9.95 774	25	10.04 226	9.86 959	12	47	6	2.6	2.5
14	9.82 747	14	9.95 799	26	10.04 201	9.86 947	11	46	7	3.0	2.9
									8	3.5	3.3
15	9.82 761	14	9.95 825	25	10.04 175	9.86 936	12	45	9	3.9	3.8
16	9.82 775	13	9.95 850	25	10.04 150	9.86 924	11	44			
17	9.82 788	14	9.95 875	26	10.04 125	9.86 913	11	43	10	4.3	4.2
18	9.82 802	14	9.95 901	25	10.04 099	9.86 902	12	42	20	8.7	8.3
19	9.82 816	14	9.95 926	26	10.04 074	9.86 890	11	41	30	13.0	12.5
									40	17.3	16.7
20	9.82 830	14	9.95 952	25	10.04 048	9.86 879	12	40	50	21.7	20.8
21	9.82 844	14	9.95 977	25	10.04 023	9.86 867	12	39			
22	9.82 858	14	9.96 002	26	10.03 998	9.86 855	11	38			
23	9.82 872	13	9.96 028	25	10.03 972	9.86 844	12	37	″	14	13
24	9.82 885	14	9.96 053	25	10.03 947	9.86 832	11	36	1	0.2	0.2
									2	0.5	0.4
25	9.82 899	14	9.96 078	26	10.03 922	9.86 821	12	35	3	0.7	0.6
26	9.82 913	14	9.96 104	25	10.03 896	9.86 809	11	34	4	0.9	0.9
27	9.82 927	14	9.96 129	26	10.03 871	9.86 798	12	33			
28	9.82 941	14	9.96 155	25	10.03 845	9.86 786	11	32	5	1.2	1.1
29	9.82 955	13	9.96 180	25	10.03 820	9.86 775	12	31	6	1.4	1.3
									7	1.6	1.5
30	9.82 968	14	9.96 205	26	10.03 795	9.86 763	11	30	8	1.9	1.7
31	9.82 982	14	9.96 231	25	10.03 769	9.86 752	12	29	9	2.1	2.0
32	9.82 996	14	9.96 256	25	10.03 744	9.86 740	12	28			
33	9.83 010	13	9.96 281	26	10.03 719	9.86 728	11	27	10	2.3	2.2
34	9.83 023	14	9.96 307	25	10.03 693	9.86 717	12	26	20	4.7	4.3
									30	7.0	6.5
35	9.83 037	14	9.96 332	25	10.03 668	9.86 705	11	25	40	9.3	8.7
36	9.83 051	14	9.96 357	26	10.03 643	9.86 694	12	24	50	11.7	10.8
37	9.83 065	13	9.96 383	25	10.03 617	9.86 682	12	23			
38	9.83 078	14	9.96 408	25	10.03 592	9.86 670	11	22			
39	9.83 092	14	9.96 433	26	10.03 567	9.86 659	12	21	″	12	11
									1	0.2	0.2
40	9.83 106	14	9.96 459	25	10.03 541	9.86 647	12	20	2	0.4	0.4
41	9.83 120	13	9.96 484	26	10.03 516	9.86 635	11	19	3	0.6	0.6
42	9.83 133	14	9.96 510	25	10.03 490	9.86 624	12	18	4	0.8	0.7
43	9.83 147	14	9.96 535	25	10.03 465	9.86 612	12	17			
44	9.83 161	13	9.96 560	26	10.03 440	9.86 600	11	16	5	1.0	0.9
									6	1.2	1.1
45	9.83 174	14	9.96 586	25	10.03 414	9.86 589	12	15	7	1.4	1.3
46	9.83 188	14	9.96 611	25	10.03 389	9.86 577	12	14	8	1.6	1.5
47	9.83 202	13	9.96 636	26	10.03 364	9.86 565	11	13	9	1.8	1.6
48	9.83 215	14	9.96 662	25	10.03 338	9.86 554	12	12			
49	9.83 229	13	9.96 687	25	10.03 313	9.86 542	12	11	10	2.0	1.8
									20	4.0	3.7
50	9.83 242	14	9.96 712	26	10.03 288	9.86 530	12	10	30	6.0	5.5
51	9.83 256	14	9.96 738	25	10.03 262	9.86 518	11	9	40	8.0	7.3
52	9.83 270	13	9.96 763	25	10.03 237	9.86 507	12	8	50	10.0	9.2
53	9.83 283	14	9.96 788	26	10.03 212	9.86 495	12	7			
54	9.83 297	13	9.96 814	25	10.03 186	9.86 483	11	6			
55	9.83 310	14	9.96 839	25	10.03 161	9.86 472	12	5			
56	9.83 324	14	9.96 864	26	10.03 136	9.86 460	12	4			
57	9.83 338	13	9.96 890	25	10.03 110	9.86 448	12	3			
58	9.83 351	14	9.96 915	25	10.03 085	9.86 436	11	2			
59	9.83 365	13	9.96 940	26	10.03 060	9.86 425	12	1			
60	9.83 378		9.96 966		10.03 034	9.86 413		0			
′	L Cos	d	L Ctn	c d	L Tan	L Sin	d	′	Proportional parts		

132° (312°)   (227°) **47°**

Table III (Cont'd)

COMMON LOGARITHMS OF TRIGONOMETRIC FUNCTIONS

43° (223°)   (316°) **136°**

′	L Sin	d	L Tan	c d	L Ctn	L Cos	d	′	Proportional parts		
0	9.83 378	14	9.96 966	25	10.03 034	9.86 413	12	60			
1	9.83 392	13	9.96 991	25	10.03 009	9.86 401	12	59			
2	9.83 405	14	9.97 016	26	10.02 984	9.86 389	12	58			
3	9.83 419	13	9.97 042	25	10.02 958	9.86 377	11	57			
4	9.83 432	14	9.97 067	25	10.02 933	9.86 366	12	56			
5	9.83 446	13	9.97 092	26	10.02 908	9.86 354	12	55		″	26	25
6	9.83 459	14	9.97 118	25	10.02 882	9.86 342	12	54				
7	9.83 473	13	9.97 143	25	10.02 857	9.86 330	12	53	″	26	25
8	9.83 486	14	9.97 168	25	10.02 832	9.86 318	12	52	1	0.4	0.4
9	9.83 500	13	9.97 193	26	10.02 807	9.86 306	11	51	2	0.9	0.8
10	9.83 513	14	9.97 219	25	10.02 781	9.86 295	12	50	3	1.3	1.2
11	9.83 527	13	9.97 244	25	10.02 756	9.86 283	12	49	4	1.7	1.7
12	9.83 540	14	9.97 269	26	10.02 731	9.86 271	12	48			
13	9.83 554	13	9.97 295	25	10.02 705	9.86 259	12	47	5	2.2	2.1
14	9.83 567	14	9.97 320	25	10.02 680	9.86 247	12	46	6	2.6	2.5
15	9.83 581	13	9.97 345	26	10.02 655	9.86 235	12	45	7	3.0	2.9
16	9.83 594	14	9.97 371	25	10.02 629	9.86 223	12	44	8	3.5	3.3
17	9.83 608	13	9.97 396	25	10.02 604	9.86 211	11	43	9	3.9	3.8
18	9.83 621	13	9.97 421	26	10.02 579	9.86 200	12	42			
19	9.83 634	14	9.97 447	25	10.02 553	9.86 188	12	41	10	4.3	4.2
20	9.83 648	13	9.97 472	25	10.02 528	9.86 176	12	40	20	8.7	8.3
21	9.83 661	13	9.97 497	26	10.02 503	9.86 164	12	39	30	13.0	12.5
22	9.83 674	14	9.97 523	25	10.02 477	9.86 152	12	38	40	17.3	16.7
23	9.83 688	13	9.97 548	25	10.02 452	9.86 140	12	37	50	21.7	20.8
24	9.83 701	14	9.97 573	25	10.02 427	9.86 128	12	36			
25	9.83 715	13	9.97 598	26	10.02 402	9.86 116	12	35	″	14	13
26	9.83 728	13	9.97 624	25	10.02 376	9.86 104	12	34	1	0.2	0.2
27	9.83 741	14	9.97 649	25	10.02 351	9.86 092	12	33	2	0.5	0.4
28	9.83 755	13	9.97 674	26	10.02 326	9.86 080	12	32	3	0.7	0.6
29	9.83 768	13	9.97 700	25	10.02 300	9.86 068	12	31	4	0.9	0.9
30	9.83 781	14	9.97 725	25	10.02 275	9.86 056	12	30	5	1.2	1.1
31	9.83 795	13	9.97 750	26	10.02 250	9.86 044	12	29	6	1.4	1.3
32	9.83 808	13	9.97 776	25	10.02 224	9.86 032	12	28	7	1.6	1.5
33	9.83 821	13	9.97 801	25	10.02 199	9.86 020	12	27	8	1.9	1.7
34	9.83 834	14	9.97 826	25	10.02 174	9.86 008	12	26	9	2.1	2.0
35	9.83 848	13	9.97 851	26	10.02 149	9.85 996	12	25	10	2.3	2.2
36	9.83 861	13	9.97 877	25	10.02 123	9.85 984	12	24	20	4.7	4.3
37	9.83 874	13	9.97 902	25	10.02 098	9.85 972	12	23	30	7.0	6.5
38	9.83 887	14	9.97 927	26	10.02 073	9.85 960	12	22	40	9.3	8.7
39	9.83 901	13	9.97 953	25	10.02 047	9.85 948	12	21	50	11.7	10.8
40	9.83 914	13	9.97 978	25	10.02 022	9.85 936	12	20			
41	9.83 927	13	9.98 003	26	10.01 997	9.85 924	12	19	″	12	11
42	9.83 940	14	9.98 029	25	10.01 971	9.85 912	12	18	1	0.2	0.2
43	9.83 954	13	9.98 054	25	10.01 946	9.85 900	12	17	2	0.4	0.4
44	9.83 967	13	9.98 079	25	10.01 921	9.85 888	12	16	3	0.6	0.6
45	9.83 980	13	9.98 104	26	10.01 896	9.85 876	12	15	4	0.8	0.7
46	9.83 993	13	9.98 130	25	10.01 870	9.85 864	13	14			
47	9.84 006	14	9.98 155	25	10.01 845	9.85 851	12	13	5	1.0	0.9
48	9.84 020	13	9.98 180	26	10.01 820	9.85 839	12	12	6	1.2	1.1
49	9.84 033	13	9.98 206	25	10.01 794	9.85 827	12	11	7	1.4	1.3
50	9.84 046	13	9.98 231	25	10.01 769	9.85 815	12	10	8	1.6	1.5
51	9.84 059	13	9.98 256	25	10.01 744	9.85 803	12	9	9	1.8	1.6
52	9.84 072	13	9.98 281	26	10.01 719	9.85 791	12	8			
53	9.84 085	13	9.98 307	25	10.01 693	9.85 779	13	7	10	2.0	1.8
54	9.84 098	14	9.98 332	25	10.01 668	9.85 766	12	6	20	4.0	3.7
55	9.84 112	13	9.98 357	26	10.01 643	9.85 754	12	5	30	6.0	5.5
56	9.84 125	13	9.98 383	25	10.01 617	9.85 742	12	4	40	8.0	7.3
57	9.84 138	13	9.98 408	25	10.01 592	9.85 730	12	3	50	10.0	9.2
58	9.84 151	13	9.98 433	25	10.01 567	9.85 718	12	2			
59	9.84 164	13	9.98 458	26	10.01 542	9.85 706	13	1			
60	9.84 177	—	9.98 484		10.01 516	9.85 693		0			
′	L Cos	d	L Ctn	c d	L Tan	L Sin	d	′	Proportional parts		

133° (313°)   (226°) **46°**

Table III (Cont'd)

COMMON LOGARITHMS OF TRIGONOMETRIC FUNCTIONS

44° (224°)   **(315°) 135°**

′	L Sin	d	L Tan	c d	L Ctn	L Cos	d	′	Proportional parts
0	9.84 177	13	9.98 484	25	10.01 516	9.85 693	12	60	
1	9.84 190	13	9.98 509	25	10.01 491	9.85 681	12	59	
2	9.84 203	13	9.98 534	26	10.01 466	9.85 669	12	58	
3	9.84 216	13	9.98 560	25	10.01 440	9.85 657	12	57	
4	9.84 229	13	9.98 585	25	10.01 415	9.85 645	13	56	
5	9.84 242	13	9.98 610	25	10.01 390	9.85 632	12	55	
6	9.84 255	14	9.98 635	26	10.01 365	9.85 620	12	54	
7	9.84 269	13	9.98 661	25	10.01 399	9.85 608	12	53	
8	9.84 282	13	9.98 686	25	10.01 314	9.85 596	13	52	
9	9.84 295	13	9.98 711	26	10.01 289	9.85 583	12	51	
10	9.84 308	13	9.98 737	25	10.01 263	9.85 571	12	50	
11	9.84 321	13	9.98 762	25	10.01 238	9.85 559	12	49	
12	9.84 334	13	9.98 787	25	10.01 213	9.85 547	13	48	
13	9.84 347	13	9.98 812	26	10.01 188	9.85 534	12	47	
14	9.84 360	13	9.98 838	25	10.01 162	9.85 522	12	46	
15	9.84 373	12	9.98 863	25	10.01 137	9.85 510	13	45	
16	9.84 385	13	9.98 888	25	10.01 112	9.85 497	12	44	
17	9.84 398	13	9.98 913	26	10.01 087	9.85 485	12	43	
18	9.84 411	13	9.98 939	25	10.01 061	9.85 473	13	42	
19	9.84 424	13	9.98 964	25	10.01 036	9.85 460	12	41	
20	9.84 437	13	9.98 989	26	10.01 011	9.85 448	12	40	
21	9.84 450	13	9.99 015	25	10.00 985	9.85 436	13	39	
22	9.84 463	13	9.99 040	25	10.00 960	9.85 423	12	38	
23	9.84 476	13	9.99 065	25	10.00 935	9.85 411	12	37	
24	9.84 489	13	9.99 090	26	10.00 910	9.85 399	13	36	
25	9.84 502	13	9.99 116	25	10.00 884	9.85 386	12	35	
26	9.84 515	13	9.99 141	25	10.00 859	9.85 374	13	34	
27	9.84 528	12	9.99 166	25	10.00 834	9.85 361	12	33	
28	9.84 540	13	9.99 191	26	10.00 809	9.85 349	12	32	
29	9.84 553	13	9.99 217	25	10.00 783	9.85 337	13	31	
30	9.84 566	13	9.99 242	25	10.00 758	9.85 324	12	30	
31	9.84 579	13	9.99 267	26	10.00 733	9.85 312	13	29	
32	9.84 592	13	9.99 293	25	10.00 707	9.85 299	12	28	
33	9.84 605	13	9.99 318	25	10.00 682	9.85 287	13	27	
34	9.84 618	12	9.99 343	25	10.00 657	9.85 274	12	26	
35	9.84 630	13	9.99 368	26	10.00 632	9.85 262	12	25	
36	9.84 643	13	9.99 394	25	10.00 606	9.85 250	13	24	
37	9.84 656	13	9.99 419	25	10.00 581	9.85 237	12	23	
38	9.84 669	13	9.99 444	25	10.00 556	9.85 225	13	22	
39	9.84 682	12	9.99 469	26	10.00 531	9.85 212	12	21	
40	9.84 694	13	9.99 495	25	10.00 505	9.85 200	13	20	
41	9.84 707	13	9.99 520	25	10.00 480	9.85 187	12	19	
42	9.84 720	13	9.99 545	25	10.00 455	9.85 175	13	18	
43	9.84 733	12	9.99 570	26	10.00 430	9.85 162	12	17	
44	9.84 745	13	9.99 596	25	10.00 404	9.85 150	13	16	
45	9.84 758	13	9.99 621	25	10.00 379	9.85 137	12	15	
46	9.84 771	13	9.99 646	26	10.00 354	9.85 125	13	14	
47	9.84 784	12	9.99 672	25	10.00 328	9.85 112	12	13	
48	9.84 796	13	9.99 697	25	10.00 303	9.85 100	13	12	
49	9.84 809	13	9.99 722	25	10.00 278	9.85 087	13	11	
50	9.84 822	13	9.99 747	26	10.00 253	9.85 074	12	10	
51	9.84 835	12	9.99 773	25	10.00 227	9.85 062	13	9	
52	9.84 847	13	9.99 798	25	10.00 202	9.85 049	12	8	
53	9.84 860	13	9.99 823	25	10.00 177	9.85 037	13	7	
54	9.84 873	12	9.99 848	26	10.00 152	9.85 024	12	6	
55	9.84 885	13	9.99 874	25	10.00 126	9.85 012	13	5	
56	9.84 898	13	9.99 899	25	10.00 101	9.84 999	13	4	
57	9.84 911	12	9.99 924	25	10.00 076	9.84 986	12	3	
58	9.84 923	13	9.99 949	25	10.00 051	9.84 974	13	2	
59	9.84 936	13	9.99 975	25	10.00 025	9.84 961	12	1	
60	9.84 949		10.00 000		10.00 000	9.84 949		0	
′	L Cos	d	L Ctn	c d	L Tan	L Sin	d	′	Proportional parts

Proportional parts:

″	26	25
1	0.4	0.4
2	0.9	0.8
3	1.3	1.2
4	1.7	1.7
5	2.2	2.1
6	2.6	2.5
7	3.0	2.9
8	3.5	3.3
9	3.9	3.8
10	4.3	4.2
20	8.7	8.3
30	13.0	12.5
40	17.3	16.7
50	21.7	20.8

″	14	13	12
1	0.2	0.2	0.2
2	0.5	0.4	0.4
3	0.7	0.6	0.6
4	0.9	0.9	0.8
5	1.2	1.1	1.0
6	1.4	1.3	1.2
7	1.6	1.5	1.4
8	1.9	1.7	1.6
9	2.1	2.0	1.8
10	2.3	2.2	2.0
20	4.7	4.3	4.0
30	7.0	6.5	6.0
40	9.3	8.7	8.0
50	11.7	10.8	10.0

134° (314°)   **(225°) 45°**

Table IV

NATURAL TRIGONOMETRIC FUNCTIONS

0° (180°)						1° (181°)				
′	Sin	Tan	Ctn	Cos	′	′	Sin	Tan	Ctn	Cos	′
0	.00000	.00000	∞	1.0000	60	0	.01745	.01746	57.290	.99985	60
1	.00029	.00029	3437.7	1.0000	59	1	.01774	.01775	56.351	.99984	59
2	.00058	.00058	1718.9	1.0000	58	2	.01803	.01804	55.442	.99984	58
3	.00087	.00087	1145.9	1.0000	57	3	.01832	.01833	54.561	.99983	57
4	.00116	.00116	859.44	1.0000	56	4	.01862	.01862	53.709	.99983	56
5	.00145	.00145	687.55	1.0000	55	5	.01891	.01891	52.882	.99982	55
6	.00175	.00175	572.96	1.0000	54	6	.01920	.01920	52.081	.99982	54
7	.00204	.00204	491.11	1.0000	53	7	.01949	.01949	51.303	.99981	53
8	.00233	.00233	429.72	1.0000	52	8	.01978	.01978	50.549	.99980	52
9	.00262	.00262	381.97	1.0000	51	9	.02007	.02007	49.816	.99980	51
10	.00291	.00291	343.77	1.0000	50	10	.02036	.02036	49.104	.99979	50
11	.00320	.00320	312.52	.99999	49	11	.02065	.02066	48.412	.99979	49
12	.00349	.00349	286.48	.99999	48	12	.02094	.02095	47.740	.99978	48
13	.00378	.00378	264.44	.99999	47	13	.02123	.02124	47.085	.99977	47
14	.00407	.00407	245.55	.99999	46	14	.02152	.02153	46.449	.99977	46
15	.00436	.00436	229.18	.99999	45	15	.02181	.02182	45.829	.99976	45
16	.00465	.00465	214.86	.99999	44	16	.02211	.02211	45.226	.99976	44
17	.00495	.00495	202.22	.99999	43	17	.02240	.02240	44.639	.99975	43
18	.00524	.00524	190.98	.99999	42	18	.02269	.02269	44.066	.99974	42
19	.00553	.00553	180.93	.99998	41	19	.02298	.02298	43.508	.99974	41
20	.00582	.00582	171.89	.99998	40	20	.02327	.02328	42.964	.99973	40
21	.00611	.00611	163.70	.99998	39	21	.02356	.02357	42.433	.99972	39
22	.00640	.00640	156.26	.99998	38	22	.02385	.02386	41.916	.99972	38
23	.00669	.00669	149.47	.99998	37	23	.02414	.02415	41.411	.99971	37
24	.00698	.00698	143.24	.99998	36	24	.02443	.02444	40.917	.99970	36
25	.00727	.00727	137.51	.99997	35	25	.02472	.02473	40.436	.99969	35
26	.00756	.00756	132.22	.99997	34	26	.02501	.02502	39.965	.99969	34
27	.00785	.00785	127.32	.99997	33	27	.02530	.02531	39.506	.99968	33
28	.00814	.00815	122.77	.99997	32	28	.02560	.02560	39.057	.99967	32
29	.00844	.00844	118.54	.99996	31	29	.02589	.02589	38.618	.99966	31
30	.00873	.00873	114.59	.99996	30	30	.02618	.02619	38.188	.99966	30
31	.00902	.00902	110.89	.99996	29	31	.02647	.02648	37.769	.99965	29
32	.00931	.00931	107.43	.99996	28	32	.02676	.02677	37.358	.99964	28
33	.00960	.00960	104.17	.99995	27	33	.02705	.02706	36.956	.99963	27
34	.00989	.00989	101.11	.99995	26	34	.02734	.02735	36.563	.99963	26
35	.01018	.01018	98.218	.99995	25	35	.02763	.02764	36.178	.99962	25
36	.01047	.01047	95.489	.99995	24	36	.02792	.02793	35.801	.99961	24
37	.01076	.01076	92.908	.99994	23	37	.02821	.02822	35.431	.99960	23
38	.01105	.01105	90.463	.99994	22	38	.02850	.02851	35.070	.99959	22
39	.01134	.01135	88.144	.99994	21	39	.02879	.02881	34.715	.99959	21
40	.01164	.01164	85.940	.99993	20	40	.02908	.02910	34.368	.99958	20
41	.01193	.01193	83.844	.99993	19	41	.02938	.02939	34.027	.99957	19
42	.01222	.01222	81.847	.99993	18	42	.02967	.02968	33.694	.99956	18
43	.01251	.01251	79.943	.99992	17	43	.02996	.02997	33.366	.99955	17
44	.01280	.01280	78.126	.99992	16	44	.03025	.03026	33.045	.99954	16
45	.01309	.01309	76.390	.99991	15	45	.03054	.03055	32.730	.99953	15
46	.01338	.01338	74.729	.99991	14	46	.03083	.03084	32.421	.99952	14
47	.01367	.01367	73.139	.99991	13	47	.03112	.03114	32.118	.99952	13
48	.01396	.01396	71.615	.99990	12	48	.03141	.03143	31.821	.99951	12
49	.01425	.01425	70.153	.99990	11	49	.03170	.03172	31.528	.99950	11
50	.01454	.01455	68.750	.99989	10	50	.03199	.03201	31.242	.99949	10
51	.01483	.01484	67.402	.99989	9	51	.03228	.03230	30.960	.99948	9
52	.01513	.01513	66.105	.99989	8	52	.03257	.03259	30.683	.99947	8
53	.01542	.01542	64.858	.99988	7	53	.03286	.03288	30.412	.99946	7
54	.01571	.01571	63.657	.99988	6	54	.03316	.03317	30.145	.99945	6
55	.01600	.01600	62.499	.99987	5	55	.03345	.03346	29.882	.99944	5
56	.01629	.01629	61.383	.99987	4	56	.03374	.03376	29.624	.99943	4
57	.01658	.01658	60.306	.99986	3	57	.03403	.03405	29.371	.99942	3
58	.01687	.01687	59.266	.99986	2	58	.03432	.03434	29.122	.99941	2
59	.01716	.01716	58.261	.99985	1	59	.03461	.03463	28.877	.99940	1
60	.01745	.01746	57.290	.99985	0	60	.03490	.03492	28.636	.99939	0
′	Cos	Ctn	Tan	Sin	′	′	Cos	Ctn	Tan	Sin	′

| 90° (270°) | | | (269°) 89° | 91° (271°) | | | (268°) 88° |

489

Table IV (Cont'd)

NATURAL TRIGONOMETRIC FUNCTIONS

2° (182°)   (357°) **177°**   **3° (183°)**   (356°) **176°**

′	Sin	Tan	Ctn	Cos	′	′	Sin	Tan	Ctn	Cos	′
0	.03490	.03492	28.636	.99939	60	0	.05234	.05241	19.081	.99863	60
1	.03519	.03521	28.399	.99938	59	1	.05263	.05270	18.976	.99861	59
2	.03548	.03550	28.166	.99937	58	2	.05292	.05299	18.871	.99860	58
3	.03577	.03579	27.937	.99936	57	3	.05321	.05328	18.768	.99858	57
4	.03606	.03609	27.712	.99935	56	4	.05350	.05357	18.666	.99857	56
5	.03635	.03638	27.490	.99934	55	5	.05379	.05387	18.564	.99855	55
6	.03664	.03667	27.271	.99933	54	6	.05408	.05416	18.464	.99854	54
7	.03693	.03696	27.057	.99932	53	7	.05437	.05445	18.366	.99852	53
8	.03723	.03725	26.845	.99931	52	8	.05466	.05474	18.268	.99851	52
9	.03752	.03754	26.637	.99930	51	9	.05495	.05503	18.171	.99849	51
10	.03781	.03783	26.432	.99929	50	10	.05524	.05533	18.075	.99847	50
11	.03810	.03812	26.230	.99927	49	11	.05553	.05562	17.980	.99846	49
12	.03839	.03842	26.031	.99926	48	12	.05582	.05591	17.886	.99844	48
13	.03868	.03871	25.835	.99925	47	13	.05611	.05620	17.793	.99842	47
14	.03897	.03900	25.642	.99924	46	14	.05640	.05649	17.702	.99841	46
15	.03926	.03929	25.452	.99923	45	15	.05669	.05678	17.611	.99839	45
16	.03955	.03958	25.264	.99922	44	16	.05698	.05708	17.521	.99838	44
17	.03984	.03987	25.080	.99921	43	17	.05727	.05737	17.431	.99836	43
18	.04013	.04016	24.898	.99919	42	18	.05756	.05766	17.343	.99834	42
19	.04042	.04046	24.719	.99918	41	19	.05785	.05795	17.256	.99833	41
20	.04071	.04075	24.542	.99917	40	20	.05814	.05824	17.169	.99831	40
21	.04100	.04104	24.368	.99916	39	21	.05844	.05854	17.084	.99829	39
22	.04129	.04133	24.196	.99915	38	22	.05873	.05883	16.999	.99827	38
23	.04159	.04162	24.026	.99913	37	23	.05902	.05912	16.915	.99826	37
24	.04188	.04191	23.859	.99912	36	24	.05931	.05941	16.832	.99824	36
25	.04217	.04220	23.695	.99911	35	25	.05960	.05970	16.750	.99822	35
26	.04246	.04250	23.532	.99910	34	26	.05989	.05999	16.668	.99821	34
27	.04275	.04279	23.372	.99909	33	27	.06018	.06029	16.587	.99819	33
28	.04304	.04308	23.214	.99907	32	28	.06047	.06058	16.507	.99817	32
29	.04333	.04337	23.058	.99906	31	29	.06076	.06087	16.428	.99815	31
30	.04362	.04366	22.904	.99905	30	30	.06105	.06116	16.350	.99813	30
31	.04391	.04395	22.752	.99904	29	31	.06134	.06145	16.272	.99812	29
32	.04420	.04424	22.602	.99902	28	32	.06163	.06175	16.195	.99810	28
33	.04449	.04454	22.454	.99901	27	33	.06192	.06204	16.119	.99808	27
34	.04478	.04483	22.308	.99900	26	34	.06221	.06233	16.043	.99806	26
35	.04507	.04512	22.164	.99898	25	35	.06250	.06262	15.969	.99804	25
36	.04536	.04541	22.022	.99897	24	36	.06279	.06291	15.895	.99803	24
37	.04565	.04570	21.881	.99896	23	37	.06308	.06321	15.821	.99801	23
38	.04594	.04599	21.743	.99894	22	38	.06337	.06350	15.748	.99799	22
39	.04623	.04628	21.606	.99893	21	39	.06366	.06379	15.676	.99797	21
40	.04653	.04658	21.470	.99892	20	40	.06395	.06408	15.605	.99795	20
41	.04682	.04687	21.337	.99890	19	41	.06424	.06438	15.534	.99793	19
42	.04711	.04716	21.205	.99889	18	42	.06453	.06467	15.464	.99792	18
43	.04740	.04745	21.075	.99888	17	43	.06482	.06496	15.394	.99790	17
44	.04769	.04774	20.946	.99886	16	44	.06511	.06525	15.325	.99788	16
45	.04798	.04803	20.819	.99885	15	45	.06540	.06554	15.257	.99786	15
46	.04827	.04833	20.693	.99883	14	46	.06569	.06584	15.189	.99784	14
47	.04856	.04862	20.569	.99882	13	47	.06598	.06613	15.122	.99782	13
48	.04885	.04891	20.446	.99881	12	48	.06627	.06642	15.056	.99780	12
49	.04914	.04920	20.325	.99879	11	49	.06656	.06671	14.990	.99778	11
50	.04943	.04949	20.206	.99878	10	50	.06685	.06700	14.924	.99776	10
51	.04972	.04978	20.087	.99876	9	51	.06714	.06730	14.860	.99774	9
52	.05001	.05007	19.970	.99875	8	52	.06743	.06759	14.795	.99772	8
53	.05030	.05037	19.855	.99873	7	53	.06773	.06788	14.732	.99770	7
54	.05059	.05066	19.740	.99872	6	54	.06802	.06817	14.669	.99768	6
55	.05088	.05095	19.627	.99870	5	55	.06831	.06847	14.606	.99766	5
56	.05117	.05124	19.516	.99869	4	56	.06860	.06876	14.544	.99764	4
57	.05146	.05153	19.405	.99867	3	57	.06889	.06905	14.482	.99762	3
58	.05175	.05182	19.296	.99866	2	58	.06918	.06934	14.421	.99760	2
59	.05205	.05212	19.188	.99864	1	59	.06947	.06963	14.361	.99758	1
60	.05234	.05241	19.081	.99863	0	60	.06976	.06993	14.301	.99756	0
′	Cos	Ctn	Tan	Sin	′	′	Cos	Ctn	Tan	Sin	′

92° (272°)   (267°) **87°**   **93° (273°)**   (266°) **86°**

Table IV (Cont'd)

NATURAL TRIGONOMETRIC FUNCTIONS

′	Sin	Tan	Ctn	Cos	′		′	Sin	Tan	Ctn	Cos	′
0	.06976	.06993	14.301	.99756	60		0	.08716	.08749	11.430	.99619	60
1	.07005	.07022	14.241	.99754	59		1	.08745	.08778	11.392	.99617	59
2	.07034	.07051	14.182	.99752	58		2	.08774	.08807	11.354	.99614	58
3	.07063	.07080	14.124	.99750	57		3	.08803	.08837	11.316	.99612	57
4	.07092	.07110	14.065	.99748	56		4	.08831	.08866	11.279	.99609	56
5	.07121	.07139	14.008	.99746	55		5	.08860	.08895	11.242	.99607	55
6	.07150	.07168	13.951	.99744	54		6	.08889	.08925	11.205	.99604	54
7	.07179	.07197	13.894	.99742	53		7	.08918	.08954	11.168	.99602	53
8	.07208	.07227	13.838	.99740	52		8	.08947	.08983	11.132	.99599	52
9	.07237	.07256	13.782	.99738	51		9	.08976	.09013	11.095	.99596	51
10	.07266	.07285	13.727	.99736	50		10	.09005	.09042	11.059	.99594	50
11	.07295	.07314	13.672	.99734	49		11	.09034	.09071	11.024	.99591	49
12	.07324	.07344	13.617	.99731	48		12	.09063	.09101	10.988	.99588	48
13	.07353	.07373	13.563	.99729	47		13	.09092	.09130	10.953	.99586	47
14	.07382	.07402	13.510	.99727	46		14	.09121	.09159	10.918	.99583	46
15	.07411	.07431	13.457	.99725	45		15	.09150	.09189	10.883	.99580	45
16	.07440	.07461	13.404	.99723	44		16	.09179	.09218	10.848	.99578	44
17	.07469	.07490	13.352	.99721	43		17	.09208	.09247	10.814	.99575	43
18	.07498	.07519	13.300	.99719	42		18	.09237	.09277	10.780	.99572	42
19	.07527	.07548	13.248	.99716	41		19	.09266	.09306	10.746	.99570	41
20	.07556	.07578	13.197	.99714	40		20	.09295	.09335	10.712	.99567	40
21	.07585	.07607	13.146	.99712	39		21	.09324	.09365	10.678	.99564	39
22	.07614	.07636	13.096	.99710	38		22	.09353	.09394	10.645	.99562	38
23	.07643	.07665	13.046	.99708	37		23	.09382	.09423	10.612	.99559	37
24	.07672	.07695	12.996	.99705	36		24	.09411	.09453	10.579	.99556	36
25	.07701	.07724	12.947	.99703	35		25	.09440	.09482	10.546	.99553	35
26	.07730	.07753	12.898	.99701	34		26	.09469	.09511	10.514	.99551	34
27	.07759	.07782	12.850	.99699	33		27	.09498	.09541	10.481	.99548	33
28	.07788	.07812	12.801	.99696	32		28	.09527	.09570	10.449	.99545	32
29	.07817	.07841	12.754	.99694	31		29	.09556	.09600	10.417	.99542	31
30	.07846	.07870	12.706	.99692	30		30	.09585	.09629	10.385	.99540	30
31	.07875	.07899	12.659	.99689	29		31	.09614	.09658	10.354	.99537	29
32	.07904	.07929	12.612	.99687	28		32	.09642	.09688	10.322	.99534	28
33	.07933	.07958	12.566	.99685	27		33	.09671	.09717	10.291	.99531	27
34	.07962	.07987	12.520	.99683	26		34	.09700	.09746	10.260	.99528	26
35	.07991	.08017	12.474	.99680	25		35	.09729	.09776	10.229	.99526	25
36	.08020	.08046	12.429	.99678	24		36	.09758	.09805	10.199	.99523	24
37	.08049	.08075	12.384	.99676	23		37	.09787	.09834	10.168	.99520	23
38	.08078	.08104	12.339	.99673	22		38	.09816	.09864	10.138	.99517	22
39	.08107	.08134	12.295	.99671	21		39	.09845	.09893	10.108	.99514	21
40	.08136	.08163	12.251	.99668	20		40	.09874	.09923	10.078	.99511	20
41	.08165	.08192	12.207	.99666	19		41	.09903	.09952	10.048	.99508	19
42	.08194	.08221	12.163	.99664	18		42	.09932	.09981	10.019	.99506	18
43	.08223	.08251	12.120	.99661	17		43	.09961	.10011	9.9893	.99503	17
44	.08252	.08280	12.077	.99659	16		44	.09990	.10040	9.9601	.99500	16
45	.08281	.08309	12.035	.99657	15		45	.10019	.10069	9.9310	.99497	15
46	.08310	.08339	11.992	.99654	14		46	.10048	.10099	9.9021	.99494	14
47	.08339	.08368	11.950	.99652	13		47	.10077	.10128	9.8734	.99491	13
48	.08368	.08397	11.909	.99649	12		48	.10106	.10158	9.8448	.99488	12
49	.08397	.08427	11.867	.99647	11		49	.10135	.10187	9.8164	.99485	11
50	.08426	.08456	11.826	.99644	10		50	.10164	.10216	9.7882	.99482	10
51	.08455	.08485	11.785	.99642	9		51	.10192	.10246	9.7601	.99479	9
52	.08484	.08514	11.745	.99639	8		52	.10221	.10275	9.7322	.99476	8
53	.08513	.08544	11.705	.99637	7		53	.10250	.10305	9.7044	.99473	7
54	.08542	.08573	11.664	.99635	6		54	.10279	.10334	9.6768	.99470	6
55	.08571	.08602	11.625	.99632	5		55	.10308	.10363	9.6493	.99467	5
56	.08600	.08632	11.585	.99630	4		56	.10337	.10393	9.6220	.99464	4
57	.08629	.08661	11.546	.99627	3		57	.10366	.10422	9.5949	.99461	3
58	.08658	.08690	11.507	.99625	2		58	.10395	.10452	9.5679	.99458	2
59	.08687	.08720	11.468	.99622	1		59	.10424	.10481	9.5411	.99455	1
60	.08716	.08749	11.430	.99619	0		60	.10453	.10510	9.5144	.99452	0
′	Cos	Ctn	Tan	Sin	′		′	Cos	Ctn	Tan	Sin	′

Table IV (Cont'd)

NATURAL TRIGONOMETRIC FUNCTIONS

6° (186°)				(353°) 173°	7° (187°)				(352°) 172°
′	Sin	Tan	Ctn	Cos	′	′	Sin	Tan	Ctn	Cos	′

′	Sin	Tan	Ctn	Cos	′	′	Sin	Tan	Ctn	Cos	′
0	.10453	.10510	9.5144	.99452	60	0	.12187	.12278	8.1443	.99255	60
1	.10482	.10540	9.4878	.99449	59	1	.12216	.12308	8.1248	.99251	59
2	.10511	.10569	9.4614	.99446	58	2	.12245	.12338	8.1054	.99248	58
3	.10540	.10599	9.4352	.99443	57	3	.12274	.12367	8.0860	.99244	57
4	.10569	.10628	9.4090	.99440	56	4	.12302	.12397	8.0667	.99240	56
5	.10597	.10657	9.3831	.99437	55	5	.12331	.12426	8.0476	.99237	55
6	.10626	.10687	9.3572	.99434	54	6	.12360	.12456	8.0285	.99233	54
7	.10655	.10716	9.3315	.99431	53	7	.12389	.12485	8.0095	.99230	53
8	.10684	.10746	9.3060	.99428	52	8	.12418	.12515	7.9906	.99226	52
9	.10713	.10775	9.2806	.99424	51	9	.12447	.12544	7.9718	.99222	51
10	.10742	.10805	9.2553	.99421	50	10	.12476	.12574	7.9530	.99219	50
11	.10771	.10834	9.2302	.99418	49	11	.12504	.12603	7.9344	.99215	49
12	.10800	.10863	9.2052	.99415	48	12	.12533	.12633	7.9158	.99211	48
13	.10829	.10893	9.1803	.99412	47	13	.12562	.12662	7.8973	.99208	47
14	.10858	.10922	9.1555	.99409	46	14	.12591	.12692	7.8789	.99204	46
15	.10887	.10952	9.1309	.99406	45	15	.12620	.12722	7.8606	.99200	45
16	.10916	.10981	9.1065	.99402	44	16	.12649	.12751	7.8424	.99197	44
17	.10945	.11011	9.0821	.99399	43	17	.12678	.12781	7.8243	.99193	43
18	.10973	.11040	9.0579	.99396	42	18	.12706	.12810	7.8062	.99189	42
19	.11002	.11070	9.0338	.99393	41	19	.12735	.12840	7.7882	.99186	41
20	.11031	.11099	9.0098	.99390	40	20	.12764	.12869	7.7704	.99182	40
21	.11060	.11128	8.9860	.99386	39	21	.12793	.12899	7.7525	.99178	39
22	.11089	.11158	8.9623	.99383	38	22	.12822	.12929	7.7348	.99175	38
23	.11118	.11187	8.9387	.99380	37	23	.12851	.12958	7.7171	.99171	37
24	.11147	.11217	8.9152	.99377	36	24	.12880	.12988	7.6996	.99167	36
25	.11176	.11246	8.8919	.99374	35	25	.12908	.13017	7.6821	.99163	35
26	.11205	.11276	8.8686	.99370	34	26	.12937	.13047	7.6647	.99160	34
27	.11234	.11305	8.8455	.99367	33	27	.12966	.13076	7.6473	.99156	33
28	.11263	.11335	8.8225	.99364	32	28	.12995	.13106	7.6301	.99152	32
29	.11291	.11364	8.7996	.99360	31	29	.13024	.13136	7.6129	.99148	31
30	.11320	.11394	8.7769	.99357	30	30	.13053	.13165	7.5958	.99144	30
31	.11349	.11423	8.7542	.99354	29	31	.13081	.13195	7.5787	.99141	29
32	.11378	.11452	8.7317	.99351	28	32	.13110	.13224	7.5618	.99137	28
33	.11407	.11482	8.7093	.99347	27	33	.13139	.13254	7.5449	.99133	27
34	.11436	.11511	8.6870	.99344	26	34	.13168	.13284	7.5281	.99129	26
35	.11465	.11541	8.6648	.99341	25	35	.13197	.13313	7.5113	.99125	25
36	.11494	.11570	8.6427	.99337	24	36	.13226	.13343	7.4947	.99122	24
37	.11523	.11600	8.6208	.99334	23	37	.13254	.13372	7.4781	.99118	23
38	.11552	.11629	8.5989	.99331	22	38	.13283	.13402	7.4615	.99114	22
39	.11580	.11659	8.5772	.99327	21	39	.13312	.13432	7.4451	.99110	21
40	.11609	.11688	8.5555	.99324	20	40	.13341	.13461	7.4287	.99106	20
41	.11638	.11718	8.5340	.99320	19	41	.13370	.13491	7.4124	.99102	19
42	.11667	.11747	8.5126	.99317	18	42	.13399	.13521	7.3962	.99098	18
43	.11696	.11777	8.4913	.99314	17	43	.13427	.13550	7.3800	.99094	17
44	.11725	.11806	8.4701	.99310	16	44	.13456	.13580	7.3639	.99091	16
45	.11754	.11836	8.4490	.99307	15	45	.13485	.13609	7.3479	.99087	15
46	.11783	.11865	8.4280	.99303	14	46	.13514	.13639	7.3319	.99083	14
47	.11812	.11895	8.4071	.99300	13	47	.13543	.13669	7.3160	.99079	13
48	.11840	.11924	8.3863	.99297	12	48	.13572	.13698	7.3002	.99075	12
49	.11869	.11954	8.3656	.99293	11	49	.13600	.13728	7.2844	.99071	11
50	.11898	.11983	8.3450	.99290	10	50	.13629	.13758	7.2687	.99067	10
51	.11927	.12013	8.3245	.99286	9	51	.13658	.13787	7.2531	.99063	9
52	.11956	.12042	8.3041	.99283	8	52	.13687	.13817	7.2375	.99059	8
53	.11985	.12072	8.2838	.99279	7	53	.13716	.13846	7.2220	.99055	7
54	.12014	.12101	8.2636	.99276	6	54	.13744	.13876	7.2066	.99051	6
55	.12043	.12131	8.2434	.99272	5	55	.13773	.13906	7.1912	.99047	5
56	.12071	.12160	8.2234	.99269	4	56	.13802	.13935	7.1759	.99043	4
57	.12100	.12190	8.2035	.99265	3	57	.13831	.13965	7.1607	.99039	3
58	.12129	.12219	8.1837	.99262	2	58	.13860	.13995	7.1455	.99035	2
59	.12158	.12249	8.1640	.99258	1	59	.13889	.14024	7.1304	.99031	1
60	.12187	.12278	8.1443	.99255	0	60	.13917	.14054	7.1154	.99027	0
′	Cos	Ctn	Tan	Sin	′	′	Cos	Ctn	Tan	Sin	′

Table IV (Cont'd)
NATURAL TRIGONOMETRIC FUNCTIONS

8° (188°)   (351°) **171°**

′	Sin	Tan	Ctn	Cos	′
0	.13917	.14054	7.1154	.99027	60
1	.13946	.14084	7.1004	.99023	59
2	.13975	.14113	7.0855	.99019	58
3	.14004	.14143	7.0706	.99015	57
4	.14033	.14173	7.0558	.99011	56
5	.14061	.14202	7.0410	.99006	55
6	.14090	.14232	7.0264	.99002	54
7	.14119	.14262	7.0117	.98998	53
8	.14148	.14291	6.9972	.98994	52
9	.14177	.14321	6.9827	.98990	51
10	.14205	.14351	6.9682	.98986	50
11	.14234	.14381	6.9538	.98982	49
12	.14263	.14410	6.9395	.98978	48
13	.14292	.14440	6.9252	.98973	47
14	.14320	.14470	6.9110	.98969	46
15	.14349	.14499	6.8969	.98965	45
16	.14378	.14529	6.8828	.98961	44
17	.14407	.14559	6.8687	.98957	43
18	.14436	.14588	6.8548	.98953	42
19	.14464	.14618	6.8408	.98948	41
20	.14493	.14648	6.8269	.98944	40
21	.14522	.14678	6.8131	.98940	39
22	.14551	.14707	6.7994	.98936	38
23	.14580	.14737	6.7856	.98931	37
24	.14608	.14767	6.7720	.98927	36
25	.14637	.14796	6.7584	.98923	35
26	.14666	.14826	6.7448	.98919	34
27	.14695	.14856	6.7313	.98914	33
28	.14723	.14886	6.7179	.98910	32
29	.14752	.14915	6.7045	.98906	31
30	.14781	.14945	6.6912	.98902	30
31	.14810	.14975	6.6779	.98897	29
32	.14838	.15005	6.6646	.98893	28
33	.14867	.15034	6.6514	.98889	27
34	.14896	.15064	6.6383	.98884	26
35	.14925	.15094	6.6252	.98880	25
36	.14954	.15124	6.6122	.98876	24
37	.14982	.15153	6.5992	.98871	23
38	.15011	.15183	6.5863	.98867	22
39	.15040	.15213	6.5734	.98863	21
40	.15069	.15243	6.5606	.98858	20
41	.15097	.15272	6.5478	.98854	19
42	.15126	.15302	6.5350	.98849	18
43	.15155	.15332	6.5223	.98845	17
44	.15184	.15362	6.5097	.98841	16
45	.15212	.15391	6.4971	.98836	15
46	.15241	.15421	6.4846	.98832	14
47	.15270	.15451	6.4721	.98827	13
48	.15299	.15481	6.4596	.98823	12
49	.15327	.15511	6.4472	.98818	11
50	.15356	.15540	6.4348	.98814	10
51	.15385	.15570	6.4225	.98809	9
52	.15414	.15600	6.4103	.98805	8
53	.15442	.15630	6.3980	.98800	7
54	.15471	.15660	6.3859	.98796	6
55	.15500	.15689	6.3737	.98791	5
56	.15529	.15719	6.3617	.98787	4
57	.15557	.15749	6.3496	.98782	3
58	.15586	.15779	6.3376	.98778	2
59	.15615	.15809	6.3257	.98773	1
60	.15643	.15838	6.3138	.98769	0
′	Cos	Ctn	Tan	Sin	′

98° (278°)   (261°) **81°**

9° (189°)   (350°) **170°**

′	Sin	Tan	Ctn	Cos	′
0	.15643	.15838	6.3138	.98769	60
1	.15672	.15868	6.3019	.98764	59
2	.15701	.15898	6.2901	.98760	58
3	.15730	.15928	6.2783	.98755	57
4	.15758	.15958	6.2666	.98751	56
5	.15787	.15988	6.2549	.98746	55
6	.15816	.16017	6.2432	.98741	54
7	.15845	.16047	6.2316	.98737	53
8	.15873	.16077	6.2200	.98732	52
9	.15902	.16107	6.2085	.98728	51
10	.15931	.16137	6.1970	.98723	50
11	.15959	.16167	6.1856	.98718	49
12	.15988	.16196	6.1742	.98714	48
13	.16017	.16226	6.1628	.98709	47
14	.16046	.16256	6.1515	.98704	46
15	.16074	.16286	6.1402	.98700	45
16	.16103	.16316	6.1290	.98695	44
17	.16132	.16346	6.1178	.98690	43
18	.16160	.16376	6.1066	.98686	42
19	.16189	.16405	6.0955	.98681	41
20	.16218	.16435	6.0844	.98676	40
21	.16246	.16465	6.0734	.98671	39
22	.16275	.16495	6.0624	.98667	38
23	.16304	.16525	6.0514	.98662	37
24	.16333	.16555	6.0405	.98657	36
25	.16361	.16585	6.0296	.98652	35
26	.16390	.16615	6.0188	.98648	34
27	.16419	.16645	6.0080	.98643	33
28	.16447	.16674	5.9972	.98638	32
29	.16476	.16704	5.9865	.98633	31
30	.16505	.16734	5.9758	.98629	30
31	.16533	.16764	5.9651	.98624	29
32	.16562	.16794	5.9545	.98619	28
33	.16591	.16824	5.9439	.98614	27
34	.16620	.16854	5.9333	.98609	26
35	.16648	.16884	5.9228	.98604	25
36	.16677	.16914	5.9124	.98600	24
37	.16706	.16944	5.9019	.98595	23
38	.16734	.16974	5.8915	.98590	22
39	.16763	.17004	5.8811	.98585	21
40	.16792	.17033	5.8708	.98580	20
41	.16820	.17063	5.8605	.98575	19
42	.16849	.17093	5.8502	.98570	18
43	.16878	.17123	5.8400	.98565	17
44	.16906	.17153	5.8298	.98561	16
45	.16935	.17183	5.8197	.98556	15
46	.16964	.17213	5.8095	.98551	14
47	.16992	.17243	5.7994	.98546	13
48	.17021	.17273	5.7894	.98541	12
49	.17050	.17303	5.7794	.98536	11
50	.17078	.17333	5.7694	.98531	10
51	.17107	.17363	5.7594	.98526	9
52	.17136	.17393	5.7495	.98521	8
53	.17164	.17423	5.7396	.98516	7
54	.17193	.17453	5.7297	.98511	6
55	.17222	.17483	5.7199	.98506	5
56	.17250	.17513	5.7101	.98501	4
57	.17279	.17543	5.7004	.98496	3
58	.17308	.17573	5.6906	.98491	2
59	.17336	.17603	5.6809	.98486	1
60	.17365	.17633	5.6713	.98481	0
′	Cos	Ctn	Tan	Sin	′

99° (279°)   (260°) **80°**

Table IV (Cont'd)

NATURAL TRIGONOMETRIC FUNCTIONS

10° (190°)				(349°) 169°		11° (191°)				(348°) 168°
′	Sin	Tan	Ctn	Cos	′	′	Sin	Tan	Ctn	Cos	′
0	.17365	.17633	5.6713	.98481	60	0	.19081	.19438	5.1446	.98163	60
1	.17393	.17663	5.6617	.98476	59	1	.19109	.19468	5.1366	.98157	59
2	.17422	.17693	5.6521	.98471	58	2	.19138	.19498	5.1286	.98152	58
3	.17451	.17723	5.6425	.98466	57	3	.19167	.19529	5.1207	.98146	57
4	.17479	.17753	5.6329	.98461	56	4	.19195	.19559	5.1128	.98140	56
5	.17508	.17783	5.6234	.98455	55	5	.19224	.19589	5.1049	.98135	55
6	.17537	.17813	5.6140	.98450	54	6	.19252	.19619	5.0970	.98129	54
7	.17565	.17843	5.6045	.98445	53	7	.19281	.19649	5.0892	.98124	53
8	.17594	.17873	5.5951	.98440	52	8	.19309	.19680	5.0814	.98118	52
9	.17623	.17903	5.5857	.98435	51	9	.19338	.19710	5.0736	.98112	51
10	.17651	.17933	5.5764	.98430	50	10	.19366	.19740	5.0658	.98107	50
11	.17680	.17963	5.5671	.98425	49	11	.19395	.19770	5.0581	.98101	49
12	.17708	.17993	5.5578	.98420	48	12	.19423	.19801	5.0504	.98096	48
13	.17737	.18023	5.5485	.98414	47	13	.19452	.19831	5.0427	.98090	47
14	.17766	.18053	5.5393	.98409	46	14	.19481	.19861	5.0350	.98084	46
15	.17794	.18083	5.5301	.98404	45	15	.19509	.19891	5.0273	.98079	45
16	.17823	.18113	5.5209	.98399	44	16	.19538	.19921	5.0197	.98073	44
17	.17852	.18143	5.5118	.98394	43	17	.19566	.19952	5.0121	.98067	43
18	.17880	.18173	5.5026	.98389	42	18	.19595	.19982	5.0045	.98061	42
19	.17909	.18203	5.4936	.98383	41	19	.19623	.20012	4.9969	.98056	41
20	.17937	.18233	5.4845	.98378	40	20	.19652	.20042	4.9894	.98050	40
21	.17966	.18263	5.4755	.98373	39	21	.19680	.20073	4.9819	.98044	39
22	.17995	.18293	5.4665	.98368	38	22	.19709	.20103	4.9744	.98039	38
23	.18023	.18323	5.4575	.98362	37	23	.19737	.20133	4.9669	.98033	37
24	.18052	.18353	5.4486	.98357	36	24	.19766	.20164	4.9594	.98027	36
25	.18081	.18384	5.4397	.98352	35	25	.19794	.20194	4.9520	.98021	35
26	.18109	.18414	5.4308	.98347	34	26	.19823	.20224	4.9446	.98016	34
27	.18138	.18444	5.4219	.98341	33	27	.19851	.20254	4.9372	.98010	33
28	.18166	.18474	5.4131	.98336	32	28	.19880	.20285	4.9298	.98004	32
29	.18195	.18504	5.4043	.98331	31	29	.19908	.20315	4.9225	.97998	31
30	.18224	.18534	5.3955	.98325	30	30	.19937	.20345	4.9152	.97992	30
31	.18252	.18564	5.3868	.98320	29	31	.19965	.20376	4.9078	.97987	29
32	.18281	.18594	5.3781	.98315	28	32	.19994	.20406	4.9006	.97981	28
33	.18309	.18624	5.3694	.98310	27	33	.20022	.20436	4.8933	.97975	27
34	.18338	.18654	5.3607	.98304	26	34	.20051	.20466	4.8860	.97969	26
35	.18367	.18684	5.3521	.98299	25	35	.20079	.20497	4.8788	.97963	25
36	.18395	.18714	5.3435	.98294	24	36	.20108	.20527	4.8716	.97958	24
37	.18424	.18745	5.3349	.98288	23	37	.20136	.20557	4.8644	.97952	23
38	.18452	.18775	5.3263	.98283	22	38	.20165	.20588	4.8573	.97946	22
39	.18481	.18805	5.3178	.98277	21	39	.20193	.20618	4.8501	.97940	21
40	.18509	.18835	5.3093	.98272	20	40	.20222	.20648	4.8430	.97934	20
41	.18538	.18865	5.3008	.98267	19	41	.20250	.20679	4.8359	.97928	19
42	.18567	.18895	5.2924	.98261	18	42	.20279	.20709	4.8288	.97922	18
43	.18595	.18925	5.2839	.98256	17	43	.20307	.20739	4.8218	.97916	17
44	.18624	.18955	5.2755	.98250	16	44	.20336	.20770	4.8147	.97910	16
45	.18652	.18986	5.2672	.98245	15	45	.20364	.20800	4.8077	.97905	15
46	.18681	.19016	5.2588	.98240	14	46	.20393	.20830	4.8007	.97899	14
47	.18710	.19046	5.2505	.98234	13	47	.20421	.20861	4.7937	.97893	13
48	.18738	.19076	5.2422	.98229	12	48	.20450	.20891	4.7867	.97887	12
49	.18767	.19106	5.2339	.98223	11	49	.20478	.20921	4.7798	.97881	11
50	.18795	.19136	5.2257	.98218	10	50	.20507	.20952	4.7729	.97875	10
51	.18824	.19166	5.2174	.98212	9	51	.20535	.20982	4.7659	.97869	9
52	.18852	.19197	5.2092	.98207	8	52	.20563	.21013	4.7591	.97863	8
53	.18881	.19227	5.2011	.98201	7	53	.20592	.21043	4.7522	.97857	7
54	.18910	.19257	5.1929	.98196	6	54	.20620	.21073	4.7453	.97851	6
55	.18938	.19287	5.1848	.98190	5	55	.20649	.21104	4.7385	.97845	5
56	.18967	.19317	5.1767	.98185	4	56	.20677	.21134	4.7317	.97839	4
57	.18995	.19347	5.1686	.98179	3	57	.20706	.21164	4.7249	.97833	3
58	.19024	.19378	5.1606	.98174	2	58	.20734	.21195	4.7181	.97827	2
59	.19052	.19408	5.1526	.98168	1	59	.20763	.21225	4.7114	.97821	1
60	.19081	.19438	5.1446	.98163	0	60	.20791	.21256	4.7046	.97815	0
′	Cos	Ctn	Tan	Sin	′	′	Cos	Ctn	Tan	Sin	′

Table IV (Cont'd)

NATURAL TRIGONOMETRIC FUNCTIONS

12° (192°)   (347°) **167°**   **13°** (193°)   (346°) **166°**

′	Sin	Tan	Ctn	Cos	′	′	Sin	Tan	Ctn	Cos	′
0	.20791	.21256	4.7046	.97815	60	0	.22495	.23087	4.3315	.97437	60
1	.20820	.21286	4.6979	.97809	59	1	.22523	.23117	4.3257	.97430	59
2	.20848	.21316	4.6912	.97803	58	2	.22552	.23148	4.3200	.97424	58
3	.20877	.21347	4.6845	.97797	57	3	.22580	.23179	4.3143	.97417	57
4	.20905	.21377	4.6779	.97791	56	4	.22608	.23209	4.3086	.97411	56
5	.20933	.21408	4.6712	.97784	55	5	.22637	.23240	4.3029	.97404	55
6	.20962	.21438	4.6646	.97778	54	6	.22665	.23271	4.2972	.97398	54
7	.20990	.21469	4.6580	.97772	53	7	.22693	.23301	4.2916	.97391	53
8	.21019	.21499	4.6514	.97766	52	8	.22722	.23332	4.2859	.97384	52
9	.21047	.21529	4.6448	.97760	51	9	.22750	.23363	4.2803	.97378	51
10	.21076	.21560	4.6382	.97754	50	10	.22778	.23393	4.2747	.97371	50
11	.21104	.21590	4.6317	.97748	49	11	.22807	.23424	4.2691	.97365	49
12	.21132	.21621	4.6252	.97742	48	12	.22835	.23455	4.2635	.97358	48
13	.21161	.21651	4.6187	.97735	47	13	.22863	.23485	4.2580	.97351	47
14	.21189	.21682	4.6122	.97729	46	14	.22892	.23516	4.2524	.97345	46
15	.21218	.21712	4.6057	.97723	45	15	.22920	.23547	4.2468	.97338	45
16	.21246	.21743	4.5993	.97717	44	16	.22948	.23578	4.2413	.97331	44
17	.21275	.21773	4.5928	.97711	43	17	.22977	.23608	4.2358	.97325	43
18	.21303	.21804	4.5864	.97705	42	18	.23005	.23639	4.2303	.97318	42
19	.21331	.21834	4.5800	.97698	41	19	.23033	.23670	4.2248	.97311	41
20	.21360	.21864	4.5736	.97692	40	20	.23062	.23700	4.2193	.97304	40
21	.21388	.21895	4.5673	.97686	39	21	.23090	.23731	4.2139	.97298	39
22	.21417	.21925	4.5609	.97680	38	22	.23118	.23762	4.2084	.97291	38
23	.21445	.21956	4.5546	.97673	37	23	.23146	.23793	4.2030	.97284	37
24	.21474	.21986	4.5483	.97667	36	24	.23175	.23823	4.1976	.97278	36
25	.21502	.22017	4.5420	.97661	35	25	.23203	.23854	4.1922	.97271	35
26	.21530	.22047	4.5357	.97655	34	26	.23231	.23885	4.1868	.97264	34
27	.21559	.22078	4.5294	.97648	33	27	.23260	.23916	4.1814	.97257	33
28	.21587	.22108	4.5232	.97642	32	28	.23288	.23946	4.1760	.97251	32
29	.21616	.22139	4.5169	.97636	31	29	.23316	.23977	4.1706	.97244	31
30	.21644	.22169	4.5107	.97630	30	30	.23345	.24008	4.1653	.97237	30
31	.21672	.22200	4.5045	.97623	29	31	.23373	.24039	4.1600	.97230	29
32	.21701	.22231	4.4983	.97617	28	32	.23401	.24069	4.1547	.97223	28
33	.21729	.22261	4.4922	.97611	27	33	.23429	.24100	4.1493	.97217	27
34	.21758	.22292	4.4860	.97604	26	34	.23458	.24131	4.1441	.97210	26
35	.21786	.22322	4.4799	.97598	25	35	.23486	.24162	4.1388	.97203	25
36	.21814	.22353	4.4737	.97592	24	36	.23514	.24193	4.1335	.97196	24
37	.21843	.22383	4.4676	.97585	23	37	.23542	.24223	4.1282	.97189	23
38	.21871	.22414	4.4615	.97579	22	38	.23571	.24254	4.1230	.97182	22
39	.21899	.22444	4.4555	.97573	21	39	.23599	.24285	4.1178	.97176	21
40	.21928	.22475	4.4494	.97566	20	40	.23627	.24316	4.1126	.97169	20
41	.21956	.22505	4.4434	.97560	19	41	.23656	.24347	4.1074	.97162	19
42	.21985	.22536	4.4373	.97553	18	42	.23684	.24377	4.1022	.97155	18
43	.22013	.22567	4.4313	.97547	17	43	.23712	.24408	4.0970	.97148	17
44	.22041	.22597	4.4253	.97541	16	44	.23740	.24439	4.0918	.97141	16
45	.22070	.22628	4.4194	.97534	15	45	.23769	.24470	4.0867	.97134	15
46	.22098	.22658	4.4134	.97528	14	46	.23797	.24501	4.0815	.97127	14
47	.22126	.22689	4.4075	.97521	13	47	.23825	.24532	4.0764	.97120	13
48	.22155	.22719	4.4015	.97515	12	48	.23853	.24562	4.0713	.97113	12
49	.22183	.22750	4.3956	.97508	11	49	.23882	.24593	4.0662	.97106	11
50	.22212	.22781	4.3897	.97502	10	50	.23910	.24624	4.0611	.97100	10
51	.22240	.22811	4.3838	.97496	9	51	.23938	.24655	4.0560	.97093	9
52	.22268	.22842	4.3779	.97489	8	52	.23966	.24686	4.0509	.97086	8
53	.22297	.22872	4.3721	.97483	7	53	.23995	.24717	4.0459	.97079	7
54	.22325	.22903	4.3662	.97476	6	54	.24023	.24747	4.0408	.97072	6
55	.22353	.22934	4.3604	.97470	5	55	.24051	.24778	4.0358	.97065	5
56	.22382	.22964	4.3546	.97463	4	56	.24079	.24809	4.0308	.97058	4
57	.22410	.22995	4.3488	.97457	3	57	.24108	.24840	4.0257	.97051	3
58	.22438	.23026	4.3430	.97450	2	58	.24136	.24871	4.0207	.97044	2
59	.22467	.23056	4.3372	.97444	1	59	.24164	.24902	4.0158	.97037	1
60	.22495	.23087	4.3315	.97437	0	60	.24192	.24933	4.0108	.97030	0
′	Cos	Ctn	Tan	Sin	′	′	Cos	Ctn	Tan	Sin	′

102° (282°)   (257°) **77°**   **103°** (283°)   (256°) **76°**

Table IV (Cont'd)

NATURAL TRIGONOMETRIC FUNCTIONS

14° (194°)   (345°) 165°

′	Sin	Tan	Ctn	Cos	′
0	.24192	.24933	4.0108	.97030	60
1	.24220	.24964	4.0058	.97023	59
2	.24249	.24995	4.0009	.97015	58
3	.24277	.25026	3.9959	.97008	57
4	.24305	.25056	3.9910	.97001	56
5	.24333	.25087	3.9861	.96994	55
6	.24362	.25118	3.9812	.96987	54
7	.24390	.25149	3.9763	.96980	53
8	.24418	.25180	3.9714	.96973	52
9	.24446	.25211	3.9665	.96966	51
10	.24474	.25242	3.9617	.96959	50
11	.24503	.25273	3.9568	.96952	49
12	.24531	.25304	3.9520	.96945	48
13	.24559	.25335	3.9471	.96937	47
14	.24587	.25366	3.9423	.96930	46
15	.24615	.25397	3.9375	.96923	45
16	.24644	.25428	3.9327	.96916	44
17	.24672	.25459	3.9279	.96909	43
18	.24700	.25490	3.9232	.96902	42
19	.24728	.25521	3.9184	.96894	41
20	.24756	.25552	3.9136	.96887	40
21	.24784	.25583	3.9089	.96880	39
22	.24813	.25614	3.9042	.96873	38
23	.24841	.25645	3.8995	.96866	37
24	.24869	.25676	3.8947	.96858	36
25	.24897	.25707	3.8900	.96851	35
26	.24925	.25738	3.8854	.96844	34
27	.24954	.25769	3.8807	.96837	33
28	.24982	.25800	3.8760	.96829	32
29	.25010	.25831	3.8714	.96822	31
30	.25038	.25862	3.8667	.96815	30
31	.25066	.25893	3.8621	.96807	29
32	.25094	.25924	3.8575	.96800	28
33	.25122	.25955	3.8528	.96793	27
34	.25151	.25986	3.8482	.96786	26
35	.25179	.26017	3.8436	.96778	25
36	.25207	.26048	3.8391	.96771	24
37	.25235	.26079	3.8345	.96764	23
38	.25263	.26110	3.8299	.96756	22
39	.25291	.26141	3.8254	.96749	21
40	.25320	.26172	3.8208	.96742	20
41	.25348	.26203	3.8163	.96734	19
42	.25376	.26235	3.8118	.96727	18
43	.25404	.26266	3.8073	.96719	17
44	.25432	.26297	3.8028	.96712	16
45	.25460	.26328	3.7983	.96705	15
46	.25488	.26359	3.7938	.96697	14
47	.25516	.26390	3.7893	.96690	13
48	.25545	.26421	3.7848	.96682	12
49	.25573	.26452	3.7804	.96675	11
50	.25601	.26483	3.7760	.96667	10
51	.25629	.26515	3.7715	.96660	9
52	.25657	.26546	3.7671	.96653	8
53	.25685	.26577	3.7627	.96645	7
54	.25713	.26608	3.7583	.96638	6
55	.25741	.26639	3.7539	.96630	5
56	.25769	.26670	3.7495	.96623	4
57	.25798	.26701	3.7451	.96615	3
58	.25826	.26733	3.7408	.96608	2
59	.25854	.26764	3.7364	.96600	1
60	.25882	.26795	3.7321	.96593	0
′	Cos	Ctn	Tan	Sin	′

104° (284°)   (255°) 75°

15° (195°)   (344°) 164°

′	Sin	Tan	Ctn	Cos	′
0	.25882	.26795	3.7321	.96593	60
1	.25910	.26826	3.7277	.96585	59
2	.25938	.26857	3.7234	.96578	58
3	.25966	.26888	3.7191	.96570	57
4	.25994	.26920	3.7148	.96562	56
5	.26022	.26951	3.7105	.96555	55
6	.26050	.26982	3.7062	.96547	54
7	.26079	.27013	3.7019	.96540	53
8	.26107	.27044	3.6976	.96532	52
9	.26135	.27076	3.6933	.96524	51
10	.26163	.27107	3.6891	.96517	50
11	.26191	.27138	3.6848	.96509	49
12	.26219	.27169	3.6806	.96502	48
13	.26247	.27201	3.6764	.96494	47
14	.26275	.27232	3.6722	.96486	46
15	.26303	.27263	3.6680	.96479	45
16	.26331	.27294	3.6638	.96471	44
17	.26359	.27326	3.6596	.96463	43
18	.26387	.27357	3.6554	.96456	42
19	.26415	.27388	3.6512	.96448	41
20	.26443	.27419	3.6470	.96440	40
21	.26471	.27451	3.6429	.96433	39
22	.26500	.27482	3.6387	.96425	38
23	.26528	.27513	3.6346	.96417	37
24	.26556	.27545	3.6305	.96410	36
25	.26584	.27576	3.6264	.96402	35
26	.26612	.27607	3.6222	.96394	34
27	.26640	.27638	3.6181	.96386	33
28	.26668	.27670	3.6140	.96379	32
29	.26696	.27701	3.6100	.96371	31
30	.26724	.27732	3.6059	.96363	30
31	.26752	.27764	3.6018	.96355	29
32	.26780	.27795	3.5978	.96347	28
33	.26808	.27826	3.5937	.96340	27
34	.26836	.27858	3.5897	.96332	26
35	.26864	.27889	3.5856	.96324	25
36	.26892	.27921	3.5816	.96316	24
37	.26920	.27952	3.5776	.96308	23
38	.26948	.27983	3.5736	.96301	22
39	.26976	.28015	3.5696	.96293	21
40	.27004	.28046	3.5656	.96285	20
41	.27032	.28077	3.5616	.96277	19
42	.27060	.28109	3.5576	.96269	18
43	.27088	.28140	3.5536	.96261	17
44	.27116	.28172	3.5497	.96253	16
45	.27144	.28203	3.5457	.96246	15
46	.27172	.28234	3.5418	.96238	14
47	.27200	.28266	3.5379	.96230	13
48	.27228	.28297	3.5339	.96222	12
49	.27256	.28329	3.5300	.96214	11
50	.27284	.28360	3.5261	.96206	10
51	.27312	.28391	3.5222	.96198	9
52	.27340	.28423	3.5183	.96190	8
53	.27368	.28454	3.5144	.96182	7
54	.27396	.28486	3.5105	.96174	6
55	.27424	.28517	3.5067	.96166	5
56	.27452	.28549	3.5028	.96158	4
57	.27480	.28580	3.4989	.96150	3
58	.27508	.28612	3.4951	.96142	2
59	.27536	.28643	3.4912	.96134	1
60	.27564	.28675	3.4874	.96126	0
′	Cos	Ctn	Tan	Sin	′

105° (285°)   (254°) 74°

Table IV (Cont'd)

NATURAL TRIGONOMETRIC FUNCTIONS

16° (196°)   (343°) 163°   17° (197°)   (342°) 162°

′	Sin	Tan	Ctn	Cos	′	′	Sin	Tan	Ctn	Cos	′
0	.27564	.28675	3.4874	.96126	60	0	.29237	.30573	3.2709	.95630	60
1	.27592	.28706	3.4836	.96118	59	1	.29265	.30605	3.2675	.95622	59
2	.27620	.28738	3.4798	.96110	58	2	.29293	.30637	3.2641	.95613	58
3	.27648	.28769	3.4760	.96102	57	3	.29321	.30669	3.2607	.95605	57
4	.27676	.28801	3.4722	.96094	56	4	.29348	.30700	3.2573	.95596	56
5	.27704	.28832	3.4684	.96086	55	5	.29376	.30732	3.2539	.95588	55
6	.27731	.28864	3.4646	.96078	54	6	.29404	.30764	3.2506	.95579	54
7	.27759	.28895	3.4608	.96070	53	7	.29432	.30796	3.2472	.95571	53
8	.27787	.28927	3.4570	.96062	52	8	.29460	.30828	3.2438	.95562	52
9	.27815	.28958	3.4533	.96054	51	9	.29487	.30860	3.2405	.95554	51
10	.27843	.28990	3.4495	.96046	50	10	.29515	.30891	3.2371	.95545	50
11	.27871	.29021	3.4458	.96037	49	11	.29543	.30923	3.2338	.95536	49
12	.27899	.29053	3.4420	.96029	48	12	.29571	.30955	3.2305	.95528	48
13	.27927	.29084	3.4383	.96021	47	13	.29599	.30987	3.2272	.95519	47
14	.27955	.29116	3.4346	.96013	46	14	.29626	.31019	3.2238	.95511	46
15	.27983	.29147	3.4308	.96005	45	15	.29654	.31051	3.2205	.95502	45
16	.28011	.29179	3.4271	.95997	44	16	.29682	.31083	3.2172	.95493	44
17	.28039	.29210	3.4234	.95989	43	17	.29710	.31115	3.2139	.95485	43
18	.28067	.29242	3.4197	.95981	42	18	.29737	.31147	3.2106	.95476	42
19	.28095	.29274	3.4160	.95972	41	19	.29765	.31178	3.2073	.95467	41
20	.28123	.29305	3.4124	.95964	40	20	.29793	.31210	3.2041	.95459	40
21	.28150	.29337	3.4087	.95956	39	21	.29821	.31242	3.2008	.95450	39
22	.28178	.29368	3.4050	.95948	38	22	.29849	.31274	3.1975	.95441	38
23	.28206	.29400	3.4014	.95940	37	23	.29876	.31306	3.1943	.95433	37
24	.28234	.29432	3.3977	.95931	36	24	.29904	.31338	3.1910	.95424	36
25	.28262	.29463	3.3941	.95923	35	25	.29932	.31370	3.1878	.95415	35
26	.28290	.29495	3.3904	.95915	34	26	.29960	.31402	3.1845	.95407	34
27	.28318	.29526	3.3868	.95907	33	27	.29987	.31434	3.1813	.95398	33
28	.28346	.29558	3.3832	.95898	32	28	.30015	.31466	3.1780	.95389	32
29	.28374	.29590	3.3796	.95890	31	29	.30043	.31498	3.1748	.95380	31
30	.28402	.29621	3.3759	.95882	30	30	.30071	.31530	3.1716	.95372	30
31	.28429	.29653	3.3723	.95874	29	31	.30098	.31562	3.1684	.95363	29
32	.28457	.29685	3.3687	.95865	28	32	.30126	.31594	3.1652	.95354	28
33	.28485	.29716	3.3652	.95857	27	33	.30154	.31626	3.1620	.95345	27
34	.28513	.29748	3.3616	.95849	26	34	.30182	.31658	3.1588	.95337	26
35	.28541	.29780	3.3580	.95841	25	35	.30209	.31690	3.1556	.95328	25
36	.28569	.29811	3.3544	.95832	24	36	.30237	.31722	3.1524	.95319	24
37	.28597	.29843	3.3509	.95824	23	37	.30265	.31754	3.1492	.95310	23
38	.28625	.29875	3.3473	.95816	22	38	.30292	.31786	3.1460	.95301	22
39	.28652	.29906	3.3438	.95807	21	39	.30320	.31818	3.1429	.95293	21
40	.28680	.29938	3.3402	.95799	20	40	.30348	.31850	3.1397	.95284	20
41	.28708	.29970	3.3367	.95791	19	41	.30376	.31882	3.1366	.95275	19
42	.28736	.30001	3.3332	.95782	18	42	.30403	.31914	3.1334	.95266	18
43	.28764	.30033	3.3297	.95774	17	43	.30431	.31946	3.1303	.95257	17
44	.28792	.30065	3.3261	.95766	16	44	.30459	.31978	3.1271	.95248	16
45	.28820	.30097	3.3226	.95757	15	45	.30486	.32010	3.1240	.95240	15
46	.28847	.30128	3.3191	.95749	14	46	.30514	.32042	3.1209	.95231	14
47	.28875	.30160	3.3156	.95740	13	47	.30542	.32074	3.1178	.95222	13
48	.28903	.30192	3.3122	.95732	12	48	.30570	.32106	3.1146	.95213	12
49	.28931	.30224	3.3087	.95724	11	49	.30597	.32139	3.1115	.95204	11
50	.28959	.30255	3.3052	.95715	10	50	.30625	.32171	3.1084	.95195	10
51	.28987	.30287	3.3017	.95707	9	51	.30653	.32203	3.1053	.95186	9
52	.29015	.30319	3.2983	.95698	8	52	.30680	.32235	3.1022	.95177	8
53	.29042	.30351	3.2948	.95690	7	53	.30708	.32267	3.0991	.95168	7
54	.29070	.30382	3.2914	.95681	6	54	.30736	.32299	3.0961	.95159	6
55	.29098	.30414	3.2879	.95673	5	55	.30763	.32331	3.0930	.95150	5
56	.29126	.30446	3.2845	.95664	4	56	.30791	.32363	3.0899	.95142	4
57	.29154	.30478	3.2811	.95656	3	57	.30819	.32396	3.0868	.95133	3
58	.29182	.30509	3.2777	.95647	2	58	.30846	.32428	3.0838	.95124	2
59	.29209	.30541	3.2743	.95639	1	59	.30874	.32460	3.0807	.95115	1
60	.29237	.30573	3.2709	.95630	0	60	.30902	.32492	3.0777	.95106	0
′	Cos	Ctn	Tan	Sin	′	′	Cos	Ctn	Tan	Sin	′

106° (286°)   (253°) 73°   107° (287°)   (252°) 72°

Table IV (Cont'd)

NATURAL TRIGONOMETRIC FUNCTIONS

18° (198°)   (341°) **161°**   **19° (199°)**   (340°) **160°**

′	Sin	Tan	Ctn	Cos	′	′	Sin	Tan	Ctn	Cos	′
0	.30902	.32492	3.0777	.95106	60	0	.32557	.34433	2.9042	.94552	60
1	.30929	.32524	3.0746	.95097	59	1	.32584	.34465	2.9015	.94542	59
2	.30957	.32556	3.0716	.95088	58	2	.32612	.34498	2.8987	.94533	58
3	.30985	.32588	3.0686	.95079	57	3	.32639	.34530	2.8960	.94523	57
4	.31012	.32621	3.0655	.95070	56	4	.32667	.34563	2.8933	.94514	56
5	.31040	.32653	3.0625	.95061	55	5	.32694	.34596	2.8905	.94504	55
6	.31068	.32685	3.0595	.95052	54	6	.32722	.34628	2.8878	.94495	54
7	.31095	.32717	3.0565	.95043	53	7	.32749	.34661	2.8851	.94485	53
8	.31123	.32749	3.0535	.95033	52	8	.32777	.34693	2.8824	.94476	52
9	.31151	.32782	3.0505	.95024	51	9	.32804	.34726	2.8797	.94466	51
10	.31178	.32814	3.0475	.95015	50	10	.32832	.34758	2.8770	.94457	50
11	.31206	.32846	3.0445	.95006	49	11	.32859	.34791	2.8743	.94447	49
12	.31233	.32878	3.0415	.94997	48	12	.32887	.34824	2.8716	.94438	48
13	.31261	.32911	3.0385	.94988	47	13	.32914	.34856	2.8689	.94428	47
14	.31289	.32943	3.0356	.94979	46	14	.32942	.34889	2.8662	.94418	46
15	.31316	.32975	3.0326	.94970	45	15	.32969	.34922	2.8636	.94409	45
16	.31344	.33007	3.0296	.94961	44	16	.32997	.34954	2.8609	.94399	44
17	.31372	.33040	3.0267	.94952	43	17	.33024	.34987	2.8582	.94390	43
18	.31399	.33072	3.0237	.94943	42	18	.33051	.35020	2.8556	.94380	42
19	.31427	.33104	3.0208	.94933	41	19	.33079	.35052	2.8529	.94370	41
20	.31454	.33136	3.0178	.94924	40	20	.33106	.35085	2.8502	.94361	40
21	.31482	.33169	3.0149	.94915	39	21	.33134	.35118	2.8476	.94351	39
22	.31510	.33201	3.0120	.94906	38	22	.33161	.35150	2.8449	.94342	38
23	.31537	.33233	3.0090	.94897	37	23	.33189	.35183	2.8423	.94332	37
24	.31565	.33266	3.0061	.94888	36	24	.33216	.35216	2.8397	.94322	36
25	.31593	.33298	3.0032	.94878	35	25	.33244	.35248	2.8370	.94313	35
26	.31620	.33330	3.0003	.94869	34	26	.33271	.35281	2.8344	.94303	34
27	.31648	.33363	2.9974	.94860	33	27	.33298	.35314	2.8318	.94293	33
28	.31675	.33395	2.9945	.94851	32	28	.33326	.35346	2.8291	.94284	32
29	.31703	.33427	2.9916	.94842	31	29	.33353	.35379	2.8265	.94274	31
30	.31730	.33460	2.9887	.94832	30	30	.33381	.35412	2.8239	.94264	30
31	.31758	.33492	2.9858	.94823	29	31	.33408	.35445	2.8213	.94254	29
32	.31786	.33524	2.9829	.94814	28	32	.33436	.35477	2.8187	.94245	28
33	.31813	.33557	2.9800	.94805	27	33	.33463	.35510	2.8161	.94235	27
34	.31841	.33589	2.9772	.94795	26	34	.33490	.35543	2.8135	.94225	26
35	.31868	.33621	2.9743	.94786	25	35	.33518	.35576	2.8109	.94215	25
36	.31896	.33654	2.9714	.94777	24	36	.33545	.35608	2.8083	.94206	24
37	.31923	.33686	2.9686	.94768	23	37	.33573	.35641	2.8057	.94196	23
38	.31951	.33718	2.9657	.94758	22	38	.33600	.35674	2.8032	.94186	22
39	.31979	.33751	2.9629	.94749	21	39	.33627	.35707	2.8006	.94176	21
40	.32006	.33783	2.9600	.94740	20	40	.33655	.35740	2.7980	.94167	20
41	.32034	.33816	2.9572	.94730	19	41	.33682	.35772	2.7955	.94157	19
42	.32061	.33848	2.9544	.94721	18	42	.33710	.35805	2.7929	.94147	18
43	.32089	.33881	2.9515	.94712	17	43	.33737	.35838	2.7903	.94137	17
44	.32116	.33913	2.9487	.94702	16	44	.33764	.35871	2.7878	.94127	16
45	.32144	.33945	2.9459	.94693	15	45	.33792	.35904	2.7852	.94118	15
46	.32171	.33978	2.9431	.94684	14	46	.33819	.35937	2.7827	.94108	14
47	.32199	.34010	2.9403	.94674	13	47	.33846	.35969	2.7801	.94098	13
48	.32227	.34043	2.9375	.94665	12	48	.33874	.36002	2.7776	.94088	12
49	.32254	.34075	2.9347	.94656	11	49	.33901	.36035	2.7751	.94078	11
50	.32282	.34108	2.9319	.94646	10	50	.33929	.36068	2.7725	.94068	10
51	.32309	.34140	2.9291	.94637	9	51	.33956	.36101	2.7700	.94058	9
52	.32337	.34173	2.9263	.94627	8	52	.33983	.36134	2.7675	.94049	8
53	.32364	.34205	2.9235	.94618	7	53	.34011	.36167	2.7650	.94039	7
54	.32392	.34238	2.9208	.94609	6	54	.34038	.36199	2.7625	.94029	6
55	.32419	.34270	2.9180	.94599	5	55	.34065	.36232	2.7600	.94019	5
56	.32447	.34303	2.9152	.94590	4	56	.34093	.36265	2.7575	.94009	4
57	.32474	.34335	2.9125	.94580	3	57	.34120	.36298	2.7550	.93999	3
58	.32502	.34368	2.9097	.94571	2	58	.34147	.36331	2.7525	.93989	2
59	.32529	.34400	2.9070	.94561	1	59	.34175	.36364	2.7500	.93979	1
60	.32557	.34433	2.9042	.94552	0	60	.34202	.36397	2.7475	.93969	0
′	Cos	Ctn	Tan	Sin	′	′	Cos	Ctn	Tan	Sin	′

Table IV (Cont'd)

NATURAL TRIGONOMETRIC FUNCTIONS

20° (200°)				(339°) 159°	21° (201°)				(338°) 158°
′	Sin	Tan	Ctn	Cos	′	′	Sin	Tan	Ctn	Cos	′

′	Sin	Tan	Ctn	Cos	′	′	Sin	Tan	Ctn	Cos	′
0	.34202	.36397	2.7475	.93969	60	0	.35837	.38386	2.6051	.93358	60
1	.34229	.36430	2.7450	.93959	59	1	.35864	.38420	2.6028	.93348	59
2	.34257	.36463	2.7425	.93949	58	2	.35891	.38453	2.6006	.93337	58
3	.34284	.36496	2.7400	.93939	57	3	.35918	.38487	2.5983	.93327	57
4	.34311	.36529	2.7376	.93929	56	4	.35945	.38520	2.5961	.93316	56
5	.34339	.36562	2.7351	.93919	55	5	.35973	.38553	2.5938	.93306	55
6	.34366	.36595	2.7326	.93909	54	6	.36000	.38587	2.5916	.93295	54
7	.34393	.36628	2.7302	.93899	53	7	.36027	.38620	2.5893	.93285	53
8	.34421	.36661	2.7277	.93889	52	8	.36054	.38654	2.5871	.93274	52
9	.34448	.36694	2.7253	.93879	51	9	.36081	.38687	2.5848	.93264	51
10	.34475	.36727	2.7228	.93869	50	10	.36108	.38721	2.5826	.93253	50
11	.34503	.36760	2.7204	.93859	49	11	.36135	.38754	2.5804	.93243	49
12	.34530	.36793	2.7179	.93849	48	12	.36162	.38787	2.5782	.93232	48
13	.34557	.36826	2.7155	.93839	47	13	.36190	.38821	2.5759	.93222	47
14	.34584	.36859	2.7130	.93829	46	14	.36217	.38854	2.5737	.93211	46
15	.34612	.36892	2.7106	.93819	45	15	.36244	.38888	2.5715	.93201	45
16	.34639	.36925	2.7082	.93809	44	16	.36271	.38921	2.5693	.93190	44
17	.34666	.36958	2.7058	.93799	43	17	.36298	.38955	2.5671	.93180	43
18	.34694	.36991	2.7034	.93789	42	18	.36325	.38988	2.5649	.93169	42
19	.34721	.37024	2.7009	.93779	41	19	.36352	.39022	2.5627	.93159	41
20	.34748	.37057	2.6985	.93769	40	20	.36379	.39055	2.5605	.93148	40
21	.34775	.37090	2.6961	.93759	39	21	.36406	.39089	2.5583	.93137	39
22	.34803	.37123	2.6937	.93748	38	22	.36434	.39122	2.5561	.93127	38
23	.34830	.37157	2.6913	.93738	37	23	.36461	.39156	2.5539	.93116	37
24	.34857	.37190	2.6889	.93728	36	24	.36488	.39190	2.5517	.93106	36
25	.34884	.37223	2.6865	.93718	35	25	.36515	.39223	2.5495	.93095	35
26	.34912	.37256	2.6841	.93708	34	26	.36542	.39257	2.5473	.93084	34
27	.34939	.37289	2.6818	.93698	33	27	.36569	.39290	2.5452	.93074	33
28	.34966	.37322	2.6794	.93688	32	28	.36596	.39324	2.5430	.93063	32
29	.34993	.37355	2.6770	.93677	31	29	.36623	.39357	2.5408	.93052	31
30	.35021	.37388	2.6746	.93667	30	30	.36650	.39391	2.5386	.93042	30
31	.35048	.37422	2.6723	.93657	29	31	.36677	.39425	2.5365	.93031	29
32	.35075	.37455	2.6699	.93647	28	32	.36704	.39458	2.5343	.93020	28
33	.35102	.37488	2.6675	.93637	27	33	.36731	.39492	2.5322	.93010	27
34	.35130	.37521	2.6652	.93626	26	34	.36758	.39526	2.5300	.92999	26
35	.35157	.37554	2.6628	.93616	25	35	.36785	.39559	2.5279	.92988	25
36	.35184	.37588	2.6605	.93606	24	36	.36812	.39593	2.5257	.92978	24
37	.35211	.37621	2.6581	.93596	23	37	.36839	.39626	2.5236	.92967	23
38	.35239	.37654	2.6558	.93585	22	38	.36867	.39660	2.5214	.92956	22
39	.35266	.37687	2.6534	.93575	21	39	.36894	.39694	2.5193	.92945	21
40	.35293	.37720	2.6511	.93565	20	40	.36921	.39727	2.5172	.92935	20
41	.35320	.37754	2.6488	.93555	19	41	.36948	.39761	2.5150	.92924	19
42	.35347	.37787	2.6464	.93544	18	42	.36975	.39795	2.5129	.92913	18
43	.35375	.37820	2.6441	.93534	17	43	.37002	.39829	2.5108	.92902	17
44	.35402	.37853	2.6418	.93524	16	44	.37029	.39862	2.5086	.92892	16
45	.35429	.37887	2.6395	.93514	15	45	.37056	.39896	2.5065	.92881	15
46	.35456	.37920	2.6371	.93503	14	46	.37083	.39930	2.5044	.92870	14
47	.35484	.37953	2.6348	.93493	13	47	.37110	.39963	2.5023	.92859	13
48	.35511	.37986	2.6325	.93483	12	48	.37137	.39997	2.5002	.92849	12
49	.35538	.38020	2.6302	.93472	11	49	.37164	.40031	2.4981	.92838	11
50	.35565	.38053	2.6279	.93462	10	50	.37191	.40065	2.4960	.92827	10
51	.35592	.38086	2.6256	.93452	9	51	.37218	.40098	2.4939	.92816	9
52	.35619	.38120	2.6233	.93441	8	52	.37245	.40132	2.4918	.92805	8
53	.35647	.38153	2.6210	.93431	7	53	.37272	.40166	2.4897	.92794	7
54	.35674	.38186	2.6187	.93420	6	54	.37299	.40200	2.4876	.92784	6
55	.35701	.38220	2.6165	.93410	5	55	.37326	.40234	2.4855	.92773	5
56	.35728	.38253	2.6142	.93400	4	56	.37353	.40267	2.4834	.92762	4
57	.35755	.38286	2.6119	.93389	3	57	.37380	.40301	2.4813	.92751	3
58	.35782	.38320	2.6096	.93379	2	58	.37407	.40335	2.4792	.92740	2
59	.35810	.38353	2.6074	.93368	1	59	.37434	.40369	2.4772	.92729	1
60	.35837	.38386	2.6051	.93358	0	60	.37461	.40403	2.4751	.92718	0
′	Cos	Ctn	Tan	Sin	′	′	Cos	Ctn	Tan	Sin	′

Table IV (Cont'd)

NATURAL TRIGONOMETRIC FUNCTIONS

22° (202°)   (337°) **157°**   **23°** (203°)   (336°) **156°**

′	Sin	Tan	Ctn	Cos	′	′	Sin	Tan	Ctn	Cos	′
0	.37461	.40403	2.4751	.92718	60	0	.39073	.42447	2.3559	.92050	60
1	.37488	.40436	2.4730	.92707	59	1	.39100	.42482	2.3539	.92039	59
2	.37515	.40470	2.4709	.92697	58	2	.39127	.42516	2.3520	.92028	58
3	.37542	.40504	2.4689	.92686	57	3	.39153	.42551	2.3501	.92016	57
4	.37569	.40538	2.4668	.92675	56	4	.39180	.42585	2.3483	.92005	56
5	.37595	.40572	2.4648	.92664	55	5	.39207	.42619	2.3464	.91994	55
6	.37622	.40606	2.4627	.92653	54	6	.39234	.42654	2.3445	.91982	54
7	.37649	.40640	2.4606	.92642	53	7	.39260	.42688	2.3426	.91971	53
8	.37676	.40674	2.4586	.92631	52	8	.39287	.42722	2.3407	.91959	52
9	.37703	.40707	2.4566	.92620	51	9	.39314	.42757	2.3388	.91948	51
10	.37730	.40741	2.4545	.92609	50	10	.39341	.42791	2.3369	.91936	50
11	.37757	.40775	2.4525	.92598	49	11	.39367	.42826	2.3351	.91925	49
12	.37784	.40809	2.4504	.92587	48	12	.39394	.42860	2.3332	.91914	48
13	.37811	.40843	2.4484	.92576	47	13	.39421	.42894	2.3313	.91902	47
14	.37838	.40877	2.4464	.92565	46	14	.39448	.42929	2.3294	.91891	46
15	.37865	.40911	2.4443	.92554	45	15	.39474	.42963	2.3276	.91879	45
16	.37892	.40945	2.4423	.92543	44	16	.39501	.42998	2.3257	.91868	44
17	.37919	.40979	2.4403	.92532	43	17	.39528	.43032	2.3238	.91856	43
18	.37946	.41013	2.4383	.92521	42	18	.39555	.43067	2.3220	.91845	42
19	.37973	.41047	2.4362	.92510	41	19	.39581	.43101	2.3201	.91833	41
20	.37999	.41081	2.4342	.92499	40	20	.39608	.43136	2.3183	.91822	40
21	.38026	.41115	2.4322	.92488	39	21	.39635	.43170	2.3164	.91810	39
22	.38053	.41149	2.4302	.92477	38	22	.39661	.43205	2.3146	.91799	38
23	.38080	.41183	2.4282	.92466	37	23	.39688	.43239	2.3127	.91787	37
24	.38107	.41217	2.4262	.92455	36	24	.39715	.43274	2.3109	.91775	36
25	.38134	.41251	2.4242	.92444	35	25	.39741	.43308	2.3090	.91764	35
26	.38161	.41285	2.4222	.92432	34	26	.39768	.43343	2.3072	.91752	34
27	.38188	.41319	2.4202	.92421	33	27	.39795	.43378	2.3053	.91741	33
28	.38215	.41353	2.4182	.92410	32	28	.39822	.43412	2.3035	.91729	32
29	.38241	.41387	2.4162	.92399	31	29	.39848	.43447	2.3017	.91718	31
30	.38268	.41421	2.4142	.92388	30	30	.39875	.43481	2.2998	.91706	30
31	.38295	.41455	2.4122	.92377	29	31	.39902	.43516	2.2980	.91694	29
32	.38322	.41490	2.4102	.92366	28	32	.39928	.43550	2.2962	.91683	28
33	.38349	.41524	2.4083	.92355	27	33	.39955	.43585	2.2944	.91671	27
34	.38376	.41558	2.4063	.92343	26	34	.39982	.43620	2.2925	.91660	26
35	.38403	.41592	2.4043	.92332	25	35	.40008	.43654	2.2907	.91648	25
36	.38430	.41626	2.4023	.92321	24	36	.40035	.43689	2.2889	.91636	24
37	.38456	.41660	2.4004	.92310	23	37	.40062	.43724	2.2871	.91625	23
38	.38483	.41694	2.3984	.92299	22	38	.40088	.43758	2.2853	.91613	22
39	.38510	.41728	2.3964	.92287	21	39	.40115	.43793	2.2835	.91601	21
40	.38537	.41763	2.3945	.92276	20	40	.40141	.43828	2.2817	.91590	20
41	.38564	.41797	2.3925	.92265	19	41	.40168	.43862	2.2799	.91578	19
42	.38591	.41831	2.3906	.92254	18	42	.40195	.43897	2.2781	.91566	18
43	.38617	.41865	2.3886	.92243	17	43	.40221	.43932	2.2763	.91555	17
44	.38644	.41899	2.3867	.92231	16	44	.40248	.43966	2.2745	.91543	16
45	.38671	.41933	2.3847	.92220	15	45	.40275	.44001	2.2727	.91531	15
46	.38698	.41968	2.3828	.92209	14	46	.40301	.44036	2.2709	.91519	14
47	.38725	.42002	2.3808	.92198	13	47	.40328	.44071	2.2691	.91508	13
48	.38752	.42036	2.3789	.92186	12	48	.40355	.44105	2.2673	.91496	12
49	.38778	.42070	2.3770	.92175	11	49	.40381	.44140	2.2655	.91484	11
50	.38805	.42105	2.3750	.92164	10	50	.40408	.44175	2.2637	.91472	10
51	.38832	.42139	2.3731	.92152	9	51	.40434	.44210	2.2620	.91461	9
52	.38859	.42173	2.3712	.92141	8	52	.40461	.44244	2.2602	.91449	8
53	.38886	.42207	2.3693	.92130	7	53	.40488	.44279	2.2584	.91437	7
54	.38912	.42242	2.3673	.92119	6	54	.40514	.44314	2.2566	.91425	6
55	.38939	.42276	2.3654	.92107	5	55	.40541	.44349	2.2549	.91414	5
56	.38966	.42310	2.3635	.92096	4	56	.40567	.44384	2.2531	.91402	4
57	.38993	.42345	2.3616	.92085	3	57	.40594	.44418	2.2513	.91390	3
58	.39020	.42379	2.3597	.92073	2	58	.40621	.44453	2.2496	.91378	2
59	.39046	.42413	2.3578	.92062	1	59	.40647	.44488	2.2478	.91366	1
60	.39073	.42447	2.3559	.92050	0	60	.40674	.44523	2.2460	.91355	0
′	Cos	Ctn	Tan	Sin	′	′	Cos	Ctn	Tan	Sin	′

112° (292°)   (247°) **67°**   **113°** (293°)   (246°) **66°**

Table IV (Cont'd)

NATURAL TRIGONOMETRIC FUNCTIONS

24° (204°)				(335°) 155°		25° (205°)				(334°) 154°
′	Sin	Tan	Ctn	Cos	′	′	Sin	Tan	Ctn	Cos	′
0	.40674	.44523	2.2460	.91355	60	0	.42262	.46631	2.1445	.90631	60
1	.40700	.44558	2.2443	.91343	59	1	.42288	.46666	2.1429	.90618	59
2	.40727	.44593	2.2425	.91331	58	2	.42315	.46702	2.1413	.90606	58
3	.40753	.44627	2.2408	.91319	57	3	.42341	.46737	2.1396	.90594	57
4	.40780	.44662	2.2390	.91307	56	4	.42367	.46772	2.1380	.90582	56
5	.40806	.44697	2.2373	.91295	55	5	.42394	.46808	2.1364	.90569	55
6	.40833	.44732	2.2355	.91283	54	6	.42420	.46843	2.1348	.90557	54
7	.40860	.44767	2.2338	.91272	53	7	.42446	.46879	2.1332	.90545	53
8	.40886	.44802	2.2320	.91260	52	8	.42473	.46914	2.1315	.90532	52
9	.40913	.44837	2.2303	.91248	51	9	.42499	.46950	2.1299	.90520	51
10	.40939	.44872	2.2286	.91236	50	10	.42525	.46985	2.1283	.90507	50
11	.40966	.44907	2.2268	.91224	49	11	.42552	.47021	2.1267	.90495	49
12	.40992	.44942	2.2251	.91212	48	12	.42578	.47056	2.1251	.90483	48
13	.41019	.44977	2.2234	.91200	47	13	.42604	.47092	2.1235	.90470	47
14	.41045	.45012	2.2216	.91188	46	14	.42631	.47128	2.1219	.90458	46
15	.41072	.45047	2.2199	.91176	45	15	.42657	.47163	2.1203	.90446	45
16	.41098	.45082	2.2182	.91164	44	16	.42683	.47199	2.1187	.90433	44
17	.41125	.45117	2.2165	.91152	43	17	.42709	.47234	2.1171	.90421	43
18	.41151	.45152	2.2148	.91140	42	18	.42736	.47270	2.1155	.90408	42
19	.41178	.45187	2.2130	.91128	41	19	.42762	.47305	2.1139	.90396	41
20	.41204	.45222	2.2113	.91116	40	20	.42788	.47341	2.1123	.90383	40
21	.41231	.45257	2.2096	.91104	39	21	.42815	.47377	2.1107	.90371	39
22	.41257	.45292	2.2079	.91092	38	22	.42841	.47412	2.1092	.90358	38
23	.41284	.45327	2.2062	.91080	37	23	.42867	.47448	2.1076	.90346	37
24	.41310	.45362	2.2045	.91068	36	24	.42894	.47483	2.1060	.90334	36
25	.41337	.45397	2.2028	.91056	35	25	.42920	.47519	2.1044	.90321	35
26	.41363	.45432	2.2011	.91044	34	26	.42946	.47555	2.1028	.90309	34
27	.41390	.45467	2.1994	.91032	33	27	.42972	.47590	2.1013	.90296	33
28	.41416	.45502	2.1977	.91020	32	28	.42999	.47626	2.0997	.90284	32
29	.41443	.45538	2.1960	.91008	31	29	.43025	.47662	2.0981	.90271	31
30	.41469	.45573	2.1943	.90996	30	30	.43051	.47698	2.0965	.90259	30
31	.41496	.45608	2.1926	.90984	29	31	.43077	.47733	2.0950	.90246	29
32	.41522	.45643	2.1909	.90972	28	32	.43104	.47769	2.0934	.90233	28
33	.41549	.45678	2.1892	.90960	27	33	.43130	.47805	2.0918	.90221	27
34	.41575	.45713	2.1876	.90948	26	34	.43156	.47840	2.0903	.90208	26
35	.41602	.45748	2.1859	.90936	25	35	.43182	.47876	2.0887	.90196	25
36	.41628	.45784	2.1842	.90924	24	36	.43209	.47912	2.0872	.90183	24
37	.41655	.45819	2.1825	.90911	23	37	.43235	.47948	2.0856	.90171	23
38	.41681	.45854	2.1808	.90899	22	38	.43261	.47984	2.0840	.90158	22
39	.41707	.45889	2.1792	.90887	21	39	.43287	.48019	2.0825	.90146	21
40	.41734	.45924	2.1775	.90875	20	40	.43313	.48055	2.0809	.90133	20
41	.41760	.45960	2.1758	.90863	19	41	.43340	.48091	2.0794	.90120	19
42	.41787	.45995	2.1742	.90851	18	42	.43366	.48127	2.0778	.90108	18
43	.41813	.46030	2.1725	.90839	17	43	.43392	.48163	2.0763	.90095	17
44	.41840	.46065	2.1708	.90826	16	44	.43418	.48198	2.0748	.90082	16
45	.41866	.46101	2.1692	.90814	15	45	.43445	.48234	2.0732	.90070	15
46	.41892	.46136	2.1675	.90802	14	46	.43471	.48270	2.0717	.90057	14
47	.41919	.46171	2.1659	.90790	13	47	.43497	.48306	2.0701	.90045	13
48	.41945	.46206	2.1642	.90778	12	48	.43523	.48342	2.0686	.90032	12
49	.41972	.46242	2.1625	.90766	11	49	.43549	.48378	2.0671	.90019	11
50	.41998	.46277	2.1609	.90753	10	50	.43575	.48414	2.0655	.90007	10
51	.42024	.46312	2.1592	.90741	9	51	.43602	.48450	2.0640	.89994	9
52	.42051	.46348	2.1576	.90729	8	52	.43628	.48486	2.0625	.89981	8
53	.42077	.46383	2.1560	.90717	7	53	.43654	.48521	2.0609	.89968	7
54	.42104	.46418	2.1543	.90704	6	54	.43680	.48557	2.0594	.89956	6
55	.42130	.46454	2.1527	.90692	5	55	.43706	.48593	2.0579	.89943	5
56	.42156	.46489	2.1510	.90680	4	56	.43733	.48629	2.0564	.89930	4
57	.42183	.46525	2.1494	.90668	3	57	.43759	.48665	2.0549	.89918	3
58	.42209	.46560	2.1478	.90655	2	58	.43785	.48701	2.0533	.89905	2
59	.42235	.46595	2.1461	.90643	1	59	.43811	.48737	2.0518	.89892	1
60	.42262	.46631	2.1445	.90631	0	60	.43837	.48773	2.0503	.89879	0
′	Cos	Ctn	Tan	Sin	′	′	Cos	Ctn	Tan	Sin	′

Table IV (Cont'd)

NATURAL TRIGONOMETRIC FUNCTIONS

26° (206°) (333°) **153°**   **27°** (207°) (332°) **152°**

′	Sin	Tan	Ctn	Cos	′	′	Sin	Tan	Ctn	Cos	′
0	.43837	.48773	2.0503	.89879	60	0	.45399	.50953	1.9626	.89101	60
1	.43863	.48809	2.0488	.89867	59	1	.45425	.50989	1.9612	.89087	59
2	.43889	.48845	2.0473	.89854	58	2	.45451	.51026	1.9598	.89074	58
3	.43916	.48881	2.0458	.89841	57	3	.45477	.51063	1.9584	.89061	57
4	.43942	.48917	2.0443	.89828	56	4	.45503	.51099	1.9570	.89048	56
5	.43968	.48953	2.0428	.89816	55	5	.45529	.51136	1.9556	.89035	55
6	.43994	.48989	2.0413	.89803	54	6	.45554	.51173	1.9542	.89021	54
7	.44020	.49026	2.0398	.89790	53	7	.45580	.51209	1.9528	.89008	53
8	.44046	.49062	2.0383	.89777	52	8	.45606	.51246	1.9514	.88995	52
9	.44072	.49098	2.0368	.89764	51	9	.45632	.51283	1.9500	.88981	51
10	.44098	.49134	2.0353	.89752	50	10	.45658	.51319	1.9486	.88968	50
11	.44124	.49170	2.0338	.89739	49	11	.45684	.51356	1.9472	.88955	49
12	.44151	.49206	2.0323	.89726	48	12	.45710	.51393	1.9458	.88942	48
13	.44177	.49242	2.0308	.89713	47	13	.45736	.51430	1.9444	.88928	47
14	.44203	.49278	2.0293	.89700	46	14	.45762	.51467	1.9430	.88915	46
15	.44229	.49315	2.0278	.89687	45	15	.45787	.51503	1.9416	.88902	45
16	.44255	.49351	2.0263	.89674	44	16	.45813	.51540	1.9402	.88888	44
17	.44281	.49387	2.0248	.89662	43	17	.45839	.51577	1.9388	.88875	43
18	.44307	.49423	2.0233	.89649	42	18	.45865	.51614	1.9375	.88862	42
19	.44333	.49459	2.0219	.89636	41	19	.45891	.51651	1.9361	.88848	41
20	.44359	.49495	2.0204	.89623	40	20	.45917	.51688	1.9347	.88835	40
21	.44385	.49532	2.0189	.89610	39	21	.45942	.51724	1.9333	.88822	39
22	.44411	.49568	2.0174	.89597	38	22	.45968	.51761	1.9319	.88808	38
23	.44437	.49604	2.0160	.89584	37	23	.45994	.51798	1.9306	.88795	37
24	.44464	.49640	2.0145	.89571	36	24	.46020	.51835	1.9292	.88782	36
25	.44490	.49677	2.0130	.89558	35	25	.46046	.51872	1.9278	.88768	35
26	.44516	.49713	2.0115	.89545	34	26	.46072	.51909	1.9265	.88755	34
27	.44542	.49749	2.0101	.89532	33	27	.46097	.51946	1.9251	.88741	33
28	.44568	.49786	2.0086	.89519	32	28	.46123	.51983	1.9237	.88728	32
29	.44594	.49822	2.0072	.89506	31	29	.46149	.52020	1.9223	.88715	31
30	.44620	.49858	2.0057	.89493	30	30	.46175	.52057	1.9210	.88701	30
31	.44646	.49894	2.0042	.89480	29	31	.46201	.52094	1.9196	.88688	29
32	.44672	.49931	2.0028	.89467	28	32	.46226	.52131	1.9183	.88674	28
33	.44698	.49967	2.0013	.89454	27	33	.46252	.52168	1.9169	.88661	27
34	.44724	.50004	1.9999	.89441	26	34	.46278	.52205	1.9155	.88647	26
35	.44750	.50040	1.9984	.89428	25	35	.46304	.52242	1.9142	.88634	25
36	.44776	.50076	1.9970	.89415	24	36	.46330	.52279	1.9128	.88620	24
37	.44802	.50113	1.9955	.89402	23	37	.46355	.52316	1.9115	.88607	23
38	.44828	.50149	1.9941	.89389	22	38	.46381	.52353	1.9101	.88593	22
39	.44854	.50185	1.9926	.89376	21	39	.46407	.52390	1.9088	.88580	21
40	.44880	.50222	1.9912	.89363	20	40	.46433	.52427	1.9074	.88566	20
41	.44906	.50258	1.9897	.89350	19	41	.46458	.52464	1.9061	.88553	19
42	.44932	.50295	1.9883	.89337	18	42	.46484	.52501	1.9047	.88539	18
43	.44958	.50331	1.9868	.89324	17	43	.46510	.52538	1.9034	.88526	17
44	.44984	.50368	1.9854	.89311	16	44	.46536	.52575	1.9020	.88512	16
45	.45010	.50404	1.9840	.89298	15	45	.46561	.52613	1.9007	.88499	15
46	.45036	.50441	1.9825	.89285	14	46	.46587	.52650	1.8993	.88485	14
47	.45062	.50477	1.9811	.89272	13	47	.46613	.52687	1.8980	.88472	13
48	.45088	.50514	1.9797	.89259	12	48	.46639	.52724	1.8967	.88458	12
49	.45114	.50550	1.9782	.89245	11	49	.46664	.52761	1.8953	.88445	11
50	.45140	.50587	1.9768	.89232	10	50	.46690	.52798	1.8940	.88431	10
51	.45166	.50623	1.9754	.89219	9	51	.46716	.52836	1.8927	.88417	9
52	.45192	.50660	1.9740	.89206	8	52	.46742	.52873	1.8913	.88404	8
53	.45218	.50696	1.9725	.89193	7	53	.46767	.52910	1.8900	.88390	7
54	.45243	.50733	1.9711	.89180	6	54	.46793	.52947	1.8887	.88377	6
55	.45269	.50769	1.9697	.89167	5	55	.46819	.52985	1.8873	.88363	5
56	.45295	.50806	1.9683	.89153	4	56	.46844	.53022	1.8860	.88349	4
57	.45321	.50843	1.9669	.89140	3	57	.46870	.53059	1.8847	.88336	3
58	.45347	.50879	1.9654	.89127	2	58	.46896	.53096	1.8834	.88322	2
59	.45373	.50916	1.9640	.89114	1	59	.46921	.53134	1.8820	.88308	1
60	.45399	.50953	1.9626	.89101	0	60	.46947	.53171	1.8807	.88295	0
′	Cos	Ctn	Tan	Sin	′	′	Cos	Ctn	Tan	Sin	′

116° (296°) (243°) **63°**   **117°** (297°) (242°) **62°**

Table IV (Cont'd)

NATURAL TRIGONOMETRIC FUNCTIONS

28° (208°)				(331°) 151°	29° (209°)				(330°) 150°
′	Sin	Tan	Ctn	Cos	′	′	Sin	Tan	Ctn	Cos	′

′	Sin	Tan	Ctn	Cos	′		′	Sin	Tan	Ctn	Cos	′
0	.46947	.53171	1.8807	.88295	60		0	.48481	.55431	1.8040	.87462	60
1	.46973	.53208	1.8794	.88281	59		1	.48506	.55469	1.8028	.87448	59
2	.46999	.53246	1.8781	.88267	58		2	.48532	.55507	1.8016	.87434	58
3	.47024	.53283	1.8768	.88254	57		3	.48557	.55545	1.8003	.87420	57
4	.47050	.53320	1.8755	.88240	56		4	.48583	.55583	1.7991	.87406	56
5	.47076	.53358	1.8741	.88226	55		5	.48608	.55621	1.7979	.87391	55
6	.47101	.53395	1.8728	.88213	54		6	.48634	.55659	1.7966	.87377	54
7	.47127	.53432	1.8715	.88199	53		7	.48659	.55697	1.7954	.87363	53
8	.47153	.53470	1.8702	.88185	52		8	.48684	.55736	1.7942	.87349	52
9	.47178	.53507	1.8689	.88172	51		9	.48710	.55774	1.7930	.87335	51
10	.47204	.53545	1.8676	.88158	50		10	.48735	.55812	1.7917	.87321	50
11	.47229	.53582	1.8663	.88144	49		11	.48761	.55850	1.7905	.87306	49
12	.47255	.53620	1.8650	.88130	48		12	.48786	.55888	1.7893	.87292	48
13	.47281	.53657	1.8637	.88117	47		13	.48811	.55926	1.7881	.87278	47
14	.47306	.53694	1.8624	.88103	46		14	.48837	.55964	1.7868	.87264	46
15	.47332	.53732	1.8611	.88089	45		15	.48862	.56003	1.7856	.87250	45
16	.47358	.53769	1.8598	.88075	44		16	.48888	.56041	1.7844	.87235	44
17	.47383	.53807	1.8585	.88062	43		17	.48913	.56079	1.7832	.87221	43
18	.47409	.53844	1.8572	.88048	42		18	.48938	.56117	1.7820	.87207	42
19	.47434	.53882	1.8559	.88034	41		19	.48964	.56156	1.7808	.87193	41
20	.47460	.53920	1.8546	.88020	40		20	.48989	.56194	1.7796	.87178	40
21	.47486	.53957	1.8533	.88006	39		21	.49014	.56232	1.7783	.87164	39
22	.47511	.53995	1.8520	.87993	38		22	.49040	.56270	1.7771	.87150	38
23	.47537	.54032	1.8507	.87979	37		23	.49065	.56309	1.7759	.87136	37
24	.47562	.54070	1.8495	.87965	36		24	.49090	.56347	1.7747	.87121	36
25	.47588	.54107	1.8482	.87951	35		25	.49116	.56385	1.7735	.87107	35
26	.47614	.54145	1.8469	.87937	34		26	.49141	.56424	1.7723	.87093	34
27	.47639	.54183	1.8456	.87923	33		27	.49166	.56462	1.7711	.87079	33
28	.47665	.54220	1.8443	.87909	32		28	.49192	.56501	1.7699	.87064	32
29	.47690	.54258	1.8430	.87896	31		29	.49217	.56539	1.7687	.87050	31
30	.47716	.54296	1.8418	.87882	30		30	.49242	.56577	1.7675	.87036	30
31	.47741	.54333	1.8405	.87868	29		31	.49268	.56616	1.7663	.87021	29
32	.47767	.54371	1.8392	.87840	28		32	.49293	.56654	1.7651	.87007	28
33	.47793	.54409	1.8379	.87840	27		33	.49318	.56693	1.7639	.86993	27
34	.47818	.54446	1.8367	.87826	26		34	.49344	.56731	1.7627	.86978	26
35	.47844	.54484	1.8354	.87812	25		35	.49369	.56769	1.7615	.86964	25
36	.47869	.54522	1.8341	.87798	24		36	.49394	.56808	1.7603	.86949	24
37	.47895	.54560	1.8329	.87784	23		37	.49419	.56846	1.7591	.86935	23
38	.47920	.54597	1.8316	.87770	22		38	.49445	.56885	1.7579	.86921	22
39	.47946	.54635	1.8303	.87756	21		39	.49470	.56923	1.7567	.86906	21
40	.47971	.54673	1.8291	.87743	20		40	.49495	.56962	1.7556	.86892	20
41	.47997	.54711	1.8278	.87729	19		41	.49521	.57000	1.7544	.86878	19
42	.48022	.54748	1.8265	.87715	18		42	.49546	.57039	1.7532	.86863	18
43	.48048	.54786	1.8253	.87701	17		43	.49571	.57078	1.7520	.86849	17
44	.48073	.54824	1.8240	.87687	16		44	.49596	.57116	1.7508	.86834	16
45	.48099	.54862	1.8228	.87673	15		45	.49622	.57155	1.7496	.86820	15
46	.48124	.54900	1.8215	.87659	14		46	.49647	.57193	1.7485	.86805	14
47	.48150	.54938	1.8202	.87645	13		47	.49672	.57232	1.7473	.86791	13
48	.48175	.54975	1.8190	.87631	12		48	.49697	.57271	1.7461	.86777	12
49	.48201	.55013	1.8177	.87617	11		49	.49723	.57309	1.7449	.86762	11
50	.48226	.55051	1.8165	.87603	10		50	.49748	.57348	1.7437	.86748	10
51	.48252	.55089	1.8152	.87589	9		51	.49773	.57386	1.7426	.86733	9
52	.48277	.55127	1.8140	.87575	8		52	.49798	.57425	1.7414	.86719	8
53	.48303	.55165	1.8127	.87561	7		53	.49824	.57464	1.7402	.86704	7
54	.48328	.55203	1.8115	.87546	6		54	.49849	.57503	1.7391	.86690	6
55	48354	55241	1 8103	87532	5		55	49874	57541	1 7379	86675	5
56	.48379	.55279	1.8090	.87518	4		56	.49899	.57580	1 7367	86661	4
57	.48405	.55317	1.8078	.87504	3		57	.49924	.57619	1.7355	.86646	3
58	.48430	.55355	1.8065	.87490	2		58	.49950	.57657	1.7344	.86632	2
59	.48456	.55393	1.8053	.87476	1		59	.49975	.57696	1.7332	.86617	1
60	.48481	.55431	1.8040	.87462	0		60	.50000	.57735	1.7321	.86603	0
′	Cos	Ctn	Tan	Sin	′		′	Cos	Ctn	Tan	Sin	′

Table IV (Cont'd)
NATURAL TRIGONOMETRIC FUNCTIONS

30° (210°)   **(329°) 149°**   **31° (211°)**   **(328°) 148°**

′	Sin	Tan	Ctn	Cos	′	′	Sin	Tan	Ctn	Cos	′
0	.50000	.57735	1.7321	.86603	60	0	.51504	.60086	1.6643	.85717	60
1	.50025	.57774	1.7309	.86588	59	1	.51529	.60126	1.6632	.85702	59
2	.50050	.57813	1.7297	.86573	58	2	.51554	.60165	1.6621	.85687	58
3	.50076	.57851	1.7286	.86559	57	3	.51579	.60205	1.6610	.85672	57
4	.50101	.57890	1.7274	.86544	56	4	.51604	.60245	1.6599	.85657	56
5	.50126	.57929	1.7262	.86530	55	5	.51628	.60284	1.6588	.85642	55
6	.50151	.57968	1.7251	.86515	54	6	.51653	.60324	1.6577	.85627	54
7	.50176	.58007	1.7239	.86501	53	7	.51678	.60364	1.6566	.85612	53
8	.50201	.58046	1.7228	.86486	52	8	.51703	.60403	1.6555	.85597	52
9	.50227	.58085	1.7216	.86471	51	9	.51728	.60443	1.6545	.85582	51
10	.50252	.58124	1.7205	.86457	50	10	.51753	.60483	1.6534	.85567	50
11	.50277	.58162	1.7193	.86442	49	11	.51778	.60522	1.6523	.85551	49
12	.50302	.48201	1.7182	.86427	48	12	.51803	.60562	1.6512	.85536	48
13	.50327	.58240	1.7170	.86413	47	13	.51828	.60602	1.6501	.85521	47
14	.50352	.58279	1.7159	.86398	46	14	.51852	.60642	1.6490	.85506	46
15	.50377	.58318	1.7147	.86384	45	15	.51877	.60681	1.6479	.85491	45
16	.50403	.58357	1.7136	.86369	44	16	.51902	.60721	1.6469	.85476	44
17	.50428	.58396	1.7124	.86354	43	17	.51927	.60761	1.6458	.85461	43
18	.50453	.58435	1.7113	.86340	42	18	.51952	.60801	1.6447	.85446	42
19	.50478	.58474	1.7102	.86325	41	19	.51977	.60841	1.6436	.85431	41
20	.50503	.58513	1.7090	.86310	40	20	.52002	.60881	1.6426	.85416	40
21	.50528	.58552	1.7079	.86295	39	21	.52026	.60921	1.6415	.85401	39
22	.50553	.58591	1.7067	.86281	38	22	.52051	.60960	1.6404	.85385	38
23	.50578	.58631	1.7056	.86266	37	23	.52076	.61000	1.6393	.85370	37
24	.50603	.58670	1.7045	.86251	36	24	.52101	.61040	1.6383	.85355	36
25	.50628	.58709	1.7033	.86237	35	25	.52126	.61080	1.6372	.85340	35
26	.50654	.58748	1.7022	.86222	34	26	.52151	.61120	1.6361	.85325	34
27	.50679	.58787	1.7011	.86207	33	27	.52175	.61160	1.6351	.85310	33
28	.50704	.58826	1.6999	.86192	32	28	.52200	.61200	1.6340	.85294	32
29	.50729	.58865	1.6988	.86178	31	29	.52225	.61240	1.6329	.85279	31
30	.50754	.58905	1.6977	.86163	30	30	.52250	.61280	1.6319	.85264	30
31	.50779	.58944	1.6965	.86148	29	31	.52275	.61320	1.6308	.85249	29
32	.50804	.58983	1.6954	.86133	28	32	.52299	.61360	1.6297	.85234	28
33	.50829	.59022	1.6943	.86119	27	33	.52324	.61400	1.6287	.85218	27
34	.50854	.59061	1.6932	.86104	26	34	.52349	.61440	1.6276	.85203	26
35	.50879	.59101	1.6920	.86089	25	35	.52374	.61480	1.6265	.85188	25
36	.50904	.59140	1.6909	.86074	24	36	.52399	.61520	1.6255	.85173	24
37	.50929	.59179	1.6898	.86059	23	37	.52423	.61561	1.6244	.85157	23
38	.50954	.59218	1.6887	.86045	22	38	.52448	.61601	1.6234	.85142	22
39	.50979	.59258	1.6875	.86030	21	39	.52473	.61641	1.6223	.85127	21
40	.51004	.59297	1.6864	.86015	20	40	.52498	.61681	1.6212	.85112	20
41	.51029	.59336	1.6853	.86000	19	41	.52522	.61721	1.6202	.85096	19
42	.51054	.59376	1.6842	.85985	18	42	.52547	.61761	1.6191	.85081	18
43	.51079	.59415	1.6831	.85970	17	43	.52572	.61801	1.6181	.85066	17
44	.51104	.59454	1.6820	.85956	16	44	.52597	.61842	1.6170	.85051	16
45	.51129	.59494	1.6808	.85941	15	45	.52621	.61882	1.6160	.85035	15
46	.51154	.59533	1.6797	.85926	14	46	.52646	.61922	1.6149	.85020	14
47	.51179	.59573	1.6786	.85911	13	47	.52671	.61962	1.6139	.85005	13
48	.51204	.59612	1.6775	.85896	12	48	.52696	.62003	1.6128	.84989	12
49	.51229	.59651	1.6764	.85881	11	49	.52720	.62043	1.6118	.84974	11
50	.51254	.59691	1.6753	.85866	10	50	.52745	.62083	1.6107	.84959	10
51	.51279	.59730	1.6742	.85851	9	51	.52770	.62124	1.6097	.84943	9
52	.51304	.59770	1.6731	.85836	8	52	.52794	.62164	1.6087	.84928	8
53	.51329	.59809	1.6720	.85821	7	53	.52819	.62204	1.6076	.84913	7
54	.51354	.59849	1.6709	.85806	6	54	.52844	.62245	1.6066	.84897	6
55	.51379	.59888	1.6698	.85792	5	55	.52869	.62285	1.6055	.84882	5
56	.51404	.59928	1.6687	.85777	4	56	.52893	.62325	1.6045	.84866	4
57	.51429	.59967	1.6676	.85762	3	57	.52918	.62366	1.6034	.84851	3
58	.51454	.60007	1.6665	.85747	2	58	.52943	.62406	1.6024	.84836	2
59	.51479	.60046	1.6654	.85732	1	59	.52967	.62446	1.6014	.84820	1
60	.51504	.60086	1.6643	.85717	0	60	.52992	.62487	1.6003	.84805	0
′	Cos	Ctn	Tan	Sin	′	′	Cos	Ctn	Tan	Sin	′

120° (300°)   **(239°) 59°**   **121° (301°)**   **(238°) 58°**

Table IV (Cont'd)

NATURAL TRIGONOMETRIC FUNCTIONS

32° (212°)				(327°) 147°
′	Sin	Tan	Ctn	Cos	′

′	Sin	Tan	Ctn	Cos	′		′	Sin	Tan	Ctn	Cos	′
0	.52992	.62487	1.6003	.84805	60		0	.54464	.64941	1.5399	.83867	60
1	.53017	.62527	1.5993	.84789	59		1	.54488	.64982	1.5389	.83851	59
2	.53041	.62568	1.5983	.84774	58		2	.54513	.65024	1.5379	.83835	58
3	.53066	.62608	1.5972	.84759	57		3	.54537	.65065	1.5369	.83819	57
4	.53091	.62649	1.5962	.84743	56		4	.54561	.65106	1.5359	.83804	56
5	.53115	.62689	1.5952	.84728	55		5	.54586	.65148	1.5350	.83788	55
6	.53140	.62730	1.5941	.84712	54		6	.54610	.65189	1.5340	.83772	54
7	.53164	.62770	1.5931	.84697	53		7	.54635	.65231	1.5330	.83756	53
8	.53189	.62811	1.5921	.84681	52		8	.54659	.65272	1.5320	.83740	52
9	.53214	.62852	1.5911	.84666	51		9	.54683	.65314	1.5311	.83724	51
10	.53238	.62892	1.5900	.84650	50		10	.54708	.65355	1.5301	.83708	50
11	.53263	.62933	1.5890	.84635	49		11	.54732	.65397	1.5291	.83692	49
12	.53288	.62973	1.5880	.84619	48		12	.54756	.65438	1.5282	.83676	48
13	.53312	.63014	1.5869	.84604	47		13	.54781	.65480	1.5272	.83660	47
14	.53337	.63055	1.5859	.84588	46		14	.54805	.65521	1.5262	.83645	46
15	.53361	.63095	1.5849	.84573	45		15	.54829	.65563	1.5253	.83629	45
16	.53386	.63136	1.5839	.84557	44		16	.54854	.65604	1.5243	.83613	44
17	.53411	.63177	1.5829	.84542	43		17	.54878	.65646	1.5233	.83597	43
18	.53435	.63217	1.5818	.84526	42		18	.54902	.65688	1.5224	.83581	42
19	.53460	.63258	1.5808	.84511	41		19	.54927	.65729	1.5214	.83565	41
20	.53484	.63299	1.5798	.84495	40		20	.54951	.65771	1.5204	.83549	40
21	.53509	.63340	1.5788	.84480	39		21	.54975	.65813	1.5195	.83533	39
22	.53534	.63380	1.5778	.84464	38		22	.54999	.65854	1.5185	.83517	38
23	.53558	.63421	1.5768	.84448	37		23	.55024	.65896	1.5175	.83501	37
24	.53583	.63462	1.5757	.84433	36		24	.55048	.65938	1.5166	.83485	36
25	.53607	.63503	1.5747	.84417	35		25	.55072	.65980	1.5156	.83469	35
26	.53632	.63544	1.5737	.84402	34		26	.55097	.66021	1.5147	.83453	34
27	.53656	.63584	1.5727	.84386	33		27	.55121	.66063	1.5137	.83437	33
28	.53681	.63625	1.5717	.84370	32		28	.55145	.66105	1.5127	.83421	32
29	.53705	.63666	1.5707	.84355	31		29	.55169	.66147	1.5118	.83405	31
30	.53730	.63707	1.5697	.84339	30		30	.55194	.66189	1.5108	.83389	30
31	.53754	.63748	1.5687	.84324	29		31	.55218	.66230	1.5099	.83373	29
32	.53779	.63789	1.5677	.84308	28		32	.55242	.66272	1.5089	.83356	28
33	.53804	.63830	1.5667	.84292	27		33	.55266	.66314	1.5080	.83340	27
34	.53828	.63871	1.5657	.84277	26		34	.55291	.66356	1.5070	.83324	26
35	.53853	.63912	1.5647	.84261	25		35	.55315	.66398	1.5061	.83308	25
36	.53877	.63953	1.5637	.84245	24		36	.55339	.66440	1.5051	.83292	24
37	.53902	.63994	1.5627	.84230	23		37	.55363	.66482	1.5042	.83276	23
38	.53926	.64035	1.5617	.84214	22		38	.55388	.66524	1.5032	.83260	22
39	.53951	.64076	1.5607	.84198	21		39	.55412	.66566	1.5023	.83244	21
40	.53975	.64117	1.5597	.84182	20		40	.55436	.66608	1.5013	.83228	20
41	.54000	.64158	1.5587	.84167	19		41	.55460	.66650	1.5004	.83212	19
42	.54024	.64199	1.5577	.84151	18		42	.55484	.66692	1.4994	.83195	18
43	.54049	.64240	1.5567	.84135	17		43	.55509	.66734	1.4985	.83179	17
44	.54073	.64281	1.5557	.84120	16		44	.55533	.66776	1.4975	.83163	16
45	.54097	.64322	1.5547	.84104	15		45	.55557	.66818	1.4966	.83147	15
46	.54122	.64363	1.5537	.84088	14		46	.55581	.66860	1.4957	.83131	14
47	.54146	.64404	1.5527	.84072	13		47	.55605	.66902	1.4947	.83115	13
48	.54171	.64446	1.5517	.84057	12		48	.55630	.66944	1.4938	.83098	12
49	.54195	.64487	1.5507	.84041	11		49	.55654	.66986	1.4928	.83082	11
50	.54220	.64528	1.5497	.84025	10		50	.55678	.67028	1.4919	.83066	10
51	.54244	.64569	1.5487	.84009	9		51	.55702	.67071	1.4910	.83050	9
52	.54269	.64610	1.5477	.83994	8		52	.55726	.67113	1.4900	.83034	8
53	.54293	.64652	1.5468	.83978	7		53	.55750	.67155	1.4891	.83017	7
54	.54317	.64693	1.5458	.83962	6		54	.55775	.67197	1.4882	.83001	6
55	.54342	.64734	1.5448	.83946	5		55	.55799	.67239	1.4872	82985	5
56	.54366	.64775	1.5438	.83930	4		56	.55823	.67282	1.4863	.82969	4
57	.54391	.64817	1.5428	.83915	3		57	.55847	.67324	1.4854	.82953	3
58	.54415	.64858	1.5418	.83899	2		58	.55871	.67366	1.4844	.82936	2
59	.54440	.64899	1.5408	.83883	1		59	.55895	.67409	1.4835	.82920	1
60	.54464	.64941	1.5399	.83867	0		60	.55919	.67451	1.4826	.82904	0
′	Cos	Ctn	Tan	Sin	′		′	Cos	Ctn	Tan	Sin	′

Table IV (Cont'd)

NATURAL TRIGONOMETRIC FUNCTIONS

34° (214°)   (325°) **145°**   **35° (215°)**   (324°) **144°**

′	Sin	Tan	Ctn	Cos	′		′	Sin	Tan	Ctn	Cos	′
0	.55919	.67451	1.4826	.82904	60		0	.57358	.70021	1.4281	.81915	60
1	.55943	.67493	1.4816	.82887	59		1	.57381	.70064	1.4273	.81899	59
2	.55968	.67536	1.4807	.82871	58		2	.57405	.70107	1.4264	.81882	58
3	.55992	.67578	1.4798	.82855	57		3	.57429	.70151	1.4255	.81865	57
4	.56016	.67620	1.4788	.82839	56		4	.57453	.70194	1.4246	.81848	56
5	.56040	.67663	1.4779	.82822	55		5	.57477	.70238	1.4237	.81832	55
6	.56064	.67705	1.4770	.82806	54		6	.57501	.70281	1.4229	.81815	54
7	.56088	.67748	1.4761	.82790	53		7	.57524	.70325	1.4220	.81798	53
8	.56112	.67790	1.4751	.82773	52		8	.57548	.70368	1.4211	.81782	52
9	.56136	.67832	1.4742	.82757	51		9	.57572	.70412	1.4202	.81765	51
10	.56160	.67875	1.4733	.82741	50		10	.57596	.70455	1.4193	.81748	50
11	.56184	.67917	1.4724	.82724	49		11	.57619	.70499	1.4185	.81731	49
12	.56208	.67960	1.4715	.82708	48		12	.57643	.70542	1.4176	.81714	48
13	.56232	.68002	1.4705	.82692	47		13	.57667	.70586	1.4167	.81698	47
14	.56256	.68045	1.4696	.82675	46		14	.57691	.70629	1.4158	.81681	46
15	.56280	.68088	1.4687	.82659	45		15	.57715	.70673	1.4150	.81664	45
16	.56305	.68130	1.4678	.82643	44		16	.57738	.70717	1.4141	.81647	44
17	.56329	.68173	1.4669	.82626	43		17	.57762	.70760	1.4132	.81631	43
18	.56353	.68215	1.4659	.82610	42		18	.57786	.70804	1.4124	.81614	42
19	.56377	.68258	1.4650	.82593	41		19	.57810	.70848	1.4115	.81597	41
20	.56401	.68301	1.4641	.82577	40		20	.57833	.70891	1.4106	.81580	40
21	.56425	.68343	1.4632	.82561	39		21	.57857	.70935	1.4097	.81563	39
22	.56449	.68386	1.4623	.82544	38		22	.57881	.70979	1.4089	.81546	38
23	.56473	.68429	1.4614	.82528	37		23	.57904	.71023	1.4080	.81530	37
24	.56497	.68471	1.4605	.82511	36		24	.57928	.71066	1.4071	.81513	36
25	.56521	.68514	1.4596	.82495	35		25	.57952	.71110	1.4063	.81496	35
26	.56545	.68557	1.4586	.82478	34		26	.57976	.71154	1.4054	.81479	34
27	.56569	.68600	1.4577	.82462	33		27	.57999	.71198	1.4045	.81462	33
28	.56593	.68642	1.4568	.82446	32		28	.58023	.71242	1.4037	.81445	32
29	.56617	.68685	1.4559	.82429	31		29	.58047	.71285	1.4028	.81428	31
30	.56641	.68728	1.4550	.82413	30		30	.58070	.71329	1.4019	.81412	30
31	.56665	.68771	1.4541	.82396	29		31	.58094	.71373	1.4011	.81395	29
32	.56689	.68814	1.4532	.82380	28		32	.58118	.71417	1.4002	.81378	28
33	.56713	.68857	1.4523	.82363	27		33	.58141	.71461	1.3994	.81361	27
34	.56736	.68900	1.4514	.82347	26		34	.58165	.71505	1.3985	.81344	26
35	.56760	.68942	1.4505	.82330	25		35	.58189	.71549	1.3976	.81327	25
36	.56784	.68985	1.4496	.82314	24		36	.58212	.71593	1.3968	.81310	24
37	.56808	.69028	1.4487	.82297	23		37	.58236	.71637	1.3959	.81293	23
38	.56832	.69071	1.4478	.82281	22		38	.58260	.71681	1.3951	.81276	22
39	.56856	.69114	1.4469	.82264	21		39	.58283	.71725	1.3942	.81259	21
40	.56880	.69157	1.4460	.82248	20		40	.58307	.71769	1.3934	.81242	20
41	.56904	.69200	1.4451	.82231	19		41	.58330	.71813	1.3925	.81225	19
42	.56928	.69243	1.4442	.82214	18		42	.58354	.71857	1.3916	.81208	18
43	.56952	.69286	1.4433	.82198	17		43	.58378	.71901	1.3908	.81191	17
44	.56976	.69329	1.4424	.82181	16		44	.58401	.71946	1.3899	.81174	16
45	.57000	.69372	1.4415	.82165	15		45	.58425	.71990	1.3891	.81157	15
46	.57024	.69416	1.4406	.82148	14		46	.58449	.72034	1.3882	.81140	14
47	.57047	.69459	1.4397	.82132	13		47	.58472	.72078	1.3874	.81123	13
48	.57071	.69502	1.4388	.82115	12		48	.58496	.72122	1.3865	.81106	12
49	.57095	.69545	1.4379	.82098	11		49	.58519	.72167	1.3857	.81089	11
50	.57119	.69588	1.4370	.82082	10		50	.58543	.72211	1.3848	.81072	10
51	.57143	.69631	1.4361	.82065	9		51	.58567	.72255	1.3840	.81055	9
52	.57167	.69675	1.4352	.82048	8		52	.58590	.72299	1.3831	.81038	8
53	.57191	.69718	1.4344	.82032	7		53	.58614	.72344	1.3823	.81021	7
54	.57215	.69761	1.4335	.82015	6		54	.58637	.72388	1.3814	.81004	6
55	.57238	.69804	1.4326	.81999	5		55	.58661	.72432	1.3806	.80987	5
56	.47262	.69847	1.4317	.81982	4		56	.58684	.72477	1.3798	.80970	4
57	.57286	.69891	1.4308	.81965	3		57	.58708	.72521	1.3789	.80953	3
58	.57310	.69934	1.4299	.81949	2		58	.58731	.72565	1.3781	.80936	2
59	.57334	.69977	1.4290	.81932	1		59	.58755	.72610	1.3772	.80919	1
60	.57358	.70021	1.4281	.81915	0		60	.58779	.72654	1.3764	.80902	0
′	Cos	Ctn	Tan	Sin	′		′	Cos	Ctn	Tan	Sin	′

124° (304°)   (235°) **55°**   **125° (305°)**   (234°) **54°**

Table IV (Cont'd)
NATURAL TRIGONOMETRIC FUNCTIONS

36° (216°)   (323°) **143°**   **37°** (217°)   (322°) **142°**

′	Sin	Tan	Ctn	Cos	′		′	Sin	Tan	Ctn	Cos	′
0	.58779	.72654	1.3764	.80902	60		0	.60182	.75355	1.3270	.79864	60
1	.58802	.72699	1.3755	.80885	59		1	.60205	.75401	1.3262	.79846	59
2	.58826	.72743	1.3747	.80867	58		2	.60228	.75447	1.3254	.79829	58
3	.58849	.72788	1.3739	.80850	57		3	.60251	.75492	1.3246	.79811	·57
4	.58873	.72832	1.3730	.80833	56		4	.60274	.75538	1.3238	.79793	56
5	.58896	.72877	1.3722	.80816	55		5	.60298	.75584	1.3230	.79776	55
6	.58920	.72921	1.3713	.80799	54		6	.60321	.75629	1.3222	.79758	54
7	.58943	.72966	1.3705	.80782	53		7	.60344	.75675	1.3214	.79741	53
8	.58967	.73010	1.3697	.80765	52		8	.60367	.75721	1.3206	.79723	52
9	.58990	.73055	1.3688	.80748	51		9	.60390	.75767	1.3198	.79706	51
10	.59014	.73100	1.3680	.80730	50		10	.60414	.75812	1.3190	.79688	50
11	.59037	.73144	1.3672	.80713	49		11	.60437	.75858	1.3182	.79671	49
12	.59061	.73189	1.3663	.80696	48		12	.60460	.75904	1.3175	.79653	48
13	.59084	.73234	1.3655	.80679	47		13	.60483	.75950	1.3167	.79635	47
14	.59108	.73278	1.3647	.80662	46		14	.60506	.75996	1.3159	.79618	46
15	.59131	.73323	1.3638	.80644	45		15	.60529	.76042	1.3151	.79600	45
16	.59154	.73368	1.3630	.80627	44		16	.60553	.76088	1.3143	.79583	44
17	.59178	.73413	1.3622	.80610	43		17	.60576	.76134	1.3135	.79565	43
18	.59201	.73457	1.3613	.80593	42		18	.60599	.76180	1.3127	.79547	42
19	.59225	.73502	1.3605	.80576	41		19	.60622	.76226	1.3119	.79530	41
20	.59248	.73547	1.3597	.80558	40		20	.60645	.76272	1.3111	.79512	40
21	.59272	.73592	1.3588	.80541	39		21	.60668	.76318	1.3103	.79494	39
22	.59295	.73637	1.3580	.80524	38		22	.60691	.76364	1.3095	.79477	38
23	.59318	.73681	1.3572	.80507	37		23	.60714	.76410	1.3087	.79459	37
24	.59342	.73726	1.3564	.80489	36		24	.60738	.76456	1.3079	.79441	36
25	.59365	.73771	1.3555	.80472	35		25	.60761	.76502	1.3072	.79424	35
26	.59389	.73816	1.3547	.80455	34		26	.60784	.76548	1.3064	.79406	34
27	.59412	.73861	1.3539	.80438	33		27	.60807	.76594	1.3056	.79388	33
28	.59436	.73906	1.3531	.80420	32		28	.60830	.76640	1.3048	.79371	32
29	.59459	.73951	1.3522	.80403	31		29	.60853	.76686	1.3040	.79353	31
30	.59482	.73996	1.3514	.80386	30		30	.60876	.76733	1.3032	.79335	30
31	.59506	.74041	1.3506	.80368	29		31	.60899	.76779	1.3024	.79318	29
32	.59529	.74086	1.3498	.80351	28		32	.60922	.76825	1.3017	.79300	28
33	.59552	.74131	1.3490	.80334	27		33	.60945	.76871	1.3009	.79282	27
34	.59576	.74176	1.3481	.80316	26		34	.60968	.76918	1.3001	.79264	26
35	.59599	.74221	1.3473	.80299	25		35	.60991	.76964	1.2993	.79247	25
36	.59622	.74267	1.3465	.80282	24		36	.61015	.77010	1.2985	.79229	24
37	.59646	.74312	1.3457	.80264	23		37	.61038	.77057	1.2977	.79211	23
38	.59669	.74357	1.3449	.80247	22		38	.61061	.77103	1.2970	.79193	22
39	.59693	.74402	1.3440	.80230	21		39	.61084	.77149	1.2962	.79176	21
40	.59716	.74447	1.3432	.80212	20		40	.61107	.77196	1.2954	.79158	20
41	.59739	.74492	1.3424	.80195	19		41	.61130	.77242	1.2946	.79140	19
42	.59763	.74538	1.3416	.80178	18		42	.61153	.77289	1.2938	.79122	18
43	.59786	.74583	1.3408	.80160	17		43	.61176	.77335	1.2931	.79105	17
44	.59809	.74628	1.3400	.80143	16		44	.61199	.77382	1.2923	.79087	16
45	.59832	.74674	1.3392	.80125	15		45	.61222	.77428	1.2915	.79069	15
46	.59856	.74719	1.3384	.80108	14		46	.61245	.77475	1.2907	.79051	14
47	.59879	.74764	1.3375	.80091	13		47	.61268	.77521	1.2900	.79033	13
48	.59902	.74810	1.3367	.80073	12		48	.61291	.77568	1.2892	.79016	12
49	.59926	.74855	1.3359	.80056	11		49	.61314	.77615	1.2884	.78998	11
50	.59949	.74900	1.3351	.80038	10		50	.61337	.77661	1.2876	.78980	10
51	.59972	.74946	1.3343	.80021	9		51	.61360	.77708	1.2869	.78962	9
52	.59995	.74991	1.3335	.80003	8		52	.61383	.77754	1.2861	.78944	8
53	.60019	.75037	1.3327	.79986	7		53	.61406	.77801	1.2853	.78926	7
54	.60042	.75082	1.3319	.79968	6		54	.61429	.77848	1.2846	.78908	6
55	.60065	.75128	1.3311	.79951	5		55	.61451	.77895	1.2838	.78891	5
56	.60089	.75173	1.3303	.79934	4		56	.61474	.77941	1.2830	.78873	4
57	.60112	.75219	1.3295	.79916	3		57	.61497	.77988	1.2822	.78855	3
58	.60135	.75264	1.3287	.79899	2		58	.61520	.78035	1.2815	.78837	2
59	.60158	.75310	1.3278	.79881	1		59	.61543	.78082	1.2807	.78819	1
60	.60182	.75355	1.3270	.79864	0		60	.61566	.78129	1.2799	.78801	0
′	Cos	Ctn	Tan	Sin	′		′	Cos	Ctn	Tan	Sin	′

126° (306°)   (233°) **53°**   **127°** (307°)   (232°) **52°**

Table IV (Cont'd)

NATURAL TRIGONOMETRIC FUNCTIONS

38° (218°)   (321°) **141°**   **39° (219°)**   (320°) **140°**

′	Sin	Tan	Ctn	Cos	′		′	Sin	Tan	Ctn	Cos	′
0	.61566	.78129	1.2799	.78801	60		0	.62932	.80978	1.2349	.77715	60
1	.61589	.78175	1.2792	.78783	59		1	.62955	.81027	1.2342	.77696	59
2	.61612	.78222	1.2784	.78765	58		2	.62977	.81075	1.2334	.77678	58
3	.61635	.78269	1.2776	.78747	57		3	.63000	.81123	1.2327	.77660	57
4	.61658	.78316	1.2769	.78729	56		4	.63022	.81171	1.2320	.77641	56
5	.61681	.78363	1.2761	.78711	55		5	.63045	.81220	1.2312	.77623	55
6	.61704	.78410	1.2753	.78694	54		6	.63068	.81268	1.2305	.77605	54
7	.61726	.78457	1.2746	.78676	53		7	.63090	.81316	1.2298	.77586	53
8	.61749	.78504	1.2738	.78658	52		8	.63113	.81364	1.2290	.77568	52
9	.61772	.78551	1.2731	.78640	51		9	.63135	.81413	1.2283	.77550	51
10	.61795	.78598	1.2723	.78622	50		10	.63158	.81461	1.2276	.77531	50
11	.61818	.78645	1.2715	.78604	49		11	.63180	.81510	1.2268	.77513	49
12	.61841	.78692	1.2708	.78586	48		12	.63203	.81558	1.2261	.77494	48
13	.61864	.78739	1.2700	.78568	47		13	.63225	.81606	1.2254	.77476	47
14	.61887	.78786	1.2693	.78550	46		14	.63248	.81655	1.2247	.77458	46
15	.61909	.78834	1.2685	.78532	45		15	.63271	.81703	1.2239	.77439	45
16	.61932	.78881	1.2677	.78514	44		16	.63293	.81752	1.2232	.77421	44
17	.61955	.78928	1.2670	.78496	43		17	.63316	.81800	1.2225	.77402	43
18	.61978	.78975	1.2662	.78478	42		18	.63338	.81849	1.2218	.77384	42
19	.62001	.79022	1.2655	.78460	41		19	.63361	.81898	1.2210	.77366	41
20	.62024	.79070	1.2647	.78442	40		20	.63383	.81946	1.2203	.77347	40
21	.62046	.79117	1.2640	.78424	39		21	.63406	.81995	1.2196	.77329	39
22	.62069	.79164	1.2632	.78405	38		22	.63428	.82044	1.2189	.77310	38
23	.62092	.79212	1.2624	.78387	37		23	.63451	.82092	1.2181	.77292	37
24	.62115	.79259	1.2617	.78369	36		24	.63473	.82141	1.2174	.77273	36
25	.62138	.79306	1.2609	.78351	35		25	.63496	.82190	1.2167	.77255	35
26	.62160	.79354	1.2602	.78333	34		26	.63518	.82238	1.2160	.77236	34
27	.62183	.79401	1.2594	.78315	33		27	.63540	.82287	1.2153	.77218	33
28	.62206	.79449	1.2587	.78297	32		28	.63563	.82336	1.2145	.77199	32
29	.62229	.79496	1.2579	.78279	31		29	.63585	.82385	1.2138	.77181	31
30	.62251	.79544	1.2572	.78261	30		30	.63608	.82434	1.2131	.77162	30
31	.62274	.79591	1.2564	.78243	29		31	.63630	.82483	1.2124	.77144	29
32	.62297	.79639	1.2557	.78225	28		32	.63653	.82531	1.2117	.77125	28
33	.62320	.79686	1.2549	.78206	27		33	.63675	.82580	1.2109	.77107	27
34	.62342	.79734	1.2542	.78188	26		34	.63698	.82629	1.2102	.77088	26
35	.62365	.79781	1.2534	.78170	25		35	.63720	.82678	1.2095	.77070	25
36	.62388	.79829	1.2527	.78152	24		36	.63742	.82727	1.2088	.77051	24
37	.62411	.79877	1.2519	.78134	23		37	.63765	.82776	1.2081	.77033	23
38	.62433	.79924	1.2512	.78116	22		38	.63787	.82825	1.2074	.77014	22
39	.62456	.79972	1.2504	.78098	21		39	.63810	.82874	1.2066	.76996	21
40	.62479	.80020	1.2497	.78079	20		40	.63832	.82923	1.2059	.76977	20
41	.62502	.80067	1.2489	.78061	19		41	.63854	.82972	1.2052	.76959	19
42	.62524	.80115	1.2482	.78043	18		42	.63877	.83022	1.2045	.76940	18
43	.62547	.80163	1.2475	.78025	17		43	.63899	.83071	1.2038	.76921	17
44	.62570	.80211	1.2467	.78007	16		44	.63922	.83120	1.2031	.76903	16
45	.62592	.80258	1.2460	.77988	15		45	.63944	.83169	1.2024	.76884	15
46	.62615	.80306	1.2452	.77970	14		46	.63966	.83218	1.2017	.76866	14
47	.62638	.80354	1.2445	.77952	13		47	.63989	.83268	1.2009	.76847	13
48	.62660	.80402	1.2437	.77934	12		48	.64011	.83317	1.2002	.76828	12
49	.62683	.80450	1.2430	.77916	11		49	.64033	.83366	1.1995	.76810	11
50	.62706	.80498	1.2423	.77897	10		50	.64056	.83415	1.1988	.76791	10
51	.62728	.80546	1.2415	.77879	9		51	.64078	.83465	1.1981	.76772	9
52	.62751	.80594	1.2408	.77861	8		52	.64100	.83514	1.1974	.76754	8
53	.62774	.80642	1.2401	.77843	7		53	.64123	.83564	1.1967	.76735	7
54	.62796	.80690	1.2393	.77824	6		54	.64145	.83613	1.1960	.76717	6
55	.62819	.80738	1.2386	.77806	5		55	.64167	.83662	1.1953	.76698	5
56	.62842	.80786	1.2378	.77788	4		56	.64190	.83712	1.1946	.76679	4
57	.62864	.80834	1.2371	.77769	3		57	.64212	.83761	1.1939	.76661	3
58	.62887	.80882	1.2364	.77751	2		58	.64234	.83811	1.1932	.76642	2
59	.62909	.80930	1.2356	.77733	1		59	.64256	.83860	1.1925	.76623	1
60	.62932	.80978	1.2349	.77715	0		60	.64279	.83910	1.1918	.76604	0
′	Cos	Ctn	Tan	Sin	′		′	Cos	Ctn	Tan	Sin	′

128° (308°)   (231°) **51°**   **129° (309°)**   (230°) **50°**

Table IV (Cont'd)

NATURAL TRIGONOMETRIC FUNCTIONS

40° (220°)   (319°) **139°**   **41° (221°)**   (318°) **138°**

′	Sin	Tan	Ctn	Cos	′	′	Sin	Tan	Ctn	Cos	′
0	.64279	.83910	1.1918	.76604	60	0	.65606	.86929	1.1504	.75471	60
1	.64301	.83960	1.1910	.76586	59	1	.65628	.86980	1.1497	.75452	59
2	.64323	.84009	1.1903	.76567	58	2	.65650	.87031	1.1490	.75433	58
3	.64346	.84059	1.1896	.76548	57	3	.65672	.87082	1.1483	.75414	57
4	.64368	.84108	1.1889	.76530	56	4	.65694	.87133	1.1477	.75395	56
5	.64390	.84158	1.1882	.76511	55	5	.65716	.87184	1.1470	.75375	55
6	.64412	.84208	1.1875	.76492	54	6	.65738	.87236	1.1463	.75356	54
7	.64435	.84258	1.1868	.76473	53	7	.65759	.87287	1.1456	.75337	53
8	.64457	.84307	1.1861	.76455	52	8	.65781	.87338	1.1450	.75318	52
9	.64479	.84357	1.1854	.76436	51	9	.65803	.87389	1.1443	.75299	51
10	.64501	.84407	1.1847	.76417	50	10	.65825	.87441	1.1436	.75280	50
11	.64524	.84457	1.1840	.76398	49	11	.65847	.87492	1.1430	.75261	49
12	.64546	.84507	1.1833	.76380	48	12	.65869	.87543	1.1423	.75241	48
13	.64568	.84556	1.1826	.76361	47	13	.65891	.87595	1.1416	.75222	47
14	.64590	.84606	1.1819	.76342	46	14	.65913	.87646	1.1410	.75203	46
15	.64612	.84656	1.1812	.76323	45	15	.65935	.87698	1.1403	.75184	45
16	.64635	.84706	1.1806	.76304	44	16	.65956	.87749	1.1396	.75165	44
17	.64657	.84756	1.1799	.76286	43	17	.65978	.87801	1.1389	.75146	43
18	.64679	.84806	1.1792	.76267	42	18	.66000	.87852	1.1383	.75126	42
19	.64701	.84856	1.1785	.76248	41	19	.66022	.87904	1.1376	.75107	41
20	.64723	.84906	1.1778	.76229	40	20	.66044	.87955	1.1369	.75088	40
21	.64746	.84956	1.1771	.76210	39	21	.66066	.88007	1.1363	.75069	39
22	.64768	.85006	1.1764	.76192	38	22	.66088	.88059	1.1356	.75050	38
23	.64790	.85057	1.1757	.76173	37	23	.66109	.88110	1.1349	.75030	37
24	.64812	.85107	1.1750	.76154	36	24	.66131	.88162	1.1343	.75011	36
25	.64834	.85157	1.1743	.76135	35	25	.66153	.88214	1.1336	.74992	35
26	.64856	.85207	1.1736	.76116	34	26	.66175	.88265	1.1329	74973	34
27	.64878	.85257	1.1729	.76097	33	27	.66197	.88317	1.1323	.74953	33
28	.64901	.85308	1.1722	.76078	32	28	.66218	.88369	1.1316	.74934	32
29	.64923	.85358	1.1715	.76059	31	29	.66240	.88421	1.1310	.74915	31
30	.64945	.85408	1.1708	.76041	30	30	.66262	.88473	1.1303	.74896	30
31	.64967	.85458	1.1702	.76022	29	31	.66284	.88524	1.1296	.74876	29
32	.64989	.85509	1.1695	.76003	28	32	.66306	.88576	1.1290	.74857	28
33	.65011	.85559	1.1688	.75984	27	33	.66327	.88628	1.1283	.74838	27
34	.65033	.85609	1.1681	.75965	26	34	.66349	.88680	1.1276	.74818	26
35	.65055	.85660	1.1674	.75946	25	35	.66371	.88732	1.1270	.74799	25
36	.65077	.85710	1.1667	.75927	24	36	.66393	.88784	1.1263	.74780	24
37	.65100	.85761	1.1660	.75908	23	37	.66414	.88836	1.1257	.74760	23
38	.65122	.85811	1.1653	.75889	22	38	.66436	.88888	1.1250	.74741	22
39	.65144	.85862	1.1647	.75870	21	39	.66458	.88940	1.1243	.74722	21
40	.65166	.85912	1.1640	.75851	20	40	.66480	.88992	1.1237	.74703	20
41	.65188	.85963	1.1633	.75832	19	41	.66501	.89045	1.1230	.74683	19
42	.65210	.86014	1.1626	.75813	18	42	.66523	.89097	1.1224	.74664	18
43	.65232	.86064	1.1619	.75794	17	43	.66545	.89149	1.1217	.74644	17
44	.65254	.86115	1.1612	.75775	16	44	.66566	.89201	1.1211	.74625	16
45	.65276	.86166	1.1606	.75756	15	45	.66588	.89253	1.1204	.74606	15
46	.65298	.86216	1.1599	.75738	14	46	.66610	.89306	1.1197	.74586	14
47	.65320	.86267	1.1592	.75719	13	47	.66632	.89358	1.1191	.74567	13
48	.65342	.86318	1.1585	.75700	12	48	.66653	.89410	1.1184	.74548	12
49	.65364	.86368	1.1578	.75680	11	49	.66675	.89463	1.1178	.74528	11
50	.65386	.86419	1.1571	.75661	10	50	.66697	.89515	1.1171	.74509	10
51	.65408	.86470	1.1565	.75642	9	51	.66718	.89567	1.1165	.74489	9
52	.65430	.86521	1.1558	.75623	8	52	.66740	.89620	1.1158	.74470	8
53	.65452	.86572	1.1551	.75604	7	53	.66762	.89672	1.1152	.74451	7
54	.65474	.86623	1.1544	.75585	6	54	.66783	.89725	1.1145	.74431	6
55	.65496	.86674	1.1538	.75566	5	55	.66805	.89777	1.1139	.74412	5
56	.65518	.86725	1.1531	.75547	4	56	.66827	.89830	1.1132	.74392	4
57	.65540	.86776	1.1524	.75528	3	57	.66848	.89883	1.1126	.74373	3
58	.65562	.86827	1.1517	.75509	2	58	.66870	.89935	1.1119	.74353	2
59	.65584	.86878	1.1510	.75490	1	59	.66891	.89988	1.1113	.74334	1
60	.65606	.86929	1.1504	.75471	0	60	.66913	.90040	1.1106	.74314	0
′	Cos	Ctn	Tan	Sin	′	′	Cos	Ctn	Tan	Sin	′

130° (310°)   (229°) **49°**   **131° (311°)**   (228°) **48°**

Table IV (Cont'd)

NATURAL TRIGONOMETRIC FUNCTIONS

′	Sin	Tan	Ctn	Cos	′	′	Sin	Tan	Ctn	Cos	′
0	.66913	.90040	1.1106	.74314	60	0	.68200	.93252	1.0724	.73135	60
1	.66935	.90093	1.1100	.74295	59	1	.68221	.93306	1.0717	.73116	59
2	.66956	.90146	1.1093	.74276	58	2	.68242	.93360	1.0711	.73096	58
3	.66978	.90199	1.1087	.74256	57	3	.68264	.93415	1.0705	.73076	57
4	.66999	.90251	1.1080	.74237	56	4	.68285	.93469	1.0699	.73056	56
5	.67021	.90304	1.1074	.74217	55	5	.68306	.93524	1.0692	.73036	55
6	.67043	.90357	1.1067	.74198	54	6	.68327	.93578	1.0686	.73016	54
7	.67064	.90410	1.1061	.74178	53	7	.68349	.93633	1.0680	.72996	53
8	.67086	.90463	1.1054	.74159	52	8	.68370	.93688	1.0674	.72976	52
9	.67107	.90516	1.1048	.74139	51	9	.68391	.93742	1.0668	.72957	51
10	.67129	.90569	1.1041	.74120	50	10	.68412	.93797	1.0661	.72937	50
11	.67151	.90621	1.1035	.74100	49	11	.68434	.93852	1.0655	.72917	49
12	.67172	.90674	1.1028	.74080	48	12	.68455	.93906	1.0649	.72897	48
13	.67194	.90727	1.1022	.74061	47	13	.68476	.93961	1.0643	.72877	47
14	.67215	.90781	1.1016	.74041	46	14	.68497	.94016	1.0637	.72857	46
15	.67237	.90834	1.1009	.74022	45	15	.68518	.94071	1.0630	.72837	45
16	.67258	.90887	1.1003	.74002	44	16	.68539	.94125	1.0624	.72817	44
17	.67280	.90940	1.0996	.73983	43	17	.68561	.94180	1.0618	.72797	43
18	.67301	.90993	1.0990	.73963	42	18	.68582	.94235	1.0612	.72777	42
19	.67323	.91046	1.0983	.73944	41	19	.68603	.94290	1.0606	.72757	41
20	.67344	.91099	1.0977	.73924	40	20	.68624	.94345	1.0599	.72737	40
21	.67366	.91153	1.0971	.73904	39	21	.68645	.94400	1.0593	.72717	39
22	.67387	.91206	1.0964	.73885	38	22	.68666	.94455	1.0587	.72697	38
23	.67409	.91259	1.0958	.73865	37	23	.68688	.94510	1.0581	.72677	37
24	.67430	.91313	1.0951	.73846	36	24	.68709	.94565	1.0575	.72657	36
25	.67452	.91366	1.0945	.73826	35	25	.68730	.94620	1.0569	.72637	35
26	.67473	.91419	1.0939	.73806	34	26	.68751	.94676	1.0562	.72617	34
27	.67495	.91473	1.0932	.73787	33	27	.68772	.94731	1.0556	.72597	33
28	.67516	.91526	1.0926	.73767	32	28	.68793	.94786	1.0550	.72577	32
29	.67538	.91580	1.0919	.73747	31	29	.68814	.94841	1.0544	.72557	31
30	.67559	.91633	1.0913	.73728	30	30	.68835	.94896	1.0538	.72537	30
31	.67580	.91687	1.0907	.73708	29	31	.68857	.94952	1.0532	.72517	29
32	.67602	.91740	1.0900	.73688	28	32	.68878	.95007	1.0526	.72497	28
33	.67623	.91794	1.0894	.73669	27	33	.68899	.95062	1.0519	.72477	27
34	.67645	.91847	1.0888	.73649	26	34	.68920	.95118	1.0513	.72457	26
35	.67666	.91901	1.0881	.73629	25	35	.68941	.95173	1.0507	.72437	25
36	.67688	.91955	1.0875	.73610	24	36	.68962	.95229	1.0501	.72417	24
37	.67709	.92008	1.0869	.73590	23	37	.68983	.95284	1.0495	.72397	23
38	.67730	.92062	1.0862	.73570	22	38	.69004	.95340	1.0489	.72377	22
39	.67752	.92116	1.0856	.73551	21	39	.69025	.95395	1.0483	.72357	21
40	.67773	.92170	1.0850	.73531	20	40	.69046	.95451	1.0477	.72337	20
41	.67795	.92224	1.0843	.73511	19	41	.69067	.95506	1.0470	.72317	19
42	.67816	.92277	1.0837	.73491	18	42	.69088	.95562	1.0464	.72297	18
43	.67837	.92331	1.0831	.73472	17	43	.69109	.95618	1.0458	.72277	17
44	.67859	.92385	1.0824	.73452	16	44	.69130	.95673	1.0452	.72257	16
45	.67880	.92439	1.0818	.73432	15	45	.69151	.95729	1.0446	.72236	15
46	.67901	.92493	1.0812	.73413	14	46	.69172	.95785	1.0440	.72216	14
47	.67923	.92547	1.0805	.73393	13	47	.69193	.95841	1.0434	.72196	13
48	.67944	.92601	1.0799	.73373	12	48	.69214	.95897	1.0428	.72176	12
49	.67965	.92655	1.0793	.73353	11	49	.69235	.95952	1.0422	.72156	11
50	.67987	.92709	1.0786	.73333	10	50	.69256	.96008	1.0416	.72136	10
51	.68008	.92763	1.0780	.73314	9	51	.69277	.96064	1.0410	.72116	9
52	.68029	.92817	1.0774	.73294	8	52	.69298	.96120	1.0404	.72095	8
53	.68051	.92872	1.0768	.73274	7	53	.69319	.96176	1.0398	.72075	7
54	.68072	.92926	1.0761	.73254	6	54	.69340	.96232	1.0392	.72055	6
55	.68093	.92980	1.0755	.73234	5	55	.69361	.96288	1.0385	.72035	5
56	.68115	.93034	1.0749	.73215	4	56	.69382	.96344	1.0379	.72015	4
57	.68136	.93088	1.0742	.73195	3	57	.69403	.96400	1.0373	.71995	3
58	.68157	.93143	1.0736	.73175	2	58	.69424	.96457	1.0367	.71974	2
59	.68179	.93197	1.0730	.73155	1	59	.69445	.96513	1.0361	.71954	1
60	.68200	.93252	1.0724	.73135	0	60	.69466	.96569	1.0355	.71934	0
′	Cos	Ctn	Tan	Sin	′	′	Cos	Ctn	Tan	Sin	′

Table IV (Cont'd)

NATURAL TRIGONOMETRIC FUNCTIONS

44° (224°)   **(315°) 135°**

′	Sin	Tan	Ctn	Cos	′
0	.69466	.96569	1.0355	.71934	60
1	.69487	.96625	1.0349	.71914	59
2	.69508	.96681	1.0343	.71894	58
3	.69529	.96738	1.0337	.71873	57
4	.69549	.96794	1.0331	.71853	56
5	.69570	.96850	1.0325	.71833	55
6	.69591	.96907	1.0319	.71813	54
7	.69612	.96963	1.0313	.71792	53
8	.69633	.97020	1.0307	.71772	52
9	.69654	.97076	1.0301	.71752	51
10	.69675	.97133	1.0295	.71732	50
11	.69696	.97189	1.0289	.71711	49
12	.69717	.97246	1.0283	.71691	48
13	.69737	.97302	1.0277	.71671	47
14	.69758	.97359	1.0271	.71650	46
15	.69779	.97416	1.0265	.71630	45
16	.69800	.97472	1.0259	.71610	44
17	.69821	.97529	1.0253	.71590	43
18	.69842	.97586	1.0247	.71569	42
19	.69862	.97643	1.0241	.71549	41
20	.69883	.97700	1.0235	.71529	40
21	.69904	.97756	1.0230	.71508	39
22	.69925	.97813	1.0224	.71488	38
23	.69946	.97870	1.0218	.71468	37
24	.69966	.97927	1.0212	.71447	36
25	.69987	.97984	1.0206	.71427	35
26	.70008	.98041	1.0200	.71407	34
27	.70029	.98098	1.0194	.71386	33
28	.70049	.98155	1.0188	.71366	32
29	.70070	.98213	1.0182	.71345	31
30	.70091	.98270	1.0176	.71325	30
31	.70112	.98327	1.0170	.71305	29
32	.70132	.98384	1.0164	.71284	28
33	.70153	.98441	1.0158	.71264	27
34	.70174	.98499	1.0152	.71243	26
35	.70195	.98556	1.0147	.71223	25
36	.70215	.98613	1.0141	.71203	24
37	.70236	.98671	1.0135	.71182	23
38	.70257	.98728	1.0129	.71162	22
39	.70277	.98786	1.0123	.71141	21
40	.70298	.98843	1.0117	.71121	20
41	.70319	.98901	1.0111	.71100	19
42	.70339	.98958	1.0105	.71080	18
43	.70360	.99016	1.0099	.71059	17
44	.70381	.99073	1.0094	.71039	16
45	.70401	.99131	1.0088	.71019	15
46	.70422	.99189	1.0082	.70998	14
47	.70443	.99247	1.0076	.70978	13
48	.70463	.99304	1.0070	.70957	12
49	.70484	.99362	1.0064	.70937	11
50	.70505	.99420	1.0058	.70916	10
51	.70525	.99478	1.0052	.70896	9
52	.70546	.99536	1.0047	.70875	8
53	.70567	.99594	1.0041	.70855	7
54	.70587	.99652	1.0035	.70834	6
55	.70608	.99710	1.0029	.70813	5
56	.70628	.99768	1.0023	.70793	4
57	.70649	.99826	1.0017	.70772	3
58	.70670	.99884	1.0012	.70752	2
59	.70690	.99942	1.0006	.70731	1
60	.70711	1.0000	1.0000	.70711	0
′	Cos	Ctn	Tan	Sin	′

134° (314°)   **(225°) 45°**

Table V

NATURAL VERSINES AND EXSECANTS

′	0° VERS.	EXSEC.	1° VERS.	EXSEC.	2° VERS.	EXSEC.	3° VERS.	EXSEC.	′
0	.00000	.00000	.00015	.00015	.00061	.00061	.00137	.00137	0
1	.00000	.00000	.00016	.00016	.00062	.00062	.00139	.00139	1
2	.00000	.00000	.00016	.00016	.00063	.00063	.00140	.00140	2
3	.00000	.00000	.00017	.00017	.00064	.00064	.00142	.00142	3
4	.00000	.00000	.00017	.00017	.00065	.00065	.00143	.00143	4
5	.00000	.00000	.00018	.00018	.00066	.00066	.00145	.00145	5
6	.00000	.00000	.00018	.00018	.00067	.00067	.00146	.00147	6
7	.00000	.00000	.00019	.00019	.00068	.00068	.00148	.00148	7
8	.00000	.00000	.00020	.00020	.00069	.00069	.00149	.00150	8
9	.00000	.00000	.00020	.00020	.00070	.00070	.00151	.00151	9
10	.00000	.00000	.00021	.00021	.00071	.00072	.00153	.00153	10
11	.00001	.00001	.00021	.00021	.00073	.00073	.00154	.00155	11
12	.00001	.00001	.00022	.00022	.00074	.00074	.00156	.00156	12
13	.00001	.00001	.00023	.00023	.00075	.00075	.00158	.00158	13
14	.00001	.00001	.00023	.00023	.00076	.00076	.00159	.00159	14
15	.00001	.00001	.00024	.00024	.00077	.00077	.00161	.00161	15
16	.00001	.00001	.00024	.00024	.00078	.00078	.00162	.00163	16
17	.00001	.00001	.00025	.00025	.00079	.00079	.00164	.00164	17
18	.00001	.00001	.00026	.00026	.00081	.00081	.00166	.00166	18
19	.00002	.00002	.00026	.00026	.00082	.00082	.00167	.00168	19
20	.00002	.00002	.00027	.00027	.00083	.00083	.00169	.00169	20
21	.00002	.00002	.00028	.00028	.00084	.00084	.00171	.00171	21
22	.00002	.00002	.00028	.00028	.00085	.00085	.00173	.00173	22
23	.00002	.00002	.00029	.00029	.00087	.00087	.00174	.00175	23
24	.00002	.00002	.00030	.00030	.00088	.00088	.00176	.00176	24
25	.00003	.00003	.00031	.00031	.00089	.00089	.00178	.00178	25
26	.00003	.00003	.00031	.00031	.00090	.00090	.00179	.00180	26
27	.00003	.00003	.00032	.00032	.00091	.00091	.00181	.00182	27
28	.00003	.00003	.00033	.00033	.00093	.00093	.00183	.00183	28
29	.00004	.00004	.00034	.00034	.00094	.00094	.00185	.00185	29
30	.00004	.00004	.00034	.00034	.00095	.00095	.00187	.00187	30
31	.00004	.00004	.00035	.00035	.00096	.00097	.00188	.00189	31
32	.00004	.00004	.00036	.00036	.00098	.00098	.00190	.00190	32
33	.00005	.00005	.00037	.00037	.00099	.00099	.00192	.00192	33
34	.00005	.00005	.00037	.00037	.00100	.00100	.00194	.00194	34
35	.00005	.00005	.00038	.00038	.00102	.00102	.00196	.00196	35
36	.00005	.00005	.00039	.00039	.00103	.00103	.00197	.00198	36
37	.00006	.00006	.00040	.00040	.00104	.00104	.00199	.00200	37
38	.00006	.00006	.00041	.00041	.00106	.00106	.00201	.00201	38
39	.00006	.00006	.00041	.00041	.00107	.00107	.00203	.00203	39
40	.00007	.00007	.00042	.00042	.00108	.00108	.00205	.00205	40
41	.00007	.00007	.00043	.00043	.00110	.00110	.00207	.00207	41
42	.00007	.00007	.00044	.00044	.00111	.00111	.00208	.00209	42
43	.00008	.00008	.00045	.00045	.00112	.00113	.00210	.00211	43
44	.00008	.00008	.00046	.00046	.00114	.00114	.00212	.00213	44
45	.00009	.00009	.00047	.00047	.00115	.00115	.00214	.00215	45
46	.00009	.00009	.00048	.00048	.00117	.00117	.00216	.00216	46
47	.00009	.00009	.00048	.00048	.00118	.00118	.00218	.00218	47
48	.00010	.00010	.00049	.00049	.00119	.00120	.00220	.00220	48
49	.00010	.00010	.00050	.00050	.00121	.00121	.00222	.00222	49
50	.00011	.00011	.00051	.00051	.00122	.00122	.00224	.00224	50
51	.00011	.00011	.00052	.00052	.00124	.00124	.00226	.00226	51
52	.00011	.00011	.00053	.00053	.00125	.00125	.00228	.00228	52
53	.00012	.00012	.00054	.00054	.00127	.00127	.00230	.00230	53
54	.00012	.00012	.00055	.00055	.00128	.00128	.00232	.00232	54
55	.00013	.00013	.00056	.00056	.00130	.00130	.00234	.00234	55
56	.00013	.00013	.00057	.00057	.00131	.00131	.00236	.00236	56
57	.00014	.00014	.00058	.00058	.00133	.00133	.00238	.00238	57
58	.00014	.00014	.00059	.00059	.00134	.00134	.00240	.00240	58
59	.00015	.00015	.00060	.00060	.00136	.00136	.00242	.00242	59
60	.00015	.00015	.00061	.00061	.00137	.00137	.00244	.00244	60

Table V (Cont'd)
NATURAL VERSINES AND EXSECANTS

′	4° VERS.	EXSEC.	5° VERS.	EXSEC.	6° VERS.	EXSEC.	7° VERS.	EXSEC.	′
0	.00244	.00244	.00381	.00382	.00548	.00551	.00745	.00751	0
1	.00246	.00246	.00383	.00385	.00551	.00554	.00749	.00755	1
2	.00248	.00248	.00386	.00387	.00554	.00557	.00752	.00758	2
3	.00250	.00250	.00388	.00390	.00557	.00560	.00756	.00762	3
4	.00252	.00252	.00391	.00392	.00560	.00563	.00760	.00765	4
5	.00254	.00254	.00393	.00395	.00563	.00566	.00763	.00769	5
6	.00256	.00257	.00396	.00397	.00566	.00569	.00767	.00773	6
7	.00258	.00259	.00398	.00400	.00569	.00573	.00770	.00776	7
8	.00260	.00261	.00401	.00403	.00572	.00576	.00774	.00780	8
9	.00262	.00263	.00404	.00405	.00576	.00579	.00778	.00784	9
10	.00264	.00265	.00406	.00408	.00579	.00582	.00781	.00787	10
11	.00266	.00267	.00409	.00411	.00582	.00585	.00785	.00791	11
12	.00269	.00269	.00412	.00413	.00585	.00588	.00789	.00795	12
13	.00271	.00271	.00414	.00416	.00588	.00592	.00792	.00799	13
14	.00273	.00274	.00417	.00419	.00591	.00595	.00796	.00802	14
15	.00275	.00276	.00420	.00421	.00594	.00598	.00800	.00806	15
16	.00277	.00278	.00422	.00424	.00598	.00601	.00803	.00810	16
17	.00279	.00280	.00425	.00427	.00601	.00604	.00807	.00813	17
18	.00281	.00282	.00428	.00429	.00604	.00608	.00811	.00817	18
19	.00284	.00284	.00430	.00432	.00607	.00611	.00814	.00821	19
20	.00286	.00287	.00433	.00435	.00610	.00614	.00818	.00825	20
21	.00288	.00289	.00436	.00438	.00614	.00617	.00822	.00828	21
22	.00290	.00291	.00438	.00440	.00617	.00621	.00825	.00832	22
23	.00292	.00293	.00441	.00443	.00620	.00624	.00829	.00836	23
24	.00295	.00296	.00444	.00446	.00623	.00627	.00833	.00840	24
25	.00297	.00298	.00447	.00449	.00626	.00630	.00837	.00844	25
26	.00299	.00300	.00449	.00451	.00630	.00634	.00840	.00848	26
27	.00301	.00302	.00452	.00454	.00633	.00637	.00844	.00851	27
28	.00304	.00305	.00455	.00457	.00636	.00640	.00848	.00855	28
29	.00306	.00307	.00458	.00460	.00640	.00644	.00852	.00859	29
30	.00308	.00309	.00460	.00463	.00643	.00647	.00856	.00863	30
31	.00311	.00312	.00463	.00465	.00646	.00650	.00859	.00867	31
32	.00313	.00314	.00466	.00468	.00649	.00654	.00863	.00871	32
33	.00315	.00316	.00469	.00471	.00653	.00657	.00867	.00875	33
34	.00317	.00318	.00472	.00474	.00656	.00660	.00871	.00878	34
35	.00320	.00321	.00474	.00477	.00659	.00664	.00875	.00882	35
36	.00322	.00323	.00477	.00480	.00663	.00667	.00878	.00886	36
37	.00324	.00326	.00480	.00482	.00666	.00671	.00882	.00890	37
38	.00327	.00328	.00483	.00485	.00669	.00674	.00886	.00894	38
39	.00329	.00330	.00486	.00488	.00673	.00677	.00890	.00898	39
40	.00332	.00333	.00489	.00491	.00676	.00681	.00894	.00902	40
41	.00334	.00335	.00492	.00494	.00680	.00684	.00898	.00906	41
42	.00336	.00337	.00494	.00497	.00683	.00688	.00902	.00910	42
43	.00339	.00340	.00497	.00500	.00686	.00691	.00906	.00914	43
44	.00341	.00342	.00500	.00503	.00690	.00695	.00909	.00918	44
45	.00343	.00345	.00503	.00506	.00693	.00698	.00913	.00922	45
46	.00346	.00347	.00506	.00509	.00697	.00701	.00917	.00926	46
47	.00348	.00349	.00509	.00512	.00700	.00705	.00921	.00930	47
48	.00351	.00352	.00512	.00515	.00703	.00708	.00925	.00934	48
49	.00353	.00354	.00515	.00518	.00707	.00712	.00929	.00938	49
50	.00356	.00357	.00518	.00521	.00710	.00715	.00933	.00942	50
51	.00358	.00359	.00521	.00524	.00714	.00719	.00937	.00946	51
52	.00361	.00362	.00524	.00527	.00717	.00722	.00941	.00950	52
53	.00363	.00364	.00527	.00530	.00721	.00726	.00945	.00954	53
54	.00365	.00367	.00530	.00533	.00724	.00730	.00949	.00958	54
55	.00368	.00369	.00533	.00536	.00728	.00733	.00953	.00962	55
56	.00370	.00372	.00536	.00539	.00731	.00737	.00957	.00966	56
57	.00373	.00374	.00539	.00542	.00735	.00740	.00961	.00970	57
58	.00375	.00377	.00542	.00545	.00738	.00744	.00965	.00975	58
59	.00378	.00379	.00545	.00548	.00742	.00747	.00969	.00979	59
60	.00381	.00382	.00548	.00551	.00745	.00751	.00973	.00983	60

Table V (Cont'd)

NATURAL VERSINES AND EXSECANTS

′	8° VERS.	8° EXSEC.	9° VERS.	9° EXSEC.	10° VERS.	10° EXSEC.	11° VERS.	11° EXSEC.	′
0	.00973	.00983	.01231	.01247	.01519	.01543	.01837	.01872	0
1	.00977	.00987	.01236	.01251	.01524	.01548	.01843	.01877	1
2	.00981	.00991	.01240	.01256	.01529	.01553	.01848	.01883	2
3	.00985	.00995	.01245	.01261	.01534	.01558	.01854	.01889	3
4	.00989	.00999	.01249	.01265	.01539	.01564	.01860	.01895	4
5	.00994	.01004	.01254	.01270	.01545	.01569	.01865	.01901	5
6	.00998	.01008	.01259	.01275	.01550	.01574	.01871	.01906	6
7	.01002	.01012	.01263	.01279	.01555	.01579	.01876	.01912	7
8	.01006	.01016	.01268	.01284	.01560	.01585	.01882	.01918	8
9	.01010	.01020	.01272	.01289	.01565	.01590	.01888	.01924	9
10	.01014	.01024	.01277	.01294	.01570	.01595	.01893	.01930	10
11	.01018	.01029	.01282	.01298	.01575	.01601	.01899	.01936	11
12	.01022	.01033	.01286	.01303	.01580	.01606	.01904	.01941	12
13	.01027	.01037	.01291	.01308	.01586	.01611	.01910	.01947	13
14	.01031	.01041	.01296	.01313	.01591	.01616	.01916	.01953	14
15	.01035	.01046	.01300	.01317	.01596	.01622	.01921	.01959	15
16	.01039	.01050	.01305	.01322	.01601	.01627	.01927	.01965	16
17	.01043	.01054	.01310	.01327	.01606	.01633	.01933	.01971	17
18	.01047	.01059	.01314	.01332	.01611	.01638	.01939	.01977	18
19	.01052	.01063	.01319	.01337	.01617	.01643	.01944	.01983	19
20	.01056	.01067	.01324	.01342	.01622	.01649	.01950	.01989	20
21	.01060	.01071	.01329	.01346	.01627	.01654	.01956	.01995	21
22	.01064	.01076	.01333	.01351	.01632	.01659	.01961	.02001	22
23	.01069	.01080	.01338	.01356	.01638	.01665	.01967	.02007	23
24	.01073	.01084	.01343	.01361	.01643	.01670	.01973	.02013	24
25	.01077	.01089	.01348	.01366	.01648	.01676	.01979	.02019	25
26	.01081	.01093	.01352	.01371	.01653	.01681	.01984	.02025	26
27	.01086	.01097	.01357	.01376	.01659	.01687	.01990	.02031	27
28	.01090	.01102	.01362	.01381	.01664	.01692	.01996	.02037	28
29	.01094	.01106	.01367	.01386	.01669	.01698	.02002	.02043	29
30	.01098	.01111	.01371	.01391	.01675	.01703	.02008	.02049	30
31	.01103	.01115	.01376	.01395	.01680	.01709	.02013	.02055	31
32	.01107	.01119	.01381	.01400	.01685	.01714	.02019	.02061	32
33	.01111	.01124	.01386	.01405	.01690	.01720	.02025	.02067	33
34	.01116	.01128	.01391	.01410	.01696	.01725	.02031	.02073	34
35	.01120	.01133	.01396	.01415	.01701	.01731	.02037	.02079	35
36	.01124	.01137	.01400	.01420	.01706	.01736	.02042	.02085	36
37	.01129	.01142	.01405	.01425	.01712	.01742	.02048	.02091	37
38	.01133	.01146	.01410	.01430	.01717	.01747	.02054	.02097	38
39	.01137	.01151	.01415	.01435	.01723	.01753	.02060	.02103	39
40	.01142	.01155	.01420	.01440	.01728	.01758	.02066	.02110	40
41	.01146	.01160	.01425	.01445	.01733	.01764	.02072	.02116	41
42	.01151	.01164	.01430	.01450	.01739	.01769	.02078	.02122	42
43	.01155	.01169	.01435	.01455	.01744	.01775	.02084	.02128	43
44	.01159	.01173	.01439	.01460	.01750	.01781	.02090	.02134	44
45	.01164	.01178	.01444	.01466	.01755	.01786	.02095	.02140	45
46	.01168	.01182	.01449	.01471	.01760	.01792	.02101	.02146	46
47	.01173	.01187	.01454	.01476	.01766	.01798	.02107	.02153	47
48	.01177	.01191	.01459	.01481	.01771	.01803	.02113	.02159	48
49	.01182	.01196	.01464	.01486	.01777	.01809	.02119	.02165	49
50	.01186	.01200	.01469	.01491	.01782	.01815	.02125	.02171	50
51	.01191	.01205	.01474	.01496	.01788	.01820	.02131	.02178	51
52	.01195	.01209	.01479	.01501	.01793	.01826	.02137	.02184	52
53	.01200	.01214	.01484	.01506	.01799	.01832	.02143	.02190	53
54	.01204	.01219	.01489	.01512	.01804	.01837	.02149	.02196	54
55	.01209	.01223	.01494	.01517	.01810	.01843	.02155	.02203	55
56	.01213	.01228	.01499	.01522	.01815	.01849	.02161	.02209	56
57	.01218	.01233	.01504	.01527	.01821	.01854	.02167	.02215	57
58	.01222	.01237	.01509	.01532	.01826	.01860	.02173	.02221	58
59	.01227	.01242	.01514	.01537	.01832	.01866	.02179	.02228	59
69	.01231	.01247	.01519	.01543	.01837	.01872	.02185	.02234	60

Table V (Cont'd)

NATURAL VERSINES AND EXSECANTS

′	12° VERS.	EXSEC.	13° VERS.	EXSEC.	14° VERS.	EXSEC.	15° VERS.	EXSEC.	′
0	.02185	.02234	.02563	.02630	.02970	.03061	.03407	.03528	0
1	.02191	.02240	.02570	.02637	.02977	.03069	.03415	.03536	1
2	.02197	.02247	.02576	.02644	.02985	.03076	.03422	.03544	2
3	.02203	.02253	.02583	.02651	.02992	.03084	.03430	.03552	3
4	.02209	.02259	.02589	.02658	.02999	.03091	.03438	.03560	4
5	.02216	.02266	.02596	.02665	.03006	.03099	.03445	.03568	5
6	.02222	.02272	.02602	.02672	.03013	.03106	.03453	.03576	6
7	.02228	.02279	.02609	.02679	.03020	.03114	.03460	.03584	7
8	.02234	.02285	.02616	.02686	.03027	.03121	.03468	.03592	8
9	.02240	.02291	.02622	.02693	.03034	.03129	.03476	.03601	9
10	.02246	.02298	.02629	.02700	.03041	.03137	.03483	.03609	10
11	.02252	.02304	.02635	.02707	.03048	.03144	.03491	.03617	11
12	.02258	.02311	.02642	.02714	.03055	.03152	.03498	.03625	12
13	.02265	.02317	.02649	.02721	.03063	.03159	.03506	.03633	13
14	.02271	.02323	.02655	.02728	.03070	.03167	.03514	.03642	14
15	.02277	.02330	.02662	.02735	.03077	.03175	.03521	.03650	15
16	.02283	.02336	.02669	.02742	.03084	.03182	.03529	.03658	16
17	.02289	.02343	.02675	.02749	.03091	.03190	.03537	.03666	17
18	.02295	.02349	.02682	.02756	.03098	.03197	.03544	.03674	18
19	.02302	.02356	.02689	.02763	.03106	.03205	.03552	.03683	19
20	.02308	.02362	.02696	.02770	.03113	.03213	.03560	.03691	20
21	.02314	.02369	.02702	.02777	.03120	.03220	.03567	.03699	21
22	.02320	.02375	.02709	.02784	.03127	.03228	.03575	.03708	22
23	.02327	.02382	.02716	.02791	.03134	.03236	.03583	.03716	23
24	.02333	.02388	.02722	.02799	.03142	.03244	.03590	.03724	24
25	.02339	.02395	.02729	.02806	.03149	.03251	.03598	.03732	25
26	.02345	.02402	.02736	.02813	.03156	.03259	.03606	.03741	26
27	.02352	.02408	.02743	.02820	.03163	.03267	.03614	.03749	27
28	.02358	.02415	.02749	.02827	.03171	.03275	.03621	.03758	28
29	.02364	.02421	.02756	.02834	.03178	.03282	.03629	.03766	29
30	.02370	.02428	.02763	.02842	.03185	.03290	.03637	.03774	30
31	.02377	.02435	.02770	.02849	.03193	.03298	.03645	.03783	31
32	.02383	.02441	.02777	.02856	.03200	.03306	.03653	.03791	32
33	.02389	.02448	.02783	.02863	.03207	.03313	.03660	.03799	33
34	.02396	.02454	.02790	.02870	.03214	.03321	.03668	.03808	34
35	.02402	.02461	.02797	.02878	.03222	.03329	.03676	.03816	35
36	.02408	.02468	.02804	.02885	.03229	.03337	.03684	.03825	36
37	.12415	.02474	.02811	.02892	.03236	.03345	.03692	.03833	37
38	.02421	.02481	.02818	.02899	.03244	.03353	.03699	.03842	38
39	.02427	.02488	.02824	.02907	.03251	.03360	.03707	.03850	39
40	.02434	.02494	.02831	.02914	.03258	.03368	.03715	.03858	40
41	.02440	.02501	.02838	.02921	.03266	.03376	.03723	.03867	41
42	.02447	.02508	.02845	.02928	.03273	.03384	.03731	.03875	42
43	.02453	.02515	.02852	.02936	.03281	.03392	.03739	.03884	43
44	.02459	.02521	.02859	.02943	.03288	.03400	.03747	.03892	44
45	.02466	.02528	.02866	.02950	.03295	.03408	.03754	.03901	45
46	.02472	.02535	.02873	.02958	.03303	.03416	.03762	.03909	46
47	.02479	.02542	.02880	.02965	.03310	.03424	.03770	.03918	47
48	.02485	.02548	.02887	.02972	.03318	.03432	.03778	.03927	48
49	.02492	.02555	.02894	.02980	.03325	.03439	.03786	.03935	49
50	.02498	.02562	.02900	.02987	.03333	.03447	.03794	.03944	50
51	.02504	.02569	.02907	.02994	.03340	.03455	.03802	.03952	51
52	.02511	.02576	.02914	.03002	.03347	.03463	.03810	.03961	52
53	.02517	.02582	.02921	.03009	.03355	.03471	.03818	.03969	53
54	.02524	.02589	.02928	.03017	.03362	.03479	.03826	.03978	54
55	.02530	.02596	.02935	.03024	.03370	.03487	.03834	.03987	55
56	.02537	.02603	.02942	.03032	.03377	.03495	.03842	.03995	56
57	.02543	.02610	.02949	.03039	.03385	.03503	.03850	.04004	57
58	.02550	.02617	.02956	.03046	.03392	.03511	.03858	.04013	58
59	.02556	.02624	.02963	.03054	.03400	.03520	.03866	.04021	59
60	.02563	.02630	.02970	.03061	.03407	.03528	.03874	.04030	60

Table V (Cont'd)
NATURAL VERSINES AND EXSECANTS

′	16° VERS.	EXSEC.	17° VERS.	EXSEC.	18° VERS.	EXSEC.	19° VERS.	EXSEC.	′
0	.03874	.04030	.04370	.04569	.04894	.05146	.05448	.05762	0
1	.03882	.04039	.04378	.04578	.04903	.05156	.05458	.05773	1
2	.03890	.04047	.04387	.04588	.04912	.05166	.05467	.05783	2
3	.03898	.04056	.04395	.04597	.04921	.05176	.05477	.05794	3
4	.03906	.04065	.04404	.04606	.04930	.05186	.05486	.05805	4
5	.03914	.04073	.04412	.04616	.04939	.05196	.05496	.05815	5
6	.03922	.04082	.04421	.04625	.04948	.05206	.05505	.05826	6
7	.03930	.04091	.04429	.04635	.04957	.05216	.05515	.05836	7
8	.03938	.04100	.04438	.04644	.04967	.05226	.05524	.05847	8
9	.03946	.04108	.04446	.04653	.04976	.05236	.05534	.05858	9
10	.03954	.04117	.04455	.04663	.04985	.05246	.05543	.05869	10
11	.03963	.04126	.04464	.04672	.04994	.05256	.05553	.05879	11
12	.03971	.04135	.04472	.04682	.05003	.05266	.05562	.05890	12
13	.03979	.04144	.04481	.04691	.05012	.05276	.05572	.05901	13
14	.03987	.04152	.04489	.04700	.05021	.05286	.05582	.05911	14
15	.03995	.04161	.04498	.04710	.05030	.05297	.05991	.05922	15
16	.04003	.04170	.04507	.04719	.05039	.05307	.05601	.05933	16
17	.04011	.04179	.04515	.04729	.05048	.05317	.05610	.05944	17
18	.04019	.04188	.04524	.04738	.05057	.05327	.05620	.05955	18
19	.04028	.04197	.04533	.04748	.05067	.05337	.05630	.05965	19
20	.04036	.04206	.04541	.04757	.05076	.05347	.05639	.05976	20
21	.04044	.04214	.04550	.04767	.05085	.05357	.05649	.05987	21
22	.04052	.04223	.04559	.04776	.05094	.05367	.05658	.05998	22
23	.04060	.04232	.04567	.04786	.05103	.05378	.05668	.06009	23
24	.04069	.04241	.04576	.04795	.05112	.05388	.05678	.06020	24
25	.04077	.04250	.04585	.04805	.05122	.05398	.05687	.06030	25
26	.04085	.04259	.04593	.04815	.05131	.05408	.05697	.06041	26
27	.04093	.04268	.04602	.04824	.05140	.05418	.05707	.06052	27
28	.04102	.04277	.04611	.04834	.05149	.05429	.05716	.06063	28
29	.04110	.04286	.04620	.04843	.05158	.05439	.05726	.06074	29
30	.04118	.04295	.04628	.04853	.05168	.05449	.05736	.06085	30
31	.04126	.04304	.04637	.04863	.05177	.05460	.05746	.06096	31
32	.04135	.04313	.04646	.04872	.05186	.05470	.05755	.06107	32
33	.04143	.04322	.04655	.04882	.05195	.05480	.05765	.06118	33
34	.04151	.04331	.04663	.04891	.05205	.05490	.05775	.06129	34
35	.04159	.04340	.04672	.04901	.05214	.05501	.05785	.06140	35
36	.04168	.04349	.04681	.04911	.05223	.05511	.05794	.06151	36
37	.04176	.04358	.04690	.04920	.05232	.05521	.05804	.06162	37
38	.04184	.04367	.04699	.04930	.05242	.05532	.05814	.06173	38
39	.04193	.04376	.04707	.04940	.05251	.05542	.05824	.06184	39
40	.04201	.04385	.04716	.04950	.05260	.05552	.05833	.06195	40
41	.04209	.04394	.04725	.04959	.05270	.05563	.05843	.06206	41
42	.04218	.04403	.04734	.04969	.05279	.05573	.05853	.06217	42
43	.04226	.04413	.04743	.04979	.05288	.05584	.05863	.06228	43
44	.04234	.04422	.04752	.04989	.05298	.05594	.05873	.06239	44
45	.04243	.04431	.04760	.04998	.05307	.05604	.05882	.06250	45
46	.04251	.04440	.04769	.05008	.05316	.05615	.05892	.06261	46
47	.04260	.04449	.04778	.05018	.05326	.05625	.05902	.06272	47
48	.04268	.04458	.04787	.05028	.05335	.05636	.05912	.06283	48
49	.04276	.04468	.04796	.05038	.05344	.05646	.05922	.06295	49
50	.04285	.04477	.04805	.05047	.05354	.05657	.05932	.06306	50
51	.04293	.04486	.04814	.05057	.05363	.05667	.05942	.06317	51
52	.04302	.04495	.04823	.05067	.05373	.05678	.05951	.06328	52
53	.04310	.04504	.04832	.05077	.05382	.05688	.05961	.06339	53
54	.04319	.04514	.04841	.05087	.05391	.05699	.05971	.06350	54
55	.04327	.04523	.04850	.05097	.05401	.05709	.05981	.06362	55
56	.04336	.04532	.04858	.05107	.05410	.05720	.05991	.06373	56
57	.04344	.04541	.04867	.05116	.05420	.05730	.06001	.06384	57
58	.04353	.04551	.04876	.05126	.05429	.05741	.06011	.06395	58
59	.04361	.04560	.04885	.05136	.05439	.05751	.06021	.06407	59
60	.04370	.04569	.04894	.05146	.05448	.05762	.06031	.06418	60

Table V (Cont'd)
NATURAL VERSINES AND EXSECANTS

′	20° VERS.	20° EXSEC.	21° VERS.	21° EXSEC.	22° VERS.	22° EXSEC.	23° VERS.	23° EXSEC.	′
0	.06031	.06418	.06642	.07114	.07282	.07853	.07950	.08636	0
1	.06041	.06429	.06652	.07126	.07293	.07866	.07961	.08649	1
2	.06051	.06440	.06663	.07138	.07303	.07879	.07972	.08663	2
3	.06061	.06452	.06673	.07150	.07314	.07892	.07984	.08676	3
4	.06071	.06463	.06684	.07162	.07325	.07904	.07995	.08690	4
5	.06081	.06474	.06694	.07174	.07336	.07917	.08006	.08703	5
6	.06091	.06486	.06705	.07186	.07347	.07930	.08018	.08717	6
7	.06101	.06497	.06715	.07199	.07358	.07943	.08029	.08730	7
8	.06111	.06508	.06726	.07211	.07369	.07955	.08041	.08744	8
9	.06121	.06520	.06736	.07223	.07380	.07968	.08052	.08757	9
10	.06131	.06531	.06747	.07235	.07391	.07981	.08064	.08771	10
11	.06141	.06542	.06757	.07247	.07402	.07994	.08075	.08784	11
12	.06151	.06554	.06768	.07259	.07413	.08006	.08086	.08798	12
13	.06161	.06565	.06778	.07271	.07424	.08019	.08098	.08811	13
14	.06171	.06577	.06789	.07283	.07435	.08032	.08109	.08825	14
15	.06181	.06588	.06799	.07295	.07446	.08045	.08121	.08839	15
16	.06191	.06600	.06810	.07307	.07457	.08058	.08132	.08852	16
17	.06201	.06611	.06820	.07320	.07468	.08071	.08144	.08866	17
18	.06211	.06622	.06831	.07332	.07479	.08084	.08155	.08880	18
19	.06221	.06634	.06841	.07344	.07490	.08097	.08167	.08893	19
20	.06231	.06645	.06852	.07356	.07501	.08109	.08178	.08907	20
21	.06241	.06657	.06863	.07368	.07512	.08122	.08190	.08920	21
22	.06252	.06668	.06873	.07380	.07523	.08135	.08201	.08934	22
23	.06262	.06680	.06884	.07393	.07534	.08148	.08213	.08948	23
24	.06272	.06691	.06894	.07405	.07545	.08161	.08225	.08962	24
25	.06282	.06703	.06905	.07417	.07556	.08174	.08236	.08975	25
26	.06292	.06715	.06916	.07429	.07568	.08187	.08248	.08989	26
27	.06302	.06726	.06926	.07442	.07579	.08200	.08259	.09003	27
28	.06312	.06738	.06937	.07454	.07590	.08213	.08271	.09017	28
29	.06323	.06749	.06948	.07466	.07601	.08226	.08282	.09030	29
30	.06333	.06761	.06958	.07479	.07612	.08239	.08294	.09044	30
31	.06343	.06773	.06969	.07491	.07623	.08252	.08306	.09058	31
32	.06353	.06784	.06980	.07503	.07634	.08265	.08317	.09072	32
33	.06363	.06796	.06990	.07516	.07645	.08278	.08329	.09086	33
34	.06374	.06807	.07001	.07528	.07657	.08291	.08340	.09099	34
35	.06384	.06819	.07012	.07540	.07668	.08305	.08352	.09113	35
36	.06394	.06831	.07022	.07553	.07679	.08318	.08364	.09127	36
37	.06404	.06842	.07033	.07565	.07690	.08331	.08375	.09141	37
38	.06415	.06854	.07044	.07578	.07701	.08344	.08387	.09155	38
39	.06425	.06866	.07055	.07590	.07713	.08357	.08399	.09169	39
40	.06435	.06878	.07065	.07602	.07724	.08370	.08410	.09183	40
41	.06445	.06889	.07076	.07615	.07735	.08383	.08422	.09197	41
42	.06456	.06901	.07087	.07627	.07746	.08397	.08434	.09211	42
43	.06466	.06913	.07098	.07640	.07757	.08410	.08445	.09224	43
44	.06476	.06925	.07108	.07652	.07769	.08423	.08457	.09238	44
45	.06486	.06936	.07119	.07665	.07780	.08436	.08469	.09252	45
46	.06497	.06948	.07130	.07677	.07791	.08449	.08481	.09266	46
47	.06507	.06960	.07141	.07690	.07802	.08463	.08492	.09280	47
48	.06517	.06972	.07151	.07702	.07814	.08476	.08504	.09294	48
49	.06528	.06984	.07162	.07715	.07825	.08489	.08516	.09308	49
50	.06538	.06995	.07173	.07727	.07836	.08503	.08528	.09323	50
51	.06548	.07007	.07184	.07740	.07848	.08516	.08539	.09337	51
52	.06559	.07019	.07195	.07752	.07859	.08529	.08551	.09351	52
53	.06569	.07031	.07206	.07765	.07870	.08542	.08563	.09365	53
54	.06580	.07043	.07216	.07778	.07881	.08556	.08575	.09379	54
55	.06590	.07055	.07227	.07790	.07893	.08569	.08586	.09393	55
56	.06600	.07067	.07238	.07803	.07904	.08582	.08598	.09407	56
57	.06611	.07079	.07249	.07816	.07915	.08596	.08610	.09421	57
58	.06621	.07091	.07260	.07828	.07927	.08609	.08622	.09435	58
59	.06632	.07103	.07271	.07841	.07938	.08623	.08634	.09449	59
60	.06642	.07114	.07282	.07853	.07950	.08636	.08645	.09464	60

Table V (Cont'd)
NATURAL VERSINES AND EXSECANTS

′	24° VERS.	EXSEC.	25° VERS.	EXSEC.	26° VERS.	EXSEC.	27° VERS.	EXSEC.	′
0	.08645	.09464	.09369	.10338	.10121	.11260	.10899	.12233	0
1	.08657	.09478	.09382	.10353	.10133	.11276	.10913	.12249	1
2	.08669	.09492	.09394	.10368	.10146	.11292	.10926	.12266	2
3	.08681	.09506	.09406	.10383	.10159	.11308	.10939	.12283	3
4	.08693	.09520	.09418	.10398	.10172	.11323	.10952	.12299	4
5	.08705	.09535	.09431	.10413	.10184	.11339	.10965	.12316	5
6	.08717	.09549	.09443	.10428	.10197	.11355	.10979	.12333	6
7	.08728	.09563	.09455	.10443	.10210	.11371	.10992	.12349	7
8	.08740	.09577	.09468	.10458	.10223	.11387	.11005	.12366	8
9	.08752	.09592	.09480	.10473	.10236	.11403	.11019	.12383	9
10	.08764	.09606	.09493	.10488	.10248	.11419	.11032	.12400	10
11	.08776	.09620	.09505	.10503	.10261	.11435	.11045	.12416	11
12	.08788	.09635	.09517	.10518	.10274	.11451	.11058	.12433	12
13	.08800	.09649	.09530	.10533	.10287	.11467	.11072	.12450	13
14	.08812	.09663	.09542	.10549	.10300	.11483	.11085	.12467	14
15	.08824	.09678	.09554	.10564	.10313	.11499	.11098	.12484	15
16	.08836	.09692	.09567	.10579	.10326	.11515	.11112	.12501	16
17	.08848	.09707	.09579	.10594	.10338	.11531	.11125	.12518	17
18	.08860	.09721	.09592	.10609	.10351	.11547	.11138	.12534	18
19	.08872	.09735	.09604	.10625	.10364	.11563	.11152	.12551	19
20	.08884	.09750	.09617	.10640	.10337	.11579	.11165	.12568	20
21	.08896	.09764	.09629	.10655	.10390	.11595	.11178	.12585	21
22	.08908	.09779	.09642	.10670	.10403	.11611	.11192	.12602	22
23	.08920	.09793	.09654	.10686	.10416	.11627	.11205	.12619	23
24	.08932	.09808	.09666	.10701	.10429	.11643	.11218	.12636	24
25	.08944	.09822	.09679	.10716	.10442	.11659	.11232	.12653	25
26	.08956	.09837	.09691	.10731	.10455	.11675	.11245	.12670	26
27	.08968	.09851	.09704	.10747	.10468	.11691	.11259	.12687	27
28	.08980	.09866	.09716	.10762	.10481	.11708	.11272	.12704	28
29	.08992	.09880	.09729	.10777	.10494	.11724	.11285	.12721	29
30	.09004	.09895	.09741	.10793	.10507	.11740	.11299	.12738	30
31	.09016	.09909	.09754	.10808	.10520	.11756	.11312	.12755	31
32	.09028	.09924	.09767	.10824	.10533	.11772	.11326	.12772	32
33	.09040	.09939	.09779	.10839	.10546	.11789	.11339	.12789	33
34	.09052	.09953	.09792	.10854	.10559	.11805	.11353	.12807	34
35	.09064	.09968	.09804	.10870	.10572	.11821	.11366	.12824	35
36	.09076	.09982	.09817	.10885	.10585	.11838	.11380	.12841	36
37	.09089	.09997	.09829	.10901	.10598	.11854	.11393	.12858	37
38	.09101	.10012	.09842	.10916	.10611	.11870	.11407	.12875	38
39	.09113	.10026	.09854	.10932	.10624	.11886	.11420	.12892	39
40	.09125	.10041	.09867	.10947	.10637	.11903	.11434	.12910	40
41	.09137	.10056	.09880	.10963	.10650	.11919	.11447	.12927	41
42	.09149	.10071	.09892	.10978	.10663	.11936	.11461	.12944	42
43	.09161	.10085	.09905	.10994	.10676	.11952	.11474	.12961	43
44	.09174	.10100	.09918	.11009	.10689	.11968	.11488	.12979	44
45	.09186	.10115	.09930	.11025	.10702	.11985	.11501	.12996	45
46	.09198	.10130	.09943	.11041	.10715	.12001	.11515	.13013	46
47	.09210	.10144	.09955	.11056	.10728	.12018	.11528	.13031	47
48	.09222	.10159	.09968	.11072	.10741	.12034	.11542	.13048	48
49	.09234	.10174	.09981	.11087	.10755	.12051	.11555	.13065	49
50	.09247	.10189	.09993	.11103	.10768	.12067	.11569	.13083	50
51	.09259	.10204	.10006	.11119	.10781	.12083	.11583	.13100	51
52	.09271	.10218	.10019	.11134	.10794	.12100	.11596	.13117	52
53	.09283	.10233	.10032	.11150	.10807	.12117	.11610	.13135	53
54	.09296	.10248	.10044	.11166	.10820	.12133	.11623	.13152	54
55	.09308	.10263	.10057	.11181	.10833	.12150	.11637	.13170	55
56	.09320	.10278	.10070	.11197	.10847	.12166	.11651	.13187	56
57	.09332	.10293	.10082	.11213	.10860	.12183	.11664	.13205	57
58	.09345	.10308	.10095	.11229	.10873	.12199	.11678	.13222	58
59	.09357	.10323	.10108	.11244	.10886	.12216	.11692	.13239	59
60	.09369	.10338	.10121	.11260	.10899	.12233	.11705	.13257	60

Table V (Cont'd)
NATURAL VERSINES AND EXSECANTS

′	28° VERS.	EXSEC.	29° VERS.	EXSEC.	30° VERS.	EXSEC.	31° VERS.	EXSEC.	′
0	.11705	.13257	.12538	.14335	.13397	.15470	.14283	.16663	0
1	.11719	.13275	.12552	.14354	.13412	.15489	.14298	.16684	1
2	.11733	.13292	.12566	.14372	.13427	.15509	.14313	.16704	2
3	.11746	.13310	.12580	.14391	.13441	.15528	.14328	.16725	3
4	.11760	.13327	.12594	.14409	.13456	.15548	.14343	.16745	4
5	.11774	.13345	.12609	.14428	.13470	.15567	.14358	.16766	5
6	.11787	.13362	.12623	.14446	.13485	.15587	.14373	.16786	6
7	.11801	.13380	.12637	.14465	.13499	.15606	.14388	.16806	7
8	.11815	.13398	.12651	.14483	.13514	.15626	.14403	.16827	8
9	.11828	.13415	.12665	.14502	.13529	.15645	.14418	.16848	9
10	.11842	.13433	.12679	.14521	.13543	.15665	.14433	.16868	10
11	.11856	.13451	.12694	.14539	.13558	.15684	.14449	.16889	11
12	.11870	.13468	.12708	.14558	.13573	.15704	.14464	.16909	12
13	.11883	.13486	.12722	.14576	.13587	.15724	.14479	.16930	13
14	.11897	.13504	.12736	.14595	.13602	.15743	.14494	.16950	14
15	.11911	.13521	.12750	.14614	.13616	.15763	.14509	.16971	15
16	.11925	.13539	.12765	.14632	.13631	.15782	.14524	.16992	16
17	.11938	.13557	.12779	.14651	.13646	.15802	.14539	.17012	17
18	.11952	.13575	.12793	.14670	.13660	.15822	.14554	.17033	18
19	.11966	.13593	.12807	.14689	.13675	.15841	.14569	.17054	19
20	.11980	.13610	.12822	.14707	.13690	.15861	.14584	.17075	20
21	.11994	.13628	.12836	.14726	.13705	.15881	.14599	.17095	21
22	.12007	.13646	.12850	.14745	.13719	.15901	.14615	.17116	22
23	.12021	.13664	.12864	.14764	.13734	.15920	.14630	.17137	23
24	.12035	.13682	.12879	.14782	.13749	.15940	.14645	.17158	24
25	.12049	.13700	.12893	.14801	.13763	.15960	.14660	.17178	25
26	.12063	.13718	.12907	.14820	.13778	.16980	.14675	.17199	26
27	.12077	.13735	.12921	.14839	.13793	.16000	.14690	.17220	27
28	.12091	.13753	.12936	.14858	.13808	.16019	.14706	.17241	28
29	.12104	.13771	.12950	.14877	.13822	.16039	.14721	.17262	29
30	.12118	.13789	.12964	.14896	.13837	.16059	.14736	.17283	30
31	.12132	.13807	.12979	.14914	.13852	.16079	.14751	.17304	31
32	.12146	.13825	.12993	.14933	.13867	.16099	.14766	.17325	32
33	.12160	.13843	.13007	.14952	.13881	.16119	.14782	.17346	33
34	.12174	.13861	.13022	.14971	.13896	.16139	.14797	.17367	34
35	.12188	.13879	.13036	.14990	.13911	.16159	.14812	.17388	35
36	.12202	.13897	.13051	.15009	.13926	.16179	.14827	.17409	36
37	.12216	.13915	.13065	.15028	.13941	.16199	.14843	.17430	37
38	.12230	.13934	.13079	.15047	.13955	.16219	.14858	.17451	38
39	.12244	.13952	.13094	.15066	.13970	.16239	.14873	.17472	39
40	.12257	.13970	.13108	.15085	.13985	.16259	.14888	.17493	40
41	.12271	.13988	.13122	.15105	.14000	.16279	.14904	.17514	41
42	.12285	.14006	.13137	.15124	.14015	.16299	.14919	.17535	42
43	.12299	.14024	.13151	.15143	.14030	.16319	.14934	.17556	43
44	.12313	.14042	.13166	.15162	.14044	.16339	.14949	.17577	44
45	.12327	.14061	.13180	.15181	.14059	.16359	.14965	.17598	45
46	.12341	.14079	.13195	.15200	.14074	.16380	.14980	.17620	46
47	.12355	.14097	.13209	.15219	.14089	.16400	.14995	.17641	47
48	.12369	.14115	.13223	.15239	.14104	.16420	.15011	.17662	48
49	.12383	.14134	.13238	.15258	.14119	.16440	.15026	.17683	49
50	.12397	.14152	.13252	.15277	.14134	.16460	.15041	.17704	50
51	.12411	.14170	.13267	.15296	.14149	.16481	.15057	.17726	51
52	.12425	.14188	.13281	.15315	.14164	.16501	.15072	.17747	52
53	.12439	.14207	.13296	.15335	.14179	.16521	.15087	.17768	53
54	.12454	.14225	.13310	.15354	.14194	.16541	.15103	.17790	54
55	.12468	.14243	.13325	.15373	.14208	.16562	.15118	.17811	55
56	.12482	.14262	.13339	.15393	.14223	.16582	.15134	.17832	56
57	.12496	.14280	.13354	.15412	.14238	.16602	.15149	.17854	57
58	.12510	.14299	.13368	.15431	.14253	.16623	.15164	.17875	58
59	.12524	.14317	.13383	.15451	.14268	.16643	.15180	.17896	59
60	.12538	.14335	.13397	.15470	.14283	.16663	.15195	.17918	60

Table V (Cont'd)

NATURAL VERSINES AND EXSECANTS

′	32° VERS.	32° EXSEC.	33° VERS.	33° EXSEC.	34° VERS.	34° EXSEC.	35° VERS.	35° EXSEC.	′
0	.15195	.17918	.16133	.19236	.17096	.20622	.18085	.22077	0
1	.15211	.17939	.16149	.19259	.17113	.20645	.18101	.22102	1
2	.15226	.17961	.16165	.19281	.17129	.20669	.18118	.22127	2
3	.15241	.17982	.16181	.19304	.17145	.20693	.18135	.22152	3
4	.15257	.18004	.16196	.19327	.17161	.20717	.18152	.22177	4
5	.15272	.18025	.16212	.19349	.17178	.20740	.18168	.22202	5
6	.15288	.18047	.16228	.19372	.17194	.20764	.18185	.22227	6
7	.15303	.18068	.16244	.19394	.17210	.20788	.18202	.22252	7
8	.15319	.18090	.16260	.19417	.17227	.20812	.18218	.22277	8
9	.15334	.18111	.16276	.19440	.17243	.20836	.18235	.22302	9
10	.15350	.18133	.16292	.19463	.17259	.20859	.18252	.22327	10
11	.15365	.18155	.16308	.19485	.17276	.20883	.18269	.22352	11
12	.15381	.18176	.16324	.19508	.17292	.20907	.18286	.22377	12
13	.15396	.18198	.16340	.19531	.17308	.20931	.18302	.22402	13
14	.15412	.18220	.16355	.19553	.17325	.20955	.18319	.22428	14
15	.15427	.18241	.16371	.19576	.17341	.20979	.18336	.22453	15
16	.15443	.18263	.16387	.19599	.17357	.21003	.18353	.22478	16
17	.15458	.18285	.16403	.19622	.17374	.21027	.18369	.22503	17
18	.15474	.18307	.16419	.19645	.17390	.21051	.18386	.22528	18
19	.15489	.18328	.16435	.19668	.17407	.21075	.18403	.22554	19
20	.15505	.18350	.16451	.19691	.17423	.21099	.18420	.22579	20
21	.15520	.18372	.16467	.19713	.17439	.21123	.18437	.22604	21
22	.15536	.18394	.16483	.19736	.17456	.21147	.18454	.22629	22
23	.15552	.18416	.16499	.19759	.17472	.21171	.18470	.22655	23
24	.15567	.18437	.16515	.19782	.17489	.21195	.18487	.22680	24
25	.15583	.18459	.16531	.19805	.17505	.21220	.18504	.22706	25
26	.15598	.18481	.16547	.19828	.17522	.21244	.18521	.22731	26
27	.15614	.18503	.16563	.19851	.17538	.21268	.18538	.22756	27
28	.15630	.18525	.16579	.19874	.17554	.21292	.18555	.22782	28
29	.15645	.18547	.16595	.19897	.17571	.21316	.18572	.22807	29
30	.15661	.18569	.16611	.19920	.17587	.21341	.18588	.22833	30
31	.15676	.18591	.16627	.19944	.17604	.21365	.18605	.22858	31
32	.15692	.18613	.16644	.19967	.17620	.21389	.18622	.22884	32
33	.15708	.18635	.16660	.19990	.17637	.21414	.18639	.22909	33
34	.15723	.18657	.16676	.20013	.17653	.21438	.18656	.22935	34
35	.15739	.18679	.16692	.20036	.17670	.21462	.18673	.22960	35
36	.15755	.18701	.16708	.20059	.17686	.21487	.18690	.22986	36
37	.15770	.18723	.16724	.20083	.17703	.21511	.18707	.23012	37
38	.15786	.18745	.16740	.20106	.17719	.21535	.18724	.23037	38
39	.15802	.18767	.16756	.20129	.17736	.21560	.18741	.23063	39
40	.15818	.18790	.16772	.20152	.17752	.21584	.18758	.23089	40
41	.15833	.18812	.16788	.20176	.17769	.21609	.18775	.23114	41
42	.15849	.18834	.16805	.20199	.17786	.21633	.18792	.23140	42
43	.15865	.18856	.16821	.20222	.17802	.21658	.18809	.23166	43
44	.15880	.18878	.16837	.20246	.17819	.21682	.18826	.23192	44
45	.15896	.18901	.16853	.20269	.17835	.21707	.18843	.23217	45
46	.15912	.18923	.16869	.20292	.17852	.21731	.18860	.23243	46
47	.15928	.18945	.16885	.20316	.17868	.21756	.18877	.23269	47
48	.15943	.18967	.16902	.20339	.17885	.21781	.18894	.23295	48
49	.15959	.18990	.16918	.20363	.17902	.21805	.18911	.23321	49
50	.15975	.19012	.16934	.20386	.17918	.21830	.18928	.23347	50
51	.15991	.19034	.16950	.20410	.17935	.21855	.18945	.23373	51
52	.16006	.19057	.16966	.20433	.17952	.21879	.18962	.23398	52
53	.16022	.19079	.16983	.20457	.17968	.21904	.18979	.23424	53
54	.16038	.19102	.16999	.20480	.17985	.21929	.18996	.23450	54
55	.16054	.19124	.17015	.20504	.18001	.21953	.19013	.23476	55
56	.16070	.19146	.17031	.20527	.18018	.21978	.19030	.23502	56
57	.16085	.19169	.17047	.20551	.18035	.22003	.19047	.23529	57
58	.16101	.19191	.17064	.20575	.18051	.22028	.19064	.23555	58
59	.16117	.19214	.17080	.20598	.18068	.22053	.19081	.23581	59
60	.16133	.19236	.17096	.20622	.18085	.22077	.19098	.23607	60

Table V (Cont'd)

NATURAL VERSINES AND EXSECANTS

′	36° VERS.	36° EXSEC.	37° VERS.	37° EXSEC.	38° VERS.	38° EXSEC.	39° VERS.	39° EXSEC.	′
0	.19098	.23607	.20136	.25214	.21199	.26902	.22285	.28676	0
1	.19115	.23633	.20154	.25241	.21217	.26931	.22304	.28706	1
2	.19133	.23659	.20171	.25269	.21235	.26960	.22322	.28737	2
3	.19150	.23685	.20189	.25296	.21253	.26988	.22340	.28767	3
4	.19167	.23711	.20207	.25324	.21271	.27017	.22359	.28797	4
5	.19184	.23738	.20224	.25351	.21289	.27046	.22377	.28828	5
6	.19201	.23764	.20242	.25379	.21306	.27075	.22395	.28858	6
7	.19218	.23790	.20259	.25406	.21324	.27104	.22414	.28889	7
8	.19235	.23816	.20277	.25434	.21342	.27133	.22432	.28919	8
9	.19252	.23843	.20294	.25462	.21360	.27162	.22450	.28950	9
10	.19270	.23869	.20312	.25489	.21378	.27191	.22469	.28980	10
11	.19287	.23895	.20329	.25517	.21396	.27221	.22487	.29011	11
12	.19304	.23922	.20347	.25545	.21414	.27250	.22506	.29042	12
13	.19321	.23948	.20365	.25572	.21432	.27279	.22524	.29072	13
14	.19338	.23975	.20382	.25600	.21450	.27308	.22542	.29103	14
15	.19356	.24001	.20400	.25628	.21468	.27337	.22561	.29133	15
16	.19373	.24028	.20417	.25656	.21486	.27366	.22579	.29164	16
17	.19390	.24054	.20435	.25683	.21504	.27396	.22598	.29195	17
18	.19407	.24081	.20453	.25711	.21522	.27425	.22616	.29226	18
19	.19424	.24107	.20470	.25739	.21540	.27454	.22634	.29256	19
20	.19442	.24134	.20488	.25767	.21558	.27483	.22653	.29287	20
21	.19459	.24160	.20506	.25795	.21576	.27513	.22671	.29318	21
22	.19476	.24187	.20523	.25823	.21595	.27542	.22690	.29349	22
23	.19493	.24213	.20541	.25851	.21613	.27572	.22708	.29380	23
24	.19511	.24240	.20559	.25879	.21631	.27601	.22727	.29411	24
25	.19528	.24267	.20576	.25907	.21649	.27630	.22745	.29442	25
26	.19545	.24293	.20594	.25935	.21667	.27660	.22764	.29473	26
27	.19562	.24320	.20612	.25963	.21685	.27689	.22782	.29504	27
28	.19580	.24347	.20629	.25991	.21703	.27719	.22801	.29535	28
29	.19597	.24373	.20647	.26019	.21721	.27748	.22819	.29566	29
30	.19614	.24400	.20665	.26047	.21739	.27778	.22838	.29597	30
31	.19632	.24427	.20682	.26075	.21757	.27807	.22856	.29628	31
32	.19649	.24454	.20700	.26104	.21775	.27837	.22875	.29659	32
33	.19666	.24481	.20718	.26132	.21794	.27867	.22893	.29690	33
34	.19684	.24508	.20736	.26160	.21812	.27896	.22912	.29721	34
35	.19701	.24534	.20753	.26188	.21830	.27926	.22930	.29752	35
36	.19718	.24561	.20771	.26216	.21848	.27956	.22949	.29784	36
37	.19736	.24588	.20789	.26245	.21866	.27985	.22967	.29815	37
38	.19753	.24615	.20807	.26273	.21884	.28015	.22986	.29846	38
39	.19770	.24642	.20824	.26301	.21902	.28045	.23004	.29877	39
40	.19788	.24669	.20842	.26330	.21921	.28075	.23023	.29909	40
41	.19805	.24696	.20860	.26358	.21939	.28105	.23041	.29940	41
42	.19822	.24723	.20878	.26387	.21957	.28134	.23060	.29971	42
43	.19840	.24750	.20895	.26415	.21975	.28164	.23079	.30003	43
44	.19857	.24777	.20913	.26443	.21993	.28194	.23097	.30034	44
45	.19875	.24804	.20931	.26472	.22012	.28224	.23116	.30066	45
46	.19892	.24832	.20949	.26500	.22030	.28254	.23134	.30097	46
47	.19909	.24859	.20967	.26529	.22048	.28284	.23153	.30129	47
48	.19927	.24886	.20984	.26557	.22066	.28314	.23172	.30160	48
49	.19944	.24913	.21002	.26586	.22084	.28344	.23190	.30192	49
50	.19962	.24940	.21020	.26615	.22103	.28374	.23209	.30223	50
51	.19979	.24967	.21038	.26643	.22121	.28404	.23228	.30255	51
52	.19997	.24995	.21056	.26672	.22139	.28434	.23246	.30287	52
53	.20014	.25022	.21074	.26701	.22157	.28464	.23265	.30318	53
54	.20032	.25049	.21092	.26729	.22176	.28495	.23283	.30350	54
55	.20049	.25077	.21109	.26758	.22194	.28525	.23302	.30382	55
56	.20066	.25104	.21127	.26787	.22212	.28555	.23321	.30413	56
57	.20084	.25131	.21145	.26815	.22231	.28585	.23339	.30445	57
58	.20101	.25159	.21163	.26844	.22249	.28615	.23358	.30477	58
59	.20119	.25186	.21181	.26873	.22267	.28646	.23377	.30509	59
60	.20136	.25214	.21199	.26902	.22285	.28676	.23396	.30541	60

Table VI
STADIA REDUCTION TABLE

Minutes	0°			1°			2°		
	Hor. Dist.	Hor. Cor.	Diff. Elev.	Hor. Dist.	Hor. Cor.	Diff. Elev.	Hor. Dist.	Hor. Cor.	Diff. Elev.
0............	100.00	0.00	0.00	99.97	0.03	1.74	99.88	0.12	3.49
2............	100.00	0.00	0.06	99.97	0.03	1.80	99.87	0.13	3.55
4............	100.00	0.00	0.12	99.97	0.03	1.86	99.87	0.13	3.60
6............	100.00	0.00	0.17	99.96	0.04	1.92	99.87	0.13	3.66
8............	100.00	0.00	0.23	99.96	0.04	1.98	99.86	0.14	3.72
10............	100.00	0.00	0.29	99.96	0.04	2.04	99.86	0.14	3.78
12............	100.00	0.00	0.35	99.96	0.04	2.09	99.85	0.15	3.84
14............	100.00	0.00	0.41	99.95	0.05	2.15	99.85	0.15	3.89
16............	100.00	0.00	0.47	99.95	0.05	2.21	99.84	0.16	3.95
18............	100.00	0.00	0.52	99.95	0.05	2.27	99.84	0.16	4.01
20............	100.00	0.00	0.58	99.95	0.05	2.33	99.83	0.17	4.07
22............	100.00	0.00	0.64	99.94	0.06	2.38	99.83	0.17	4.13
24............	100.00	0.00	0.70	99.94	0.06	2.44	99.82	0.18	4.18
26............	99.99	0.01	0.76	99.94	0.06	2.50	99.82	0.18	4.24
28............	99.99	0.01	0.81	99.93	0.07	2.56	99.81	0.19	4.30
30............	99.99	0.01	0.87	99.93	0.07	2.62	99.81	0.19	4.36
32............	99.99	0.01	0.93	99.93	0.07	2.67	99.80	0.20	4.42
34............	99.99	0.01	0.99	99.93	0.07	2.73	99.80	0.20	4.47
36............	99.99	0.01	1.05	99.92	0.08	2.79	99.79	0.21	4.53
38............	99.99	0.01	1.11	99.92	0.08	2.85	99.79	0.21	4.59
40............	99.99	0.01	1.16	99.92	0.08	2.91	99.78	0.22	4.65
42............	99.99	0.01	1.22	99.91	0.09	2.97	99.78	0.22	4.71
44............	99.98	0.02	1.28	99.91	0.09	3.02	99.77	0.23	4.76
46............	99.98	0.02	1.34	99.90	0.10	3.08	99.77	0.23	4.82
48............	99.98	0.02	1.40	99.90	0.10	3.14	99.76	0.24	4.88
50............	99.98	0.02	1.45	99.90	0.10	3.20	99.76	0.24	4.94
52............	99.98	0.02	1.51	99.89	0.11	3.26	99.75	0.25	4.99
54............	99.98	0.02	1.57	99.89	0.11	3.31	99.74	0.26	5.05
56............	99.97	0.03	1.63	99.89	0.11	3.37	99.74	0.26	5.11
58............	99.97	0.03	1.69	99.88	0.12	3.43	99.73	0.27	5.17
60............	99.97	0.03	1.74	99.88	0.12	3.49	99.73	0.27	5.23
C = 0.75......	0.75	0.00	0.01	0.75	0.00	0.02	0.75	0.00	0.03
C = 1.00......	1.00	0.00	0.01	1.00	0.00	0.03	1.00	0.00	0.04
C = 1.25......	1.25	0.00	0.02	1.25	0.00	0.03	1.25	0.00	0.05

Table VI (Cont'd)

Minutes	3° Hor. Dist.	3° Hor. Cor.	3° Diff. Elev.	4° Hor. Dist.	4° Hor. Cor.	4° Diff. Elev.	5° Hor. Dist.	5° Hor. Cor.	5° Diff. Elev.
0	99.73	0.27	5.23	99.51	0.49	6.96	99.24	0.76	8.68
2	99.72	0.28	5.28	99.51	0.49	7.02	99.23	0.77	8.74
4	99.71	0.29	5.34	99.50	0.50	7.07	99.22	0.78	8.80
6	99.71	0.29	5.40	99.49	0.51	7.13	99.21	0.79	8.85
8	99.70	0.30	5.46	99.48	0.52	7.19	99.20	0.80	8.91
10	99.69	0.31	5.52	99.47	0.53	7.25	99.19	0.81	8.97
12	99.69	0.31	5.57	99.46	0.54	7.30	99.18	0.82	9.03
14	99.68	0.32	5.63	99.46	0.54	7.36	99.17	0.83	9.08
16	99.68	0.32	5.69	99.45	0.55	7.42	99.16	0.84	9.14
18	99.67	0.33	5.75	99.44	0.56	7.48	99.15	0.85	9.20
20	99.66	0.34	5.80	99.43	0.57	7.53	99.14	0.86	9.25
22	99.66	0.34	5.86	99.42	0.58	7.59	99.13	0.87	9.31
24	99.65	0.35	5.92	99.41	0.59	7.65	99.11	0.89	9.37
26	99.64	0.36	5.98	99.40	0.60	7.71	99.10	0.90	9.43
28	99.63	0.37	6.04	99.39	0.61	7.76	99.09	0.91	9.48
30	99.63	0.37	6.09	99.38	0.62	7.82	99.08	0.92	9.54
32	99.62	0.38	6.15	99.38	0.62	7.88	99.07	0.93	9.60
34	99.62	0.38	6.21	99.37	0.63	7.94	99.06	0.94	9.65
36	99.61	0.39	6.27	99.36	0.64	7.99	99.05	0.95	9.71
38	99.60	0.40	6.32	99.35	0.65	8.05	99.04	0.96	9.77
40	99.59	0.41	6.38	99.34	0.66	8.11	99.03	0.97	9.83
42	99.59	0.41	6.44	99.33	0.67	8.17	99.01	0.99	9.88
44	99.58	0.42	6.50	99.32	0.68	8.22	99.00	1.00	9.94
46	99.57	0.43	6.56	99.31	0.69	8.28	98.99	1.01	10.00
48	99.56	0.44	6.61	99.30	0.70	8.34	98.98	1.02	10.05
50	99.56	0.44	6.67	99.29	0.71	8.40	98.97	1.03	10.11
52	99.55	0.45	6.73	99.28	0.72	8.45	98.96	1.04	10.17
54	99.54	0.46	6.79	99.27	0.73	8.51	98.94	1.06	10.22
56	99.53	0.47	6.84	99.26	0.74	8.57	98.93	1.07	10.28
58	99.52	0.48	6.90	99.25	0.75	8.63	98.92	1.08	10.34
60	99.51	0.49	6.96	99.24	0.76	8.68	98.91	1.09	10.40
C = 0.75	0.75	0.00	0.05	0.75	0.00	0.06	0.75	0.00	0.07
C = 1.00	1.00	0.00	0.06	1.00	0.00	0.08	0.99	0.01	0.09
C = 1.25	1.25	0.00	0.08	1.25	0.00	0.10	1.24	0.01	0.11

Table VI (Cont'd)

Minutes	12°			13°			14°		
	Hor. Dist.	Hor. Cor.	Diff. Elev.	Hor. Dist.	Hor. Cor.	Diff. Elev.	Hor. Dist.	Hor. Cor.	Diff. Elev.
0.............	95.68	4.32	20.34	94.94	5.06	21.92	94.15	5.85	23.47
2.............	95.65	4.35	20.39	94.91	5.09	21.97	94.12	5.88	23.52
4.............	95.63	4.37	20.44	94.89	5.11	22.02	94.09	5.91	23.58
6.............	95.61	4.39	20.50	94.86	5.14	22.08	94.07	5.93	23.63
8.............	95.58	4.42	20.55	94.84	5.16	22.13	94.04	5.96	23.68
10............	95.56	4.44	20.60	94.81	5.19	22.18	94.01	5.99	23.73
12............	95.53	4.47	20.66	94.79	5.21	22.23	93.98	6.02	23.78
14............	95.51	4.49	20.71	94.76	5.24	22.28	93.95	6.05	23.83
16............	95.49	4.51	20.76	94.73	5.27	22.34	93.93	6.07	23.88
18............	95.46	4.54	20.81	94.71	5.29	22.39	93.90	6.10	23.93
20............	95.44	4.56	20.87	94.68	5.32	22.44	93.87	6.13	23.99
22............	95.41	4.59	20.92	94.66	5.34	22.49	93.84	6.16	24.04
24............	95.39	4.61	20.97	94.63	5.37	22.54	93.81	6.19	24.09
26............	95.36	4.64	21.03	94.60	5.40	22.60	93.79	6.21	24.14
28............	95.34	4.66	21.08	94.58	5.42	22.65	93.76	6.24	24.19
30............	95.32	4.68	21.13	94.55	5.45	22.70	93.73	6.27	24.24
32............	95.29	4.71	21.18	94.52	5.48	22.75	93.70	6.30	24.29
34............	95.27	4.73	21.24	94.50	5.50	22.80	93.67	6.33	24.34
36............	95.24	4.76	21.29	94.47	5.53	22.85	93.65	6.35	24.39
38............	95.22	4.78	21.34	94.44	5.56	22.91	93.62	6.38	24.44
40............	95.19	4.81	21.39	94.42	5.58	22.96	93.59	6.41	24.49
42............	95.17	4.83	21.45	94.39	5.61	23.01	93.56	6.44	24.55
44............	95.14	4.86	21.50	94.36	5.64	23.06	93.53	6.47	24.60
46............	95.12	4.88	21.55	94.34	5.66	23.11	93.50	6.50	24.65
48............	95.09	4.91	21.60	94.31	5.69	23.16	93.47	6.53	24.70
50............	95.07	4.93	21.66	94.28	5.72	23.22	93.45	6.55	24.75
52............	95.04	4.96	21.71	94.26	5.74	23.27	93.42	6.58	24.80
54............	95.02	4.98	21.76	94.23	5.77	23.32	93.39	6.61	24.85
56............	94.99	5.01	21.81	94.20	5.80	23.37	93.36	6.64	24.90
58............	94.97	5.03	21.87	94.17	5.83	23.42	93.33	6.67	24.95
60............	94.94	5.06	21.92	94.15	5.85	23.47	93.30	6.70	25.00
C = 0.75......	0.73	0.02	0.16	0.73	0.02	0.17	0.73	0.02	0.19
C = 1.00......	0.98	0.02	0.22	0.97	0.03	0.23	0.97	0.03	0.25
C = 1.25......	1.22	0.03	0.27	1.21	0.04	0.29	1.21	0.04	0.31

Table VI (Cont'd)

Minutes	15°			16°			17°		
	Hor. Dist.	Hor. Cor.	Diff. Elev.	Hor. Dist.	Hor. Cor.	Diff. Elev.	Hor. Dist.	Hor. Cor.	Diff. Elev.
0	93.30	6.70	25.00	92.40	7.60	26.50	91.45	8.55	27.96
2	93.27	6.73	25.05	92.37	7.63	26.55	91.42	8.58	28.01
4	93.24	6.76	25.10	92.34	7.66	26.59	91.39	8.61	28.06
6	93.21	6.79	25.15	92.31	7.69	26.64	91.35	8.65	28.10
8	93.18	6.82	25.20	92.28	7.72	26.69	91.32	8.68	28.15
10	93.16	6.84	25.25	92.25	7.75	26.74	91.29	8.71	28.20
12	93.13	6.87	25.30	92.22	7.78	26.79	91.26	8.74	28.25
14	93.10	6.90	25.35	92.19	7.81	26.84	91.22	8.78	28.30
16	93.07	6.93	25.40	92.15	7.85	26.89	91.19	8.81	28.34
18	93.04	6.96	25.45	92.12	7.88	26.94	91.16	8.84	28.39
20	93.01	6.99	25.50	92.09	7.91	26.99	91.12	8.88	28.44
22	92.98	7.02	25.55	92.06	7.94	27.04	91.09	8.91	28.49
24	92.95	7.05	25.60	92.03	7.97	27.09	91.06	8.94	28.54
26	92.92	7.08	25.65	92.00	8.00	27.13	91.02	8.98	28.58
28	92.89	7.11	25.70	91.97	8.03	27.18	90.99	9.01	28.63
30	92.86	7.14	25.75	91.93	8.07	27.23	90.96	9.04	28.68
32	92.83	7.17	25.80	91.90	8.10	27.28	90.92	9.08	28.73
34	92.80	7.20	25.85	91.87	8.13	27.33	90.89	9.11	28.77
36	92.77	7.23	25.90	91.84	8.16	27.38	90.86	9.14	28.82
38	92.74	7.26	25.95	91.81	8.19	27.43	90.82	9.18	28.87
40	92.71	7.29	26.00	91.77	8.23	27.48	90.79	9.21	28.92
42	92.68	7.32	26.05	91.74	8.26	27.52	90.76	9.24	28.96
44	92.65	7.35	26.10	91.71	8.29	27.57	90.72	9.28	29.01
46	92.62	7.38	26.15	91.68	8.32	27.62	90.69	9.31	29.06
48	92.59	7.41	26.20	91.65	8.35	27.67	90.66	9.34	29.11
50	92.56	7.44	26.25	91.61	8.39	27.72	90.62	9.38	29.15
52	92.53	7.47	26.30	91.58	8.42	27.77	90.59	9.41	29.20
54	92.49	7.51	26.35	91.55	8.45	27.81	90.55	9.45	29.25
56	92.46	7.54	26.40	91.52	8.48	27.86	90.52	9.48	29.30
58	92.43	7.57	26.45	91.48	8.52	27.91	90.48	9.52	29.34
60	92.40	7.60	26.50	91.45	8.55	27.96	90.45	9.55	29.39
C = 0.75	0.72	0.03	0.20	0.72	0.03	0.21	0.72	0.03	0.23
C = 1.00	0.96	0.04	0.27	0.96	0.04	0.28	0.95	0.05	0.30
C = 1.25	1.20	0.05	0.34	1.20	0.05	0.35	1.19	0.06	0.38

Table VI (Cont'd)

Minutes	18°			19°			20°		
	Hor. Dist.	Hor. Cor.	Diff. Elev.	Hor. Dist.	Hor. Cor.	Diff. Elev.	Hor. Dist.	Hor. Cor	Diff. Elev.
0............	90.45	9.55	29.39	89.40	10.60	30.78	88.30	11.70	32.14
2............	90.42	9.58	29.44	89.36	10.64	30.83	88.26	11.74	32.18
4............	90.38	9.62	29.48	89.33	10.67	30.87	88.23	11.77	32.23
6............	90.35	9.65	29.53	89.29	10.71	30.92	88.19	11.81	32.27
8............	90.31	9.69	29.58	89.26	10.74	30.97	88.15	11.85	32 32
10............	90.28	9.72	29.62	89.22	10.78	31.01	88.11	11.89	32.36
12............	90.24	9.76	29.67	89.18	10.82	31.06	88.08	11.92	32.41
14............	90.21	9.79	29.72	89.15	10 85	31.10	88.04	11.96	32.45
16............	90.18	9.82	29.76	89.11	10.89	31.15	88.00	12.00	32.49
18............	90.14	9.86	29.81	89.08	10.92	31.19	87.96	12.04	32.54
20............	90.11	9.89	29.86	89.04	10.96	31.24	87.93	12.07	32.58
22............	90.07	9.93	29.90	89.00	11.00	31.28	87.89	12.11	32.63
24............	90.04	9.96	29.95	88.96	11.04	31.33	87.85	12.15	32.67
26............	90.00	10.00	30.00	88.93	11.07	31.38	87.81	12.19	32.72
28............	89.97	10.03	30.04	88.89	11.11	31.42	87.77	12.23	32.76
30............	89.93	10.07	30.09	88.86	11.14	31.47	87.74	12.26	32.80
32............	89.90	10.10	30.14	88.82	11.18	31.51	87:70	12.30	32.85
34............	89.86	10.14	30.19	88.78	11.22	31.56	87.66	12.34	32.89
36............	89.83	10.17	30.23	88.75	11.25	31.60	87.62	12.38	32.93
38............	89.79	10.21	30.28	88.71	11.29	31.65	87.58	12.42	32.98
40............	89.76	10.24	30.32	88.67	11.33	31.69	87.54	12.46	33.02
42............	89.72	10.28	30.37	88.64	11.36	31.74	87.51	12.49	33.07
44............	89.69	10.31	30.41	88.60	11.40	31.78	87.47	12.53	33.11
46............	89.65	10.35	30.46	88.56	11.44	31.83	87.43	12.57	33.15
48............	89.61	10.39	30.51	88.53	11.47	31.87	87.39	12.61	33.20
50............	89.58	10.42	30.55	88.49	11.51	31.92	87.35	12.65	33.24
52............	89.54	10.46	30.60	88.45	11.55	31.96	87.31	12.69	33.28
54............	89.51	10.49	30.65	88.41	11.59	32.01	87.27	12.73	33.33
56............	89.47	10.53	30.69	88.38	11.62	32.05	87.24	12.76	33.37
58............	89.44	10.56	30.74	88.34	11.66	32.09	87.20	12.80	33.41
60............	89.40	10.60	30.78	88.30	11.70	32.14	87.16	12.84	33.46
C = 0.75......	0.71	0.04	0.24	0.71	0.04	0.25	0.70	0.05	0.26
C = 1.00......	0.95	0.05	0.32	0.94	0.06	0.33	0.94	0.06	0.35
C = 1.25......	1.19	0.06	0.40	1.18	0.07	0.42	1.17	0.08	0.44

Table VI (Cont'd)

Minutes	21° Hor. Dist.	21° Hor. Cor.	21° Diff. Elev.	22° Hor. Dist.	22° Hor. Cor.	22° Diff. Elev.	23° Hor. Dist.	23° Hor. Cor.	23° Diff. Elev.
0	87.16	12.84	33.46	85.97	14.03	34.73	84.73	15.27	35.97
2	87.12	12.88	33.50	85.93	14.07	34.77	84.69	15.31	36.01
4	87.08	12.92	33.54	85.89	14.11	34.82	84.65	15.35	36.05
6	87.04	12.96	33.59	85.85	14.15	34.86	84.61	15.39	36.09
8	87.00	13.00	33.63	85.80	14.20	34.90	84.57	15.43	36.13
10	86.96	13.04	33.67	85.76	14.24	34.94	84.52	15.48	36.17
12	86.92	13.08	33.72	85.72	14.28	34.98	84.48	15.52	36.21
14	86.88	13.12	33.76	85.68	14.32	35.02	84.44	15.56	36.25
16	86.84	13.16	33.80	85.64	14.36	35.07	84.40	15.60	36.29
18	86.80	13.20	33.84	85.60	14.40	35.11	84.35	15.65	36.33
20	86.77	13.23	33.89	85.56	14.44	35.15	84.31	15.69	36.37
22	86.73	13.27	33.93	85.52	14.48	35.19	84.27	15.73	36.41
24	86.69	13.31	33.97	85.48	14.52	35.23	84.23	15.77	36.45
26	86.65	13.35	34.01	85.44	14.56	35.27	84.18	15.82	36.49
28	86.61	13.39	34.06	85.40	14.60	35.31	84.14	15.86	36.53
30	86.57	13.43	34.10	85.36	14.64	35.36	84.10	15.90	36.57
32	86.53	13.47	34.14	85.31	14.69	35.40	84.06	15.94	36 61
34	86.49	13.51	34.18	85.27	14.73	35.44	84.01	15.99	36.65
36	86.45	13.55	34.23	85.23	14.77	35.48	83.97	16.03	36.69
38	86.41	13.59	34.27	85.19	14.81	35.52	82.93	16.07	36.73
40	86.37	13.63	34.31	85.15	14.85	35.56	83.89	16.11	36.77
42	86.33	13.67	34.35	85.11	14.89	35.60	83.84	16.16	36.80
44	86.29	13.71	34.40	85.07	14.93	35.64	83.80	16.20	36 84
46	86.25	13.75	34.44	85.02	14.98	35.68	83.76	16.24	36.88
48	86.21	13.79	34.48	84.98	15.02	35.72	83.72	16.28	36.92
50	86.17	13.83	34.52	84.94	15.06	35.76	83.67	16.33	36.96
52	86.13	13.87	34.57	84.90	15.10	35.80	83 63	16.37	37.00
54	86.09	13.91	34.61	84.86	15.14	35.85	83.59	16.41	37.04
56	86.05	13.95	34.65	84.82	15.18	35.89	83.54	16.46	37.08
58	86.01	13.99	34.69	84.77	15.23	35.93	83.50	16.50	37.12
60	85.97	14.03	34.73	84.73	15.27	35.97	83.46	16.54	37.16
C = 0.75	0.70	0.05	0.27	0.69	0.06	0.29	0.69	0.06	0.30
C = 1.00	0.93	0.07	0.37	0.92	0.08	0.38	0.92	0.08	0.40
C = 1.25	1.16	0.09	0.46	1.15	0.10	0.48	1.15	0.10	0.50

Table VI (Cont'd)

Minutes	24° Hor. Dist.	24° Hor. Cor.	24° Diff. Elev.	25° Hor. Dist.	25° Hor. Cor.	25° Diff. Elev.	26° Hor. Dist.	26° Hor. Cor.	26° Diff. Elev.
0	83.46	16.54	37.16	82.14	17.86	38.30	80.78	19.22	39.40
2	83.41	16.59	37.20	82.09	17.91	38.34	80.74	19.26	39.44
4	83.37	16.63	37.23	82.05	17.95	38.38	80.69	19.31	39.47
6	83.33	16.67	37.27	82.01	17.99	38.41	80.65	19.35	39.51
8	83.28	16.72	37.31	81.96	18.04	38.45	80.60	19.40	39.54
10	83.24	16.76	37.35	81.92	18.08	38.49	80.55	19.45	39.58
12	83.20	16.80	37.39	81.87	18.13	38.53	80.51	19.49	39.61
14	83.15	16.85	37.43	81.83	18.17	38.56	80.46	19.54	39.65
16	83.11	16.89	37.47	81.78	18.22	38.60	80.41	19.59	39.69
18	83.07	16.93	37.51	81.74	18.26	38.64	80.37	19.63	39.72
20	83.02	16.98	37.54	81.69	18.31	38.67	80.32	19.68	39.76
22	82.98	17.02	37.58	81.65	18.35	38.71	80.28	19.72	39.79
24	82.93	17.07	37.62	81.60	18.40	38.75	80.23	19.77	39.83
26	82.89	17.11	37.66	81.56	18.44	38.78	80.18	19.82	39.86
28	82.85	17.15	37.70	81.51	18.49	38.82	80.14	19.86	39.90
30	82.80	17.20	37.74	81.47	18.53	38.86	80.09	19.91	39.93
32	82.76	17.24	37.77	81.42	18.58	38.89	80.04	19.96	39.97
34	82.72	17.28	37.81	81.38	18.62	38.93	80.00	20.00	40.00
36	82.67	17.33	37.85	81.33	18.67	38.97	79.95	20.05	40.04
38	82.63	17.37	37.89	81.28	18.72	39.00	79.90	20.10	40.07
40	82.58	17.42	37.93	81.24	18.76	39.04	79.86	20.14	40.11
42	82.54	17.46	37.96	81.19	18.81	39.08	79.81	20.19	40.14
44	82.49	17.51	38.00	81.15	18.85	39.11	79.76	20.24	40.18
46	82.45	17.55	38.04	81.10	18.90	39.15	79.72	20.28	40.21
48	82.41	17.59	38.08	81.06	18.94	39.18	79.67	20.33	40.24
50	82.36	17.64	38.11	81.01	18.99	39.22	79.62	20.38	40.28
52	82.32	17.68	38.15	80.97	19.03	39.26	79.58	20.42	40.31
54	82.27	17.73	38.19	80.92	19.08	39.29	79.53	20.47	40.35
56	82.23	17.77	38.23	80.87	19.13	39.33	79.48	20.52	40.38
58	82.18	17.82	38.26	80.83	19.17	39.36	79.44	20.56	40.42
60	82.14	17.86	38.30	80.78	19.22	39.40	79.39	20.61	40.45
C = 0.75	0.68	0.07	0.31	0.68	0.07	0.32	0.67	0.08	0.33
C = 1.00	0.91	0.09	0.41	0.90	0.10	0.43	0.89	0.11	0.45
C = 1.25	1.14	0.11	0.52	1.13	0.12	0.54	1.12	0.13	0.56

Table VI (Cont'd)

Minutes	27° Hor. Dist.	27° Hor. Cor.	27° Diff. Elev.	28° Hor. Dist.	28° Hor. Cor.	28° Diff. Elev.
0	79.39	20.61	40.45	77.96	22.04	41.45
2	79.34	20.66	40.49	77.91	22.09	41.48
4	79.30	20.70	40.52	77.86	22.14	41.52
6	79.25	20.75	40.55	77.81	22.19	41.55
8	79.20	20.80	40.59	77.77	22.23	41.58
10	79.15	20.85	40.62	77.72	22.28	41.61
12	79.11	20.89	40.66	77.67	22.33	41.65
14	79.06	20.94	40.69	77.62	22.38	41.68
16	79.01	20.99	40.72	77.57	22.43	41.71
18	78.96	21.04	40.76	77.52	22.48	41.74
20	78.92	21.08	40.79	77.48	22.52	41.77
22	78.87	21.13	40.82	77.43	22.57	41.81
24	78.82	21.18	40.86	77.38	22.62	41.84
26	78.77	21.23	40.89	77.33	22.67	41.87
28	78.73	21.27	40.92	77.28	22.72	41.90
30	78.68	21.32	40.96	77.23	22.77	41.93
32	78.63	21.37	40.99	77.18	22.82	41.97
34	78.58	21.42	41.02	77.13	22.87	42.00
36	78.54	21.46	41.06	77.09	22.91	42.03
38	78.49	21.51	41.09	77.04	22.96	42.06
40	78.44	21.56	41.12	76.99	23.01	42.09
42	78.39	21.61	41.16	76.94	23.06	42.12
44	78.34	21.66	41.19	76.89	23.11	42.15
46	78.30	21.70	41.22	76.84	23.16	42.19
48	78.25	21.75	41.26	76.79	23.21	42.22
50	78.20	21.80	41.29	76.74	23.26	42.25
52	78.15	21.85	41.32	76.69	23.31	42.28
54	78.10	21.90	41.35	76.64	23.36	42.31
56	78.06	21.94	41.39	76.59	23.41	42.34
58	78.01	21.99	41.42	76.55	23.45	42.37
60	77.96	22.04	41.45	76.50	23.50	42.40
C = 0.75	0.66	0.09	0.35	0.66	0.09	0.36
C = 1.00	0.89	0.11	0.46	0.88	0.12	0.48
C = 1.25	1.11	0.14	0.58	1.10	0.15	0.60

Table VI (Cont'd)

Minutes	29°			30°		
	Hor. Dist.	Hor. Cor.	Diff. Elev.	Hor. Dist.	Hor. Cor.	Diff. Elev.
0............	76.50	23.50	42.40	75.00	25.00	43.30
2............	76.45	23.55	42.43	74.95	25.05	43.33
4............	76.40	23.60	42.46	74.90	25.10	43.36
6............	76.35	23.65	42.49	74.85	25.15	43.39
8............	76.30	23.70	42.53	74.80	25.20	43.42
10............	76.25	23.75	42.56	74.75	25.25	43.45
12............	76.20	23.80	42.59	74.70	25.30	43.47
14............	76.15	23.85	42.62	74.65	25.35	43.50
16............	76.10	23.90	42.65	74.60	25.40	43.53
18............	76.05	23.95	42.68	74.55	25.45	43.56
20............	76.00	24.00	42.71	74.49	25.51	43.59
22............	75.95	24.05	42.74	74.44	25.56	43.62
24............	75.90	24.10	42.77	74.39	25.61	43.65
26............	75.85	24.15	42.80	74.34	25.66	43.67
28............	75.80	24.20	42.83	74.29	25.71	43.70
30............	75.75	24.25	42.86	74.24	25.76	43.73
32............	75.70	24.30	42.80	74.19	25.81	43.76
34............	75.65	24.35	42.92	74.14	25.86	43.79
36............	75.60	24.40	42.95	74.09	25.91	43.82
38............	75.55	24.45	42.98	74.04	25.96	43.84
40............	75.50	24.50	43.01	73.99	26.01	43.87
42............	75.45	24.55	43.04	73.93	26.07	43.90
44............	75.40	24.60	43.07	73.88	26.12	43.93
46............	75.35	24.65	43.10	73.83	26.17	43.95
48............	75.30	24.70	43.13	73.78	26.22	43.98
50............	75.25	24.75	43.16	73.73	26.27	44.01
52............	75.20	24.80	43.18	73.68	26.32	44.04
54............	75.15	24.85	43.21	73.63	26.37	44.07
56............	75.10	24.90	43.24	73.58	26.42	44.09
58............	75.05	24.95	43.27	73.52	26.48	44.12
60............	75.00	25.00	43.30	73.47	26.53	44.15
C = 0.75........	0.65	0.10	0.37	0.65	0.10	0.38
C = 1.00........	0.87	0.13	0.49	0.86	0.14	0.51
C = 1.25........	1.09	0.16	0.62	1.08	0.17	0.64

Index

Second order: